A NEW GENERAL ARITHMETIC — COMPLETE EDITION

NOTE:

A New General Arithmetic is also offered in separate parts:

Part A   (ISBN 0 85950 112 4)
Part B   (ISBN 0 85950 130 2)
Answers   (ISBN 0 85950 132 9)

The publishers will be pleased to supply further information about this series, or other books from the same author on request. A full list of Stanley Thornes (Publishers) mathematics titles is also available.

A New
General Arithmetic

Complete Edition

Ewart Smith MSc

Head of Mathematics Department
Tredegar Comprehensive School

Stanley Thornes (Publishers) Ltd

First published in 1983 by:

Stanley Thornes (Publishers) Ltd
Old Station Drive
Leckhampton
CHELTENHAM GL53 0DN

Reprinted 1984 with minor corrections
Reprinted 1985 with minor corrections

British Library Cataloguing in Publication Data

    Smith, Ewart
      A new general arithmetic
      Pts. A + B
      1. Arithmetic—1961—
      I. Title
      513   QA107

      ISBN 0-85950-131-0

Typeset by Tech-Set, Gateshead, Tyne & Wear.
Printed and bound in Great Britain at The Bath Press, Avon.

CONTENTS

PREFACE   ix

PART A

1 **WHOLE NUMBERS** — words into figures and figures into words — the four rules — miscellaneous examples — sequences and series.   **1**

2 **FACTORS AND MULTIPLES** — prime numbers — expressing numbers in terms of prime numbers using index notation — finding square roots and cube roots using factors and indices — highest common factor (HCF) — least common multiple (LCM).   **15**

3 **FRACTIONS** — proper and improper fractions — equal fractions — mixed numbers — arranging fractions in ascending or descending order — the four rules — expressing one quantity as a fraction of another — miscellaneous examples.   **22**

4 **DECIMALS** — conversion of common fractions and mixed numbers into decimals and vice versa — the four rules — decimal places — significant figures — standard form.   **39**

5 **DIRECTED NUMBERS** — positive and negative numbers — the four rules.   **58**

6 **THE METRIC SYSTEM** — the four rules — miscellaneous examples.   **64**

REVISION PAPERS 1–25   **72**

7 **NUMBER SYSTEMS INCLUDING BINARY** — conversion from one base to another — the four rules for different number bases — binary numbers.   **81**

8 **MONEY** — the four rules — miscellaneous examples.   **91**

9 **AVERAGES**   **100**

10 **RATIO AND PROPORTION** — ratio of two quantities — simplest form — increase or decrease in a given ratio — representative fraction of a map — proportional parts — direct proportion — inverse proportion — compound proportion.   **104**

11 **PERCENTAGES** — conversion of common and decimal fractions into percentages and vice versa — one number as a percentage of another — percentage change — cost price — selling price — percentage profit and loss — to find a percentage of a given value — miscellaneous examples.   **121**

12 **AREA AND VOLUME** — area of an irregular shape by counting squares — area of the square and rectangle and combinations of these — area of the parallelogram, triangle and trapezium — volume of a cuboid — open and closed rectangular box — volumes of solids with uniform cross-section.   **135**

REVISION PAPERS 26–50   **155**

PART B

13 **SIMPLE GRAPHS** — drawing a graph — currency conversion graphs — travel graphs.   **167**

14 **STATISTICS** — pictographs — pie charts — bar charts — histograms — mean — median — mode — probability.   **178**

15 **CALCULATORS AND TABLES** — squares — square roots — Pythagoras' theorem — reciprocals.   **200**

16 **LOGARITHMS** — indices — logarithms.   **210**

17 **FURTHER AREAS AND VOLUMES** — the prism — the pyramid — the circle — the annulus — arc length and sector of a circle — the cylinder — the right circular cone — the sphere — flow of liquid in a pipe — similar shapes — miscellaneous examples.   **226**

18 **TAXES** — income tax — PAYE — value added tax (VAT) — capital gains tax — capital transfer tax. **268**

19 **INCOME** — methods of payment: hourly, piecework, commission, salaries — gross and net wages/salaries — deductions: income tax, national insurance, pension schemes — social benefits. **280**

REVISION PAPERS 51–75 **298**

20 **SIMPLE AND COMPOUND INTEREST** — simple interest including inverse problems — compound interest: compound interest table, compound interest formula — appreciation and depreciation. **315**

21 **BORROWING MONEY** — mortgages — hire-purchase — credit cards. **338**

22 **HOUSEHOLD AND MOTOR EXPENSES** — rates — gas, electricity and telephone bills — cost of running a motorcycle or car — insurance on house, contents, car and motorcycle. **351**

23 **HOLIDAYS AND TRAVEL** — distance tables — the 24 hour clock — timetables — time zones — foreign exchange — package holidays — travel insurance. **382**

24 **STOCKS AND SHARES; BANKRUPTCY** — buying and selling stocks — brokerage — types of shares — buying and selling shares — bankruptcy. **399**

25 **IMPERIAL UNITS** **419**

26 **CHANGE OF UNITS** **426**

REVISION PAPERS 76–100 **430**

EXAMINATION QUESTIONS PAPERS 1–15 **446**

USEFUL FACTS AND FORMULAE **467**

ANSWERS **471**

INDEX **519**

PREFACE

This two-part book offers a complete course in General Arithmetic covering all the topics examined at CSE and 'O' level by the various examining boards. It may also be used by students following RSA, BEC and TEC courses, as well as those hoping to obtain certificates of proficiency in arithmetic including the new AEB examinations in Basic Arithmetic and Proficiency in Arithmetic.

A comprehensive range of examples is offered, supported by a simple down-to-earth text which includes several hundred worked examples. The number and range of difficulty of the exercises is such that, while there is sufficient to keep the weaker student fully occupied, there are also numerous questions which the best of students will find demanding.

The book is presented in two parts:

Part A covers the basic arithmetic normally studied during the first three years in the secondary school, which inevitably requires reinforcement in the fourth and subsequent years.

Part B is mainly concerned with civic and social arithmetic. While some of the topics are frequently introduced in the third year, its primary aim is to satisfy fourth and fifth-year students, as well as those 16+ students who, in various educational establishments, are aiming to make their knowledge of the subject as complete as possible.

Revision papers are given at regular intervals and a chapter is included specifically dealing with imperial units, since these are still required by many industries and certain examining bodies.

Another aim of the book is to provide a reservoir of examples at all levels, which I hope will enable readers to become better informed and more useful citizens.

Many of those who use this book will be the proud owners of electronic calculators. Provided the examination rules allow it, their use should be encouraged, for I believe that they will open a new door to the many students who previously became bogged down in the mechanics of the four rules when any numbers other than the simplest occurred.

It should be realised that the use of a calculator places an even greater emphasis on estimation and approximation and, therefore, on the understanding of basic arithmetic.

I would like to thank my former colleague, Mr Tom Thomas, for all the hard work he has put in checking through the answers, as well as Mr John Roberts, MA, and Mr Wyn Davies, BA, for the kind suggestions they made after reading the typescript. Finally I am indebted to the following examining boards for permission to use their questions:

Associated Examining Board (AEB)
Joint Matriculation Board (JMB)
Oxford and Cambridge Schools Examination Board (O & C)
Southern Universities Joint Board (SU)
Welsh Joint Education Committee (WJEC)

Ewart Smith
1983

PART
A

1

WHOLE NUMBERS

EXERCISE 1   NUMBERS IN WORDS AND FIGURES

Write the following numbers in figures:

1. Three thousand and twenty-seven
2. Five thousand one hundred and seventy-six
3. Nine thousand five hundred
4. Four thousand eight hundred and forty-two
5. Sixteen thousand and fifty
6. Twelve thousand eight hundred and seventy-two
7. One thousand seven hundred and eighty-three
8. Twenty-two thousand nine hundred
9. Four hundred thousand
10. One hundred and ten thousand
11. Eighteen thousand and forty
12. Four thousand and three
13. Thirteen hundred thousand
14. Eight thousand six hundred and thirty
15. One hundred thousand and seventy-two
16. Seven thousand and eighty-seven
17. Forty-seven thousand eight hundred and sixty-five
18. Five hundred and fifty thousand seven hundred
19. Two million five hundred thousand
20. Thirteen million five hundred and seventy-two.

Write the following numbers in words:

21. 426   **22.** 927   **23.** 126   **24.** 430

25. 655   **26.** 926   **27.** 1500   **28.** 3750

29. 82 000   **30.** 67 500   **31.** 347 005   **32.** 592 070

33. 142 560   **34.** 872 660   **35.** 394 000   **36.** 462 500

37. 500 873   **38.** 892 660   **39.** 1 270 000

40. 3 050 047.

EXERCISE 2   ADDITION

1. 34
43
—

2. 62
15
—

3. 47
51
—

4. 71
18
—

5. 45
53
—

6. 27
43
—

7. 35
55
—

8. 52
38
—

9. 44
36
—

10. 29
41
—

11. 16
25
—

12. 27
44
—

13. 65
29
—

14. 56
35
—

15. 47
39
—

16. 27
83
—

17. 49
57
—

18. 63
79
—

19. 48
56
—

20. 33
88
—

21. 31
214
512
—

22. 22
703
154
—

23. 315
42
420
—

24. 155
510
23
—

25. 430
521
47
—

26. 134
212
431
—

27. 514
142
223
—

28. 641
233
113
—

29. 270
309
120
—

30. 105
482
312
—

31. 127
314
124
—

32. 315
414
123
—

33. 516
     214
     233
     ───

34. 142
     326
     534
     ───

35. 138
     128
     714
     ───

36. 731
     148
     170
     ───

37. 233
     581
     174
     ───

38. 282
     351
     366
     ───

39. 114
     238
     429
     ───

40. 331
     269
     307
     ───

41. 921
     342
     625
     ───

42. 711
     822
     353
     ───

43. 931
     223
     444
     ───

44. 731
     823
     925
     ───

45. 622
     651
     716
     ───

46. 374
     255
     165
     ───

47. 516
     434
     915
     ───

48. 372
     149
     165
     ───

49. 527
     443
     849
     ───

50. 748
     627
     324
     ───

51. 493
     614
     728
     ───

52. 592
     115
     638
     ───

53. 421
     537
     654
     ───

54. 792
     535
     292
     ───

55. 817
     443
     593
     ───

56. 463
     592
     137
     ───

57. 926
     321
     743
     ───

58. 517
     728
     395
     ───

59. 826
     430
     994
     ───

60. 621
     126
     632
     ───

61.   24
      317
     9280
     ───

62.   142
       37
     8034
     ───

63. 5319
      928
       64
     ───

64.   584
     6741
       93
     ───

65. 8264
       73
      547
     ───

66.   923
      417
     2934
     ───

67. 6214
      327
      436
     ───

68.   423
     5911
      732
     ───

69.	2656	70.	716	71.	9261	72.	627
	431		593		437		5219
	724		3714		563		856

73.	736	74.	927	75.	8624	76.	2064
	391		7814		698		5214
	6241		338		532		1828

77.	5129	78.	2174	79.	3893	80.	5624
	1427		3924		2636		3093
	2173		4315		1418		1174

81.	5936	82.	6923	83.	9537	84.	4079
	4285		5473		2143		5321
	7261		3364		6572		1505

85.	7438	86.	2420	87.	5390	88.	9281
	6537		263		537		4416
	1293		5142		829		327
			619		7241		782

89.	176	90.	362	91.	7241	92.	2451
	2439		9211		3789		4157
	7210		655		5253		3624
	826		3140		742		931

93.	4319	94.	9280	95.	320	96.	4261
	526		4265		4217		5372
	3345		371		5235		3649
	2785		5117		9629		2143

97.	5921	98.	7437	99.	1049	100.	9210
	3726		4126		8216		8571
	2937		3324		5566		2239
	6273		3324		7243		3591

101.	47 321	102.	65 784	103.	46 357	104.	22 533
	52 164		56 225		83 465		77 345
	39 207		13 567		43 678		56 920
	15 367		30 057		67 448		36 378

4

105.	84 567 98 254 30 574 12 217	**106.**	21 437 37 214 92 956 72 140 36 210	**107.**	68 433 76 843 13 568 54 763 57 802	**108.**	33 245 46 233 26 354 66 833 50 764

109.	22 647 12 997 84 562 45 267 77 880	**110.**	85 572 53 882 43 378 99 837 56 600

111. $262 + 345 + 826$

112. $592 + 437 + 127$

113. $927 + 412 + 816$

114. $347 + 727 + 839$

115. $614 + 824 + 334$

116. $539 + 224 + 739$

117. $2436 + 413 + 7264$

118. $5146 + 2475 + 9265$

119. $1342 + 6149 + 7343$

120. $2143 + 5114 + 8263$

121. $9624 + 41\,739 + 536$

122. $724 + 4165 + 16\,347$

123. $11\,434 + 2963 + 736$

124. $32\,692 + 515 + 8173$

125. $36\,424 + 59\,364 + 1166$

126. $8164 + 14\,392 + 31\,519$

127. $87\,419 + 23\,550 + 51\,962$

128. $15\,437 + 75\,392 + 63\,420$

129. $32\,711 + 59\,267 + 22\,624$

130. $31\,415 + 51\,163 + 72\,344$

131. Find the sum of all the numbers from 1 to 20.

132. Find the sum of all the even numbers from 98 to 124.

133. Find the sum of all the odd numbers from 159 to 163.

134. Find the sum of all the whole numbers between 19 and 43 which are exactly divisible by 5.

135. In a local election Mrs Addicott receives 1264 votes, Mr Beanham 972 votes, Mrs Capstick 53 votes and Mr Dearnley 474 votes. How many people voted?

136. In a parliamentary election the votes cast were as follows: Miss Edwards 8492, Mrs Shorey 24 537, Mr Grafter 16 934 and Mr Gibson 4219. In addition there were 143 spoilt voting papers and 7246 registered voters failed to record their vote. Find the size of the total electorate.

137. During the first six months of the year the following numbers visited a zoo: 1649, 2434, 4621, 12 047, 27 267 and 35 937. Find the total number of visitors during the six month period.

138. Motorway exits along a certain section of the M4 are numbered 5 to 27. How many exits are there in that section?

139. Last year the number of vehicles each month failing to obtain an MOT certificate at Bryant's Vehicle Testing Station were as follows: 26, 13, 8, 15, 41, 12, 9, 17, 24, 19, 17, 24. Find the total number of failures for the year.

140. During the last week of January the number of new cars leaving a factory was: Monday 934, Tuesday 1026, Wednesday 1139, Thursday 1243 and Friday 976. How many cars left the factory during the week?

EXERCISE 3   SUBTRACTION

1. 57 42 —	2. 95 64 —	3. 47 36 —	4. 79 57 —
5. 68 25 —	6. 429 217 —	7. 538 307 —	8. 792 682 —
9. 645 531 —	10. 384 213 —	11. 82 64 —	12. 56 39 —
13. 42 37 —	14. 83 67 —	15. 73 27 —	16. 242 127 —
17. 638 309 —	18. 436 219 —	19. 584 156 —	20. 725 518 —
21. 572 284 —	22. 415 187 —	23. 633 268 —	24. 725 589 —
25. 814 276 —	26. 4462 3421 —	27. 3718 1407 —	28. 4231 3111 —
29. 5926 2615 —	30. 8756 3423 —	31. 5934 2155 —	32. 8261 3189 —

33.	9114	34.	3720	35.	6535	36.	3178
	1076		1077		3489		1689

37.	4629	38.	5198	39.	7266	40.	8431
	2733		1589		2378		4597

41.	73 400	42.	56 592	43.	14 634	44.	32 420
	24 387		39 447		11 894		15 555

45. 92 705
    24 887

Subtract the second number from the first:

46. 5437, 2466   47. 8293, 1739

48. 4537, 934   49. 16 421, 8734

50. 24 214, 16 845.

Subtract the first number from the second:

51. 473, 5294   52. 892, 1004

53. 3412, 20 040   54. 15 721, 24 827

55. 3492, 10 477.

Simplify:

56. $526 + 137 + 293 - 756$ 57. $743 - 93 - 47 - 236$

58. $127 + 539 - 464 - 98$ 59. $35 + 242 - 63 - 129$

60. $1000 - 327 - 113 - 424$ 61. $446 - 314 + 27 - 68$

62. $2000 - 573 - 78 - 498$

63. $5274 - 167 - 87 - 3421 - 245$

64. $1263 - 2114 + 1737 - 142 - 34$

65. $154 - 726 - 2241 + 3440.$

66. What number must be added to 1472 to give 5664?

67. What number must be added to 732 to give 1021?

68. What number must be added to 5637 to give 24 371?

69. What number must be added to 1249 to give 7374?

70. Subtract three hundred and thirty-four from seven hundred and ninety-seven.

71. Subtract two hundred and forty-nine from five hundred and fifty-six.

72. Subtract three hundred and fifty-seven from nine hundred and seventy-three.

73. Subtract four thousand three hundred and seventy-one from sixteen thousand.

74. Subtract five thousand five hundred and forty-seven from ten thousand.

75. Subtract nine thousand two hundred and sixty-four from twenty-nine thousand seven hundred and seventy-six.

76. The crowd at Old Trafford for a first division game on a particular Saturday was 45 427 but on the following Saturday 4937 fewer spectators turned up. What was the attendance for the second game?

77. On consecutive Saturdays the attendance at Portman Road was 35 472 and 32 789. Find the decrease in attendance.

78. In a large school there are 127 fewer pupils this year than last year, and it is expected that there will be a further fall of 88 pupils next year. If there are 1347 pupils in the school this year, calculate the number of pupils (a) in the school last year, (b) expected to be in the school next year.

79. In a school with 1395 pupils there are 47 more girls than boys. How many boys are there?

80. In a factory with a workforce consisting of 265 men, 569 women and 102 young people, 788 people are paid a weekly wage while the remainder receive an annual salary. How many are paid a salary?

EXERCISE 4   MULTIPLICATION

1. 34×5	2. 42×6	3. 29×7	4. 52×8
5. 72×4	6. 94×5	7. 78×3	8. 47×9
9. 242×5	10. 163×7	11. 521×4	12. 763×2
13. 372×7	14. 314×9	15. 824×6	16. 916×4
17. 615×3	18. 342×8	19. 241×7	20. 528×5
21. 154×20	22. 213×30	23. 621×40	24. 451×50
25. 759×60	26. 448×70	27. 139×80	28. 291×90
29. 49×53	30. 37×42	31. 14×53	32. 56×27
33. 67×32	34. 75×47	35. 53×16	36. 44×73

37.	98 × 56	38.	82 × 41	39.	57 × 24	40.	27 × 54
41.	87 × 21	42.	42 × 29	43.	63 × 51	44.	72 × 43
45.	65 × 98	46.	43 × 55	47.	73 × 32	48.	31 × 82
49.	13 × 19	50.	27 × 54	51.	73 × 32	52.	67 × 44
53.	73 × 83	54.	84 × 92	55.	96 × 97	56.	34 × 95
57.	220 × 21	58.	162 × 24	59	313 × 32	60.	415 × 33
61.	520 × 26	62.	724 × 42	63.	272 × 51	64.	413 × 46
65.	372 × 61	66.	518 × 72	67.	472 × 81	68.	754 × 84
69.	425 × 56	70.	671 × 44	71.	824 × 36	72.	339 × 27
73.	812 × 74	74.	641 × 56	75.	592 × 68	76.	392 × 85
77.	558 × 91	78.	637 × 94	79.	748 × 97	80.	829 × 96
81.	220 × 124	82.	720 × 222	83.	635 × 321		
84.	913 × 504	85.	421 × 312	86.	527 × 213		
87.	641 × 421	88.	513 × 632	89.	531 × 748		
90.	293 × 678	91.	913 × 543	92.	816 × 378		
93.	917 × 413	94.	921 × 173	95.	492 × 317		
96.	646 × 821	97.	636 × 325	98.	749 × 527		
99.	827 × 514	100.	752 × 926				

101. Multiply the sum of 42 and 93 by their difference.

102. Multiply the sum of 59 and 104 by their difference.

103. Multiply the sum of 72 and 237 by their difference.

104. Multiply the sum of 242 and 173 by their difference.

105. Multiply the sum of 372 and 843 by their difference.

106. On a particular day a supermarket sells 76 large packets of ginger biscuits, 47 medium packets and 82 small packets. If a large packet contains 36 biscuits, a medium packet 24 and a small packet 18, how many biscuits were sold on that day?

107. A bus company operates 27 fifty-seater buses, 14 forty-five-seater buses and 5 eighteen-seater buses. How many seats does the bus company have available?

108. At a concert 247 seats were sold at £7 each, 534 at £5 each and 413 at £3 each. Find the total amount of money taken.

109. A soccer player estimates that he runs 9 miles during a match. If he plays twice a week for a thirty-six week season, find the total distance he has run during the season's matches.

110. A bus from Franton to Highlow travels a distance of 28 miles
each way. Each day, a bus starts from Franton at 7 a.m. and takes
4 hours for a round trip. It returns to Franton for the last time at
11 p.m. Find the total distance travelled by the bus in (a) a week,
(b) a year.

EXERCISE 5 DIVISION

Divide:

1.	612 by 4	2.	1535 by 5
3.	1446 by 6	4.	5341 by 7
5.	336 by 8	6.	1575 by 9
7.	6545 by 11	8.	1176 by 12
9.	8112 by 13	10.	5936 by 14
11.	1397 by 11	12.	4644 by 9
13.	6258 by 21	14.	4064 by 16
15.	1258 by 17	16.	7536 by 24
17.	6020 by 35	18.	2277 by 33
19.	26 164 by 62	20.	12 528 by 54
21.	6888 by 84	22.	44 091 by 71
23.	19 928 by 47	24.	13 230 by 54
25.	98 332 by 124	26.	40 812 by 76
27.	28 213 by 89	28.	202 370 by 245
29.	53 573 by 317	30.	77 322 by 789.

Divide, giving quotient and remainder:

31.	436 by 9	32.	529 by 7
33.	613 by 8	34.	873 by 6
35.	447 by 8	36.	693 by 9
37.	443 by 11	38.	926 by 12
39.	734 by 14	40.	1429 by 16
41.	2936 by 17	42.	4453 by 13
43.	8264 by 19	44.	7436 by 24
45.	5916 by 18	46.	2426 by 54
47.	9264 by 63	48.	3373 by 42

49.	4246 by 37	50.	7369 by 49

51. 2537 by 82   52. 92 984 by 126

53. 71 564 by 361   54. 33 925 by 417

55. 11 424 by 314   56. 53 615 by 424

57. 49 937 by 636   58. 245 678 by 597

59. 89 345 by 852   60. 714 394 by 948.

61. Divide twenty-two thousand seven hundred and twenty-four by ninety-two.

62. Divide eighteen thousand seven hundred and forty-six by two hundred and thirty-two.

63. Divide two hundred and twenty-two thousand four hundred and forty by six hundred and sixty-four.

64. Divide ninety-one thousand two hundred and sixty-four by seven hundred and thirty-six.

65. Divide fifty-nine thousand five hundred and eight by one thousand and forty-four.

66. Divide the sum of 959 and 685 by their difference.

67. Divide the sum of 1455 and 873 by their difference.

68. Divide the product of 357 and 408 by their difference.

69. Divide the product of 64 and 35 by their sum.

70. Divide the product of 126 and 84 by their sum.

71. In a library a bookshelf will take 47 books. How many shelves are required for 4371 books?

72. Forty-nine-seater coaches are available to transport air passengers from the airport to the city centre. If 1255 passengers are to be transported, how many coaches will be required, and how many spare seats will there be on the last coach assuming that all the others are full?

73. My car burns 1 gallon of petrol for every 38 miles. How many gallons will be required for a journey of 608 miles?

74. There are 1428 pupils in a school with a teaching staff of 84. How many pupils is this for each teacher?

75. A cardboard carton will hold 72 tins of baked beans. How many cartons are required to pack 4680 tins of beans?

76. Cigars are packed in packets of 3. How many packets are required to pack 855 cigars?

77. A factory produces 3545 car wheels in a week. If each car requires 5 wheels, how many cars does this cater for?

78. The borough council allocates £7 627 000 for new houses. If each house is estimated to cost £14 500 to build, how many houses do they intend to build?

79. How many 2 kilogram packets of sugar may be filled from a 5 tonne delivery? (1 tonne = 1000 kilograms)

80. How many egg boxes, each of which will hold 6 eggs, are required to pack 1000 eggs? How many eggs are there in the last box?

81. If sound travels at 330 metres per second, how long will it take for a person 1980 metres away to hear a clap of thunder?

82. Lamp standards are placed at 50 metre intervals. If the last standard on a stretch of road is 2150 metres from the first, how many standards are there?

83. A mail order firm has £14 000 to spend on promoting a new product. If it costs 35p to send to each household, how many households will they be able to send to?

84. How many years, each with 365 days, are there in 16 425 days?

85. There are 321 516 voters in the county of Centreshire. For local elections the county is divided into regions, each region having 2748 voters. Into how many regions will the county be divided?

EXERCISE 6   MISCELLANEOUS EXAMPLES

1. A palette of building blocks consists of five layers each containing 27 blocks. How many palettes of blocks must be ordered if a particular building is expected to require 112 000 blocks?

2. There are 12 460 cans of peas in the stock room of a hypermarket. If 76 boxes, each containing 72 cans, are taken from the stock to display on the shelves, how many cans remain in stock?

3. In a school with 743 pupils it is estimated that each pupil uses 15 exercise books in a year. At the beginning of the school year there are 2434 new books in stock, and during the year the school receives two deliveries, each of 5500 new books. How many books remain in stock at the end of the school year?

4. A 1600 metre length of road is to be fenced off on both sides. If a roll of fencing is 33 metres long, how many rolls are required, and how much is left over?

5. A catering pack for a certain jam contains 5000 grams of jam. If 12 grams of jam is used in each jam tart, how many tarts may be made from five catering packs?

6. Thirty-two children in a class collect tokens in order to send for games which are advertised on a cornflakes packet. Each child collects 17 tokens and 50 tokens are required for each game. How many games would they be able to send for?

7. A bookseller purchases 42 packets of a new book, each packet containing 24 books. He stores them in his shop on shelves. How many shelves would be required if each shelf will house 56 books?

8. At a concert 245 people pay £8 each, 413 pay £5 each and 349 pay £3 each. Calculate (a) the total receipts, (b) the profit after expenses of £3785 have been paid.

9. It costs £17 925 for an aeroplane to fly between two cities. If 264 passengers make the flight, travelling either first class or tourist, calculate the profit on the flight given that the 52 first class passengers each pay a fare twice that of the tourist class passenger's fare of £63.

10. A lorry proprietor owns twelve 20 tonne lorries, five 15 tonne lorries and forty-two 10 tonne lorries. How many journeys would each lorry make to remove 30 870 tonnes of materials, assuming that all the lorries make the same number of journeys?

SEQUENCES AND SERIES

Consider the sets of numbers:

(a)   2, 4, 6, 8, ...
(b)   4, 16, 36, 64, ...

In each set the numbers are in a definite order and there is a rule for obtaining any number from the number which comes before it. For example in (a) the even numbers are listed in order, the next two being 10 and 12, whereas in (b) the even numbers have been squared, the next two being 100 and 144. Such a set of numbers is called a *sequence*.

When terms are added together we have a *series*. Thus $2 + 4 + 6 + 8 + 10 + 12$ ... and $4 + 16 + 36 + 64 + ...$ are examples of series. Whether we consider the next term for a sequence or for a series, the rule for finding it is the same.

EXAMPLE 1   Write down the next two terms in the sequence $0, 3, 8, 15, \ldots$.

The next two terms will be 24 and 35 since the sequence is formed by squaring the natural numbers $1, 2, 3, 4, 5, 6, \ldots$, and subtracting 1 each time; or $0, {}^{+3}3, {}^{+5}8, {}^{+7}15, {}^{+9}24, {}^{+11}35$.

EXAMPLE 2   Write down the next two terms in the sequence 1, 3, 9, 27, ...

This time the rule is to multiply the preceding term by 3. The next two terms are therefore 81 and 243.

EXAMPLE 3   Find the next two terms in the series $1 + 7 + 15 + 25 + \ldots$.

The rth term is $r^2 + 3(r-1)$

i.e. $r = 1$ gives $1^2 + 3(1-1) = 1$
      $r = 2$ gives $2^2 + 3(2-1) = 7$
      $r = 3$ gives $3^2 + 3(3-1) = 15$
      $r = 4$ gives $4^2 + 3(4-1) = 25$
      $r = 5$ gives $5^2 + 3(5-1) = 37$
      $r = 6$ gives $6^2 + 3(6-1) = 51$

$\therefore$ The next two terms are 37 and 51.

EXERCISE 7

Find the next two terms in each of the following sequences:

1. $1, 2, 3, 4, \ldots$ 2. $4, 0, -4, -8, \ldots$

3. $4, 6, 8, 10, \ldots$ 4. $1, 2, 4, 8, \ldots$

5. $4, 7, 10, 13, 16, \ldots$ 6. $24, 12, 6, 3, \ldots$

7. $1, 8, 27, 64, \ldots$ 8. $3, -4, -11, \ldots$

9. $1, -8, 27, -64, \ldots$ 10. $20, 27, 34, 41, \ldots$

11. $1, -2, -5, -8, \ldots$ 12. $8, 4, 1, -1, \ldots$

13. $3, 7, 12, 18, \ldots$ 14. $0, 2, 6, 12, \ldots$.

Find the next two terms in each of the following series:

15. $1 + 3 + 5 + 7 + \ldots$ 16. $1 + 4 + 9 + 16 + \ldots$

17. $10 + 15 + 20 + 25 + \ldots$ 18. $1 - 4 + 9 - 16 + \ldots$

19. $30 + 20 + 10 + \ldots$ 20. $10 + 9 + 8 + 7 + \ldots$

21. $12 - 10 + 8 - 6 + \ldots$ 22. $50 - 35 + 20 - 5 + \ldots$

23. $100 + 10 + 1 + \ldots$ 24. $100 + 20 + 4 + \ldots$

25. $19 + 15 + 11 + 7 \ldots$ 26. $3 + 5 + 9 + 17 + \ldots$

27. $19 + 18 + 16 + 13 + \ldots$ 28. $72 + 50 + 32 + 18 + \ldots$

29. $-11 + 7 - 3 + \ldots$ 30. $0 + 4 + 18 + 48 + \ldots$.

2

FACTORS
AND MULTIPLES

PRIME NUMBERS

Since 12 is exactly divisible by 2 we say that 2 is a *factor* of 12, and 12
is a *multiple* of 2. Similarly, 2, 3, 4 and 6 are factors of 24 and 24 is a
multiple of each of the numbers 2, 3, 4 and 6. A number which has no
factor apart from itself and 1 is called a *prime number*. Prime numbers
in ascending order are 2, 3, 5, 7, 11, 13, 17, 19, 23, 29, 31, ... (Note
that 1 is not a prime number.)

It is often convenient to express a number in terms of prime numbers

e.g. $\qquad 12 = 2 \times 2 \times 3$

and $\qquad 378 = 2 \times 3 \times 3 \times 3 \times 7$

In mathematics we are often trying to reduce the amount of writing,
and here we can write:

$\qquad 2 \times 2 \qquad$ as $\qquad 2^2$

and $\qquad 3 \times 3 \times 3 \qquad$ as $\qquad 3^3$

We read these as '2 *to the power or index of* 2', or two squared and '3
to the power or index of 3' or three cubed.

Similarly $\qquad 5 \times 5 \times 5 \times 5 = 5^4 \qquad$ (5 to the power 4)

and $\qquad 7 \times 7 \times 7 = 7^3 \qquad$ (7 to the power 3)

Extending the idea to the two numbers given above:

$\qquad 12 = 2^2 \times 3 \qquad$ and $\qquad 378 = 2 \times 3^3 \times 7$

EXAMPLE 1 Express $2 \times 2 \times 3 \times 3 \times 3 \times 5 \times 3 \times 2$ in index form.

In index form this becomes $2^3 \times 3^4 \times 5$.

EXAMPLE 2 Multiply $2^4 \times 2^3$.

$$2^4 \times 2^3 = (2 \times 2 \times 2 \times 2) \times (2 \times 2 \times 2)$$
$$= 2 \times 2 \times 2 \times 2 \times 2 \times 2 \times 2$$
$$= 2^7$$

(Note that the indices are *added* together i.e. $4 + 3 = 7$.)

Similarly $3^5 \times 3^2 = 3^7$

and $5^8 \times 5^3 = 5^{11}$

EXAMPLE 3 Find the value of $3^3 \times 5^2$.

$$3^3 \times 5^2 = 27 \times 25$$
$$= 675$$

EXAMPLE 4 Express $3^4 \times 3^5 \div 3^7$ in prime factors in index form.

$$\frac{3^4 \times 3^5}{3^7} = \frac{3^9}{3^7} \qquad (Add\ the\ indices\ when\ multiplying)$$

$$= 3^2 \qquad (Subtract\ the\ indices\ when\ dividing)$$

EXAMPLE 5 Express 5096 in prime factors.

$$
\begin{array}{r|r}
2 & 5096 \\
2 & 2548 \\
2 & 1274 \\
7 & 637 \\
7 & 91 \\
13 & 13 \\
& 1
\end{array}
$$

$\therefore\ 5096 = 2^3 \times 7^2 \times 13$

The square root of a number is the number which when multiplied by itself gives the given number. It is denoted by the symbol $\sqrt{\ }$.

e.g. $\sqrt{16} = 4$ since $4 \times 4 = 16$

$\sqrt{144} = 12$ since $12 \times 12 = 144$

EXAMPLE 6   Express 19 600 in prime factors and hence find its square root.

$$\begin{array}{r|r}
2 & 19\,600 \\
2 & 9800 \\
2 & 4900 \\
2 & 2450 \\
5 & 1225 \\
5 & 245 \\
7 & 49 \\
7 & 7 \\
& 1
\end{array}$$

$\therefore\ 19\,600 = 2^4 \times 5^2 \times 7^2$

or $19\,600 = (2^2 \times 5 \times 7) \times (2^2 \times 5 \times 7)$

$= (2^2 \times 5 \times 7)^2$

$\therefore\ \sqrt{19\,600} = 2^2 \times 5 \times 7 = 140$

i.e. the square root is found by halving each index.

Similarly $\sqrt{54\,756} = \sqrt{2^2 \times 3^4 \times 13^2} = 2 \times 3^2 \times 13 = 234$.

EXERCISE 8

Express the following in prime factors in index form:

1. $3 \times 3 \times 3 \times 5 \times 7 \times 7 \times 5 \times 3$
2. $2 \times 2 \times 11 \times 11 \times 11$
3. $3 \times 2 \times 2 \times 5 \times 2 \times 2 \times 5 \times 2$
4. $3 \times 3 \times 5 \times 7 \times 3 \times 5 \times 5 \times 7$
5. $3^2 \times 3^5$
6. $2^4 \times 2^2 \times 2$
7. $5^8 \div 5^4$
8. $3^4 \times 3^2 \div 3^3$
9. 3×12
10. $4 \times 8 \times 16$
11. $10^2 \times 10^3$
12. $10^3 \times 10^4 \div 100$
13. $2^5 \times 2^2 \div 2^3$
14. $5^5 \div (5^2 \times 5^3)$
15. 12×27.

Find the values of:

16. $2^2 \times 3^2$
17. $2^2 \times 3^2 \times 5$
18. $2^3 \times 3^2 \times 5^2$
19. $2^4 \times 3^3$
20. $2^2 \times 3^3 \times 5^2$.

Express the following in prime factors:

21. 36
22. 48
23. 108
24. 252
25. 144
26. 675
27. 1715
28. 216
29. 1568
30. 210
31. 864
32. 875
33. 1125
34. 2835
35. 6075
36. 1280
37. 1936
38. 1144
39. 41 503
40. 30 030.

Which of the following numbers are perfect squares?

41. $2^2 \times 3^2 \times 5$

42. $2^{..} \times 3^2 \times 5^2$

43. $2^4 \times 3^2 \times 11^2$

44. $3^3 \times 5^2$

45. $3^2 \times 5^4$

46. $2^2 \times 3^3 \times 5^2$

47. $3^4 \times 5^6$

48. $2^4 \times 3 \times 7^3$.

Which of the following numbers are perfect cubes?

49. $2^2 \times 3^3$ 50. $3^3 \times 5^6$ 51. $2^3 \times 5^2$ 52. $2^3 \times 5^9$.

What is the least integer (whole number) by which the following numbers must be multiplied to make them perfect squares?

53. $2^3 \times 3^2$ 54. 2×3^3 55. $2^2 \times 3^3 \times 5$

56. $2^4 \times 3^3 \times 7^2$.

What is the least integer by which the following numbers must be multiplied to make them perfect cubes?

57. $2^3 \times 3^2$ 58. $2^6 \times 3 \times 5^3$ 59. $2^4 \times 7^3$

60. $3^3 \times 5^6 \times 7^8$.

61. What is the smallest number by which 441 must be multiplied to make it a multiple of 42?

62. What is the smallest number by which 360 must be multiplied to make it a multiple of 35?

63. What is the smallest number by which 1600 must be multiplied to make it a multiple of 84?

Express each of the following numbers in prime factors using index notation and hence find their square roots:

64. 576   65. 2025   66. 1225   67. 2304

68. 2916   69. 5184   70. 5625   71. 193 600.

Express each of the following in prime numbers using index notation and hence find their cube roots:

72. 216   73. 729   74. 1728   75. 3375

76. 5832   77. 13 824.

Find the least integers by which the following numbers must be multiplied to make them perfect squares. Find the square roots of the resulting products:

78. 5200   79. 1188   80. 15 125   81. 18 375.

Find the least integers by which the following numbers must be multiplied to make them perfect cubes. Find the cube roots of the resulting products:

82. 72   83. 864   84. 27 783   85. 8575.

HIGHEST COMMON FACTOR (HCF)

A number which is a factor of two or more numbers is a common factor, e.g. 4 is a factor of 12 and 20 and thus it is a common factor of these two numbers. The largest number which is a common factor of two or more numbers is called the *highest common factor* or HCF. In the above example the HCF is 4.

Probably the easiest way of finding the HCF of two or more numbers is to express the numbers in powers of prime factors.

EXAMPLE 7   Find the HCF of 72, 252 and 600.

Expressing each number as powers of prime factors:

$$72 = 2^3 \times 3^2$$
$$252 = 2^2 \times 3^2 \times 7$$
$$600 = 2^3 \times 3 \times 5^2$$

The highest power of 2 which is a factor of each is 2^2, and the highest power of 3 is 3^1, there being no other common factor.

$$\therefore \text{HCF} = 2^2 \times 3 = 12$$

It is worth noticing that any common factor of a given set of numbers is also a factor of their difference. This can often be of use in spotting common factors.

LEAST COMMON MULTIPLE (LCM)

The *least common multiple* of two or more numbers is the least number into which each of them will divide without remainder.

EXAMPLE 8   Write down the LCM of 8 and 10.

By inspection the least common multiple of these two numbers is 40.

EXAMPLE 9   Write down the LCM of $2^2 \times 3 \times 7$ and 2×3^2 in index form.

$$LCM = 2^2 \times 3^2 \times 7$$

Each of the factors 2, 3 and 7 must be included in the LCM, the power used being the highest occurring.

EXAMPLE 10   Find the LCM of 1176, 630, 300 and 1323.

Expressing each number in prime factors in index form:

$$1176 = 2^3 \times 3 \times 7^2$$
$$630 = 2 \times 3^2 \times 5 \times 7$$
$$300 = 2^2 \times 3 \times 5^2$$
$$1323 = 3^3 \times 7^2$$

The LCM is found by taking every factor which is found in these to the highest power occurring.

Thus $LCM = 2^3 \times 3^3 \times 7^2 \times 5^2$

Since LCMs are often very large numbers they are normally left in factor form.

EXERCISE 9

Write down by inspection the HCF of:

1. 12, 16   2. 20, 30   3. 15, 20, 25   4. 18, 48

5. 12, 18   6. 51, 34   7. 8, 10, 16

8. 30, 45, 60   9. 18, 27   10. 35, 42

11. 12, 18, 42 12. 49, 84   13. 6, 12, 32

14. 9, 24, 39   15. 64, 72   16. 35, 52, 56

17. 18, 54, 72 18. 85, 68   19. 18, 27, 105

20. 42, 70, 84.

Find the HCF of the following sets of numbers, giving your answers as products of prime factors:

21. 45, 60   22. 245, 385   23. 333, 243   24. 175, 448

25. 96, 720   26. 324, 720   27. 120, 408   28. 351, 648

29. 24, 42, 54   30. 432, 768

31. 108, 162, 270   32. 224, 504, 952

33. 96, 192, 216   34. 105, 147, 196

35. 378, 462, 630   36. 624, 832, 1072
37. 275, 100, 225   38. 1485, 4725
39. 168, 392, 448   40. 456, 551, 589
41. 224, 352, 600   42. 432, 558, 702
43. 273, 975, 1638   44. 476, 672, 812
45. 350, 425, 600   46. 294, 735, 1323
47. 882, 1134, 1638   48. 792, 1296, 1728
49. 504, 952, 1176   50. 420, 525, 735.

EXERCISE 10

Write down the LCM of:

1. 5, 10   2. 10, 25   3. 12, 36   4. 3, 4, 5
5. 9, 18, 36   6. 5, 15, 20   7. 9, 18, 27   8. 21, 28
9. 15, 30, 60   10. 3, 5, 7.

Write down, in index form, the LCM of:

11. $2 \times 3^2, 2^2 \times 3$ 12. $2^3 \times 5, 2^2 \times 5^2$
13. $2^2 \times 3^4, 2^2 \times 3^2$ 14. $2^2 \times 5, 2 \times 5^3$
15. $2^2 \times 3^2, 2 \times 3^4$ 16. $3^2 \times 5, 3^3 \times 5^2$
17. $3 \times 5^3, 3^3 \times 5$ 18. $2^2 \times 3 \times 5, 3^2 \times 5^3$
19. $2 \times 3^2 \times 5, 2^2 \times 3$ 20. $2^4 \times 3 \times 5^2, 2^2 \times 3^3 \times 5^2$.

Find the LCM of the following, giving your answers in prime factors:

21. 5, 10, 15   22. 16, 18, 24
23. 16, 56, 84   24. 63, 81, 147
25. 100, 125, 150   26. 27, 36, 42
27. 64, 80, 84   28. 39, 104, 169
29. 44, 121, 66   30. 36, 48, 108
31. 18, 24, 36, 42   32. 12, 21, 28, 42
33. 25, 35, 45, 65   34. 66, 121, 143, 165
35. 84, 63, 36, 108.

FRACTIONS

COMMON FRACTIONS

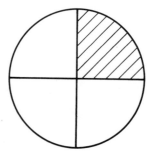

The diagram illustrates an apple tart which is divided into four equal parts (called quarters) for a family with very healthy appetites. The shaded area represents one of these parts and is one-quarter of the whole. This is written $\frac{1}{4}$ and is called a fraction. The lower number (or in this case the number of parts we divide the whole into) is called the *denominator*. The upper number indicates the number of fourth parts taken, and is called the *numerator*. Similarly the unshaded area represents three pieces, each of which is one-quarter of the whole. We write this as $\frac{3}{4}$, the denominator is 4 and the numerator 3.

EXERCISE 11

1. Write the following as fractions: one-half, five-eighths, seven-twentieths, thirteen-sixty-fourths, nine-thirty-seconds.

2. Write the following fractions in words:

$$\frac{9}{20}, \frac{3}{8}, \frac{21}{29}, \frac{31}{100}, \frac{137}{200}.$$

3. Write down the value of: half of 10 p, three-quarters of £1, seven-eighths of £2, four-twentieths of 1 metre, one-tenth of an hour, two-thirds of a day.

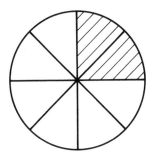

To return to our apple tart, if it had been divided into eight equal parts, each part as a fraction would be written $\frac{1}{8}$. The shaded area is two such parts or $\frac{2}{8}$ and is obviously exactly the same as the shaded area given earlier i.e. $\frac{2}{8} = \frac{1}{4}$.

Similarly we could show that $\frac{5}{20} = \frac{4}{16} = \frac{3}{12} = \frac{2}{8} = \frac{1}{4}$.

All these fractions are equal in value. We thus see that the value of a fraction is unchanged if the numerator and denominator are divided (or multiplied) by the same number.

Thus
$$\frac{12}{18} = \frac{2}{3} = \frac{30}{45}$$

EXAMPLE 1   Reduce $\dfrac{63}{81}$ to its lowest terms.

Dividing the numerator and denominator by 9 gives:

$$\frac{63}{81} = \frac{7}{9}$$

EXAMPLE 2   Reduce $\dfrac{1260}{2016}$ to its lowest terms.

$$\frac{1260}{2016} = \frac{315}{504} \qquad \text{(dividing numerator and denominator by 4)}$$

$$= \frac{45}{72} \qquad \text{(dividing numerator and denominator by 7)}$$

$$= \frac{5}{8} \qquad \text{(dividing numerator and denominator by 9)}$$

$$\therefore \quad \frac{1260}{2016} = \frac{5}{8}$$

EXAMPLE 3   Express $\dfrac{5}{9}$ with a denominator of 36.

$$\frac{5}{9} = \frac{20}{36} \qquad \text{(multiplying top and bottom by 4)}$$

It is frequently convenient to place fractions in ascending or descending order by expressing all of them with the same denominator.

EXAMPLE 4   Arrange the following in ascending order:

$$\frac{1}{2}, \ \frac{5}{8}, \ \frac{9}{12}, \ \frac{7}{16}.$$

We require the LCM of the denominator, i.e. the lowest number they will all divide into exactly. LCM is 48.

Then $\dfrac{1}{2} = \dfrac{24}{48}, \quad \dfrac{5}{8} = \dfrac{30}{48}, \quad \dfrac{9}{12} = \dfrac{36}{48}, \quad \dfrac{7}{16} = \dfrac{21}{48}$

i.e. the numbers placed in ascending order are $\dfrac{21}{48}, \dfrac{24}{48}, \dfrac{30}{48}, \dfrac{36}{48}$ or $\dfrac{7}{16}, \dfrac{1}{2}, \dfrac{5}{8}, \dfrac{9}{12}.$

EXAMPLE 5   Arrange the following in descending order:

$$\frac{1}{4}, \ \frac{9}{16}, \ \frac{3}{5}, \ \frac{7}{20}.$$

The LCM of the denominator is 80.

Then $\dfrac{1}{4} = \dfrac{20}{80}, \quad \dfrac{9}{16} = \dfrac{45}{80}, \quad \dfrac{3}{5} = \dfrac{48}{80}, \quad \dfrac{11}{20} = \dfrac{44}{80}$

i.e. the numbers placed in descending order are $\dfrac{48}{80}, \dfrac{45}{80}, \dfrac{44}{80}, \dfrac{20}{80}$ or $\dfrac{3}{5}, \dfrac{9}{16}, \dfrac{11}{20}, \dfrac{1}{4}.$

A fraction in which the numerator is less than the denominator is called a *proper fraction* e.g. $\frac{1}{2}, \frac{3}{4}, \frac{4}{5}$, etc., whereas a fraction in which the numerator is greater than the denominator is called an *improper fraction* e.g. $\frac{3}{2}, \frac{4}{3}, \frac{5}{4}$, etc.

Both proper and improper fractions are examples of common or vulgar fractions.

An improper fraction may be expressed as a *mixed number*, consisting of a whole number together with a fraction.

e.g.
$$\frac{5}{4} = \frac{4}{4} + \frac{1}{4}$$
$$= 1 + \frac{1}{4}$$
$$= 1\frac{1}{4}$$

and
$$\frac{31}{9} = \frac{27}{9} + \frac{4}{9}$$
$$= 3 + \frac{4}{9}$$
$$= 3\frac{4}{9}$$

Do not leave an answer as an improper fraction — change it to a mixed number.

EXERCISE 12

1. Reduce the following fractions to their lowest terms:

(a) $\dfrac{36}{60}$ (b) $\dfrac{75}{100}$ (c) $\dfrac{144}{324}$ (d) $\dfrac{48}{400}$

(e) $\dfrac{63}{112}$ (f) $\dfrac{115}{276}$ (g) $\dfrac{362}{676}$ (h) $\dfrac{147}{315}$

(i) $\dfrac{529}{667}$ (j) $\dfrac{207}{351}$ (k) $\dfrac{252}{684}$ (l) $\dfrac{272}{952}$

(m) $\dfrac{714}{882}$ (n) $\dfrac{465}{540}$ (o) $\dfrac{1368}{1728}$.

2. Complete:

(a) $\dfrac{3}{4} = \dfrac{}{16}$ (b) $\dfrac{3}{4} = \dfrac{15}{}$ (c) $\dfrac{2}{5} = \dfrac{}{20}$ (d) $\dfrac{5}{9} = \dfrac{35}{}$

(e) $\dfrac{8}{7} = \dfrac{}{56}$ (f) $\dfrac{2}{9} = \dfrac{}{63}$ (g) $\dfrac{}{11} = \dfrac{96}{132}$

(h) $\dfrac{7}{} = \dfrac{56}{64}$ (i) $\dfrac{5}{} = \dfrac{65}{117}$ (j) $\dfrac{7}{12} = \dfrac{252}{}$.

3. Arrange the following fractions in ascending order:

(a) $\dfrac{1}{4}, \dfrac{1}{3}, \dfrac{3}{8}$ (b) $\dfrac{5}{9}, \dfrac{4}{7}, \dfrac{2}{3}$

(c) $\dfrac{1}{3}, \dfrac{7}{16}, \dfrac{7}{20}$ (d) $\dfrac{7}{16}, \dfrac{3}{8}, \dfrac{5}{12}, \dfrac{23}{48}$

(e) $\dfrac{41}{45}, \dfrac{31}{36}, \dfrac{15}{16}, \dfrac{77}{81}$

(f) $\dfrac{49}{120}, \dfrac{23}{60}, \dfrac{13}{30}, \dfrac{37}{90}$

(g) $\dfrac{22}{45}, \dfrac{29}{60}, \dfrac{39}{80}, \dfrac{12}{25}$

(h) $\dfrac{7}{30}, \dfrac{13}{60}, \dfrac{2}{9}, \dfrac{4}{15}.$

4. Arrange the following fractions in descending order:

(a) $\dfrac{3}{4}, \dfrac{5}{8}, \dfrac{11}{16}$

(b) $\dfrac{8}{25}, \dfrac{36}{125}, \dfrac{1}{5}$

(c) $\dfrac{5}{7}, \dfrac{11}{14}, \dfrac{13}{20}$

(d) $\dfrac{4}{9}, \dfrac{1}{3}, \dfrac{2}{7}, \dfrac{1}{5}$

(e) $\dfrac{2}{3}, \dfrac{9}{14}, \dfrac{11}{18}, \dfrac{10}{21}$

(f) $\dfrac{2}{9}, \dfrac{5}{21}, \dfrac{2}{7}, \dfrac{5}{28}$

(g) $\dfrac{11}{12}, \dfrac{19}{24}, \dfrac{13}{15}, \dfrac{23}{32}$

(h) $\dfrac{11}{42}, \dfrac{7}{30}, \dfrac{8}{35}, \dfrac{13}{60}.$

5. Express as mixed or whole numbers:

(a) $\dfrac{40}{12}$

(b) $\dfrac{12}{8}$

(c) $\dfrac{44}{3}$

(d) $\dfrac{15}{3}$

(e) $\dfrac{60}{15}$

(f) $\dfrac{70}{13}$

(g) $\dfrac{520}{13}$

(h) $\dfrac{29}{4}$

(i) $\dfrac{37}{8}$

(j) $\dfrac{420}{14}$

(k) $\dfrac{45}{8}$

(l) $\dfrac{94}{13}$

(m) $\dfrac{73}{21}$

(n) $\dfrac{112}{8}$

(o) $\dfrac{51}{13}$

(p) $\dfrac{72}{16}$

(q) $\dfrac{666}{24}$

(r) $\dfrac{241}{19}$

(s) $\dfrac{68}{31}$

(t) $\dfrac{1550}{73}.$

6. Express as improper fractions:

(a) $5\frac{1}{3}$ (b) $4\frac{3}{7}$ (c) $10\frac{1}{9}$ (d) $13\frac{2}{3}$

(e) $14\frac{1}{4}$ (f) $7\frac{3}{4}$ (g) $8\frac{2}{5}$ (h) $9\frac{5}{8}$

(i) $21\frac{1}{6}$ (j) $14\frac{8}{11}$ (k) $16\frac{1}{5}$ (l) $42\frac{4}{9}$

(m) $6\frac{16}{19}$ (n) $4\frac{29}{32}$ (o) $7\frac{11}{31}$ (p) $14\frac{2}{23}$

(q) $72\frac{4}{7}$ (r) $37\frac{5}{8}$ (s) $102\frac{3}{7}$ (t) $240\frac{5}{17}.$

ADDITION

The fractions to be added must be rewritten so that they all have a common denominator.

EXAMPLE 6   Simplify $\dfrac{1}{4} + \dfrac{2}{3}$.

The common denominator of 4 and 3 is 12. We therefore express each fraction in twelfths

i.e. $\dfrac{1}{4} + \dfrac{2}{3} = \dfrac{3}{12} + \dfrac{8}{12}$

$\qquad\qquad\quad = \dfrac{11}{12}$

EXAMPLE 7   Simplify $\dfrac{1}{5} + \dfrac{1}{3} + \dfrac{3}{7}$.

The common denominator is 105.

Then $\dfrac{1}{5} + \dfrac{1}{3} + \dfrac{3}{7} = \dfrac{21}{105} + \dfrac{35}{105} + \dfrac{45}{105}$

$\qquad\qquad\qquad\quad = \dfrac{101}{105}$

EXAMPLE 8   Simplify $\dfrac{4}{5} + \dfrac{1}{3} + \dfrac{11}{15}$.

The common denominator is 15.

Then $\dfrac{4}{5} + \dfrac{1}{3} + \dfrac{11}{15} = \dfrac{12}{15} + \dfrac{5}{15} + \dfrac{11}{15}$

$\qquad\qquad\qquad\quad = \dfrac{28}{15}$

$\qquad\qquad\qquad\quad = 1\frac{13}{15}$

When a question involves whole numbers or improper fractions it is usual in addition questions to express any improper fraction as a mixed number and to total the whole numbers before considering the fractions.

EXAMPLE 9   Simplify $5\dfrac{1}{3} + 3\dfrac{3}{4} + 7\dfrac{2}{5}$.

$5\dfrac{1}{3} + 3\dfrac{3}{4} + 7\dfrac{2}{5} = 5 + 3 + 7 + \dfrac{1}{3} + \dfrac{3}{4} + \dfrac{2}{5}$

$$= 15 + \frac{20}{60} + \frac{45}{60} + \frac{24}{60}$$

(expressing each fraction in terms of the common denominator)

$$= 15 + \frac{89}{60}$$

$$= 15 + 1 + \frac{29}{60}$$

$$= 16\tfrac{29}{60}$$

When the method is fully understood the solution may be set out as follows:

$$5\frac{1}{3} + 3\frac{3}{4} + 7\frac{2}{5} = 15\frac{20 + 45 + 24}{60}$$

$$= 15\tfrac{89}{60}$$

$$= 16\tfrac{29}{60}$$

EXAMPLE 10   Simplify $4\dfrac{2}{7} + \dfrac{22}{9} + \dfrac{61}{14}$.

$$4\frac{2}{7} + \frac{22}{9} + \frac{61}{14} = 4\frac{2}{7} + 2\frac{4}{9} + 4\frac{5}{14}$$

$$= 10\frac{36 + 56 + 45}{126}$$

$$= 10\tfrac{137}{126}$$

$$= 11\tfrac{11}{126}$$

EXERCISE 13

Simplify:

1. $\dfrac{3}{10} + \dfrac{7}{10}$

2. $\dfrac{3}{15} + \dfrac{7}{15}$

3. $\dfrac{5}{17} + \dfrac{4}{17}$

4. $\dfrac{1}{12} + \dfrac{5}{12}$

5. $\dfrac{9}{20} + \dfrac{3}{20}$

6. $\dfrac{5}{8} + \dfrac{3}{8}$

7. $\dfrac{11}{30} + \dfrac{19}{30}$

8. $\dfrac{1}{4} + \dfrac{3}{8}$

9. $\dfrac{7}{8} + \dfrac{7}{12}$

10. $\dfrac{3}{5} + \dfrac{1}{2}$

11. $\dfrac{4}{5} + \dfrac{5}{8}$

12. $\dfrac{3}{11} + \dfrac{5}{9}$

13. $\dfrac{7}{16} + \dfrac{3}{8}$

14. $\dfrac{1}{4} + \dfrac{11}{16}$

15. $\dfrac{19}{32} + \dfrac{3}{8}$

16. $\dfrac{7}{24} + \dfrac{1}{6}$

17. $\dfrac{1}{2} + \dfrac{1}{3} + \dfrac{1}{4}$

18. $\dfrac{2}{5} + \dfrac{1}{3} + \dfrac{3}{4}$

19. $\dfrac{7}{12} + \dfrac{2}{3} + \dfrac{1}{6}$

20. $\dfrac{5}{6} + \dfrac{1}{2} + \dfrac{7}{12}$

21. $\dfrac{4}{15} + \dfrac{7}{10} + \dfrac{3}{5}$

22. $\dfrac{1}{12} + \dfrac{1}{4} + \dfrac{1}{8}$

23. $\dfrac{11}{36} + \dfrac{7}{12} + \dfrac{5}{6}$

24. $\dfrac{2}{3} + \dfrac{7}{18} + \dfrac{5}{6}$

25. $1\dfrac{1}{2} + \dfrac{3}{4}$

26. $2\dfrac{1}{4} + 1\dfrac{1}{2}$

27. $5\dfrac{1}{3} + 2\dfrac{1}{6}$

28. $4\dfrac{3}{4} + 1\dfrac{7}{8}$

29. $7\dfrac{5}{8} + 2\dfrac{1}{2}$

30. $9\dfrac{1}{3} + 4\dfrac{5}{6}$

31. $12\dfrac{1}{2} + 5\dfrac{3}{7}$

32. $2\dfrac{7}{13} + 1\dfrac{1}{2}$

33. $3\dfrac{11}{12} + 1\dfrac{1}{4}$

34. $2\dfrac{3}{7} + 1\dfrac{1}{4}$

35. $3\dfrac{7}{12} + 3\dfrac{5}{8}$

36. $10\dfrac{3}{8} + 4\dfrac{7}{16}$

37. $1\dfrac{3}{4} + \dfrac{2}{5} + 2\dfrac{1}{10}$

38. $3\dfrac{1}{2} + 2\dfrac{1}{4} + 1\dfrac{1}{8}$

39. $7\dfrac{3}{10} + 2\dfrac{5}{8} + 3\dfrac{1}{2}$

40. $5\dfrac{3}{20} + 8\dfrac{1}{5} + 4\dfrac{1}{4}$

41. $4\dfrac{7}{8} + 5\dfrac{3}{4} + 7\dfrac{1}{2}$

42. $1\dfrac{1}{3} + 3\dfrac{5}{6} + \dfrac{1}{2}$

43. $3\dfrac{1}{7} + 1\dfrac{9}{14} + 2\dfrac{1}{2}$

44. $5\dfrac{1}{5} + 3\dfrac{7}{20} + 5\dfrac{3}{4}$

45. $\dfrac{7}{8} + \dfrac{4}{3} + \dfrac{7}{9}$

46. $\dfrac{15}{8} + \dfrac{9}{4} + \dfrac{7}{2}$

47. $\dfrac{25}{18} + \dfrac{13}{6} + \dfrac{23}{12}$

48. $\dfrac{10}{3} + \dfrac{29}{21} + \dfrac{13}{7}$

49. $4\dfrac{2}{3} + \dfrac{16}{9} + \dfrac{41}{18} + 5\dfrac{7}{12}$

50. $\dfrac{73}{15} + \dfrac{41}{10} + 3\dfrac{1}{5} + \dfrac{7}{30}.$

SUBTRACTION

The following examples illustrate subtraction. Whole numbers are dealt with first.

EXAMPLE 11   Simplify $5\dfrac{3}{5}-2\dfrac{1}{4}$.

$$5\frac{3}{5}-2\frac{1}{4} = 3+\frac{3}{5}-\frac{1}{4}$$

$$= 3+\frac{12}{20}-\frac{5}{20}$$

$$= 3+\frac{7}{20}$$

$$= 3\tfrac{7}{20}$$

Or if preferred:

$$5\frac{3}{5}-2\frac{1}{4} = 3\frac{12-5}{20}$$

$$= 3\tfrac{7}{20}$$

EXAMPLE 12   Simplify $7\dfrac{1}{4}-3\dfrac{4}{9}$.

$$7\frac{1}{4}-3\frac{4}{9} = 4+\frac{1}{4}-\frac{4}{9}$$

$$= 4+\frac{9-16}{36}$$

$$= 3+\frac{36+9-16}{36}$$

$$= 3\tfrac{29}{36}$$

We next consider an example involving addition and subtraction.

EXAMPLE 13   Simplify $5\dfrac{1}{3}-2\dfrac{2}{5}+3\dfrac{3}{4}-1\dfrac{7}{8}$.

$$5\frac{1}{3} - 2\frac{2}{5} + 3\frac{3}{4} - 1\frac{7}{8} = 5\frac{40 - 48 + 90 - 105}{120}$$

$$= 5\frac{130 - 153}{120}$$

(combining the whole numbers and expressing the fractions with a common denominator)

$$= 4\frac{120 + 130 - 153}{120} \qquad \left(\text{rewriting 5 as } 4 + \frac{120}{120}\right)$$

$$= 4\tfrac{97}{120}$$

EXERCISE 14

1. $\dfrac{7}{10} - \dfrac{3}{10}$

2. $\dfrac{7}{15} - \dfrac{3}{15}$

3. $\dfrac{7}{12} - \dfrac{1}{12}$

4. $\dfrac{5}{17} - \dfrac{2}{17}$

5. $\dfrac{9}{24} - \dfrac{1}{12}$

6. $\dfrac{3}{4} - \dfrac{1}{3}$

7. $\dfrac{7}{8} - \dfrac{3}{4}$

8. $\dfrac{17}{18} - \dfrac{5}{6}$

9. $\dfrac{19}{32} - \dfrac{3}{8}$

10. $\dfrac{49}{100} - \dfrac{3}{10}$

11. $\dfrac{9}{14} - \dfrac{2}{21}$

12. $\dfrac{19}{48} - \dfrac{3}{24}$

13. $\dfrac{34}{35} - \dfrac{5}{7}$

14. $\dfrac{4}{5} - \dfrac{5}{7}$

15. $\dfrac{7}{16} - \dfrac{3}{8}$

16. $\dfrac{5}{6} - \dfrac{11}{18}$

17. $\dfrac{2}{3} - \dfrac{1}{4} - \dfrac{1}{6}$

18. $\dfrac{11}{12} - \dfrac{1}{4} - \dfrac{2}{3}$

19. $\dfrac{23}{25} - \dfrac{3}{10} - \dfrac{1}{5}$

20. $\dfrac{17}{30} - \dfrac{2}{5} - \dfrac{1}{16}$

21. $\dfrac{5}{6} - \dfrac{5}{12} + \dfrac{1}{2}$

22. $\dfrac{4}{9} + \dfrac{2}{3} - \dfrac{11}{12}$

23. $\dfrac{4}{7} + \dfrac{10}{21} - \dfrac{3}{14}$

24. $\dfrac{19}{20} - \dfrac{3}{5} + \dfrac{3}{4}$

25. $3\dfrac{2}{3} - 2\dfrac{1}{2}$

26. $5\dfrac{3}{4} - 2\dfrac{3}{8}$

27. $7\dfrac{1}{2} - \dfrac{1}{3}$

28. $9\dfrac{7}{12} - 3\dfrac{1}{3}$

29. $4\dfrac{7}{12} - 2\dfrac{1}{6}$

30. $10\dfrac{3}{4} - 7\dfrac{5}{8}$

31. $2\dfrac{1}{2} - 1\dfrac{3}{4}$

32. $6\dfrac{1}{4} - 1\dfrac{5}{8}$

33. $7\dfrac{3}{8} - 4\dfrac{11}{12}$

34. $3\dfrac{7}{20} - 2\dfrac{11}{15}$

35. $12\dfrac{4}{7} - 5\dfrac{1}{3}$

36. $5\dfrac{3}{5} - 3\dfrac{9}{10}$

37. $5\dfrac{7}{8} - 2\dfrac{1}{2} - 1\dfrac{1}{4}$

38. $10 - 2\dfrac{1}{12} - 3\dfrac{5}{6}$

39. $8 - 4\dfrac{4}{7} - 2\dfrac{2}{5}$

40. $6\dfrac{3}{4} - \dfrac{7}{12} - 3\dfrac{9}{16}$

41. $7\dfrac{3}{7} - 2\dfrac{3}{14} - 3\dfrac{1}{2}$

42. $3\dfrac{1}{4} + 4\dfrac{1}{3} - 5\dfrac{1}{6}$

43. $4\dfrac{7}{12} - 3\dfrac{5}{8} + 1\dfrac{2}{3}$

44. $12\dfrac{1}{4} - 7\dfrac{5}{6} + 4\dfrac{11}{12}$

45. $\dfrac{11}{6} - \dfrac{4}{3} - \dfrac{4}{9}$

46. $\dfrac{21}{4} - \dfrac{5}{3} - \dfrac{7}{2}$

47. $\dfrac{52}{25} + \dfrac{12}{5} - \dfrac{23}{20}$

48. $\dfrac{49}{36} + \dfrac{17}{12} - \dfrac{9}{8}$

49. $5\dfrac{1}{3} - \dfrac{19}{4} + \dfrac{31}{6} - 2\dfrac{1}{2}$

50. $\dfrac{17}{5} + 5\dfrac{1}{4} - \dfrac{33}{8} - \dfrac{11}{10}$

MULTIPLICATION

If 4 boys each have $£\frac{1}{5}$, then the total amount of money they have between them is:

$$£\left(\dfrac{1}{5} + \dfrac{1}{5} + \dfrac{1}{5} + \dfrac{1}{5}\right) = £\dfrac{4}{5}$$

or $\qquad 4 \times £\dfrac{1}{5} = £\dfrac{4}{5}$

i.e. to multiply a fraction by an integer we multiply the numerator by that integer, leaving the denominator unchanged.

e.g. $\qquad 3 \times \dfrac{1}{7} = \dfrac{3}{7}, \qquad 5 \times \dfrac{2}{13} = \dfrac{10}{13},$

$$7 \times \dfrac{3}{14} = \dfrac{21}{14} = \dfrac{3}{2} = 1\dfrac{1}{2}$$

A simple solution for $7 \times \dfrac{3}{14}$ would be to write $7 \times \dfrac{3}{14} = \dfrac{3}{2}$ (dividing numerator and denominator by 7).

To multiply proper fractions together, multiply their numerators to give the numerator of the answer, and their denominators to give the denominator of the answer.

e.g. $\qquad \dfrac{5}{7} \times \dfrac{3}{4} = \dfrac{15}{28} \qquad$ and $\qquad \dfrac{7}{12} \times \dfrac{13}{23} = \dfrac{91}{276}$

If a mixed number is involved it must first be expressed as an improper fraction

thus $\qquad 1\dfrac{1}{2} \times \dfrac{7}{8} = \dfrac{3}{2} \times \dfrac{7}{8} = \dfrac{21}{16} = 1\dfrac{5}{16}$

and $\qquad 4\dfrac{1}{4} \times 2\dfrac{1}{2} = \dfrac{17}{4} \times \dfrac{5}{2} = \dfrac{85}{8} = 10\dfrac{5}{8}$

Frequently a number will divide into the numerator of one of the fractions being multiplied and the denominator of another thus simplifying the calculations.

e.g. $\qquad 7\dfrac{1}{2} \times 2\dfrac{4}{5} = \dfrac{\overset{3}{\cancel{15}}}{\underset{1}{\cancel{2}}} \times \dfrac{\overset{7}{\cancel{14}}}{\underset{1}{\cancel{5}}} = 21$

and $\qquad 3\dfrac{3}{7} \times 1\dfrac{5}{12} \times 4\dfrac{2}{3} = \dfrac{\overset{2}{\cancel{24}}}{\underset{1}{\cancel{7}}} \times \dfrac{17}{\underset{1}{\cancel{12}}} \times \dfrac{\overset{2}{\cancel{14}}}{3} = \dfrac{68}{3} = 22\dfrac{2}{3}$

(Reducing can only be carried out when the fractions are multiplied. It cannot be done with $\frac{24}{7} + \frac{17}{12}$ or $\frac{24}{7} - \frac{17}{12}$ or $\frac{24}{7} \div \frac{17}{12}$.)

When 'of' occurs between two fractions it may always be replaced by multiplication.

e.g. $\qquad \dfrac{2}{5}$ of $2\dfrac{1}{3}$ means $\dfrac{2}{5} \times 2\dfrac{1}{3} = \dfrac{2}{5} \times \dfrac{7}{3} = \dfrac{14}{15}$

and $\qquad \dfrac{8}{9}$ of $5\dfrac{2}{5} = \dfrac{8}{9} \times \dfrac{27}{5} = \dfrac{24}{5} = 4\dfrac{4}{5}$

EXERCISE 15

Find the value of:

1. $\dfrac{7}{8}$ cm $\times 4$

2. $\dfrac{3}{4}$ m $\times 3$

3. $£\dfrac{7}{12} \times 8$

4. $\dfrac{5}{13} \times 5$

5. $\dfrac{4}{5}p \times 12$

6. $3 \times \dfrac{7}{2}$ litres

7. $5 \times \dfrac{2}{3}$ pints

8. $4 \times \dfrac{3}{4}$ gallons

9. $12 \times \dfrac{3}{5}$ grams

10. $6 \times \dfrac{4}{9}$ seconds

11. $8 \times \dfrac{3}{4}p$

12. $9 \times \dfrac{5}{12}$ kg

13. $\dfrac{4}{5} \times 12$

14. $\dfrac{3}{25} \times 10$

15. $\dfrac{4}{13} \times 6$

16. $\dfrac{5}{9} \times 24$

17. $10 \times \dfrac{3}{5}$

18. $20 \times \dfrac{7}{4}$

19. $36 \times \dfrac{4}{9}$

20. $27 \times \dfrac{4}{3}$

21. $2\dfrac{1}{4} \times 8$

22. $3\dfrac{2}{3} \times 12$

23. $5\dfrac{1}{7} \times 14$

24. $4\dfrac{7}{8} \times 6$

25. $7 \times 3\dfrac{1}{2}$

26. $13 \times 1\dfrac{1}{4}$

27. $18 \times \dfrac{7}{9}$

28. $15 \times \dfrac{7}{24}$

29. $\dfrac{2}{3} \times \dfrac{5}{9}$

30. $\dfrac{7}{12} \times \dfrac{3}{5}$

31. $\dfrac{8}{13} \times \dfrac{5}{12}$

32. $\dfrac{20}{21} \times \dfrac{7}{4}$

33. $\dfrac{3}{14} \times \dfrac{21}{49}$

34. $\dfrac{7}{64} \times \dfrac{16}{21}$

35. $\dfrac{5}{8}$ of 4

36. $\dfrac{3}{7}$ of $\dfrac{14}{19}$

37. $4\dfrac{1}{2} \times \dfrac{4}{9}$

38. $4\dfrac{1}{4} \times \dfrac{13}{34}$

39. $7\dfrac{3}{5} \times \dfrac{5}{19}$

40. $5\dfrac{2}{5} \times \dfrac{7}{8}$

41. $\dfrac{11}{15}$ of $2\dfrac{3}{22}$

42. $\dfrac{4}{7}$ of $4\dfrac{3}{8}$

43. $2\dfrac{5}{8} \times \dfrac{3}{7} \times 2\dfrac{2}{5}$

44. $\dfrac{2}{17} \times 3\dfrac{1}{8} \times 1\dfrac{7}{10}$

45. $3\dfrac{1}{6} \times 1\dfrac{5}{7} \times 5\dfrac{1}{4}$

46. $3\dfrac{3}{7} \times 1\dfrac{5}{9} \times 2\dfrac{1}{8}$

47. $4\dfrac{1}{2} \times 3\dfrac{2}{3} \times 1\dfrac{1}{11}$

48. $1\dfrac{2}{5} \times 2\dfrac{1}{4} \times 4\dfrac{1}{3}$

49. $\dfrac{2}{3}$ of $\left(2\dfrac{1}{2} \times 1\dfrac{4}{5}\right)^2$

50. $\left(1\dfrac{5}{7} \times 2\dfrac{1}{3}\right)^2 \times \dfrac{3}{16}.$

DIVISION

If you divide £1 or 100 p into 4 equal parts you divide it into quarters, e.g. one-quarter of 100 p is 25 p.

We write this $\frac{1}{4} \times 100p = 25p$

Thus to divide a number by 4 we multiply it by $\frac{1}{4}$

e.g.
$$7 \div 4 = 7 \times \frac{1}{4} = \frac{7}{4} = 1\frac{3}{4}$$

$$\frac{3}{4} \div 4 = \frac{3}{4} \times \frac{1}{4} = \frac{3}{16}$$

Similarly $\frac{3}{4}$ divided by $\frac{2}{3}$ is written:

$$\frac{3}{4} \div \frac{2}{3} = \frac{3}{4} \times \frac{3}{2} = \frac{9}{8} = 1\frac{1}{8}$$

and
$$\frac{5}{7} \div \frac{3}{4} = \frac{5}{7} \times \frac{4}{3} = \frac{20}{21}$$

To divide a number by a fraction, multiply by the fraction turned upside down. The word we use for this in mathematics is *reciprocal* or *inverse*.

The reciprocal of 7 is $\frac{1}{7}$

The reciprocal of $\frac{2}{3}$ is $\frac{3}{2}$

The reciprocal of $\frac{5}{9}$ is $\frac{9}{5}$

The reciprocal of $\frac{1}{13}$ is 13

NOTE: Any number multiplied by its reciprocal gives an answer of 1.

EXAMPLE 14
$$3\frac{1}{5} \div \frac{4}{7} = \frac{16}{5} \div \frac{4}{7}$$

$$= \frac{16}{5} \times \frac{7}{4}$$

$$= \frac{28}{5}$$

$$= 5\frac{3}{5}$$

EXAMPLE 15

$$8\frac{2}{7} \div 5\frac{4}{5} = \frac{58}{7} \div \frac{29}{5}$$

$$= \frac{58}{7} \times \frac{5}{29}$$

$$= \frac{10}{7}$$

$$= 1\frac{3}{7}$$

EXERCISE 16

Find the value of:

1. $\frac{1}{2}$ divided by 4

2. $\frac{1}{3}$ divided by 3

3. $\frac{1}{4}$ divided by 2

4. $\frac{2}{3}$ divided by 7

5. $\frac{5}{13}$ divided by 10

6. $\frac{4}{7}$ divided by 2

7. $2\frac{1}{2}$ divided by 5

8. $7\frac{1}{3}$ divided by 11

9. $4 \div \frac{1}{2}$

10. $6 \div \frac{1}{3}$

11. $5 \div \frac{1}{2}$

12. $12 \div \frac{1}{8}$

13. $\frac{1}{4} \div \frac{1}{2}$

14. $\frac{1}{2} \div \frac{1}{3}$

15. $\frac{1}{20} \div \frac{1}{5}$

16. $\frac{1}{4} \div \frac{1}{20}$

17. $\frac{3}{8} \div \frac{2}{3}$

18. $\frac{7}{12} \div \frac{2}{5}$

19. $\frac{8}{9} \div \frac{2}{7}$

20. $\frac{9}{16} \div \frac{3}{4}$

21. $1 \div \frac{1}{3}$

22. $1 \div \frac{4}{3}$

23. $1 \div \frac{9}{10}$

24. $1 \div \frac{20}{21}$

25. $\frac{15}{4} \div \frac{5}{2}$

26. $\frac{12}{7} \div \frac{3}{14}$

27. $\frac{18}{11} \div \frac{27}{22}$

28. $\frac{5}{13} \div \frac{10}{19}$

29. $1\frac{1}{2} \div \frac{2}{3}$

30. $2\frac{1}{3} \div 1\frac{5}{9}$

31. $4\frac{1}{7} \div 2\frac{5}{12}$

32. $3\frac{3}{5} \div 2\frac{7}{10}$

33. $\frac{\frac{1}{3}}{5}$

34. $\frac{1}{2\frac{1}{4}}$

35. $\frac{\frac{1}{7}}{3}$

36. $\frac{1}{4\frac{4}{7}}$

37. $1\frac{1}{2} \div 1\frac{1}{5}$

38. $5\frac{1}{3} \div 1\frac{1}{7}$

39. $4\frac{2}{5} \div 5\frac{1}{2}$

40. $4\frac{1}{3} \div 9\frac{3}{4}$

41. $8\frac{4}{13} \div 5\frac{2}{5}$

42. $6\frac{2}{5} \div 9\frac{3}{5}$

43. $6\frac{1}{2} \div 2\frac{3}{5}$

44. $9\frac{2}{3} \div 8\frac{2}{7}$

45. $2\frac{5}{8} \div 12\frac{1}{4}$

46. $17\frac{3}{5} \div 3\frac{3}{10}$

47. $6\frac{3}{8} \div 21\frac{1}{4}$

48. $8\frac{1}{8} \div 7\frac{3}{7}$

49. $31\frac{2}{7} \div 4\frac{13}{15}$

50. $5\frac{5}{14} \div 19\frac{4}{9}$.

EXERCISE 17 MISCELLANEOUS EXAMPLES

1. A box contains 120 oranges but $\frac{3}{8}$ of them are found to be bad. How many are satisfactory?

2. My electricity bill for heating and lighting was £324. If $\frac{7}{9}$ of the cost was for heating, how much did I pay for lighting?

3. In a secondary school $\frac{7}{12}$ of the third-year pupils are girls and 105 are boys. How many girls are there?

4. In a mathematics textbook $\frac{2}{5}$ deals with arithmetic, $\frac{3}{7}$ algebra and the remainder geometry. If the book has 210 pages, how many pages of geometry are there?

5. During a 6 hour coach journey the rest periods amount to $\frac{1}{5}$ of the time. If the average speed of the coach when it is moving is 50 mph, how long is the journey?

6. A petrol storage tank is three-quarters full. After 75 gallons have been drawn off it is three-fifths full. What is the capacity of the tank?

7. The local council agrees to pay $\frac{3}{7}$ of the cost of running a leisure centre, with the county council paying the remainder. If the county council pays £490 000, find the total running cost.

8. After spending $\frac{5}{6}$ of my pocket money I have 80 p remaining. How much pocket money do I receive?

9. A man poured $\frac{5}{8}$ of a can of oil into his car engine and had 3 litres left over. How much did he use?

10. A retailer bought a quantity of eggs. 46 were broken, the remainder being $\frac{8}{9}$ of the original. How many eggs did he buy?

11. John and Fred go into business together, John putting up $\frac{7}{12}$ of the capital and Fred the remainder of £10 400. How much did John contribute?

12. Anne, Betty and Cheryl decide to open a hairdressing salon. To do this they require £2680. Anne contributes $\frac{7}{20}$ of it, Betty $\frac{3}{10}$ and Cheryl the remainder. How much does each contribute?

13. In a book containing four short stories, the first is $\frac{1}{6}$ of the whole, the second $\frac{1}{8}$, the third 126 pages and the fourth $\frac{1}{3}$. How many pages are in the book?

14. The product of two numbers is 8. If one of the numbers is $3\frac{1}{3}$, find the other.

15. The product of two numbers is 21. If one of the numbers is $2\frac{4}{7}$, find the other.

16. How many jars, each of which holds $\frac{3}{8}$ kg, may be filled from a tin containing 21 kg?

17. The area of a blackboard is $8\frac{3}{4}$ square metres. If the board is $1\frac{2}{3}$ m wide, how long is it?

18. If it takes $3\frac{1}{3}$ minutes to fill $\frac{3}{8}$ of a water storage tank, how long will it take to fill it completely?

19. When the larger of two fractions is divided by the smaller, the result is $1\frac{7}{18}$. If the smaller fraction is $2\frac{2}{5}$, find the larger.

20. When the smaller of two fractions is divided by the larger, the result is $\frac{7}{9}$. If the smaller fraction is $2\frac{2}{3}$, find the larger.

DECIMALS

DECIMALS AND COMMON FRACTIONS

Consider the number 5555:

$$5555 = 5\text{ thousands} + 5\text{ hundreds} + 5\text{ tens} + 5\text{ units}$$

Each figure in the number 5555 has a value which is 10 times the value of the number immediately following it. It would seem quite reasonable to extend this system to fractional quantities or quantities which are less than unity. If we place a dot or decimal point at the change-over position from whole numbers to fractional or decimal parts, then

$$5555.555 = 5\text{ thousands} + 5\text{ hundreds} + 5\text{ tens}$$
$$+ 5\text{ units} + 5\text{ tenths} + 5\text{ hundredths}$$
$$+ 5\text{ thousandths}$$

The decimal point is necessary to determine where the change-over occurs.

Hence
$$.555 = 5\text{ tenths} + 5\text{ hundredths} + 5\text{ thousandths}$$

$$= \frac{5}{10} + \frac{5}{100} + \frac{5}{1000}$$

$$= \frac{555}{1000}$$

A decimal is therefore a fraction whose denominator is a power of 10. As in 505 where the zero tells us that there are no tens, so in .505 there are five tenths, no hundredths and five thousandths. The zero holds the position if all non-zero digits are absent. It is common practice if there is no whole number before the decimal point to write a zero in front of it, e.g. instead of .505 we write 0.505.

Any decimal fraction may be written as a common fraction quite easily, but frequently this fraction is not in its lowest terms.

e.g. $$0.5 = \frac{5}{10} = \frac{1}{2}$$

and $$0.555 = \frac{555}{1000} = \frac{111}{200}$$

EXAMPLE 1

Write (a) $\dfrac{7}{10}$, (b) $\dfrac{4}{10} + \dfrac{5}{100} + \dfrac{7}{1000}$ as decimals.

(a) $\dfrac{7}{10} = 0.7$

(b) $\dfrac{4}{10} + \dfrac{5}{100} + \dfrac{7}{1000} = 0.457$

EXAMPLE 2

Express (a) 0.8, (b) 0.359 as the sums of vulgar fractions whose denominators are 10, 100, 1000.

(a) $0.8 = \dfrac{8}{10}$

(b) $0.359 = \dfrac{3}{10} + \dfrac{5}{100} + \dfrac{9}{1000}$

EXAMPLE 3

Express (a) 0.535, (b) 0.074 as single vulgar fractions with a power of 10 as the denominator.

(a) $0.535 = \dfrac{535}{1000}$

(b) $0.074 = \dfrac{74}{1000}$

EXAMPLE 4

Express (a) 0.65, (b) 0.624 as vulgar fractions in their lowest terms.

(a) $0.65 = \dfrac{65}{100} = \dfrac{13}{20}$

(b) $0.624 = \dfrac{624}{1000} = \dfrac{78}{125}$

EXERCISE 18

Rewrite each of the following in decimal form:

	THOUSANDS	HUNDREDS	TENS	UNITS	TENTHS	HUNDREDTHS	THOUSANDTHS
1.			1	2	3		
2.				4	5	6	
3.			8	3	7	3	
4.				7	3	4	6
5.			2	4		5	
6.		1		5	6		4
7.		7	2	6		8	
8.			1		5	3	6
9.		4			2	3	
10.	6	1		4	5		8

Express each of the following in table form as shown above:

11. 8.6   12. 4.27   13. 26.83   14. 4.926

15. 27.942   16. 636.421   17. 16.04   18. 33.005

19. 30.92   20. 406.507   21. 126.543   22. 500.063

23. 735.707   24. 3007.607   25. 7305.042   26. 0.64

27. 0.247   28. 0.093   29. 0.114   30. 0.008.

Write the following as decimals:

31. $\dfrac{3}{10}$ 32. $\dfrac{7}{10}$ 33. $\dfrac{3}{10}+\dfrac{7}{100}$ 34. $\dfrac{5}{10}+\dfrac{4}{100}$

35. $\dfrac{3}{10}+\dfrac{5}{100}+\dfrac{7}{1000}$ 36. $\dfrac{1}{10}+\dfrac{7}{100}+\dfrac{4}{1000}$

37. $\dfrac{35}{100}+\dfrac{2}{1000}$ 38. $\dfrac{49}{100}+\dfrac{7}{1000}$

39. $\dfrac{9}{10}+\dfrac{13}{1000}$ 40. $\dfrac{7}{10}+\dfrac{5}{1000}$

41. $\dfrac{37}{1000}$ 　　　 42. $\dfrac{52}{1000}$ 　　　 43. $\dfrac{234}{1000}$ 　　　 44. $\dfrac{53}{10}$

45. $\dfrac{472}{100}$ 　　　 46. $\dfrac{12}{10} + \dfrac{3}{100}$.

Express each of the following as the sum of common fractions whose denominators are 10, 100, 1000, etc.:

47. 0.4 　　　 48. 0.27 　　　 49. 0.83 　　　 50. 0.246

51. 0.737 　　 52. 0.829 　　 53. 0.062 　　 54. 0.0359

55. 5.37 　　　 56. 4.29 　　　 57. 10.07 　　 58. 35.903.

Express each of the following as a single common fraction with a power of 10 as the denominator:

59. 0.3 　　　 60. 0.38 　　　 61. 0.94 　　　 62. 0.357

63. 0.848 　　 64. 0.718 　　 65. 0.051 　　 66. 0.0248

67. 4.73 　　　 68. 82.4 　　　 69. 6.945 　　 70. 23.052.

Express each of the following as a common fraction in its lowest terms:

71. 0.8 　　　 72. 0.75 　　　 73. 0.45 　　　 74. 0.65

75. 0.375 　　 76. 0.625 　　 77. 0.64 　　　 78. 0.28

79. 0.36 　　　 80. 0.628 　　 81. 0.444 　　 82. 0.875

83. 0.55 　　　 84. 0.78 　　　 85. 0.125.

MULTIPLICATION AND DIVISION BY 10 OR A POWER OF 10

Since $25 \times 10 = 250$, the 5 units when multiplied by 10 become 5 tens and the 2 tens become 2 hundreds i.e. each figure in the original number is moved one place to the left in relation to the decimal point. Put another way, the decimal point is moved one place to the right. In the same way:

$$42.64 \times 10 = 426.4$$

and
$$7.26 \times 100 = 7.26 \times 10 \times 10 = 72.6 \times 10$$
$$= 726$$

i.e. if we multiply by 100 the decimal point is moved two places to the right.

Similarly $\times 1000$ moves the decimal point 3 places to the right,
$\times 10\,000$ moves the decimal point 4 places to the right,

and so on.

Division by 10 makes tens become units, hundreds become tens, and so on.

e.g. $$64.2 \div 10 = 6.42$$

To divide by 10 we move the decimal point 1 place to the left. Similarly, to divide by 100 we move the decimal point 2 places to the left, to divide by 1000 we move the decimal point 3 places to the left, and so on.

EXAMPLE 5 (a) $927.4 \times 100 = 92\,740$
(b) $50.38 \times 10 = 503.8$
(c) $0.0349 \times 1000 = 34.9$

EXAMPLE 6 (a) $67.4 \div 100 = 0.674$
(b) $423.8 \div 10\,000 = 0.042\,38$
(c) $0.72 \div 1000 = 0.000\,72$

EXERCISE 19

Simplify:

1. 6.73×10
2. 14.21×10
3. 0.892×10
4. 36.14×100
5. 0.0429×100
6. 1.642×100
7. 4.96×1000
8. 0.235×1000
9. 0.0964×1000
10. $0.428 \times 10\,000$
11. 3.943×10
12. 16.92×100
13. 239.2×10
14. 43.68×100
15. 0.912×1000
16. 0.007×1000
17. 1.229×100
18. $0.0264 \times 10\,000$
19. $0.734 \times 10\,000$
20. $0.82 \times 100\,000$
21. $70.2 \div 10$
22. $8.42 \div 10$
23. $246.4 \div 10$
24. $0.526 \div 10$
25. $431.5 \div 100$
26. $62.3 \div 100$
27. $5.176 \div 100$
28. $0.916 \div 100$
29. $734 \div 1000$
30. $1920 \div 1000$

31. $8.264 \div 100$ **32.** $43.4 \div 10$

33. $0.9 \div 1000$ **34.** $90 \div 100$

35. $742 \div 1000$ **36.** $60.6 \div 10$

37. $0.634 \div 100$ **38.** $0.074 \div 100$

39. $436 \div 10\,000$ **40.** $909.6 \div 1000.$

ADDITION AND SUBTRACTION

Addition and subtraction of decimals are carried out in the same way as with whole numbers. The most important thing to remember is that the decimal points must be placed underneath one another. This ensures that all digits with the same place value are written in the same column.

EXAMPLE 7   Add 5.16, 37.4, 0.361 and 162.04.

```
  5.16
 37.4
  0.361
162.04
204.961
```

EXAMPLE 8   Subtract 73.649 from 243.94.

```
243.94
 73.649
170.291
```

EXERCISE 20

Addition

1. 4.3
2.5
—

2. 7.5
2.3
—

3. 6.1
1.8
—

4. 3.6
5.2
—

5. 3.8
6.1
—

6. 7.3
1.9
—

7. 6.8
2.7
—

8. 4.4
3.8
—

9. 5.9
7.4
—

10. 6.7
5.8
—

11. 7.61
1.25
—

12. 2.33
5.41
—

13. 4.55
     3.43
     ———

14. 6.45
     7.95
     ———

15. 8.73
     4.28
     ———

16. 40.15
     16.23
     ———

17. 71.04
     13.82
     ———

18. 32.41
     11.83
     ———

19. 45.71
     59.09
     ———

20. 18.72
     52.53
     ———

21.   17.31
     124.97
     ———

22.   82.58
     243.04
     ———

23. 173.4
      59.73
     ———

24. 521.4
      58.97
     ———

25. 373.9
      48.62
     ———

26.   9.372
     14.142
     ———

27. 15.043
      7.994
     ———

28. 62.3
     15.895
     ———

29. 4.437
     0.975
     ———

30. 37.914
      3.009
     ———

31.   7.334
     18.21
     54.095
     ———

32. 16.04
     93.87
      5.927
     ———

33. 34.92
     27.36
     50.25
     ———

34. 127.9
      38.72
       5.947
     ———

35.   4.926
      27.35
     337.9
     ———

36.   0.536
      1.904
     25.88
     ———

37.   64.9
       8.345
     136.48
     ———

38.   31.92
       8.437
     463.8
     ———

39. 42.76
     90.04
     37.095
     ———

40. 731.4
        9.537
       38.92
     ———

41.   50.21
     134.92
      16.73
      58.56
     ———

42.   4.926
      73.35
       4.728
     516.045
     ———

43.   6.92
     27.668
      5.931
     48.043
     ———

44. 76.009
      0.926
      3.741
     54.8
     ———

45. 344.59
      84.47
       0.927
      36.5
     ———

46. 540.73
     349.2
      16.34
       9.454
      62.09
     ———

47. 13.43
      8.2
      9.67
     34.53
      5.98
     ———

48. 44.91
     33.675
     18.9
     66.35
      0.925
     ———

49. 842.1
      36.93
       8.445
       0.737
     ———

50.   2.142
      36.085
      50.92
     845.2
     ———

Add :

51. $9.4 + 3.7 + 16.2$ 52. $51.2 + 19.4 + 37.26$

53. $18.09 + 62.14 + 7.9$ 54. $83.74 + 7.447 + 3.92$

55. $56.92 + 247.1 + 8.993$ 56. $37.85 + 334.8 + 9.75$

57. $4 + 0.25 + 0.873$ 58. $15.2 + 3.004 + 1.732$

59. $73.91 + 253.34 + 47.936$ 60. $22.04 + 85.904 + 17.88.$

Subtraction

61. 8.5 6.3	**62.** 4.9 1.7	**63.** 12.8 1.5	**64.** 36.4 25.2
65. 59.7 35.4	**66.** 5.97 3.45	**67.** 16.82 3.71	**68.** 42.76 31.34
69. 9.453 1.232	**70.** 64.95 53.71	**71.** 32.4 19.3	**72.** 6.74 3.78
73. 72.64 18.25	**74.** 40.92 36.37	**75.** 5.84 1.87	**76.** 40.982 16.389
77. 51.253 34.937	**78.** 341.43 27.94	**79.** 621.42 344.93	**80.** 54.217 3.778
81. 200.43 167.97	**82.** 516.9 47.36	**83.** 16.493 8.56	**84.** 84.17 9.385
85. 4.835 0.996	**86.** 5.6 1.447	**87.** 18.4 7.346	**88.** 50.2 8.345
89. 30.2 19.731	**90.** 84.000 58.886		

91. Subtract 6.49 from 12.97.

92. Subtract 15.23 from 38.09.

93. Subtract 0.935 from 2.

94. Subtract 7.543 from 10.

95. Subtract 249.66 from 500.

96. From 27.2 subtract 7.39.

97. From 84.92 subtract 57.37.

98. From 100 subtract 49.35.

99. From 300 subtract 247.924.

100. From 80 subtract 0.737.

MULTIPLICATION

EXAMPLE 9   Multiply 5.3 by 4.71.

(Rough answer $5 \times 5 = 25$.)

Since $5.3 = \dfrac{53}{10}$ and $4.71 = \dfrac{471}{100}$

$5.3 \times 4.71 = \dfrac{53}{10} \times \dfrac{471}{100} = \dfrac{24\,963}{1000} = 24.963$

We may therefore multiply the two numbers together using long multiplication, then count the total number of decimal places *after* the decimal point in the two numbers (1 from 5.3 and 2 from 4.71), and place the decimal point in the answer so that this number of places (i.e. 3) comes *after* the decimal point.

EXAMPLE 10   Find 5.64×3.45.

(Rough answer $6 \times 3 = 18$.)

        5.64   2 places after the point
        3.45   2 places after the point
        ─────
        2820
       22 560
      169 200
       ─────
       19.4580 $\therefore$ 4 places after the point in the answer

$\therefore$ $5.64 \times 3.45 = 19.4580$

EXAMPLE 11   Find 70.16×0.293.

(Rough answer $70 \times 0.3 = 21$.)

        70.16   2 places after the point
         0.293   3 places after the point
        ─────
        21 048
       631 440
     1 403 200
       ─────
       20.556 88 $\therefore$ 5 places after the point in the answer

$\therefore$ $70.16 \times 0.293 = 20.556\,88$

EXERCISE 21

Find:

1. 0.2×5	2. 0.3×4	3. 0.7×8
4. 0.4×6	5. 0.03×7	6. 0.08×5
7. 0.06×8	8. 0.02×9	9. 0.12×4
10. 0.35×6	11. 0.26×7	12. 0.78×3
13. 1.73×5	14. 2.84×4	15. 5.93×8
16. 7.24×6	17. 6.37×3	18. 8.78×7
19. 7.82×2	20. 9.35×5	21. 0.52×20
22. 0.71×50	23. 0.36×80	24. 0.73×30
25. 0.042×30	26. 0.07×500	27. 0.033×60
28. 4.35×40	29. 8.92×90	30. 36.5×70
31. 7.34×50	32. 4.2×1.3	33. 9.7×2.5
34. 6.9×8.4	35. 3.4×6.3	36. 0.6×0.3
37. 0.7×0.5	38. 0.9×0.8	39. 0.2×0.4
40. 0.54×0.27	41. 0.018×4000	42. 0.34×0.72
43. 0.88×0.51	44. 0.67×0.24	45. 2.42×0.81
46. 0.93×0.24	47. 4.37×0.82	48. 9.16×0.38
49. 36.2×1.4	50. 91.7×2.7	51. 43.6×5.3
52. 70.9×8.6	53. 16.4×7.04	54. 51.6×8.09
55. 36.21×18.2	56. 61.3×37.5	57. 52.41×0.423
58. 4.59×1.237	59. 78.91×4.64	60. 60.24×0.4153

61. $(1.732)^2$

62. $(1.414)^2$

63. $(2.236)^2$

64. $(3.142)^2$

65. 731.4×0.0043

66. $450 \times 0.009\,31$

67. 672×0.0531

68. 89.4×0.0229

69. $0.2 \times 0.3 \times 0.4$

70. $1.2 \times 0.5 \times 0.4$

71. $5.1 \times 0.8 \times 0.4$

72. $2.4 \times 0.5 \times 0.7$

73. $0.3 \times 5.2 \times 0.7$

74. $0.8 \times 3.1 \times 0.5$

75. $0.9 \times 8.2 \times 0.4$

76. $0.6 \times 7.3 \times 0.7$

77. $3.14 \times 0.5 \times 0.5$

78. $2.61 \times 0.7 \times 0.3$

79. $47.4 \times 0.4 \times 0.9$

80. $61.2 \times 0.12 \times 0.8$.

DIVISION

SHORT DIVISION

EXAMPLE 12

Divide 30.08 by 8.

(Rough answer $30 \div 8 \approx 4$.)

8)30.08
  3.76

$\therefore \quad 30.08 \div 8 = 3.76$

EXAMPLE 13

Divide 90.72 by 7.

(Rough answer $90 \div 7 \approx 13$.)

7)90.72
  12.96

$\therefore \quad 90.72 \div 7 = 12.96$

EXERCISE 22

Find:

1. $5.28 \div 4$
2. $7.35 \div 5$
3. $14.24 \div 8$
4. $213.6 \div 6$
5. $35.98 \div 7$
6. $54.68 \div 2$
7. $23.79 \div 3$
8. $38.43 \div 9$
9. $5 \div 4$
10. $4 \div 5$
11. $3 \div 5$
12. $5 \div 3$
13. $0.964 \div 2$
14. $0.636 \div 3$
15. $0.918 \div 6$
16. $0.944 \div 8$
17. $0.093 \div 3$
18. $0.168 \div 4$
19. $0.124 \div 8$
20. $0.049 \div 5$
21. $11 \div 5$
22. $15 \div 4$
23. $9 \div 4$
24. $11 \div 8$
25. $3 \div 8$
26. $31 \div 5$
27. $7 \div 8$
28. $15 \div 6$
29. $27 \div 4$
30. $14 \div 4$
31. $43 \div 5$
32. $17 \div 8$
33. $33.04 \div 7$
34. $35.55 \div 9$
35. $25.413 \div 3$
36. $31.52 \div 5$
37. $0.0372 \div 4$
38. $0.1512 \div 7$
39. $0.005\,872 \div 8$
40. $0.2655 \div 9$.

LONG DIVISION

The most common approach to the long division of decimals is to make the divisor (the decimal on the bottom) a whole number.

EXAMPLE 14

Divide 22.386 by 3.64.

(Rough answer $24 \div 4 = 6$.)

$$\frac{22.386}{3.64} = \frac{2238.6}{364}$$

(we have multiplied the numerator and denominator by 100)

```
        6.15
364)2238.6
    2184
     546
     364
    1820
    1820
     . . .
```

$\therefore$ $22.386 \div 3.64 = 6.15$

EXAMPLE 15

Divide 42.054 by 0.815.

(Rough answer $42 \div 0.8 = 420 \div 8 \approx \overset{.}{5}2$.)

$$\frac{42.054}{0.815} = \frac{42\,054}{815}$$

(we have multiplied the top and the bottom by 1000)

```
        51.6
815)42 054.
    4075
    1304
     815
    4890
    4890
     . . .
```

$\therefore$ $42.054 \div 0.815 = 51.6$

EXERCISE 23

Find:

1. $35.49 \div 13$

2. $29.44 \div 16$

3. $118.23 \div 21$

4. $310.8 \div 37$

5. $202.86 \div 63$

6. $130.08 \div 24$

7. $17.01 \div 2.7$

8. $31.05 \div 6.9$

9. $54.76 \div 7.4$

10. $28.38 \div 3.3$

11. $67.24 \div 8.2$

12. $56.32 \div 6.4$

13. $964.8 \div 134$

14. $955.5 \div 735$

15. $2820.7 \div 421$

16. $14.98 \div 0.7$

17. $49.322 \div 0.91$

18. $110.51 \div 0.43$

19. $0.231 \div 0.525$

20. $0.3991 \div 0.614$

21. $0.8507 \div 0.905$

22. $4.29 \div 0.066$

23. $4.6434 \div 0.071$

24. $8.256 \div 0.048$

25. $629.67 \div 83.4$

26. $14.8836 \div 4.74$

27. $1.94208 \div 0.476$

28. $23.1504 \div 4.134$

29. $287.7135 \div 97.53$

30. $9885.7 \div 163.4$

31. $177.48 \div 48$

32. $535.5 \div 15.3$

33. $2130.6 \div 40.2$

34. $10122 \div 241$

35. $6411.6 \div 93.6$.

DECIMAL PLACES, NEAREST WHOLE NUMBER, ETC.

It must not be assumed that one decimal will always divide exactly into another.

EXAMPLE 16   Consider $324.6 \div 16.7$.

$$\frac{324.6}{16.7} = \frac{3246}{167}$$

(multiply the top and bottom by 10 to make the denominator a whole number)

```
            19.437 ...
      167)3246.
           167
          1576
          1503
           730
           668
           620
           501
          1190
          1169
            21
```

The difference between 19.44 and 19.437 is 0.003, while the difference between 19.43 and 19.437 is 0.007, i.e. 19.44 is nearer to 19.437 than 19.43 is to it. We say that 19.437 ... correct to two decimal places is 19.44.

Correct to two decimal places means correct to the second figure after the decimal point. This is determined by looking at the number in the third decimal place — if this number is 5 or greater than 5, the number in the second place is increased by 1; if the number in the third place is less than 5, the number in the second place is the number already there.

Example 17 shows numbers correct to two decimal places:

EXAMPLE 17   (a) 14.943   14.94
                 (b) 39.456   39.46
                 (c) 227.004   227.00
                 (d) 79.996   80.00

Similarly:

EXAMPLE 18   (a) 92.75 correct to one decimal place is 92.8.
                 (b) 0.9247 correct to three decimal places is 0.925.

In a similar way Example 19 gives numbers correct to the nearest whole number, the nearest ten and the nearest hundred.

EXAMPLE 19   (a) 15.72 correct to the nearest whole number is 16.
                 (b) 539.73 correct to the nearest ten is 540.
                 (c) 539.73 correct to the nearest hundred is 500.

EXERCISE 24

Give the following correct to one decimal place:

1. 14.37	2. 39.45	3. 8.927	4. 12.924
5. 3.427	6. 294.95	7. 1027.64	8. 54.99
9. 7.646	10. 73.921	11. 0.934	12. 0.276
13. 0.3727	14. 0.5927	15. 0.8747	16. 0.092
17. 0.076	18. 92.637	19. 61.05	20. 40.08.

Give the following correct to two decimal places:

21. 14.274	22. 50.097	23. 37.345	24. 9.293

25. 7.666	26. 70.249	27. 63.597	28. 42.564
29. 8.257	30. 3.495	31. 0.926	32. 0.998
33. 0.678	34. 0.345	35. 0.143	36. 0.6235
37. 0.4218	38. 0.7374	39. 0.8264	40. 0.1937.

Give the following correct to the nearest whole number:

41. 4.274	42. 3.923	43. 16.45	44. 27.64
45. 35.55	46. 19.28	47. 53.47	48. 41.82
49. 73.44	50. 127.74	51. 231.92	52. 527.64
53. 413.9	54. 300.27	55. 404.58	56. 0.927
57. 0.88	58. 8.74	59. 7.39	60. 713.98.

Give the following correct to the nearest ten:

61. 74.9	62. 35.46	63. 216.4	64. 593.7
65. 168.2	66. 824	67. 936	68. 224
69. 523	70. 6844	71. 55.46	72. 14.9
73. 9.267	74. 19.94	75. 73.94	76. 5643
77. 4978	78. 7999	79. 61.94	80. 47.27.

Give the following correct to the nearest hundred:

81. 7420	82. 6180	83. 198.2	84. 589.4
85. 442.4	86. 76.6	87. 3424	88. 1760
89. 59.2	90. 727.9	91. 5379	92. 1264
93. 33 994	94. 56 375	95. 673 492	96. 394.2
97. 829.7	98. 31 455	99. 83 846	100. 9999.

SIGNIFICANT FIGURES

Many questions ask for the answer correct to a certain number of significant figures. A few examples will indicate exactly what this means. A rule worth remembering is that if the first figure to be discarded is a 5 or a figure greater than 5, the previous figure is increased by 1.

EXAMPLE 20

37.4789 is 37.479 correct to five significant figures

37.48 correct to four significant figures

37.5 correct to three significant figures

37 correct to two significant figures

EXAMPLE 21   0.905 36 is 0.9054 correct to four significant figures

0.905   correct to three significant figures

0.91   correct to two significant figures

EXAMPLE 22   0.007 384 is 0.007 38 correct to three significant figures

0.0074 correct to two significant figures

0.007 correct to the first significant figure

EXERCISE 25

Give the following correct to three significant figures:

1. 327.6	2. 413.4	3. 762.5	4. 843.4
5. 192.6	6. 61.29	7. 80.92	8. 36.66
9. 40.33	10. 59.27	11. 2.341	12. 3.927
13. 5.663	14. 9.887	15. 7.342	16. 0.5555
17. 0.6214	18. 0.7378	19. 0.8115	20. 0.5439
21. 1240	22. 6927	23. 8275	24. 4336
25. 3929	26. 0.064 74	27. 0.029 45	28. 0.085 67
29. 0.059 16	30. 0.022 48	31. 36 495	32. 27 644
33. 813 999	34. 54 737	35. 50 098	36. 5.926 43
37. 16.9115	38. 207.462	39. 62 648	40. 0.554 372
41. 73.6429	42. 192 937	43. 0.009 2745	
44. 5.4474	45. 920 064	46. 0.002 937 4	
47. 0.045 67	48. 604 009	49. 82.916	50. 327.4465.

Give the following correct to two significant figures:

51. 543	52. 731	53. 54.24	54. 16.93
55. 34.74	56. 26 745	57. 9.493	58. 18.45
59. 392.61	60. 4.3343	61. 0.927	62. 0.3924
63. 0.7261	64. 0.009 45	65. 0.037 45	66. 204.04
67. 16.09	68. 9.009	69. 8.249	70. 54 643.

Give the following correct to four significant figures:

71. 52 734   **72.** 17 424   **73.** 39 245   **74.** 724.96

75. 362.98   **76.** 44.246   **77.** 32.937   **78.** 3.141 59

79. 2.9876   **80.** 0.643 21   **81.** 0.567 89   **82.** 0.028 673

83. 8.6248   **84.** 37.1423   **85.** 98.9481   **86.** 23.564

87. 0.045 937   **88.** 473 790   **89.** 83.456   **90.** 0.354 28.

Give the following numbers correct to
(a) the nearest whole number
(b) three significant figures
(c) two decimal places:

91. 74.6243   **92.** 18.5437   **93.** 24.927   **94.** 524.147

95. 618.332   **96.** 828.186   **97.** 7.924   **98.** 42.434

99. 8.547   **100.** 364.624.

EXAMPLE 23   Find $354.3 \div 19.2$ giving your answer

(a) correct to two decimal places
(b) correct to three significant figures.

(Rough answer $350 \div 20 = 17.5$.)

$$\frac{354.3}{19.2} = \frac{3543}{192}$$

$$
\begin{array}{r}
18.453 \\
192\overline{)3543.} \\
\underline{192} \\
1623 \\
\underline{1536} \\
870 \\
\underline{768} \\
1020 \\
\underline{960} \\
600 \\
\underline{576} \\
24
\end{array}
$$

(to obtain the answer correct to 2 decimal places we find the quotient to 3 decimal places)

$\therefore$ $354.3 \div 19.2 = 18.45$ correct to two decimal places

             $= 18.5$ correct to three significant figures

EXERCISE 26

Evaluate the following correct to two decimal places:

1. $20.4 \div 8.3$
2. $37.2 \div 5.7$
3. $75.4 \div 9.2$
4. $48.2 \div 4.9$
5. $13.7 \div 2.6$
6. $61.4 \div 7.2$
7. $50.1 \div 5.3$
8. $89.2 \div 137$
9. $4.21 \div 17.3$
10. $0.93 \div 1.8$
11. $0.41 \div 2.6$
12. $0.93 \div 0.17$
13. $723.4 \div 93.6$
14. $241.2 \div 64.3$
15. $556.9 \div 327.1$
16. $0.937 \div 26.4$
17. $0.873 \div 0.047$
18. $0.293 \div 0.074$
19. $654.1 \div 926.2$
20. $0.573 \div 31.3.$

Evaluate the following correct to three decimal places:

21. $52.4 \div 49.2$
22. $73.6 \div 94.2$
23. $18.92 \div 9.47$
24. $92.4 \div 137$
25. $42.7 \div 60.2$
26. $5.36 \div 10.9$
27. $0.541 \div 0.23$
28. $0.643 \div 0.55$
29. $0.734 \div 0.452$
30. $0.731 \div 1.84$
31. $0.848 \div 9.21$
32. $0.378 \div 21.4$
33. $592.3 \div 347.8$
34. $754.3 \div 864$
35. $6142 \div 839.$

Evaluate the following correct to three significant figures:

36. $243 \div 62.4$
37. $9.87 \div 2.34$
38. $536.4 \div 337.2$
39. $6.351 \div 4.92$
40. $18.36 \div 46.2$
41. $87.14 \div 236.1$
42. $0.145 \div 7.35$
43. $0.44 \div 26.3$
44. $0.92 \div 62.1$
45. $40.1 \div 0.076$
46. $237 \div 0.36$
47. $884.2 \div 0.093$
48. $3.21 \div 0.004\ 34$
49. $16.3 \div 0.0876$
50. $536.1 \div 0.0924.$

STANDARD FORM

When a number is expressed in the form $a \times 10^n$, where a is a number between 1 and 10 and n is zero or an integer, the number is said to be in *standard form*.

EXAMPLE 24   Express each of the following in standard form:
(a) 512.3, (b) 42.6, (c) 702 000, (d) 0.75,
(e) 0.000 432.

(a) $512.3 = 5.123 \times 100 = 5.123 \times 10^2$

(b) $42.64 = 4.264 \times 10^1$

(c) $702\,000 = 7.02 \times 100\,000 = 7.02 \times 10^5$

(d) $0.75 = \dfrac{7.5}{10} = 7.5 \times 10^{-1}$

(e) $0.000\,432 = \dfrac{4.32}{10\,000} = \dfrac{4.32}{10^4} = 4.32 \times 10^{-4}$

EXERCISE 27

Express each of the following in standard form:

1. 72.6
2. 183.4
3. 5000
4. 424.2
5. 82 400
6. 1 230 000
7. 0.5
8. 0.43
9. 0.842
10. 0.07
11. 0.009
12. 0.0412
13. 0.0093
14. 0.000 02
15. 0.000 054 3.

16. If $a = 1.2 \times 10^4$ and $b = 3 \times 10^2$, find (i) $a + b$, (ii) ab, (iii) $a \div b$, expressing each answer in standard form.

17. If $a = 5 \times 10^4$ and $b = 25 \times 10^3$, find (i) $a + b$, (ii) ab, (iii) $a \div b$, (iv) $b \div a$, giving each answer in standard form.

18. If $a = 3.6 \times 10^4$ and $b = 4 \times 10^{-3}$, find (i) ab, (ii) $a \div b$, expressing each answer in standard form.

19. If $a = 4.2 \times 10^{-3}$ and $b = 6 \times 10^{-5}$, find (i) $a + b$, (ii) $a - b$, (iii) ab, (iv) $a \div b$, expressing each answer in standard form.

20. If $a = 8.4 \times 10^{-5}$ and $b = 2.1 \times 10^6$, find (i) ab, (ii) $a \div b$, expressing each answer in standard form.

DIRECTED NUMBERS

ADDITION AND SUBTRACTION

We are all familiar with the temperatures given on the TV weather charts for different parts of the country at different times of the year. During the summer, temperatures everywhere are + numbers, but in the winter we frequently see − numbers. On the centigrade scale the temperature at which water freezes is marked $0°$. Temperatures above this are referred to as + temperatures, and those below as − temperatures. If the temperature was $8°$ at 8 a.m. but $11°$ at noon, it would have risen by $3°$. We denote rising by $3°$ as $+3°$, therefore $8°$ plus $(+3°) = 11°$.

If the temperature at 6 p.m. on the same day is $6°$, it has fallen by $5°$, and we denote this fall by $-5°$, i.e. $11°$ plus $(-5°) = 6°$.

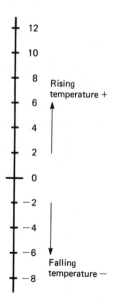

If the initial temperature is $4°$ and it falls $6°$, then the thermometer reads $-2°$

i.e. $\qquad 4°$ plus $(-6°) = -2°$

If the initial temperature is $-2°$ and it falls $5°$, then the thermometer reads $-7°$

i.e. $\qquad -2°$ plus $(-5°) = -7°$

Numbers such as $+3$ and -7 are called *directed numbers*. The $-$ sign therefore means 'in the opposite direction to $+$'.

In this context we can therefore say that:

(a) a loss of £10 is the same as a profit of $-£10$,

(b) -15 minutes late is the same as 15 minutes early,

(c) -40 metres above ground is the same as 40 metres below ground,

(d) paying £100 into the bank is the same as withdrawing $-£100$ from it.

EXERCISE 28

Give alternative statements for each of the following:

1. The clock is -3 minutes fast.

2. The clock is 5 minutes slow.

3. I pay $-£20$ into my bank account.

4. I withdraw $-£50$ from my bank account.

5. Peter climbs -100 metres up a mountain.

6. Jane walks down 6 stairs.

7. -50 litres of water flows into the bath.

8. Tom walks -3 kilometres due south.

9. Mary receives a pay rise of -6%.

10. The price of gold decreases by 20%.

11. The population of Eastmouth increases by -2000.

12. Bolton beat Hyde by -2 goals.

We are therefore able to conclude that a rise of -2 is the same as a fall of 2, and that a fall of -2 is the same as a rise of 2. Denoting a rise by $+$ and a fall by $-$ we can therefore write:

$$+(-2) = -2$$

and $\qquad -(-2) = +2$

EXAMPLE 1   (a) $5 + (-2) = 5 - 2 = 3$
(b) $-5 + (-2) = -5 - 2 = -7$
(c) $8 - (-2) = 8 + 2 = 10$
(d) $-8 - (-3) = -8 + 3 = -5$

EXAMPLE 2   (a) Add -2 to 8.
$$8 + (-2) = 8 - 2 = 6$$

(b) Add -4 to -7.
$$-7 + (-4) = -7 - 4 = -11$$

(c) Subtract -3 from 12.
$$12 - (-3) = 12 + 3 = 15$$

(d) Subtract -7 from -9.
$$-9 - (-7) = -9 + 7 = -2$$

EXAMPLE 3   Simplify:
(a) $8 - 2 - 10 = 8 - 12 = -4$
(b) $7 - (5 - 2) = 7 - 3 = 4$
(c) $-10 + (3 - 7) - 4 = -10 + (-4) - 4$
$$= -10 - 4 - 4 = -18$$

EXERCISE 29

Simplify:

1. $10 + (-5)$
2. $7 + (-3)$
3. $12 + (-9)$
4. $20 + (-17)$
5. $8 + (-10)$
6. $6 + (-14)$
7. $10 + (-20)$
8. $15 + (-21)$
9. $(-4) + (-3)$
10. $(-10) + (-2)$
11. $(-8) + (-5)$
12. $(-14) + (-16)$
13. $(15) - (-2)$
14. $(16) - (-8)$
15. $(-14) - (-3)$
16. $(-8) - (-12)$
17. $10 - (-5)$
18. $(-16) - (-4)$
19. $(-9) - (-7)$
20. $(-18) + (-7)$
21. $5 + (-3) + (-2)$
22. $12 + (-6) + (-4)$
23. $8 + (-5) + (-3)$
24. $12 + (-8) + (-6)$
25. $9 - (-4) + (-5)$
26. $6 + (-3) - (-8)$
27. $4 - (-2) + (-3)$
28. $10 + (-5) - (-5)$

29. $(-8)+(-4)+(-2)$ **30.** $(-5)+(-3)+(-7)$

31. $(-12)-(-2)+(-8)$ **32.** $(-5)+(-6)-(-4)$

33. $(-7)-(-8)+(-4)$ **34.** $(-10)+(-8)-(-3)$

35. $-(-3)+(-2)+(-4)$ **36.** $-(-5)+(-6)$

37. $-(-8)-(-4)+(-2)$ **38.** $-(-10)-(-6)+(-5)$

39. $-(-7)+(-2)-(-6)$ **40.** $-(-9)+(-7)-(-5)$

MULTIPLICATION AND DIVISION

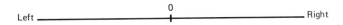

Left ——————— 0 ——————— Right

Imagine a boy walking along the half-way line on a football pitch. Suppose he walks at 2 metres per second (m/s) and starts walking on the hour.

A speed of $+2$ m/s means that he walks to the right, while a speed of -2 m/s means that he walks to the left. Similarly for time: $+5$ seconds means 5 seconds after the hour, and -5 seconds means 5 seconds before the hour.

If he walks from the centre 0 for $+5$ seconds at a speed of $+2$ m/s where is he?

$\qquad$ 10 metres to the right of 0 or $(+5)\times(+2)=+10$ m

If he walks from the centre for $+5$ seconds at a speed of -2 m/s where is he?

$\qquad$ 10 metres to the left of 0 or $(+5)\times(-2)=-10$ m

If he walks from the centre for -5 seconds at a speed of 2 m/s where is he?

$\qquad$ 10 metres to the left of 0 or $(-5)\times(+2)=-10$ m

If he walks from the centre for -5 seconds at a speed of -2 m/s where is he?

$\qquad$ 10 metres to the right of 0 or $(-5)\times(-2)=+10$ m

If he is at 0 at time 0 seconds, then 5 seconds previous to this (i.e. at -5 seconds) he was 10 metres to the right of 0).

The above four results enable us to formulate the rule that: like signs *multiplied together* give a plus sign while unlike signs *multiplied together* give a minus sign.

It follows that if $(-5)\times(-2)=+10$

then $\qquad\qquad (+10)\div(-2)=-5$

61

Similarly since $(+5) \times (-2) = -10$

$$(-10) \div (-2) = 5$$

Hence: division of like signs gives a plus sign while division of unlike signs gives a minus sign.

EXAMPLE 4   (a) $(+10) \times (-6) = -60$

(b) $(-24) \times (+3) = -72$

(c) $(-6) \times (-5) = +30$

EXAMPLE 5   (a) $(-20) \div 4 = -5$

(b) $(30) \div (-6) = -5$

(c) $(-24) \div (-4) = 6$

EXAMPLE 6   (a) $(-5) \times (4) \times (-3) = (-20) \times (-3) = 60$

(b) $\dfrac{(-6) \times 4}{(-12)} = \dfrac{(-24)}{(-12)} = 2$

(c) $(-8 \div 4) \times (-2) = (-2) \times (-2) = 4$

(d) $(-4)^3 \div 16 = \dfrac{(-4) \times (-4) \times (-4)}{16} = \dfrac{-64}{16} = -4$

EXERCISE 30

Simplify:

1. $4 \times (-3)$	2. $(-4) \times 2$	3. $(-5) \times (-4)$
4. $(-14) \times 3$	5. $-(14 \times 3)$	6. $14 \times (-5)$
7. $(-13) \times (-3)$	8. $(-5) \times 3$	9. $(-12) \div 12$
10. $12 \div (-3)$	11. $(-24) \div 3$	12. $(-36) \div (-12)$
13. $8 \div (-4)$	14. $(-16) \div 4$	15. $(-27) \div (-9)$
16. $(-15) \div (-5)$	17. $\dfrac{99}{-11}$	18. $\dfrac{-88}{11}$
19. $\dfrac{-55}{-5}$	20. $\dfrac{16}{-4}$	21. $\dfrac{-28}{7}$
22. $\dfrac{-16}{-8}$	23. $\dfrac{24}{-3}$	24. $\dfrac{-48}{-24}$
25. $\dfrac{-14}{7}$	26. $\dfrac{24}{-8}$	27. $\dfrac{-144}{-16}$
28. $\dfrac{-9}{-27}$	29. $3(4-2)$	30. $5(-3-4)$

31. $6(-7+9)$

32. $5(-3+4)$

33. $-3(7-2)$

34. $-8(-5+4)$

35. $-6(-6-2)$

36. $-6(-8-1)$

37. $\dfrac{9-3}{3}$

38. $\dfrac{-17-8}{5}$

39. $\dfrac{-5-7}{4}$

40. $\dfrac{-28-8}{12}$

41. $\dfrac{21-3}{-6}$

42. $\dfrac{-9-7}{-8}$

43. $\dfrac{-19+7}{-2}$

44. $\dfrac{-31-19}{-10}$

45. $(8-4)\times 2$

46. $(8-4)\div 2$

47. $8\div(4-2)$

48. $8\div(-4+2)$

49. $(8\div 4)-2$

50. $8\times(4\times 2)$

51. $8\times 4\times(-2)$

52. $8\times(-4)\times 2$

53. $8\times(-4)\times(-2)$

54. $(8\div 4)\times 2$

55. $(8\div 4)\times(-2)$

56. $(8\div 4)\times 4$

57. $(-8\div 4)\times 2$

58. $(-8\div 4)-2$

59. $(-8\div 4)+2$

60. $8\div(4\div 2)$

61. $8-(4\div 2)$

62. $8\div(4-2)$

63. $8\div(4\times 2)$

64. $8\div(-4\times 2)$

65. $8+(-4\div 2)$

66. $(8+4)\div(-2)$

67. $4\div(8\times 2)$

68. $(-4\div 8)\times 2$

69. $\dfrac{(-3)\times(-4)\times(-5)}{-60}$

70. $\dfrac{(-1)\times 4\times(-6)}{-36}$

71. $\dfrac{(-3)^2\times(-4)}{12}$

72. $(-3)^2\times(-2)^3$

73. $\dfrac{(-4)^2\times(-3)}{2(-6-2)}$

74. $\dfrac{8\times(-4)\times(-2)^2}{(-12)\times(-2)}$

75. $\dfrac{(-12)\times(-4)}{12\div(-4)}$.

THE METRIC SYSTEM

The metric system of units is a simplified version of a system of weights and measures which was introduced in France in 1790 during the French Revolution. It is essentially a decimal system, the standard unit of length being the metre (m) and the standard unit of mass being the kilogram (kg), although the gram (g) is frequently used.

The metre was intended to be one ten-millionth of the distance from the equator to the North Pole as measured along the line of longitude through Paris. Its exact value is now defined by reference to a particular wavelength of electromagnetic radiation.

The same prefixes occur several times in the metric system, and outside it. It is therefore important to learn these: *kilo* means thousand, *centi* means one hundredth and *milli* means one thousandth.

LENGTH

The basic unit of length is the *metre*. A length of one thousand metres is called a *kilometre*. The metre may be divided into one hundred equal parts each of which is called a *centimetre*. It may also be divided into one thousand equal parts each of which is called a *millimetre*.

Hence

$$1 \text{ kilometre (km)} = 1000 \text{ metres (m)}$$

$$1 \text{ centimetre (cm)} = \frac{1}{100} \text{ metre (m)}$$

$$1 \text{ millimetre (mm)} = \frac{1}{1000} \text{ metre (m)}$$

It follows that:

$$1\,\text{km} = 1000\,\text{m}$$

$$100\,\text{cm} = 1\,\text{m}$$

$$1000\,\text{mm} = 1\,\text{m}$$

and

$$10\,\text{mm} = 1\,\text{cm}$$

EXAMPLE 1 Convert $5.264\,\text{m}$ into (a) centimetres, (b) milli-metres.

$$5.264\,\text{m} = 5.264 \times 100\,\text{cm} = 526.4\,\text{cm}$$

$$5.264\,\text{m} = 5.264 \times 1000\,\text{m} = 5264\,\text{mm}$$

EXAMPLE 2 Convert $0.458\,\text{km}$ into metres.

$$0.458\,\text{km} = 0.458 \times 1000\,\text{m} = 458\,\text{m}$$

EXAMPLE 3 Express (a) 5 cm 4 mm in millimetres, (b) 3 m 84 cm 5 mm in centimetres.

(a) $5\,\text{cm}\,4\,\text{mm} = 50\,\text{mm} + 4\,\text{mm} = 54\,\text{mm}$

(b) $3\,\text{m}\,84\,\text{cm}\,5\,\text{mm} = 300\,\text{cm} + 84\,\text{cm} + 0.5\,\text{cm}$
$$= 384.5\,\text{cm}$$

When adding or subtracting metric quantities it is important that all quantities are converted into a common unit.

EXAMPLE 4 Add 2 m 37 cm, 84 cm and 534 mm giving your answer in (a) millimetres, (b) metres.

(a)
$$2\,\text{m}\,37\,\text{cm} = 2370\,\text{mm}$$
$$84\,\text{cm} = 840\,\text{mm}$$
$$534\,\text{mm} = 534\,\text{mm}$$
$$\therefore\ \text{Sum} = 3744\,\text{mm}$$

(b) $3744\,\text{mm} = 3.744\,\text{m}$

EXAMPLE 5 Subtract 434 m 84 cm from 2 km. Give your answer in metres.

$$2\,\text{km} = 2000\quad\text{m}$$
$$434\,\text{m}\,84\,\text{cm} = 434.84\,\text{m}$$
$$\therefore\ \text{Difference} = 1565.16\,\text{m}$$

EXAMPLE 6 From a ball of string 50 m long one hundred and five lengths, each 45 cm, are cut. What length of string remains?

65

Total length of 105 pieces each of length 45 cm
= 105 × 45 cm = 4725 cm.

Original length of ball = 50 m = 5000 cm.

∴ Amount remaining = (5000 − 4725) cm

= 275 cm

EXERCISE 31

1. Measure each of the following straight lines correct to the nearest centimetre:
   (a) ——————————
   (b) ————————————
   (c) ——————
   (d) ————————————

2. Measure each of the following straight lines correct to the nearest millimetre:
   (a) ————
   (b) ——————————
   (c) ————————
   (d) ————————————

3. Measure each of the following straight lines in (i) centimetres, (ii) millimetres:
   (a) ——————————
   (b) —————————
   (c) ————————
   (d) ——————————————

4. Draw straight lines of the following lengths:
   (a) 3 cm   (b) 7 cm   (c) 12 cm   (d) 9.5 cm.

5. Draw straight lines of the following lengths:
   (a) 35 mm   (b) 82 mm   (c) 58 mm   (d) 26 mm.

6. Which metric unit would it be most sensible to use to measure:
   (a) the width of the nearest road
   (b) your height
   (c) the height of a lamp standard
   (d) the distance between Paris and Rome
   (e) the thickness of a piece of window glass.

7. Convert into metres:
   (a) 12 km   (b) 4.32 km   (c) 0.68 km   (d) 529 cm
   (e) 4360 cm   (f) 26 cm   (g) 734 mm   (h) 38 mm
   (i) 60.24 km   (j) 49.7 cm.

8. Convert into centimetres:
   (a) 24 m   (b) 3.6 m   (c) 0.49 m   (d) 0.026 m
   (e) 44 mm   (f) 634 mm   (g) 7.31 mm   (h) 0.04 mm
   (i) 1.732 km   (j) 0.0264 km.

9. Convert into millimetres:
   (a) 37 cm   (b) 13.5 cm   (c) 9.12 cm   (d) 0.46 cm
   (e) 8.4 m   (f) 27 m   (g) 0.73 m   (h) 0.024 m
   (i) 1.243 km   (j) 0.092 km.

10. Convert into kilometres:
    (a) 5000 m   (b) 10 000 m   (c) 750 m   (d) 4360 m
    (e) 830 m   (f) 17 630 cm   (g) 49 360 cm
    (h) 763 cm   (i) 143 400 mm
    (j) 7 230 000 mm.

11. Add the following, giving each answer in metres:
    (a) 3 m, 42 cm, 1 m 50 cm, 8 m 74 cm
    (b) 59 cm, 84 cm, 2430 mm
    (c) 643 cm, 842 mm, 3914 mm
    (d) 2.1 km, 904 m, 8640 cm
    (e) 0.04 km, 53 m, 892 m.

12. Subtract the second length from the first, giving your answer in metres:
    (a) 12 m, 200 cm   (b) 34 m, 14.3 m
    (c) 60 m, 4930 cm   (d) 45.2 cm, 164 mm
    (e) 2934 mm, 1.36 m.

13. Express the following as mixed quantities in terms of metres, centimetres and millimetres:
    (a) 30.24 m   (b) 2436 cm   (c) 7490 mm   (d) 0.024 16 km
    (e) 92 600 mm   (f) 6724 cm   (g) 10 304 cm.

14. Find the following giving each answer in metres:
    (a) 4 m − 264 cm + 930 mm
    (b) 7.2 m − 437 cm + 2600 mm
    (c) 826 cm − 2.45 m + 200 mm
    (d) 1400 cm − 3940 mm − 8.36 m
    (e) 2640 mm + 0.92 m − 356 cm.

15. The diameter of a penny is 2 cm. How many pennies placed side by side will extend a distance of 5 m?

16. A 2 p coin has a diameter of 2.5 cm. How many 2 p coins placed side by side are required to extend a distance of 100 m?

17. How many pencils of length 18 cm, placed end to end, are required to stretch 100 m?

18. How many concrete blocks, each 22 cm high, are required to reach a height of 1.76 m?

19. How many concrete blocks, each 60 cm long, are required to build one course of a wall 33.6 m long?

20. A book is 6.6 mm thick. How many similar books may be stored on a shelf 1.65 m long?

MASS

The basic unit of mass is the kilogram (kg), which is defined from a standard block of metal kept near Paris.

$$1 \text{ kilogram (kg)} = 1000 \text{ grams (g)}$$

and

$$1 \text{ milligram (mg)} = \frac{1}{1000} \text{ gram (g)} = \frac{1}{1\,000\,000} \text{ kg}$$

For large masses we use the metric tonne (t) where 1 tonne = 1000 kilograms

$$\therefore \qquad 1 \text{ kg} = 1000 \text{ g}$$

$$1 \text{ g} = 1000 \text{ mg}$$

and

$$1 \text{ t} = 1000 \text{ kg}$$

EXAMPLE 7   Convert:

(a) 1.93 kg into grams

(b) 0.043 t into kilograms

(c) 73 400 mg into grams

(d) 59 300 g into kilograms

(a) Since $1 \text{ kg} = 1000 \text{ g}$

$$1.93 \text{ kg} = 1.93 \times 1000 \text{ g} = 1930 \text{ g}$$

(b) Since $1 \text{ t} = 1000 \text{ kg}$

$$0.043 \text{ t} = 0.043 \times 1000 \text{ kg} = 43 \text{ kg}$$

(c) Since $1000 \text{ mg} = 1 \text{ g}$

$$73\,400 \text{ mg} = \frac{73\,400}{1000} \text{ g} = 73.4 \text{ g}$$

(d) Since $1000 \text{ g} = 1 \text{ kg}$

$$59\,300 \text{ g} = \frac{59\,300}{1000} \text{ kg} = 59.3 \text{ kg}$$

EXAMPLE 8   Add 5.43 kg, 8640 g, 293 400 mg and 0.0443 t, giving your answer in kilograms.

$$5.43 \text{ kg} = 5.43 \text{ kg}$$

$$8640 \text{ g} = 8.64 \text{ kg}$$

$$293\,400 \text{ mg} = 0.2934 \text{ kg}$$

$$0.0443 \text{ t} = 44.3 \text{ kg}$$

$$\therefore \quad \text{Total mass} = 58.6634 \text{ kg}$$

EXAMPLE 9   Express 54 346 g in terms of kilograms and grams.

$$54\,346\,g = 54\,000\,g + 346\,g$$

$$= 54\,kg\,346\,g$$

EXAMPLE 10   A van carries a load of 0.5 t which is made up of 30 boxes, each containing 36 tins of cooked meat, together with 2 boxes of fresh fruit each of mass 4.3 kg. Calculate the mass of 1 tin of cooked meat.

Total mass of load $= 0.5\,t = 500\,kg$

Mass of 2 boxes of fruit at 4.3 kg per box $= 8.6\,kg$

∴   Mass of 30 boxes of cooked meat $= 491.4\,kg$

∴   Mass of 1 box of cooked meat $= \dfrac{491.4}{30}$

$$= 16.38\,kg$$

i.e.   Mass of 36 tins of cooked meat $= 16.38\,kg$

$$= 16\,380\,g$$

∴   Mass of 1 tin of cooked meat $= \dfrac{16\,380}{36}$

$$= 455\,g$$

∴   Each tin has a mass of 455 g

EXERCISE 32   MISCELLANEOUS EXAMPLES

1. What units would you expect to use to measure the mass of each of the following?
    (a)   a car
    (b)   a loaded petrol tanker
    (c)   a saccharin tablet
    (d)   one page from this book
    (e)   a bag of potatoes.

2. Convert into grams:
    (a)   250 mg   (b)   5700 mg   (c)   73 400 mg
    (d)   4730 mg   (e)   5.42 kg   (f)   20.4 kg   (g)   0.73 kg
    (h)   0.0493 kg.

3. Convert into kilograms:
    (a)   7600 g   (b)   491 g   (c)   97.2 g   (d)   6040 g
    (e)   926 400 mg   (f)   55 450 mg
    (g)   374 mg   (h)   8497 mg.

4. Convert into milligrams:
   (a) 54 g   (b) 429 g   (c) 1.24 g   (d) 0.46 g
   (e) 1.2 kg   (f) 0.044 kg   (g) 0.217 kg   (h) 0.000 84 kg.

5. Convert:
   (a) 3420 kg into tonnes
   (b) 1.74 t into kilograms
   (c) 0.047 t into kilograms
   (d) 83 440 kg into tonnes
   (e) 504 600 kg into tonnes.

6. Add the following masses, giving your answers in kilograms:
   (a) 240 kg, 0.42 t, 34 kg   (b) 3 kg, 864 g, 736 g
   (c) 544 g, 1.24 kg, 64 g   (d) 65 000 mg, 434 g, 0.244 kg
   (e) 0.06 t, 240 kg, 0.416 t.

7. Add the following masses, giving your answers in grams:
   (a) 7340 mg, 25.4 g, 1350 mg   (b) 2.6 g, 0.0042 kg, 55 400 mg
   (c) 270 mg, 16.4 g, 550 mg   (d) 0.074 kg, 8640 mg, 65.5 g.

8. Subtract the first mass from the second, giving your answer in grams:
   (a) 760 g, 1.46 kg   (b) 2.57 kg, 6480 g
   (c) 640 mg, 1.26 g   (d) 1870 mg, 0.004 88 kg
   (e) 0.000 092 kg, 687 mg.

9. Express in mixed quantities in terms of kilograms and grams:
   (a) 9430 g   (b) 1691 g   (c) 3450 g   (d) 13.74 kg
   (e) 28.4 kg.

10. A tin of tomatoes has a mass of 230 g. What is the mass, in kilograms, of a case containing 72 such tins?

11. A jar of marmalade has a mass of 454 g. What is the mass, in kilograms, of a carton containing 48 such jars?

12. If the mass of a 2 p coin is 7.12 g, find the mass in kilograms of a bag containing £20 of such coins.

13. A bag containing penny coins has a mass of 5.34 kg. If each coin has a mass of 3.56 g what is the total value of the coins in the bag?

14. A lorry has an unladen mass of 5 t 40 kg, and carries a load of 180 bags of potatoes, each with mass 25 kg. What is the combined mass, in tonnes, of the lorry plus the potatoes?

15. Into an empty carton of mass 80 g are placed six cakes, each of mass 195 g. Calculate the mass of the carton when full.

16. A tin of fruit cocktail has a mass of 326 g. Find the mass, in kilograms, of a box which contains 36 such tins, allowing 1 kg for the mass of the empty box.

17. A fifty-four-seater coach leaves for a package holiday with every seat taken. If the passengers are of average mass 82 kg and each passenger has 35 kg of luggage, find the total mass of the passengers plus their luggage.

18. Ham is sold in tins, each tin having a mass of 198 g. Find the total mass of a carton containing 72 such tins if the carton has a mass of 550 g.

19. The mass of a can of Bucko corned beef is 340 g. If 48 such cans are packed into a case of mass 600 g, find the mass of 50 full cases.

20. Fifty-four tins of tomato soup are placed in a box of mass 456 g. If the combined mass of tins and box is 24 kg, find the mass, in grams, of one tin of soup.

21. Forty-eight tins of pineapple cubes together with their packaging have a mass of 22 kg. If the mass of the packaging is 928 g, calculate the mass of five tins of pineapple cubes.

22. A housewife returns from the supermarket with:

    6 bags of sugar, each of mass 2.2 kg
    12 cans of beans, each of mass 425 g
    4 packets of cereal, each of mass 440 g and
    8 jars of jam, each of mass 454 g.

    Calculate the total mass of her purchases.

23. A lorry is loaded with:

    64 boxes, each of mass 22 kg
    44 boxes, each of mass 34 kg
    152 boxes, each of mass 18 kg and
    98 boxes, each of mass 26 kg.

    Find the total mass of the load in tonnes.

24. Table salt is sold in boxes of mass 1.5 kg. If a salt cellar requires 35.5 g of salt to fill it, how many times could it be filled from one box of table salt? Give your answer correct to the nearest whole number.

25. An aircraft has 320 seats. If all the seats are occupied with passengers of average mass 78 kg, and each passenger is allowed 20 kg of luggage, calculate the total potential mass of passengers plus their luggage.

REVISION PAPERS
1-25

PAPER 1

1. Add 143, 7264, 92 and 736.

2. Multiply 437 by 55.

3. Express 5184 in prime factors and hence find its square root.

4. Reduce $\dfrac{2160}{5040}$ to its lowest terms.

5. How many lengths of cloth, each 3.25 m long may be cut from a 100 m roll? How much is left over?

PAPER 2

1. Subtract 3659 from 5000.

2. Divide 9648 by 72.

3. Express 5733 in prime factors. What is the smallest number by which 5733 must be multiplied to make it a perfect square?

4. Calculate the total mass in kilograms of 84 packets each containing a mass of 476 g.

5. Write down the next two numbers in the sequence 19, 14, 9, ...

PAPER 3

1. Add 2764, 3419, 83 and 9264.

2. A train leaves Manchester at 3.36 p.m. and arrives in London 117 minutes later. Find its time of arrival.

3. Divide fourteen thousand three hundred and thirty-eight by two hundred and fourteen.

4. Express 9261 in prime factors and hence find its cube root.

5. Simplify (a) $\dfrac{5}{8} \times \dfrac{4}{3}$, (b) $\dfrac{7}{8} \div \dfrac{3}{4}$.

PAPER 4

1. Find the sum of all the whole numbers between 16 and 31 which are exactly divisible by 3.

2. Write down the next two terms in the series $8 + 9 + 11 + 14 + \ldots$.

3. Express 630 and 1728 in prime factors. Hence find their HCF and LCM.

4. Simplify (a) $\dfrac{5}{7} + \dfrac{5}{14}$, (b) $\dfrac{5}{7} - \dfrac{5}{14}$.

5. A factory worker, on a five day week, starts work at 7.30 a.m. and works until 4 p.m. with three-quarters of an hour off for lunch. How many hours does he work in a week?

PAPER 5

1. Find $7261 - 4395 + 743 - 1436$.

2. Find the mass, in kilograms, of 34 articles each with mass 127 g. How much more, or less, is this than the mass of 18 articles each with a mass 248 g?

3. Simplify $5\dfrac{1}{4} \times 1\dfrac{7}{9}$.

4. Evaluate (a) 123.5×0.89, (b) $123.5 \div 0.89$, giving each answer correct to one decimal place.

5. Lamp standards, which are set at 50 m intervals along a straight road, are numbered consecutively. If Jane walks from standard number 67 to standard number 127, how far does she walk in kilometres?

PAPER 6

1. Express 375 m as a fraction of 2 km, giving your answer in its lowest terms.

2. Simplify $5\frac{1}{7} \div 1\frac{23}{49}$.

3. Simplify (a) $1.24 + 0.36 - 0.84$, (b) 0.8×0.4.

4. A school opens at 8.45 a.m. and closes at 3.35 p.m. The lunch break is from 12.20 p.m. to 1.35 p.m. and there is a 15 minute mid-morning break. How long are the pupils at work in (a) a day, (b) a week, (c) a school year consisting of 195 days?

5. At a local election with three candidates, Mr Brown received $\frac{1}{3}$ of the votes cast, Mrs Collard $\frac{2}{5}$ and Miss Durley $\frac{1}{4}$. If there were 73 spoilt papers, how many people voted and how many votes did the winner receive?

PAPER 7

1. A football supporters' club hires fifty-four-seater coaches to transport 4364 supporters to an away match. How many coaches are required?

2. How much larger is the sum of 842 and 736 than the difference between 1000 and 136?

3. Multiply 924 by 234 and divide the result by 273.

4. Find (a) 1.2×0.7, (b) $0.024 \div 12$.

5. Write down the next three numbers in the sequence 10, 15, 19, 22, ...

PAPER 8

1. The product of three numbers, two of which are 13 and 17, is 4199. Find the third number.

2. The length of a man's pace is 90 cm. How many paces does he take to walk $2\frac{2}{5}$ km?

3. Find (a) 4.2×1.6, (b) $371 \div 0.7$.

4. Twelve cars, each of length 4.72 m, are parked nose to tail with a 65 cm gap between each car and the next. Calculate the total distance from the front of the first to the back of the last.

5. Simplify (a) $8 - 4(-2)$, (b) $-24 \div (-6 + 2)$.

PAPER 9

1. Find the sum of 34.62, 7.09, 0.845 and 40.

2. Subtract the difference between 8950 and 4689 from the sum of 5376 and 1294.

3. Divide 42.64 by 12.3 giving your answer correct to two decimal places.

4. Four auto parts in a set have masses 17.5 g, 21 g, 28 g and 33.5 g. Find the mass, in kilograms, of twelve such sets.

5. In the fourth year of a school $\frac{3}{5}$ of the pupils study geography and $\frac{1}{3}$ of those who do not study geography study history. If 120 fourth formers study neither history nor geography, how many pupils are there in the fourth year?

PAPER 10

1. Simplify $\left(2\frac{1}{4} - 1\frac{1}{3}\right) \div \frac{11}{24}$.

2. Find the quotient and remainder when 7345 is divided by 126.

3. A load of coal was divided between four brothers. The first received $\frac{1}{3}$ of it, the second $\frac{2}{5}$, the third $\frac{1}{7}$ and the fourth 273 kg. Calculate the original mass of coal and the amount received by the first brother.

4. Give 293.746 correct to (a) the nearest hundred, (b) three significant figures, (c) two decimal places.

5. There are 1511 pupils in a school. If there are 43 fewer boys than girls, how many girls are there?

PAPER 11

1. Express 14 896 in prime factors. Hence find the smallest number by which it must be multiplied to make it a perfect square.

2. Express (a) $\frac{73}{36}$ as a decimal, (b) 5.016 as a mixed number in its lowest terms.

3. Multiply 1.732 by 44.6.

4. Simplify (a) $(-14 \div 4) \div 2$, (b) $(-5 \div 10) \times (-2)$.

5. A tennis ball bounces to $\frac{2}{3}$ of the height from which it is dropped. If it is dropped from a height of 6 m, how high will it rise after it has struck the ground for the second time?

PAPER 12

1. Find the sum of all the whole numbers between 24 and 36 which are not multiples of 3.

2. Divide 10.6026 by 0.431.

3. Evaluate $404 \div 63.2$ correct to two decimal places.

4. Find the HCF of 5100 and 2100 giving your answer as the product of prime factors.

5. Simplify $1\frac{1}{3} \times 1\frac{8}{9} \div 3\frac{7}{9}$.

PAPER 13

1. Find $\frac{3}{7}$ of 393.4 m.

2. Write down the next two numbers in the series $7 + 23 + 48 + 84 + \dots$.

3. Express (a) 0.775, (b) 0.268, as common fractions in their lowest terms.

4. Evaluate $926.43 \div 154.2$ correct to two decimal places.

5. Mr Ali buys a new car which it is claimed should give 42 miles per gallon. He finds it gives 38 miles per gallon. How much extra petrol will he require in a year when he travels 11 172 miles?

PAPER 14

1. Express 70.748 correct to (a) the nearest whole number, (b) two decimal places, (c) three significant figures.

2. Simplify (a) $\dfrac{7.2 \times 0.4}{36}$, (b) $0.3 \times 0.3 \times 0.3$.

3. Simplify $\left(4\frac{1}{3} - 2\frac{2}{7}\right) \times \dfrac{49}{86}$.

4. A lorry is loaded with 84 cases each of mass 112 kg. If the mass of the lorry when loaded is 13 908 kg, calculate its unladen mass.

5. A bag of marbles is divided between three boys. Kevin had $\frac{1}{6}$ of them, Brian twice as many as Kevin, and Donald had 84. How many does Brian have?

PAPER 15

1. Express 5880 as the product of prime numbers. Hence determine whether or not 5880 is exactly divisible by 105.

2. Patsy Kagan uses the train to go to work taking 55 seconds for each mile. Her train journey is 26 miles each way. Calculate the total time she spends on the train each week if she works a $5\frac{1}{2}$ day week.

3. Arrange $\dfrac{5}{13}, \dfrac{7}{15}, \dfrac{4}{7}$ in ascending order.

4. Simplify (a) 0.043×8.06, (b) $11.6232 \div 0.348$.

5. A greengrocer bought 207 oranges and found that $\frac{1}{9}$ were bad. How many were fit to eat?

PAPER 16

1. Express 493.078 correct to (a) the nearest 10, (b) three significant figures, (c) one decimal place.

2. Write down the next two terms in the sequence $\dfrac{7}{8}, \dfrac{8}{9}, \dfrac{9}{10}, \cdots$

3. Arrange $\dfrac{9}{20}, \dfrac{11}{24}, \dfrac{9}{16}$ in descending order.

4. If 2.54 cm equals 1 inch and 12 inches equals one foot, express 100 m in feet correct to two decimal places.

5. How many hours will it take a train to travel 420 km at 175 km per hour?

PAPER 17

1. Multiply 2.64 by 0.492. Give your answer correct to (a) three significant figures, (b) three decimal places.

2. By what must $3\frac{4}{7}$ be multiplied to make $\frac{2}{5}$?

3. Simplify $\left(1\frac{3}{8}+2\frac{3}{4}\right)-\left(\frac{1}{3}+\frac{5}{6}\right)$.

4. Express 0.906 25 as a common fraction in its lowest terms.

5. A man walks 144 miles in 4 days by walking for 12 hours each day. How many days will he take to cover 216 miles walking for 9 hours a day if he walks at the same rate?

PAPER 18

1. Simplify $5\frac{3}{7}\times7-12\frac{4}{5}$.

2. Calculate $(45-3\times13)\div(-2)$.

3. Express $2\frac{2}{21}$ as a decimal.

4. How long is the sun up if it rises at 4.45 a.m. and sets at 7.12 p.m.?

5. A retailer buys a quantity of apples. $\frac{2}{7}$ were sold on Thursday, $\frac{3}{8}$ on Friday and $\frac{1}{5}$ on Saturday. If 156 apples remain unsold, how many were sold on Friday?

PAPER 19

1. Calculate (a) 4.8×0.9, (b) $4.8\div0.9$, (c) $4.8-0.9$.

2. Express 3600 as a product of prime numbers in index form and hence find its square root.

3. Express 67.459 correct to (a) the nearest whole number, (b) one decimal place, (c) four significant figures.

4. The government increased the price of petrol by $\frac{1}{5}$ and the following year increased the new price by a further $\frac{1}{5}$. By what fraction has the original price been increased to give the final price?

5. Allowing 2 mm for each saw cut, how many pieces, each 54 cm long, may be cut from a 3 m length of timber? What length will remain?

PAPER 20

1. Simplify $2\frac{1}{2} - 1\frac{7}{8} + \frac{3}{4}$.

2. Calculate (a) $(36 - 24) \div (-8)$, (b) $36 - 24 \div 8$.

3. Write down the next two numbers in the sequence 5, 6, 8, 11, ...

4. Find the sum of all the numbers between 20 and 50 which are multiples of 8.

5. Two men walk at the same rate beginning with the same foot at the same time. If the first takes a pace of 75 cm and the second a pace of 80 cm, how far will they walk before they are in step again?

PAPER 21

1. Calculate (a) $9 - 3(6 - 4)$, (b) $(9 - 3)(6 - 4)$.

2. Express (a) $\frac{5}{16}$, (b) $\frac{4}{125}$ in decimals.

3. Divide 3.2 kg of potatoes between Susan and Christine so that Christine has 70 g more than Susan.

4. Find the HCF of 620, 1116 and 1488.

5. A clock loses 5 seconds every hour. If it is correct at 8 a.m. on Monday morning, how much will it have lost by the following Monday at the same time?

PAPER 22

1. Simplify $1\frac{2}{3} + 5\frac{1}{12} - 4\frac{3}{4}$.

2. Express (a) 0.875, (b) 0.218 75, as common fractions in their lowest terms.

3. Calculate (a) $6.4 \times 1.6 \times 2.4$, (b) $9.01 \div 1.7$.

4. How many packets, each containing 450 g, may be filled from a crate containing three-quarters of a tonne of mixed fruit? How much remains?

5. What is the smallest number of records that can be divided between 20, 24 or 30 girls?

PAPER 23

1. Simplify $\dfrac{4}{3}\left(1\dfrac{1}{4}-\dfrac{1}{5}\right)$.

2. Calculate $\dfrac{2^3\times 3\times 5^2}{2\times 5^3}$.

3. (a) Find $217-0.217$. (b) Divide 0.2484 by 0.9.

4. Reduce 468 kg to a common fraction of 1 t in its lowest terms.

5. A journey by car which lasted 6 hours 37 minutes ended at 1 p.m. What time did it start?

PAPER 24

1. Express 960.747 correct to (a) the nearest hundred, (b) three significant figures, (c) one decimal place.

2. Which is the greater and by how much, $2\dfrac{1}{2}\times\dfrac{2}{3}$ or $2\dfrac{1}{2}\div\dfrac{2}{3}$?

3. Express 120 cm as a fraction of 8 m in its lowest terms.

4. Find the number which is half-way between -4 and 8.

5. If I give 0.375 of my ball of string to my sister, then half of what remains to my brother, I still have 4.3 m. How much string did I have to start with?

PAPER 25

1. Simplify $2\dfrac{13}{95}\div 2\dfrac{2}{57}$.

2. Find (a) 4.8×0.4, (b) $4.8\div 0.04$, (c) $0.48\div 40$.

3. Express 0.92554 correct to (a) the nearest whole number, (b) two decimal places, (c) three significant figures.

4. State what part 85 cm is of 4 m as (a) a common fraction in its lowest terms, (b) a decimal fraction.

5. A water tank is $\frac{7}{8}$ full. If 5 litres is drawn off the tank is $\frac{13}{16}$ full. What quantity will the tank hold when full?

7

NUMBER SYSTEMS INCLUDING BINARY

EXAMPLE 1
$$
\begin{array}{r}
37 \\
26\,+ \\
\hline
65 \\
\hline
\end{array}
$$

EXAMPLE 2
$$
\begin{array}{r}
16 \\
14 \\
12\,+ \\
\hline
44 \\
\hline
\end{array}
$$

At first sight the above examples seem very strange additions. Using the system we are most familiar with (the *denary* system) we would write:

$$
\begin{array}{r}
37 \\
26 \\
\hline
63 \\
\hline
\end{array}
\qquad \text{and} \qquad
\begin{array}{r}
16 \\
14 \\
12 \\
\hline
42 \\
\hline
\end{array}
$$

These additions have been made in the scale of ten, i.e. we have used the rule: as soon as your total is 10, it is equal to one unit belonging to the next column to the left.

But if in Example 1 we give further information, and say that the first number refers to gallons while the second refers to pints, we can understand the addition that has taken place. The first line could be the amount of milk delivered to a canteen on Monday, while the second line could show the amount delivered on Tuesday. It follows that by adding the two together we have 6 gallons 5 pints, which is the amount delivered during the two days. Since 8 pints is equal to 1 gallon, the addition is correct. Here we have counted in base 8, or *octal* numbers.

81

Similarly, the second example shows the distances of three races in which the thoroughbred *Demur* ran. The distances are given in miles and furlongs, 8 furlongs being equivalent to 1 mile. Again we have counted in octal numbers.

These examples have only shown a single addition from one column to another, but they may be extended into the 'four rules' involving any base.

When we write 14_8 we refer to it as a number 'to the base 8'. The 1 to the left of the 4 is equal to 8 units. Thus $14_8 = (1 \times 8) + 4 = 8 + 4 = 12$ in our most commonly used system i.e. to the base 10 or in denary form.

Similarly
$$235_8 = (2 \times 8^2) + (3 \times 8) + 5$$
$$= 128 + 24 + 5$$
$$= 157_{10}$$

If we consider a base 5 number:
$$231_5 = (2 \times 5^2) + (3 \times 5) + 1$$
$$= 50 + 15 + 1$$
$$= 66_{10}$$

or a base 3 number:
$$121_3 = (1 \times 3^2) + (2 \times 3) + 1$$
$$= 9 + 6 + 1$$
$$= 16_{10}$$

Conversely, we may wish to convert a denary number into a number with a different base.

Thus
$$374 \text{ or } 374_{10} = (5 \times 64) + (6 \times 8) + 6$$

(arranging 374 as the sum of multiples of powers of 8)

i.e.
$$374_{10} = (5 \times 8^2) + (6 \times 8) + 6$$
$$= 566_8$$

The same result may also be obtained by dividing and writing remainders:

$$
\begin{array}{r|l}
8\,\lfloor 374 \rfloor & \\
8\,\boxed{46} & \text{Rem 6} \\
8\,\boxed{5} & \text{Rem 6} \\
0 & \text{Rem 5}
\end{array}
$$

Writing the remainders from the bottom up gives:

$$374_{10} = 566_8$$

EXAMPLE 3   Convert the denary number 287 into a number to the base 5.

$$5\lfloor 287 \rfloor$$
$$5\lfloor 57 \rfloor \text{ Rem 2}$$
$$5\lfloor 11 \rfloor \text{ Rem 2}$$
$$5\lfloor 2 \rfloor \text{ Rem 1}$$
$$0\rfloor \text{ Rem 2}$$

$$\therefore \quad 287_{10} = 2122_5$$

The following examples show how the 'four rules' operate for different bases.

EXAMPLE 4   Find:

(a) $134_5 + 23_5$,

(b) $124_5 - 31_5$,

(c) $232_5 \times 12_5$,

(d) $121_5 \div 14_5$.

(a)		(b)		(c)		(d)	
	134		124		232		4
	23		31		12		14)121
	212		43		1014		121
					2320		. . .
					3334		

EXAMPLE 5   Find:

(a) $574_8 + 261_8$,

(b) $1543_8 - 725_8$,

(c) $342_8 \times 35_8$,

(d) $3410_8 \div 31_8$.

(a)		(b)		(c)		(d)	
	574		1543		342		110
	261		725		35		31)3410
	1055		616		2152		31
					10 460		31
					12 632		31
							0
							0

EXERCISE 33

Find:

1. $235_8 + 6$
2. $542_8 + 5$
3. $424_5 + 4$
4. $134_5 + 3$
5. $212_3 + 2$
6. $532_7 + 5$
7. $342_8 - 7$
8. $572_8 - 5$
9. $421_5 - 4$
10. $341_5 - 3$
11. $352_6 - 5$.

12. Convert the following octal numbers into denary numbers: 23_8, 542_8, 267_8, 534_8.

13. Convert the following base 3 numbers into denary numbers: 22_3, 212_3, 1212_3, 2111_3.

14. Convert the following base 4 four numbers into denary numbers: 32_4, 123_4, 322_4, 1232_4.

15. Convert the denary numbers 34, 267 and 534 into (a) numbers to the base 5, (b) numbers to the base 7.

16. Find (a) $424_5 + 133_5$, (b) $213_5 - 34_5$.

17. Find (a) $374_8 + 166_8$, (b) $525_8 - 266_8$.

18. Find (a) $327_8 \times 121_8$, (b) $6335_8 \div 45_8$.

19. Find (a) $341_5 \times 223_5$, (b) $200222_3 \div 121_3$.

20. Calculate (a) $346_7 + 214_7 + 523_7$, (b) $331_4 + 123_4 - 231_4$.

Find each of the following, working in the given base:

21. (a) $212_3 + 112_3$, (b) $214_6 \times 23_6$, (c) $1220_6 \div 41_6$.

22. (a) $2345_9 - 1264_9$, (b) $225_7 \times 46_7$, (c) $2134_5 \div 3_5$.

23. (a) $4341_5 + 3122_5$, (b) $7533_8 - 3452_8$, (c) $221_3 \times 111_3$.

24. (a) $6453_7 - 655_7$, (b) $332_4 \times 213_4$, (c) $5027_8 \div 173_8$.

25. (a) $677_8 \div 245_8$, (b) $4332_5 \div 2113_5$.

BINARY NUMBERS

The smallest base we can use is 2. The only two symbols then required are 0 and 1. This system is called the *binary* system. It is extremely important in computer work because the electronic circuits can only be in one of two states —*on* or *off*. A binary number is built up of powers of 2.

i.e. $\qquad 10101_2 = (1 \times 2^4) + (0 \times 2^3) + (1 \times 2^2) + (0 \times 2^1) + (1 \times 2^0)$

NOTE: $a^0 = 1$ for any non-zero value of a. In particular, $2^0 = 1$ or $1 = 2^0$.

$$= 16 + 0 + 4 + 0 + 1$$

$$= 21_{10}$$

and $\qquad 1110111_2 = (1 \times 2^6) + (1 \times 2^5) + (1 \times 2^4) + (0 \times 2^3)$

$$+ (1 \times 2^2) + (1 \times 2^1) + (1 \times 2^0)$$

$$= 64 + 32 + 16 + 0 + 4 + 2 + 1$$

$$= 119_{10}$$

EXAMPLE 6   Convert 78_{10} into a binary number.

Method 1 $78 = 64 + 8 + 4 + 2$

$$= 2^6 + 2^3 + 2^2 + 2^1$$

If we now introduce zeros for the powers of 2 which are missing, $78 = 2^6 + 0 + 0 + 2^3 + 2^2 + 2^1 + 0$

$\therefore$ $78_{10} = 1001110_2$

Method 2   Using division by 2 and remainders we have:

```
2 | 78 |
2 | 39 | Rem 0
2 | 19 | Rem 1
2 | 9  | Rem 1
2 | 4  | Rem 1
2 | 2  | Rem 0
2 | 1  | Rem 0
  | 0  | Rem 1
```

i.e. the binary equivalent, writing from the bottom up, is 1001110_2.

EXAMPLE 7   Convert the binary number 11100111_2 to denary.

$$11100111_2 = 2^7 + 2^6 + 2^5 + 2^2 + 2^1 + 2^0$$

$$= 128 + 64 + 32 + 4 + 2 + 1$$

$$= 231_{10}$$

EXERCISE 34

Convert the following denary numbers into binary:

1. 9	2. 11	3. 17	4. 19
5. 24	6. 27	7. 36	8. 45
9. 57	10. 69	11. 96	12. 105
13. 126	14. 137	15. 153	16. 172
17. 193	18. 218	19. 253	20. 342.

Convert the following binary numbers into denary:

21. 110	22. 111	23. 1001	24. 1100
25. 1011	26. 1101	27. 10110	28. 11001
29. 10111	30. 10011	31. 11111	
32. 101010	33. 110011	34. 101110	
35. 100111	36. 111001.		

37. What is the largest denary number which can be represented by five binary digits?

38. What is the largest denary number which can be represented by seven binary digits?

Which is the larger of the following pairs of binary numbers?

39. 110, 101

40. 1011, 1100

41. 10101, 1111

42. 110101, 111000.

Which is the smaller of the following pairs of binary numbers?

43. 1011, 1100

44. 10111, 10101

45. 11000, 11001

46. 101011, 101100.

47. Which of the following binary numbers are even?
    (a) 100   (b) 1000   (c) 1101   (d) 11001
    (e) 11000.

48. Which of the following binary numbers are odd?
    (a) 1001   (b) 1100   (c) 10001   (d) 11111
    (e) 10000.

49. Which of the following binary numbers are multiples of 4?
    (a) 101   (b) 100   (c) 100100
    (d) 1100110   (e) 111110.

50. Which of the following binary numbers are multiples of 8?
    (a) 1010   (b) 10110   (c) 11000   (d) 101100
    (e) 10001.

51. Write down:
    (a) the next three binary numbers after 1101110
    (b) the next three odd numbers after 1101011
    (c) the next two even numbers after 101101.

52. Write down the binary number which is 4 more than 101111.

53. Write down the binary number which is 6 more than 10111.

54. Write down the binary number which is 2 less than 110110.

55. Write down the binary number which is 5 less than 110011.

BINARY ADDITION

Facts worth learning are:

$$1 + 1 = 10$$
$$1 + 1 + 1 = 11$$

and
$$1 + 1 + 1 + 1 = 100$$

EXAMPLE 8

```
  1011
   111
 10010
   111
```

In the right hand column $1+1=10$ i.e. 0 down carry 1. In the second column we have $1+1+1$ (carried) $=11$ i.e. 1 down carry 1, and so on. When your total is 2 in any column it is 'worth' 1 in the next column to the left.

EXAMPLE 9

```
   1110
    101
  11101
   1011
 111011
   1111
     11
```

BINARY SUBTRACTION

EXAMPLE 10   (a)
```
 1101
  111 −
  110
```
(b)
```
 10011
  1110 −
   101
```

When you use 1 from the previous column it is worth 2 in the column in which it is used.

BINARY MULTIPLICATION

EXAMPLE 11   (a)
```
    111
     11 ×
    111
   1110
  10101
```
(b)
```
    1101
     110 ×
   11010
  110100
 1001110
```

BINARY DIVISION

With binary division, instead of thinking 'How many times?', think 'Will it divide?'. If the answer is 'Yes', a 1 goes in the answer, but if the answer is 'No', then a 0 goes in the answer.

EXAMPLE 12   (a) Divide 10101 by 111.

(b) Divide 11011 by 101.

(c) Divide 10011101 by 1011.

(a)
```
            11
      111 ) 10101
            111
            111
            111
            . . .
```

(b)
```
         101
101)11011
     101
      111
      101
       10
```
i.e. 1 0 1 remainder 10

(c)
```
              1110
1011)10011101
     1011
     10001
      1011
      1100
      1011
        11
```
i.e. 1 1 1 0 remainder 11

EXERCISE 35

Working in the binary system, add:

1. 1 0 1 0
       1 1
    ———

2. 1 1 0 1
      1 0 1
    ———

3. 1 0 1 0
      1 1 1
    ———

4. 1 1 1
    1 1 1
    ——

5. 1 0 1 1
    1 1 0 0
    ———

6. 1 1 0 0 1
     1 1 1 1
    ———

7. 1 1 0 1 1
     1 0 1 1
    ———

8. 1 0 1 1 1 0
     1 1 1 0 1
    ———

9.   1 0 1
     1 1 1
    1 0 0 1
    ———

10. 1 1 1
      1 1
    1 1 0 0
    ———

11. 1 0 1 1
     1 1 1
    1 1 0 0
    ———

12. 1 1 0 0 1
     1 1 0 0
      1 1 1
    ———

13. 1 1 0 0 1 1
       1 1 1 1
      1 0 1 0 1
        1 0 1
    ———

14. 1 0 0 0 1 1
     1 0 0 1 1
      1 1 1 1
    1 0 0 0 1
    ———

Working in the binary system, perform the following subtractions:

15. 1 1 0
      1 1
    ——

16. 1 0 0 1
     1 1 1
    ———

17. 1 1 0 0
     1 1 1
    ———

18. 1 1 0 1
      1 1
    ———

19. 1 1 1 0 0
      1 0 1
    ———

20. 1 0 1 0 1
      1 1 1
    ———

21. 1 1 0 0 1 1
      1 1 1 0
    ———

22. 1 0 1 1 0 1
     1 0 1 1 0
    ———

Working in the binary system, perform the following multiplications:

23. 110×11

24. 1011×11

25. 1100×11

26. 1010×110

27. 1100×101

28. 1010×111

29. 1100×1010

30. 1011×1011

31. 101010×110.

Working in the binary system, divide:

32. 1010 by 10

33. 11011 by 11

34. 111000 by 1110

35. 10011010 by 1011

36. 10010110 by 1010

37. 1101 by 110

38. 101110 by 111

39. 110110 by 101

40. 100011 by 110.

8

MONEY

THE UK SYSTEM

In the United Kingdom the basic unit of currency is the pound sterling
(£) which is divided into 100 pence (p)

i.e. £1 = 100 p

A decimal point is used to separate the pounds from the pence, hence
£7.43 means seven pounds and forty-three pence. When the £ sign has
been used it is unnecessary to write the pence sign after the pence.

There are two ways of writing amounts less than one pound. Forty-three
pence may be written either £0.43 or 43 p. If the number of pence is
less than ten, we place a zero in front of the number if we use the £ sign;
e.g. three pence may be written 3 p or £0.03.

The smallest unit of money used is the half-penny, which is written as
a common fraction i.e. $\frac{1}{2}$. Three and a half pence is thus written $3\frac{1}{2}$ p or
£0.03$\frac{1}{2}$. It is worth noting that this is equivalent to £0.035, a fact which
is useful in some questions.

ADDITION

EXERCISE 36

Add:

1. £	2. £	3. £	4. £
0.42	0.24	0.15	0.11
0.16	0.35	0.42	0.22
0.21	0.40	0.31	0.55

5. £
0.14
0.47
0.34
———

6. £
0.22
0.39
0.17
———

7. £
0.35
0.26
0.37
———

8. £
0.54
0.12
0.29
———

9. £
0.44
0.37
0.92
———

10. £
0.53
0.74
0.66
———

11. £
0.73
0.94
0.36
———

12. £
0.84
0.78
0.59
———

13. £
1.26
5.93
7.21
———

14. £
4.62
3.93
8.21
———

15. £
5.66
14.29
3.24
———

16. £
21.43
9.26
8.73
———

17. £
8.17
2.04
8.36
———

18. £
12.24
23.61
14.40
———

19. £
8.30
4.75
2.99
———

20. £
3.17
4.92
7.36
———

21. £
$0.37\frac{1}{2}$
$0.42\frac{1}{2}$
$0.83\frac{1}{2}$
———

22. £
$0.15\frac{1}{2}$
$0.74\frac{1}{2}$
$0.30\frac{1}{2}$
———

23. £
$0.29\frac{1}{2}$
$0.13\frac{1}{2}$
$0.48\frac{1}{2}$
———

24. £
$0.16\frac{1}{2}$
$0.42\frac{1}{2}$
$0.78\frac{1}{2}$
———

25. £
$4.09\frac{1}{2}$
$6.33\frac{1}{2}$
$4.58\frac{1}{2}$
———

26. £
$3.72\frac{1}{2}$
1.36
$4.97\frac{1}{2}$
———

27. £
$6.90\frac{1}{2}$
$5.46\frac{1}{2}$
1.32
———

28. £
4.68
$9.39\frac{1}{2}$
$8.21\frac{1}{2}$
———

29. £
14.34
$8.92\frac{1}{2}$
76.40
4.62
———

30. £
42.40
$17.26\frac{1}{2}$
8.37
50.21
———

31. £
127.41
4.93
18.21
227.03
———

32. £
5.92
36.14
127.03
9.78
———

91

33.	£	34.	£	35.	£	36.	£
	14.90		30.21		4.36		$8.14\frac{1}{2}$
	7.36		520.72		413.74		33.54
	532.40		18.43		8.93		$4.92\frac{1}{2}$
	0.67		227.16		55.29		127.30

37.	£	38.	£	39.	£	40.	£
	226.41		154.14		$246.44\frac{1}{2}$		$726.43\frac{1}{2}$
	128.49		726.80		893.53		436.13
	307.52		819.56		$254.62\frac{1}{2}$		$293.59\frac{1}{2}$
	78.90		334.72		726.18		$874.73\frac{1}{2}$

41. $£8.23\frac{1}{2} + £37.40 + £14.04$

42. $£48.26\frac{1}{2} + £59.13 + £88.47$

43. $£73.74 + £16.92 + £57.26\frac{1}{2}$

44. $£80.21 + £18.28\frac{1}{2} + £66.90\frac{1}{2}$

45. $£246.40 + £82 + £2.76 + £34.42$

46. $£52.42 + £218.74 + 99\,p + £7.62$

47. $£8.32\frac{1}{2} + £346.74 + £72.58\frac{1}{2} + £19.87\frac{1}{2}$

48. $£17.62\frac{1}{2} + £843.42 + £78.13\frac{1}{2} + £227.13\frac{1}{2}$

49. $£26.42\frac{1}{2} + 44\frac{1}{2}\,p + 16\,p + £5.14$

50. The table below shows the daily takings (in £) in a shop over a four week period:

	M	T	W	T	F	S	
WEEK 1	20.16	54.91	70.14	737.93	1036.14	942.10	g
WEEK 2	50.92	16.31	53.56	623.87	873.59	837.31	h
WEEK 3	78.44	34.80	49.08	672.74	1137.44	742.78	i
WEEK 4	18.44	93.72	61.82	852.68	936.95	529.37	j
	a	b	c	d	e	f	k

Add the columns and rows. Find the total by adding the answers for the rows and check your answer by totalling the answers to the columns.

SUBTRACTION

EXERCISE 37

Subtract:

1. £
    7.36
    4.14
    ———

2. £
    9.35
    6.31
    ———

3. £
    3.94
    1.82
    ———

4. £
    6.67
    4.36
    ———

5. £
    9.27
    4.63
    ———

6. £
    6.14
    1.82
    ———

7. £
    4.47
    2.98
    ———

8. £
    8.13
    5.95
    ———

9. £
    $4.27\frac{1}{2}$
    1.82
    ———

10. £
    $7.42\frac{1}{2}$
    3.58
    ———

11. £
    $8.59\frac{1}{2}$
    5.62
    ———

12. £
    $13.29\frac{1}{2}$
    7.36
    ———

13. £
    24.16
    $18.09\frac{1}{2}$
    ———

14. £
    52.43
    $9.27\frac{1}{2}$
    ———

15. £
    38.19
    $9.36\frac{1}{2}$
    ———

16. £
    82.76
    $34.83\frac{1}{2}$
    ———

17. £
    50.00
    9.38
    ———

18. £
    170.00
    54.16
    ———

19. £
    280.00
    137.94
    ———

20. £
    200.00
    184.14
    ———

21. £
    529.00
    $136.87\frac{1}{2}$
    ———

22. £
    706.44
    $519.27\frac{1}{2}$
    ———

23. £
    400.49
    $126.84\frac{1}{2}$
    ———

24. £
    563.92
    $398.77\frac{1}{2}$
    ———

25. £
    2000.00
    816.94
    ———

26. £
    5000.00
    4937.61
    ———

27. £
    4396.14
    $2847.38\frac{1}{2}$
    ———

28. £
    $9264.08\frac{1}{2}$
    5648.29
    ———

29. £50 − £28.34

30. £82 − £69.87

31. £180 − £93.51

32. £260.40 − £127.84

33. £349.21 − £253.97

34. £545.06 − £387.93

35. £413.40 − £278.65

36. £47.04 − £$38.58\frac{1}{2}$

37. £134.92 − £82.76$\frac{1}{2}$

38. £9.82$\frac{1}{2}$ − £3.76$\frac{1}{2}$

39. £349.20$\frac{1}{2}$ − £261.08$\frac{1}{2}$

40. £1600.12$\frac{1}{2}$ − £834.37$\frac{1}{2}$.

Subtract the first amount from the second:

41. 87 p, £4.22

42. 15$\frac{1}{2}$ p, £8.00

43. £2.44, £12.16

44. £76.84$\frac{1}{2}$, £100

45. £382.79$\frac{1}{2}$, £579.06.

Subtract the second amount from the first:

46. £10, £8.16

47. £40, £26.49$\frac{1}{2}$

48. £57.44, £42.83$\frac{1}{2}$

49. £826.93, £536.28

50. £714.47, £73.84$\frac{1}{2}$.

MULTIPLICATION

EXERCISE 38

Multiply:

1. £2.44 by 3

2. £6.13 by 4

3. £4.73 by 5

4. £1.63 by 6

5. £5.19 by 7

6. £8.59 by 8

7. £3.74 by 10

8. £9.73 by 9

9. £4.32 by 11

10. £6.64 by 7

11. £8.84 by 8

12. £3.68 by 5

13. £4.87 by 4

14. £9.26 by 6

15. £1.37 by 8

16. £5.82$\frac{1}{2}$ by 6

17. £7.51$\frac{1}{2}$ by 8

18. £3.18$\frac{1}{2}$ by 10

19. £6.74$\frac{1}{2}$ by 3

20. £4.42$\frac{1}{2}$ by 5

21. £8.27$\frac{1}{2}$ by 9

22. £5.92 by 14

23. £6.59 by 16

24. £9.32 by 18

25. £1.47 by 15

26. £3.92 by 17

27. £8.62 by 19

28. £6.73$\frac{1}{2}$ by 12

29. £7.16$\frac{1}{2}$ by 15

30. £4.29$\frac{1}{2}$ by 18

31. £24.16 by 26

32. £73.34 by 33

33. £49.37 by 54

34. £16.49 by 37

35. £92.03 by 57

36. £70.64 by 83

37. £36.24$\frac{1}{2}$ by 46

38. £19.87$\frac{1}{2}$ by 54

39. £23.64$\frac{1}{2}$ by 82

40. £84.73$\frac{1}{2}$ by 53

41. £39.27$\frac{1}{2}$ by 77

42. £60.58$\frac{1}{2}$ by 39

43. £136.40 by 46

44. £234.56 by 36

45. £343.82 by 86

46. £413.90 by 73

47. £291.50 by 95

48. £186.43 by 47

49. £182.61$\frac{1}{2}$ by 34

50. £763.90 by 47.

Division

Exercise 39

Divide:

1. £4.89 by 3

2. £11.35 by 5

3. £7.98 by 7

4. £16.64 by 8

5. £12.15 by 9

6. £23.76 by 11

7. £43.36 by 8

8. £39.24 by 9

9. £32.76 by 12

10. £93.08 by 13

11. £74.34 by 18

12. £39.69 by 21

13. £149.58 by 27

14. £134.64 by 17

15. £223.72 by 34

16. £156.94 by 38

17. £231.50 by 25

18. £71.82 by 19

19. £69.66 by 43

20. £151.28 by 62

21. £290.08 by 56

22. £133.28 by 28

23. £245.29 by 19

24. £421.82 by 23

25. £449.28 by 72

26. £589.38 by 66

27. £374.36 by 49

28. £399.36 by 39

29. £75.44 by 46

30. £511.56 by 28

31. £511.98 by 53

32. £351.96 by 42

33. £795.63 by 33

34. £23.76 by 54 p

35. £27.36 by 72 p

36. £39.56 by 43 p

37. £48 by 75 p

38. £22.62 by 29 p

39. £48.14 by 83 p

40. £51.12 by £1.42

41. £168.54 by £3.18

42. £214.08 by £4.46

43. £192.78 by £1.89

44. £962.88 by £4.72

45. £783.96 by £8.34

46. £54.90 by 36

47. £204.39 by 54

48. £585.23 by 86

49. £1190.99$\frac{1}{2}$ by 73

50. £143.37$\frac{1}{2}$ by 31

51. £465.40$\frac{1}{2}$ by 57

52. £239.94 by 124

53. £555.45 by 230

54. £1351.35 by 182

55. £5.51 by 14$\frac{1}{2}$p

56. £15.67$\frac{1}{2}$ by 27$\frac{1}{2}$p

57. £46.35$\frac{1}{2}$ by 63$\frac{1}{2}$p

58. £1435.50 by £12.37$\frac{1}{2}$

59. £5516.08 by £18.14$\frac{1}{2}$

60. £7686.22$\frac{1}{2}$ by £39.82$\frac{1}{2}$.

EXERCISE 40   MISCELLANEOUS EXAMPLES

1. A father changes a £5 note and gives £1.27 to each of his three children. How much is left over?

2. How many complete metres of cloth at £3.80 a metre may be bought for £20? What sum of money is left over?

3. Calculate the cost of 760 units of electricity at 4.55 p per unit.

4. Calculate the cost of 376 therms of gas at 32.5 p per therm.

5. During a day's work a bus driver collected 184 fares at 72 p each, 147 at 54 p each and 34 at 44 p each. How much did he collect during the day?

6. The total tickets sold for a concert were as follows: 154 at £6, 243 at £4 and 193 at £3. Find the total amount of money collected.

7. If a 2 p piece is 2.6 cm in diameter, find the value of 1 km of 2 p pieces laid side by side.

8. Jane Goldspink went shopping with the knowledge that she had £216.40 in her bank account. She wrote cheques to the value of

£41.67, £16.93, £53.19 and £39.47. How much remained in her account after these cheques had been passed?

9. A book of postage stamps contains 12 stamps at $22\frac{1}{2}$ p each, 6 stamps at 18 p each and 6 stamps at $16\frac{1}{2}$ p each. Find the total value of the book.

10. A family of five bought their Christmas cards. Father bought 42 at 16 p each, mother 45 at 18 p each, John 16 at 10 p each, Joan 18 at 9 p each and Jack 26 at 8 p each. How many cards did they buy? How much did they spend on cards altogether? How much would it cost to send all these cards if the postage for each was 18 p?

11. In a school canteen 85 pupils bought the 65 p meal, 64 the 58 p meal and 116 the meal costing 52 p. Find the total takings.

12. A school decided that they could afford to give £360 away in book tokens for Prize Day. If they gave tokens to the value of £5 but each token cost an extra 5 p, find the maximum number of prizes they could afford.

13. How many 50 g balls of wool could be purchased for £20 if each ball cost 76 p? How much cash was left over?

14. Bread rolls for refreshments at a disco cost 15 p each. How many rolls could be purchased for £12?

15. When milk costs 25 p per pint a family take 4 pints every day except Tuesday and Thursday when they take 3. Calculate the weekly milk bill.

16. Find the cost of buying 748 roofing tiles at 96 p each.

17. Four tyres for a car cost £45.13 each. What change would there be from £200?

18. A generous teacher gave Christmas presents to his class. He gave $\frac{1}{2}$ p to the first pupil, 1 p to the second, 2 p to the third, 4 p to the fourth, 8 p to the fifth, and so on. If there were 12 children in the class, how much did it cost him?

19. In one week in a school tuck shop they sold 162 bars of chocolate at 44 p each, 247 cans of squash at 35 p each and 942 packets of crisps at 15 p each. Find the total takings for the week.

20. The Hussett's daily newspaper costs 32 p, the Sunday paper 45 p, and in addition they take magazines each week to the value of £1.54. How much change will there be if they pay for the week's papers with a £5 note?

21. A money box contains £14 in 5 p, 10 p and 50 p coins. If there are twenty-three 50 p coins and eighteen 10 p coins, how many 5 p coins are there?

22. A collecting box contains £9.41 in coins of value 2 p, 5 p and 10 p. If there are twenty-seven 5 p coins and seventy 10 p coins, how many 2 p coins are there?

23. When the collecting box for the blind on the counter of the local shop is opened it is found to contain the following coins: 48 at 1 p, 55 at 2 p, 37 at 10 p and five at 50 p. How much was in the box?

24. Sandra takes part in a sponsored 8 mile walk. Thirteen people sponsor her for 2 p a mile, twenty-one for 5 p a mile and eight people for 50 p a mile. How much should she collect if she walks the whole distance?

25. Find the cost of 4.5 t at £133.60 per tonne.

26. Anthony Thompson's 'take-home' pay is £98.70 per week for a five day week. If it costs him 84 p per day in bus fares, £1.44 per day for lunch, and he pays £22.50 each week towards his keep, how much remains?

27. A builder sells a new house for £38 000. If the materials cost him £14 550 and he employed eight men for 52 days at £48 each per day, how much profit did he make?

28. A school decides to spend £6000 on re-equipping the school library. An Open Day in aid of this raises £2543.80, and 563 parents each promise to donate £2.50. How much is still required?

29. Seven hundred and thirty-two factory workers negotiate a pay increase of 6 p per hour for a thirty-eight hour week. How much will this cost the company?

30. Forty-seven office workers negotiate an 8 p per hour increase for a thirty-seven hour week. Find the increase in the firm's weekly wage bill.

31. A group of forty-two fourth formers pay £142 each to go on a short holiday to France. In addition they each pay in £45 for pocket money. Calculate the total amount of money collected.

32. A man's 'take-home' pay, after all deductions, is £94.50 per week. How much is his 'take-home' pay for the year?

33. The school under-12 soccer team, plus a teacher and one reserve, go to an away game by bus. If the teacher's return fare is £2.42, but all the boys travel for half fare, find the total paid in fares.

34. A woman's annual salary is £10 400. If she pays £832 pension contribution and £191 per calendar month in income tax, calculate her net annual salary.

35. A dining table costs £345.50, a dining chair £85.40 and a carver (a dining chair with arms) £112.37. What would be the total cost of a table and eight chairs, two of which are carvers?

36. A gardener is paid £2.54 per hour, and his helper £1.86 per hour. How much would they earn between them in a four week month if each works for 38 hours a week?

37. The return fare to London, which is 144 miles away, is £21.60. How much is this per mile?

38. The single fare to Manchester, which is 276 km away is £17.94. What is the charge per kilometre?

39. If there are 158 people employed in a department store and each employee earns on average £94 per week, calculate the weekly wage bill.

40. A company agrees to the weekly wages of its 764 employees being increased from £144 to £156.50 if fifty-five employees retire early. Does the weekly wage bill increase or decrease, and by how much?

41. Ernie Tamplin buys a second hand car for £760, spends £25 each on four new tyres, and spends a further £158 on repairs. Later he sells it for £1050. Find his profit (or loss).

42. Mr Cooper pays for his car by making a down payment of £520 followed by 24 monthly payments of £84.36. How much does his car cost him?

43. In the January sales a man buys three shirts at £7.50 each (reduced from £14.50), two ties at £1.75 each (reduced from £2.25) and six pairs of socks at 80 p per pair (reduced from £1.20). How much did he save by waiting for the sale?

44. A housewife makes 14 kg of marmalade using 4 kg of oranges at 60 p per kg, 8 kg of sugar at 44 p per kg and 10 lemons at 15 p each. Find the cost per kilogram of the marmalade.

45. Mrs Miles changes £156 into French francs, and for each £ she receives 9 francs. How many francs does she receive?

46. Mr Woodward changes 968 US dollars into sterling. If he receives 55 p for each dollar, how many £s does he receive?

47. A cashier in a bank has a bundle of £10 notes which are numbered consecutively from S52 001013 to S52 001246. What is the value of the bundle?

48. John Shepherd buys a motorcycle by paying a deposit of £72 followed by thirty-six monthly payments of £14.56. Paying on terms costs him £22.66 more than the cash price. Calculate the cash price.

49. 357 000 people enter for a 'Win-a-car' competition in a newspaper. If the entry fee is 25 p, and the prizes are five cars, each car being valued at £8450, find the profit made by the newspaper.

50. An ironmonger mixes 12 kg of nails costing £3.60 per kilogram with 36 kg of nails costing £4.20 per kilogram. What is the cost per kilogram of the mixture?

AVERAGES

If a batsman scores 56, 49, 81 and 34 in four completed innings we say that his average score is $\dfrac{56 + 49 + 81 + 34}{4} = 55$. While he has not scored exactly 55 in any particular innings, the figure enables us to compare him with another batsman who has scored 520 in 10 completed innings and has an average of 52.

Similarly, if a train travels 150 miles in $1\frac{1}{2}$ hours, we say that the average speed of the train is $\dfrac{150}{1\frac{1}{2}}$ mph $= 100$ mph.

The *average* (or *mean*) of a number of quantities is the total of all the quantities divided by the number of quantities.

i.e. the average of $N_1, N_2, N_3, \ldots, N_m$

$$= \frac{N_1 + N_2 + N_3 + \ldots + N_m}{m}$$

It is particularly important to remember that you cannot add or subtract averages. Always deal in totals.

EXAMPLE 1 The Saturday takings of a small shop over a four week period are £212, £164, £178 and £174. Find the average Saturday takings over the four weeks.

$$\text{Average takings} = £\frac{212 + 164 + 178 + 174}{4}$$

$$= £\frac{728}{4}$$

$$= £182$$

EXAMPLE 2

In a rugby team the average weight of the seven backs is 76 kg and the average weight of the eight forwards is 90 kg. Find the average weight of the team, giving your answer correct to one decimal place.

Total weight of the seven backs $= 7 \times 76$ kg
$$= 532 \text{ kg}$$

Total weight of the eight forwards $= 8 \times 90$ kg
$$= 720 \text{ kg}$$

Total weight of the fifteen team members $= 1252$ kg

$\therefore$ Average weight of team $= \dfrac{1252}{15}$ kg $= 83.47$ kg

$= 83.5$ kg correct to one decimal place

EXAMPLE 3

A girl sets out on a 7 mile journey on her bicycle. She rides for 5 miles at an average speed of 15 mph until her bicycle breaks down, forcing her to push the bicycle the remaining distance at a speed of 3 mph. Find her average speed for the whole journey.

Time spent riding $= \dfrac{5 \text{ miles}}{15 \text{ mph}} = \dfrac{1}{3}$ hour

Time spent pushing $= \dfrac{2}{3}$ hour

$\therefore$ Total time for journey $= \left(\dfrac{1}{3} + \dfrac{2}{3}\right)$ hours

$= 1$ hour

Average speed for whole journey $= \dfrac{\text{total distance}}{\text{total time}}$

$= \dfrac{7 \text{ miles}}{1 \text{ hour}}$

$= 7$ mph

EXERCISE 41

Find the average of:

1. 10, 12, 14, 16, 18
2. 56, 48, 60, 57, 49
3. 57, 34, 42, 29, 38
4. 8.2, 12.4, 16.5, 9.9, 11.2, 17.4
5. 27.2, 34.9, 46.7, 39.4, 53.1, 39.9.

6. The number of hours of sunshine in Corfu for successive days during a certain week were 10.4, 12.6, 11.4, 8.2, 12.2, 12.4, 9.8. Find the daily average.

7. A car takes $2\frac{1}{4}$ hours for a journey of $128\frac{1}{4}$ miles. Calculate its average speed.

8. A coach takes $3\frac{1}{3}$ hours for a journey of 300 kilometres. Calculate its average speed.

9. Joan takes 8 minutes to walk the $\frac{1}{2}$ mile to school. Find her average walking speed in mph.

10. George cycles from school to his home, a distance of $4\frac{1}{2}$ miles, in 15 minutes. Find his average speed in mph.

11. Caroline takes 24 minutes to walk to her friend's home which is 2 km away. Find her average walking speed in kilometres per hour.

12. In an ice-dancing competition the marks awarded to a couple were: 5.4, 4.9, 5.8, 5.5, 5.7, 5.5, 5.5, 5.4. Their score is found by finding the average of these marks but ignoring the highest and lowest marks. Calculate the couple's score.

13. A county bowler takes 110 wickets for 1267 runs. Find his bowling average correct to two decimal places.

14. An opening batsman scores 1976 runs in a season in 46 completed innings. Calculate his average correct to two decimal places.

15. Last season a batsman scored 976 runs in 38 completed innings, while the season before he scored 1242 runs in 43 completed innings. Calculate his average over the two seasons, giving your answer correct to one decimal place.

16. In the first 20 innings of a season a batsman scored 1124 runs. In the next innings he scored 136. By how much will this increase his average?

17. The average number of newspapers sold by a newsagent from Monday to Friday during a certain week was 483, while the average number sold from Monday to Saturday of the same week was 516. How many papers were sold on the Saturday?

18. The average height of 25 girls in a form was 152.2 cm. When one girl joined the class the average fell to 152 cm. How tall was she?

19. My average petrol consumption for a 280 mile journey was 35 mpg. If the average consumption for 220 miles of the journey when I used the motorway was 40 mpg, calculate the number of miles per gallon for the 60 miles of urban driving.

20. A boy walks the $\frac{1}{4}$ mile from his home to the bus stop at an average speed of 3 mph. There he catches the bus which takes him the 10 miles to school at an average speed of 30 mph. Find his average speed for the whole journey.

21. A bus travels from Rainhill to Puddletown, a distance of 10 miles, at an average speed of 20 mph, and continues its journey to Wetside, a further 20 miles beyond Puddletown, at an average speed of 15 mph. Find its average speed for the whole journey from Rainhill to Wetside.

22. A motorist leaves home on a journey of 200 miles. The journey is in two distinct parts: the first 20 miles to the motorway is driven at an average speed of 20 mph, but once on the motorway he is able to average 60 mph. Calculate his average speed for the whole journey.

23. The area of the County of Eastshire is $50\,000\,\text{km}^2$ while the area of the County of Westshire is $20\,000\,\text{km}^2$. If the average annual rainfall for Eastshire is 254 cm while the average annual rainfall for Westshire is 317 cm, find the average annual rainfall for the two counties taken as a whole.

24. The average weight of the 12 boys in a class is 54.2 kg while the average weight of the 16 girls is 56.8 kg. Calculate the average weight for the whole class, giving your answer correct to one decimal place.

25. The average height of the 18 girls in a needlework class is 154 cm. If one girl leaves, the average height falls to 153.8 cm. How tall is she?

26. The area of the Republic of Ireland is approximately 27 000 square miles, while the area of Northern Ireland is approximately 5500 square miles. During a certain year the average rainfall in the Republic amounted to 920 mm, while the average rainfall in the North was 1040 mm. Calculate the average rainfall for Ireland. Give your answer correct to the nearest millimetre.

27. In a boat race the average mass of a crew is 67.8 kg. If the mass of the cox is 43 kg, find the average mass of the oarsmen.

28. A first division football club had an average 'home' gate of 21 400 for the first half of the season when they played 12 games, but an average 'home' gate of 23 700 for the 9 games played during the second half of the season. Find the average 'home' gate for the season, giving your answer correct to the nearest 100.

29. Peter's journey from home to London consisted of three distinct parts. He walked the $\frac{1}{2}$ mile from home to the bus stop at 4 mph, travelled the 10 miles by bus to the station at an average speed of 20 mph, and the 150 miles from the station to London at an average speed of 100 mph. Calculate his average speed from home to London.

30. A motorist wanted to make a 110 mile journey in 2 hours. He travelled the first 60 miles at an average speed of 45 mph, and the next 30 miles at an average speed of 90 mph. What must be his average speed for the final 20 miles if he is to arrive on time?

10 RATIO AND PROPORTION

If the length of the model of a railway carriage is 25 cm while the actual carriage is 18 m long, there is a relation between the two lengths. We say that the model is $\frac{1}{72}$ the length of the carriage. If the model is accurate, every linear dimension will be $\frac{1}{72}$ that of the actual carriage. We call this fraction the *ratio* between the lengths for the model and the corresponding lengths for the carriage. It is also convenient to write the ratio $\frac{1}{72}$ as $1:72$.

A ratio can exist only between two quantities of the same kind which have been expressed in the same units. It is always equivalent to a fraction which is an abstract number, and should be expressed as simply as possible.

If Joan has 20 p and Terry £1.35, the ratio

$$\frac{\text{Amount of money Joan has}}{\text{Amount of money Terry has}} = \frac{20\,\text{p}}{135\,\text{p}} = \frac{4}{27}$$

Conversely
$$\frac{\text{Amount of money Terry has}}{\text{Amount of money Joan has}} = \frac{27}{4}$$

A ratio is unaltered if the top and bottom are multiplied (or divided) by the same number.

e.g.
$$\frac{20}{135} = \frac{4}{27} = \frac{80}{540}$$

or
$$20:135 = 4:27 = 80:540$$

EXAMPLE 1

Find the ratio of $45\,mm$ to $15\,cm$ in its simplest form.

$$\text{Ratio} = \frac{45\,mm}{150\,mm}$$

$$= \frac{3}{10} \qquad \text{(dividing top and bottom by 15)}$$

EXAMPLE 2

Which ratio is the greater, $2:3$ or $5:8$?

$$\frac{2}{3} = \frac{16}{24} \quad \text{and} \quad \frac{5}{8} = \frac{15}{24}$$

$\therefore\ 2:3$ is the greater ratio.

EXAMPLE 3

Fill in the blanks in the following ratios:

$$\frac{5}{3} = \frac{15}{} = \frac{}{48}$$

$$\frac{5}{3} = \frac{15}{9} \qquad (15 = 5 \times 3 \ \therefore \text{ denominator is multiplied by 3 to give 9})$$

$$= \frac{80}{48} \qquad (48 = 3 \times 16 \ \therefore \text{ numerator is multiplied by 16 to give 80})$$

EXAMPLE 4

Increase £5 in the ratio $12:5$.

$$\text{Required amount} = £5 \times \frac{12}{5} = £12$$

EXAMPLE 5

Decrease $36\,cm$ in the ratio $4:9$.

$$\text{Required length} = 36 \times \frac{4}{9}\ cm = 16\,cm$$

EXAMPLE 6

When the cost of gas increases in the ratio $7:5$ a household cuts its use of gas in the ratio $3:4$. In what ratio will the total cost alter?

The increase in the cost of gas causes the bill to be multiplied by a factor of $\frac{7}{5}$.

The reduction in use causes the bill to be multiplied by a factor of $\frac{3}{4}$.

$\therefore$ The effect of the two changes is to multiply the bill by $\frac{7}{5} \times \frac{3}{4}$ or $\frac{21}{20}$, i.e. the bill will be increased in the ratio $21:20$.

EXERCISE 42

Express the following ratios as fractions in their lowest terms:

1. $20:30$ 2. $25:45$ 3. $48:72$ 4. $63:81$

5. $63:147$ 6. $8.1:9.9$ 7. $13:7.8$

8. $44.8:39.2$ 9. $\dfrac{1}{4}:\dfrac{3}{4}$ 10. $\dfrac{3}{8}:\dfrac{1}{2}$ 11. $2\dfrac{1}{4}:1\dfrac{3}{4}$

12. $4\dfrac{1}{2}:1\dfrac{2}{5}$ 13. $56\,p:80\,p$ 14. $42\,p:63\,p$

15. £$120:$£15 16. £$18:$£42

17. $40\,cm:130\,cm$ 18. $52\,m:78\,m$

19. $8.8\,m:24.2\,m$ 20. $42\,km:63\,km$

21. $5\,mm:2\,cm$ 22. $2\,m:55\,cm$

23. $150\,cm:3\,m$ 24. $4.2\,m:6000\,cm$

25. $650\,cm^3:1\dfrac{1}{2}\,litres$ 26. $72\,p:$£2.16

27. £$8.40:42\,p$ 28. $1500\,mm:2\,m$

29. $30\,min:2\,h$ 30. $2\dfrac{1}{4}\,h:5\,h$

31. $3\,h:48\,min$ 32. $245\,min:70\,min$

33. $1.5\,kg:500\,g$ 34. $1750\,g:3\,kg$

35. $49\,g:108\,g$ 36. $5.4\,kg:7.2\,kg.$

Which ratio is the greater?

37. $4:5$ or $8:9$ 38. $9:2$ or $7:3$

39. $4:3$ or $10:7$ 40. $14:9$ or $23:16.$

Which ratio is the smaller?

41. $3:4$ or $5:7$ 42. $7:8$ or $14:15$

43. $9:5$ or $26:17$ 44. $7:3$ or $20:9.$

Fill in the blanks in the following:

45. $\dfrac{2}{5}=\dfrac{}{20}=\dfrac{14}{}$ 46. $\dfrac{3}{7}=\dfrac{12}{}=\dfrac{}{56}$

47. $\dfrac{14}{13}=\dfrac{}{39}=\dfrac{70}{}$ 48. $\dfrac{7}{11}=\dfrac{56}{}=\dfrac{}{121}$

49. $\dfrac{}{9} = \dfrac{12}{27} = \dfrac{60}{}$

50. $\dfrac{7}{} = \dfrac{49}{56} = \dfrac{}{168}.$

51. Increase £10 in the ratio $5:2$.

52. Increase £5.60 in the ratio $13:8$.

53. Increase 588 cm in the ratio $12:7$.

54. Increase 15.3 m in the ratio $4:3$.

55. Increase 165 g in the ratio $9:5$.

56. Decrease £16.36 in the ratio $3:4$.

57. Decrease 84 p in the ratio $7:12$.

58. Decrease 323 mm in the ratio $6:19$.

59. Decrease 28 km in the ratio $5:8$.

60. Decrease 39.1 kg in the ratio $12:17$.

61. In a mixed class of 32 there are 14 boys. Find the ratio of boys to girls.

62. In a year group there are 216 boys and 288 girls. Find the ratio of girls to boys.

63. There are 1920 pupils in a school of whom 864 are boys. Find the ratio of:
    (a) the number of boys to the number of girls
    (b) the number of girls to the number of pupils.

64. John earns £200 per week while Jim earns £1000 per calendar month. Find the ratio of their yearly earnings.

65. A salesman spends $3\frac{1}{2}$ hours of his working day of $10\frac{1}{2}$ hours travelling. Find the ratio of:
    (a) the time he is driving to the time he is not driving
    (b) the time he is not driving to the length of his working day.

66. The number of children receiving free meals in a school increases from 161 to 184. In what ratio have the number of free meals increased?

67. The population of a village rose from 153 to 238. In what ratio did the population increase?

68. The air fare between two American cities is £545 at high season and £436 at low season. Find the ratio of these fares.

69. Find the ratio of the area of Wales, which is 7450 square miles, to the area of Scotland, which is 30 396 square miles.

70. Find the ratio of the area of Northern Ireland (5420 square miles) to that of the Republic of Ireland (27 100 square miles).

71. Find the ratio of the length of the River Seine, 768 km, to the length of the River Loire, 972 km.

72. Find the ratio of the areas of two squares whose sides are 2 cm and 3 cm.

73. A joint of frozen pork, weighing 2200 g, loses 88 g when thawed. In what ratio is its weight reduced?

74. A child sleeps $10\frac{1}{2}$ hours every day. Find the ratio of the time he is awake to the time he sleeps.

75. A boy is 12 years old now and his father is 42 years old. Find:
    (a) the ratio of their present ages
    (b) the ratio of their ages in 3 years' time.

76. A mother is 56 years old now and her daughter is 24. Find the ratio of their ages (a) now, (b) 12 years ago.

77. One car travels at 50 miles per hour while another travels at 1 mile per minute. Find the ratio of their speeds.

78. A woman's gross pay is £142 while her deductions amount to £42.60. Find the ratio of her deductions to her net pay.

79. A record shop increases its stock of records in the ratio 7:6. If its original stock was 2166 records, find:
    (a) the total new stock
    (b) the increase in the number of records.

80. The population of a rural area decreased from 2091 to 1845. In what ratio did the population decrease?

81. When the price of petrol increases in the ratio 6:5 a motorist reduces his mileage in the ratio 9:11. Find the ratio in which his petrol costs change.

82. When the price of tobacco increases in the ratio 9:7 a smoker reduces his consumption in the ratio 2:3. Find the ratio in which his smoking costs change.

83. In a sale goods are reduced by one-fifth. In what ratio are the prices reduced?

84. A man earns £12 480 in a year and spends £10 560. Find the ratio of:
    (a) his income to his expenditure
    (b) his savings to his income.

85. The following recipe will make 7 kg of marmalade: 2 kg oranges, 4 kg sugar, 1 lemon, 1 litre water. What quantities would be required to make 63 kg of marmalade?

86. The following recipe will make sufficient swiss roll for six people:

120 g flour, 125 g castor sugar, 2 eggs, 2 tablespoons jam. What quantities would be required to make sufficient swiss roll for 63 people?

87. The hours a man worked increased in the ratio 9:8 and the hourly rate he was paid increased in the ratio 7:6. In what ratio does his income increase?

88. The hours a woman worked increased in the ratio 13:10 but her hourly rate of pay decreased in the ratio 8:9. Was she better or worse off, and in what ratio?

89. A shopkeeper reduced the price of every article in his shop by 25 p in the £. What would be the new price of an article previously selling for £5.96?

90. A shopkeeper reduced the price of every article in her shop by 20 p in the £. What would be the original price of an article she now sold for £12.28?

REPRESENTATIVE FRACTION

The scale of a map is often given as a ratio. For example the current Ordnance Survey maps in most common use are in the ratio 1:50 000. This means that 1 cm on the map represents 50 000 cm or 500 m on the ground. Any two places on the map which are 5.5 cm apart will be 5.5 × 500 m = 2750 m = 2.75 km apart on the ground. Conversely any places which are 5.45 km apart on the ground will be:

$$\frac{5.45 \text{ km}}{50\,000} = \frac{5.45 \times 1000 \times 100 \text{ cm}}{50\,000}$$

$$= 10.9 \text{ cm apart on the map}$$

The fraction $\dfrac{1}{50\,000}$ is called the *representative fraction*, or RF of the map.

EXAMPLE 7   The RF of a map is $\dfrac{1}{50\,000}$. Find the distance in kilometres between two villages which are 14.4 cm apart on the map.

1 cm represents 50 000 cm

i.e. 1 cm represents 500 m

i.e. 1 cm represents 0.5 km

∴   14.4 cm represents 14.4 × 0.5 km = 7.2 km.

The distance between the villages is therefore 7.2 km.

EXAMPLE 8   The area of a lake is 4.5 square kilometres. What area will represent the lake on a map whose RF is $\frac{1}{50\,000}$?

50 000 cm is represented on the map by 1 cm

i.e.   0.5 km is represented on the map by 1 cm

∴   1 km is represented on the map by 2 cm

i.e. $1\,km^2$ is represented on the map by
$2 \times 2\,cm^2 = 4\,cm^2$

∴ $4.5\,km^2$ is represented on the map by

$4 \times 4.5\,cm^2 = 18\,cm^2$

The area representing the lake on the map will therefore be $18\,cm^2$.

EXERCISE 43

1.   The scale of a map is 1 cm represents 1 km. Find its RF.

2.   The scale of a map is 1 cm represents 400 m. Find its RF.

3.   The scale of a map is 20 cm to 1 km. Find its RF.

4.   The plan of a house is 1 cm to 2 m. Find the RF of the plan. Find the length and breadth of the lounge on the plan if it measures 6 m by 4 m.

5.   The plan of a house is 1 cm to $2\frac{1}{2}$ m. Find the RF of the plan. Find the dimensions of a room which measures 1.6 cm by 2.4 cm on the plan.

6.   The plan of a house has an RF of $\frac{1}{50}$. Find the dimensions, on the plan, of a room which measures 5.5 m by 4 m.

7.   The scale of a map is 1:10 000. What area in square kilometres is represented by $1\,cm^2$ on the map?

8.   The RF of a map is $\frac{1}{50\,000}$. What area on a map (in square centimetres) represents a farm of area 8 square kilometres?

9.   The scale of a map is 1:1 000 000. Find, in square kilometres, the area of a stretch of water which has an area of $8.46\,cm^2$ on the map.

10.   Two landmarks are found to be 132 mm apart on a map whose scale is 1:30 000. How many kilometres separate them?

11. The area of a pond is $53\,\text{m}^2$ and on a map it has an area of $0.53\,\text{cm}^2$. Find the RF of the map.

12. On a map a reservoir is represented by an area of $8.52\,\text{cm}^2$. If the scale of the map is $1:500\,000$, find the area of the reservoir in hectares. (1 hectare = 1000 square metres.)

13. The distance between two towns is 26 miles. Find the distance between these towns in centimetres on a map with RF $\dfrac{1}{50\,000}$. (1 mile = 1.61 km.)

14. On a map two schools are 140 mm apart. If the scale of the map is $1:20\,000$, find their distance apart (a) in kilometres, (b) in miles. (1 km = 0.621 mile.)

15. A three hundred acre farm is shown on a map. If the RF of the map is $\dfrac{1}{50\,000}$, find the area in square centimetres representing it on the map. (1 hectare = 2.471 acres.)

PROPORTIONAL PARTS

If a father divides £10 between his two children giving £7 to one and £3 to the other, we can consider the £10 as having 10 parts, of which he gives 7 to one child and 3 to the other. We say that he has divided the money between his children in the ratio $7:3$.

Conversely if we have a 45 cm length of copper tube and wish to divide it into three lengths which are in the ratio $2:3:4$, we think of the tube as having $2+3+4$ or 9 parts, each part being $\dfrac{45}{9}\,\text{cm} = 5\,\text{cm}$ long.

The three pieces of tube will then have lengths 10 cm (2 parts), 15 cm (3 parts) and 20 cm (4 parts) respectively.

EXAMPLE 9

Divide £840 between A, B and C in the ratio $5:7:9$.

Consider the £840 to be divided into $5+7+9$ i.e. 21 equal parts.

Then one part $= £\dfrac{840}{21} = £40.$

$\therefore$ A's share $= £5 \times 40 = £200$

B's share $= £7 \times 40 = £280$

and C's share $= £9 \times 40 = £360$

EXERCISE 44

1. Divide £42 in the ratio 4:3.

2. Divide 55 p in the ratio 2:3.

3. Divide 54 cm in the ratio 7:11.

4. Divide 3.6 m in the ratio 4:5.

5. Divide 20 km in the ratio 3:7.

6. Divide £66 in the ratio 2:4:5.

7. Divide 70 p in the ratio 2:3:5.

8. Divide 156 mm in the ratio 5:4:3.

9. Divide 322 cm in the ratio 2:5:7.

10. Divide 450 g in the ratio 5:7:13.

11. Divide £39 in the ratio $\frac{1}{2}:\frac{1}{3}:\frac{1}{4}$.

12. Divide 88 p in the ratio $\frac{1}{2}:\frac{1}{4}:\frac{1}{6}$.

13. Divide 960 g in the ratio 1.5:2:2.5.

14. Divide 154 cm in the ratio 0.5:0.8:0.9.

15. Divide 154 cm in the ratio 8:6.4:3.2.

16. Find two numbers whose sum is 144 and whose ratio is 9:7.

17. Find two numbers whose sum is 104 and whose ratio is 4:9.

18. Find two numbers whose difference is 15 and whose ratio is 4:3.

19. Find two numbers whose difference is 44 and whose ratio is 7:11.

20. The length, width and height of a room are in the ratio 4:3:2. If the sum of all three quantities is 11.25 m, find the dimensions of the room.

21. Divide 98 p between three girls, Alison, Beryl and Chris in the ratio 2:5:7.

22. Divide an 80 cm rod into three parts in the ratio 4:7:9.

23. The sides of a triangle are in the ratio 5:6:7. If the distance around the triangle is 63 cm, find the length of each side.

24. Three people A, B and C enter into partnership in a business. They agree to find capital in the ratio 4:5:6. If C puts up £14 400, calculate (a) the total capital required, (b) how much B invests in the business.

25. A quantity of coal weighing 36.75 t is to be carried by three lorries in the ratio 7:5:9. How much will each lorry carry?

26. Two youth clubs are to receive a grant from the local authority in proportion to their respective memberships. If one has 338 members and the other 494, how would a grant of £2560 be divided between them?

27. If $A:B = 3:4$ and $B:C = 2:5$, find $A:B:C$.

28. If $X:Y = 4:5$ and $Y:Z = 3:4$, find $X:Y:Z$.

29. If $a:b = 3:5$ and $b:c = 3:5$, find $a:b:c$.

30. If $p:q = \frac{1}{2}:\frac{1}{3}$ and $q:r = \frac{3}{4}:\frac{1}{4}$, find $p:q:r$.

31. Divide £55 between A, B and C so that A's share is twice B's share and three times C's share.

32. Divide £250 between A, B and C so that B's share is one-half of A's, and C's share is one-third of B's share.

33. Profits in a business amounting to £957 are to be divided between the partners John, Joan and Jim in the ratio of the capital they invested. If John invested £1320, Joan £1056, and Jim £528, how much does Joan receive?

34. An alloy consists of copper and zinc in the ratio 5:7. What weight of copper will be required to add to 931 kg of zinc? How much alloy will this give?

35. An alloy consists of zinc, copper and tin in the ratio of 2:7:4. Find the amount of each metal in 65 g of alloy.

DIRECT PROPORTION

If   1 jar of jam costs 80 p

then   3 jars of jam will cost $3 \times 80\,p = 240\,p$

and   7 jars of jam will cost $7 \times 80\,p = 560\,p$

Since the total cost increases as the number of jars increases, the cost is said to increase in *direct proportion* to the number of jars bought.

EXAMPLE 10   If a car uses 3 gallons of petrol for a journey of 162 miles, how far will it travel on 8 gallons?

On 3 gallons the car will travel 162 miles.

$\therefore$ on 1 gallon it will travel $\dfrac{162}{3}$ miles $= 54$ miles

$\therefore$ on 8 gallons it will travel 54×8 miles
$= 432$ miles

EXAMPLE 11   If five coaches are required to transport 260 supporters to a football match, how many similar coaches would be required to transport 1092 supporters?

260 supporters require 5 coaches

∴   1 supporter requires $\dfrac{5}{260}$ coaches

then 1092 supporters will require $\dfrac{5}{260} \times 1092$ coaches

∴   1092 supporters require 21 coaches.

EXERCISE 45

1. If 12 bars of soap cost £8.52, how much will 20 cost?

2. If 5 packets of tea cost £3.35, how much will 12 cost?

3. Twenty-seven articles cost £4.59. Find the cost of 44 at the same rate.

4. Thirty-five packets of sweets cost £12.60. Find the cost of 53 similar packets.

5. If 7 bananas cost £1.26 find the cost of 32.

6. If 12 oranges cost £1.68 find the cost of 25.

7. A man earns £288 by working for 36 hours. How much would he earn by working for 44 hours at the same rate?

8. A car travels $192\frac{1}{2}$ miles on 5 gallons of petrol. How far will it travel on 8 gallons?

9. A car requires 7 gallons of petrol for a journey of 245 miles. How many gallons will be required for a journey of 455 miles?

10. A small car will run for 266 km on 19 litres of petrol. How far will it run on 32 litres?

11. A motorcycle requires 14 litres of petrol to cover 308 km. How many litres will be required for a journey of 341 km?

12. A hotel charges £259 per person per week. What would be the charge for 16 days at the same rate?

13. The airfare for a 1350 mile flight is £202.50. What would be the fare for a flight of 3440 miles at the same rate?

14. The cost of publishing a book with 105 pages is £3.36. How many pages could be expected in a book costing £7.52 if the cost per page is considered constant?

15. A television set cost £65.52 to hire for 7 months. How much would it cost to hire for 2 years?

16. A new candle which is 18 cm tall will burn for $4\frac{1}{2}$ hours. What height remains when it has been burning for 2 hours 40 minutes?

17. If 544 people attend a concert, the takings amount to £3916.80. How many attended on the following evening when the takings amounted to £2858.40? (Assume that all seats were sold at the same price.

18. Mr Brown paid £319.60 in rates on his house which had a rateable value of £340. If he moved to a new house with a rateable value of £516, how much would he expect to pay in rates?

19. An alloy is made by mixing copper with lead in the ratio 7:9 by mass. What mass of lead would be required to mix with 266 kg of copper, and what mass of alloy would result?

20. Railway freight charges were increased from $7\frac{1}{2}$ p to $9\frac{1}{2}$ p for each article dispatched from a factory. What is the new freight charge for an order which used to cost £19.20?

21. It used to cost 15 p each to send certain articles by post. If the cost of posting a parcel containing a given number of articles increases from £22.20 to £25.90, find the new cost of posting a single article.

22. If three-sevenths of a load of hay has a mass of 1728 kg, what is the mass of four-ninths of the same load?

23. If five-twelfths of a sum of money is £24.50, what is four-sevenths of the same sum?

24. If fifteen machines cost £9465, what would be the cost of eighteen similar machines?

25. It costs £253.75 to carpet a rectangular lounge measuring 3.5 metres by 5 metres. How much would it cost to cover the dining room measuring 2.5 metres by 3 metres with a similar carpet?

INVERSE PROPORTION

Suppose it takes 7 men 60 days to lay a section of motorway. The same section would be laid by:

> 1 man in 420 days
> 2 men in 210 days
> 3 men in 140 days
> 4 men in 105 days
> 5 men in 84 days
> 6 men in 70 days
> 7 men in 60 days and so on.

Selecting two of these lines at random and rewriting:

and
> 3 men will lay the section in 140 days
>
> 7 men will lay the section in 60 days

The ratio of the number of men is $3:7$ or $\dfrac{3}{7}$ and the ratio of the number of days they take is:

$$\frac{140}{60} = \frac{7}{3}$$

Thus if the number of men employed is increased in the ratio $7:3$, the time taken decreases in the ratio $3:7$. This is an example of *inverse proportion*. Two quantities are said to vary inversely or be in inverse proportion if an increase (or decrease) in one causes a corresponding decrease (or increase) in the other.

EXAMPLE 12   If it takes 64 men 42 hours to assemble a light aeroplane, how long would it take 21 men?

Method 1   If the number of men is reduced in the ratio $\dfrac{21}{64}$, the time they will take will be increased in the ratio $\dfrac{64}{21}$.

$$\therefore \quad \text{Time taken} = 42 \times \frac{64}{21} \text{ hours} = 128 \text{ hours}$$

Method 2   Arrange the data:

NO. OF MEN	TIME TAKEN IN HOURS
64	42
21	x

Since the values are in inverse proportion

$$\frac{64}{21} = \frac{x}{42}$$

i.e. $21x = 64 \times 42$

$$\therefore \quad x = \frac{64 \times 42}{21} = 128$$

$\therefore$ Time taken $= 128$ hours

Method 3 (The unitary method). If 64 men take 42 hours to assemble the aeroplane, then 1 man takes 64×42 hours to assemble the aeroplane.

$$\therefore \quad 21 \text{ men take } \frac{64 \times 42}{21} \text{ hours } = 128 \text{ hours}$$

EXERCISE 46

1. A coach takes 2 hours to make a journey when travelling at 60 mph. How long would the journey take if the coach travelled at 40 mph?

2. A car takes 6 hours to make a journey when travelling at 70 mph. What would be its average speed if it took 5 hours for the same journey?

3. If it takes 21 men 4 days to mark out an athletics stadium, how long would it take 12 men to do the same job?

4. A small boat has sufficient food to last its crew of 12 for 9 days. If it rescues six people from the sea, how long will the same food last?

5. A school boiler which consumes 0.75 t of fuel a day has a 12 day supply. If cold weather causes the consumption to increase to 0.9 t a day, how many days will it last?

6. If it takes 360 square tiles of side 10 cm to cover a wall, how many of side 15 cm would be required to cover the same wall?

7. If the volume of a given mass of gas is 4.2 cm^3 when its pressure is 30 cm of mercury, find the volume when the pressure is increased to 36 cm of mercury. (Assume that volume and pressure are inversely related.)

8. When a box of chocolates is divided among 5 people they have 8 chocolates each. If the box was divided between 4 people, how many chocolates would each receive?

9. A fruit farmer employs 34 men to harvest his apples. If they take 9 days to do the job, how many men would be required to do the job in 6 days?

10. A factory requires 45 sewing machines to produce a given quantity of dresses in 22 days. How many machines would be required to produce the same number of dresses in 18 days?

11. My bookshelf will hold 360 books of average thickness 2 cm. How many copies of *National Geographic* will it hold if the average copy is 6 mm thick?

12. The average waiting time at a supermarket when 12 check-outs are available is 8 minutes. How many check-outs would be required to reduce the waiting time to 3 minutes?

13. A brass band and a theatre group receive equal grants from the local authority. The band has 44 members and receives the equivalent of £7 for each member, while the theatre group only receives the equivalent of £4 per member. How many members are there in the theatre group?

14. Water in a rectangular tank with a base area of 1.5 m² is 24 cm deep. If it is run off into another rectangular tank of base area 1.2 m², to what height will it rise?

15. If the cost of gas for heating 12 greenhouses for 5 days is £70, how many greenhouses could be heated for 4 days at the same cost?

16. A cog wheel with 60 cogs meshes with a cog wheel with 35 cogs. If the former makes 84 revolutions in a minute, how many does the other make?

17. Two gear wheels mesh together, one making 60 revolutions per minute and the other 80. If the smaller wheel has 30 teeth, how many teeth does the larger wheel have?

18. A boys' camp has enough stores to support 42 boys for 14 days. If 49 boys attend the camp how long will the stores last?

19. A ball of string may be cut into 45 pieces, each of length 28 cm. How many pieces 63 cm long could be cut from the same ball?

20. In a school 44 classrooms are required if each class size is 30 pupils. How many more classrooms would be required if all the class sizes are cut to 24?

COMPOUND PROPORTION

In simple proportion only two quantities are involved, but in compound proportion we are concerned with more than two quantities. It is often convenient to introduce special units, e.g. if 8 men work for 6 hours we could say that they have produced $8 \times 6 = 48$ man-hours' work, or if an aeroplane carries 120 passengers for 350 miles, the airline is able to charge for 120×350 passenger-miles.

EXAMPLE 13

If 6 men earn £360 for 12 hours' work, how much will 8 men earn for 20 hours' work at the same rate?

Method 1 Let us call 1 man working for 1 hour a man-hour.

Then 6×12 man-hours costs £360

i.e. 1 man-hour costs $£\dfrac{360}{6 \times 12} = £5$

$\therefore$ 8×20 man-hours will cost $£8 \times 20 \times 5 = £800$

i.e. 8 men working for 20 hours will earn £800.

Method 2 Question: Will 8 men earn more or less than 6?

Answer: More. Therefore multiply by $\dfrac{8}{6}$.

Question: Will a given number of men earn more or less in 20 hours than in 12 hours?

Answer: More. Therefore multiply by $\dfrac{20}{12}$.

i.e. Amount earned by 8 men in 20 hours

$$= £360 \times \frac{8}{6} \times \frac{20}{12} = £800$$

EXERCISE 47

1. If 8 men earn £288 for 9 hours' work, how much will 11 men earn for 7 hours' work?

2. Six girls earn £90 for 5 hours' work. How much should 8 girls earn for 4 hours' work?

3. If 6 boys earn £300 in 5 days, how much will 4 boys earn in 12 days?

4. Eight gas heaters running for 4 hours cost £3.84. How much will nine heaters cost to run for 7 hours?

5. The income received by hiring 7 mixing machines for 8 days is £448. What would be the income if 4 machines were hired for 15 days?

6. In a packing department 16 women pack 1568 boxes in 7 hours. How many boxes should be packed by 21 women in 6 hours?

7. If a workforce of 15 is required to produce 945 articles in 7 hours, what workforce is required to produce 864 articles in 8 hours?

8. The cost of transporting 8 t of goods 30 miles is £320. How many tonnes of goods could be expected to be transported 100 miles for £600?

9. In a certain school 80 teachers are required if each teaches a 34 period week. How many teachers will be required if the teaching week is reduced to 32 periods?

10. If a field contains enough grass to graze 36 sheep for 18 days, how many sheep could graze a field 3 times as large for 8 days?

11. A bank charges £21 for a loan of £300 for 6 months. What would be the charge for a loan of £5000 for 14 months?

12. Eighteen college staff can enrol 1980 students in 5 hours. How many staff are required to enrol 1056 students in 4 hours?

13. The cost of petrol for a 120 km journey for a car which travels 20 km on each litre of petrol is £2.40. What would be the cost for a 300 km journey in a car which travels 15 km on each litre?

14. Last quarter my electricity bill was £60 when I used 1200 units of electricity, each unit costing 5 p. This quarter I intend cutting my use by $\frac{1}{5}$ since the cost of electricity has increased by 1 p per unit. What should my next electricity bill be?

15. In a school canteen the food bill for a week when they are catering for 380 pupils is £760. How much should it rise or fall if the cost of a meal increases by 25% while the number of pupils served falls by 100?

PERCENTAGES

Per cent means per hundred, e.g. 12 per cent means 12 per hundred. If 12 per cent of the pupils in a school are absent, then for every 100 pupils on the register 12 of them are absent. If there are 1400 i.e. 14×100 pupils in the school, $14 \times 12 = 168$ will be absent.

In mathematics we are always looking for shorter ways of writing things and especially for symbols instead of words. Instead of the 'per cent' we write %. Therefore 12% and 12 per cent have exactly the same meaning.

It follows that 12% can be written in fraction form as $\dfrac{12}{100}$ or $\dfrac{3}{25}$ i.e. 12% is equivalent to $\dfrac{3}{25}$.

Percentages are fractions with a denominator of 100

e.g. $\qquad \dfrac{3}{20} = \dfrac{15}{100} \qquad$ or $\qquad 15\%$

Percentages may be expressed as fractions and fractions are easily converted into percentages.

A percentage is converted into a fraction by dividing by 100 and simplifying

e.g. $\qquad 20\% = \dfrac{20}{100} = \dfrac{1}{5} = 0.2$

and $\qquad 65\% = \dfrac{65}{100} = \dfrac{13}{20} = 0.65$

A fraction is converted into a percentage by multiplying by 100

e.g. $\qquad \dfrac{3}{5} = \dfrac{3}{5} \times 100\% = 60\%$

121

and
$$\frac{17}{20} = \frac{17}{20} \times 100\% = 85\%$$

It is only a short step from the above to 'Express 35 cm as a percentage of 2 m'.

The first quantity as a fraction of the second is $\dfrac{35}{200}$ (taking great care to see that both are in the same units).

Then
$$\frac{35}{200} = \frac{35}{200} \times 100\% = 17\tfrac{1}{2}\%$$

EXERCISE 48

Express the following as percentages:

1. $\frac{1}{2}, \frac{1}{4}, \frac{1}{8}, \frac{3}{8}, \frac{5}{8}$

2. $\frac{7}{8}, \frac{1}{3}, \frac{2}{3}, \frac{9}{8}, \frac{17}{8}$

3. $\frac{1}{5}, \frac{2}{5}, \frac{4}{5}, \frac{6}{5}, \frac{8}{5}$

4. $\frac{11}{20}, \frac{3}{25}, \frac{5}{6}, \frac{9}{20}, \frac{17}{50}$

5. $\frac{29}{25}, 1\frac{1}{3}, 2\frac{9}{10}, 1\frac{1}{10}, 1\frac{7}{8}$

6. $0.25, 0.35, 0.47, 0.06, 0.72$

7. $1.23, 2, 3.04, 0.655, 12.24.$

Express the following percentages as (a) common fractions in their lowest terms, (b) decimals:

8. $25\%, 50\%, 75\%, 40\%, 60\%$

9. $55\%, 48\%, 64\%, 76\%, 35\%$

10. $12\frac{1}{2}\%, 37\frac{1}{2}\%, 62\frac{1}{2}\%, 87\frac{1}{2}\%, 16\frac{2}{3}\%.$

11. If 32% of the boys in a year group take woodwork, what percentage do not?

12. A man spends 43% of his income on household expenses, 28% on pleasure, saves 8% and spends the remainder on his car. What percentage is spent on his car?

13. If 72% of the cost of a cigarette is tax, how much is not?

14. An object is 43% animal, 29% vegetable and the remainder is mineral. What percentage is mineral?

15. The cost of running a car is 28% petrol, 35% road tax, insurance and repairs, and the remainder depreciation. What percentage accounts for depreciation?

16. Marmalade consists of 28% fruit, 58% sugar and the remainder water. Find the percentage of water.

17. At an election 31% vote Labour, 31% vote Conservative and the remainder for the SDP. What percentage vote for the SDP?

Express the first quantity as a percentage of the second:

18. (a) 5, 20   (b) 4, 40   (c) 16, 64   (d) 50, 25
    (e) 15, 60

19. (a) 12 cm, 60 cm   (b) 33 cm, 1 m   (c) 4 m, 3 m
    (d) 400 m, 1 km   (e) 243 mm, 30 cm

20. (a) 24 cm^2, 96 cm^2 (b) 200 mm^2, 40 cm^2
    (c) 1000 cm^2, 1 m^2 (d) 550 cm^3, 1 litre
    (e) 844 cm^3, 2 litres

21. (a) 1600 g, 2 kg   (b) 2.64 kg, 8.8 kg
    (c) 850 kg, 1 t   (d) $157\frac{1}{2}$ g, 450 g
    (e) 36 g, 50 g.

Find the value of:

22. (a) 30% of 8 m   (b) 65% of 5 cm
    (c) 85% of 2.5 km

23. (a) $12\frac{1}{2}$% of 720 g   (b) $66\frac{2}{3}$% of 369 kg
    (c) 125% of 36 g

24. (a) 37% of 84   (b) $16\frac{2}{3}$% of 159 cm
    (c) $58\frac{1}{2}$% of 44 m.

25. In a third year 52% of the 250 pupils study French. How many do not study French?

26. Deductions from a man's wage amount to 40%. What is his wage after deductions if he earns £320?

27. In a biology test a girl scores 26 marks out of 40. What percentage is this?

28. The constituents of gunpowder are: nitre 75%, charcoal 15% and sulphur 10%. How many kilograms of gunpowder may be made from 12 kg of charcoal?

29. In an election 47% of the electorate voted Labour, 15% Conservative and the remainder for the Nationalist candidate. If there were 64 500 voters, how many voted for the Nationalist?

30. In a local election 56% of the electorate voted Conservative, 37% Labour and the remainder Liberal. If 44 400 are eligible to vote, how many more votes did the Conservative candidate receive than the Liberal?

31. In a form 75% are boys and 9 are girls. How many pupils are there in the form?

32. In a year group 65% are girls and 84 are boys. How many girls are there?

33. In a form of 30, 9 study cookery. What percentage do not?

34. If 50% of a number is 20, find the number.

35. If 20% of a number is 25, find the number.

36. If 60% of a sum of money is £3.60, find the sum of money.

37. If 75% of a sum of money is £7.20, find the sum of money.

38. If 35% of a sum of money is £43.40, find the sum of money.

39. In a family 40% are males. What is the smallest number of females in the family?

40. A house was sold for £60 000 which was 96% of what it cost to build. How much did it cost to build?

41. In a sale a shopkeeper reduced his prices by 30 p in the pound. What percentage was this?

42. In a sale an article was marked down from £21.40 to £18.19. What percentage reduction was this?

43. In a sale a coat was marked down from £134 to £87.10. What percentage reduction was this?

44. A piece of frozen fish lost 4% of its mass when thawed. If its mass was 1.44 kg when thawed, what was its mass when frozen?

45. A packet of cornflakes was full when it left the factory but 'settling' caused the volume taken by the cornflakes to reduce by 8%. If the volume of the packet was $3000\,cm^3$, find the volume taken by the cornflakes when they had settled.

46. In end of term examinations a pupil scored a total of 572 marks out of a possible 800. Express this result as a percentage.

47. In an examination a pupil gained 221 marks out of a possible 340. What percentage is this?

48. In a test a boy gained 85% of the marks. How many marks did he receive if the total possible was 460?

49. A girl sat three mathematics papers and had an average mark of 66%. If she scored 52 out of a hundred in the first paper and 73 out of a hundred in the second, how many did she score out of 100 in the third?

50. A broker charges $1\frac{1}{2}\%$ commission on shares he sells. If he sells 5420 shares at £4.40 each for a client, calculate his commission.

PERCENTAGE CHANGE

When the government announces that prices have increased by 10% it means that for every £100 we previously needed to buy goods and services we now need £110. For example:

A car which cost £15 000 would increase to

$$£15\,000 \times \frac{110}{100} = £16\,500$$

A can of fruit which cost £1.40 would increase to

$$£1.40 \times \frac{110}{100} = £1.54$$

A holiday which cost £1250 would rise to

$$£1250 \times \frac{110}{100} = £1375$$

If the original price is represented by 100, the new price is represented by 110, i.e. the new price may be calculated by multiplying the original cost by $\frac{110}{100}$ which is called the *multiplying factor*.

Similarly if a car depreciates by 20% during its first year, every £100 of value has decreased by £20 to £80, i.e. the new value is found by multiplying the purchase price by the multiplying factor $\frac{80}{100}$.

If the car was bought for £20 000 it would be worth:

$$£20\,000 \times \frac{80}{100} = £16\,000 \qquad \text{after one year}$$

EXERCISE 49

1. What multiplying factor increases a number by:
   (a) 20%   (b) 50%   (c) 35%   (d) 120%
   (e) 200%?

2. What multiplying factor decreases a number by:
   (a) 20%   (b) 60%   (c) 12%   (d) 35%
   (e) 75%?

3. Increase the given numbers by the given percentage:
   (a) 100, 30%   (b) 240, 60%
   (c) 30, 80%   (d) 66, $33\frac{1}{3}$%
   (e) 64, $12\frac{1}{2}$%.

4. Decrease the given numbers by the given percentage:
   (a) 200, 40%   (b) 175, 30%
   (c) 21, $66\frac{2}{3}$%   (d) 64, $12\frac{1}{2}$%.

5. The price of a watch marked £60 rises by 12%. Find its new price.

6. A man's weekly wage of £550 rises by 15%. Find his new wage.

7. A girl's weight increased by 8% on holiday. If she weighed 65 kg before she went, how much did she weigh on her return?

8. A boy's height increased by 20% between his twelfth and fourteenth birthdays. If he was 145 cm on his twelfth birthday, how tall was he on his fourteenth?

9. Water increases in volume by 4% when frozen. Find the volume of 525 cm^3 of water when converted into ice.

10. The water rate on a property is 18% higher this year than last year. If it was £160 last year, what will it be this year?

11. A girl is 25% taller now than she was 3 years ago. If she is 160 cm now, how tall was she 3 years ago?

12. The number of children attending school in the county of Peaceshire is 6% fewer this year than last year. If 63 200 were attending school last year, how many are attending this year?

13. In a sale the price of an article marked at £74 is reduced by 15%. What is its sale price?

14. A car, bought for £16 000, loses 72% of its value over a 5 year period. Find its value after 5 years.

15. A woman's height decreased by 5% between her fiftieth and seventy-fifth birthdays. If her height was 1.82 m when she was fifty, how tall was she 25 years later?

16. A man's weight increased by 63% between his twentieth and fortieth birthdays. At twenty he weighed 48 kg. How much did he weigh on his fortieth birthday?

17. When making a model stool a boy estimated that he had 72% of the wood he started with in the finished model. If the model weighed 2.52 kg, what weight of wood did he start with?

18. A retailer sold an article for £54 thus gaining $12\frac{1}{2}$% on the amount it cost him. How much did it cost him?

19. The percentage of staff in a school decreased by 5%. If 114 staff remain, how many left?

20. The widening of a road results in the garden of a house being reduced in area by 35%. If the area of the garden is $546\,\text{m}^2$ after widening, what was its original area?

PERCENTAGE PROFIT AND LOSS

When a retailer buys goods and is able to sell them at a higher price, a profit is made, which is the difference between the selling price (SP) and the cost price (CP). The percentage profit made is always calculated by expressing the *profit as a percentage of the cost price*.

Thus $\text{Percentage profit} = \dfrac{\text{profit}}{\text{cost price}} \times 100$

i.e. $\% \text{ Profit} = \dfrac{\text{SP} - \text{CP}}{\text{CP}} \times 100$

Similarly $\% \text{ Loss} = \dfrac{\text{loss}}{\text{CP}} \times 100$ i.e. $\% \text{ Loss} = \dfrac{\text{CP} - \text{SP}}{\text{CP}} \times 100$

EXAMPLE 1   A retailer bought a clock for £55 and sold it for £77. Find his percentage profit.

$$\text{Profit} = \text{SP} - \text{CP}$$

$$= £77 - £55$$

$$= £22$$

$$\% \text{ Profit} = \dfrac{\text{profit}}{\text{CP}} \times 100$$

$$= \dfrac{£22}{£55} \times 100$$

i.e. $\text{Profit} = 40\%$

EXAMPLE 2   A retailer bought a can of fruit for 80 p and sold it at a profit of 25%. Find the selling price.

Method 1   Profit is 25% or $\dfrac{25}{100}$ of the CP

i.e. $\text{Profit} = 80 \times \dfrac{25}{100}\text{p}$

$$= 20\,\text{p}$$

$\therefore$ $\text{SP} = \text{CP} + \text{profit}$

$$= 80\,\text{p} + 20\,\text{p}$$

$$= £1$$

127

Method 2

$$SP = CP + \frac{25}{100} CP$$

$$= \frac{125}{100} CP$$

$$= CP \times \frac{125}{100}$$

$$= 80 \times \frac{125}{100} p$$

$$= 100 p$$

$$= £1$$

In general terms, if the profit is *P%*

$$SP = CP \times \frac{(100 + P)}{100}$$

For example if CP = £5 and profit is 35%

$$SP = £5 \times \frac{(100 + 35)}{100}$$

$$= £5 \times \frac{135}{100}$$

$$= £6.75$$

EXAMPLE 3 Linda buys a record for £6 but decides she does not like it very much so she sells it to a friend at a loss of 15%. How much does the friend pay for it?

Method 1

Loss is 15% or $\frac{15}{100}$ of the cost price

i.e.   Loss $= £6 \times \frac{15}{100}$

$$= £0.90$$

$\therefore$ SP $=$ CP $-$ loss

$$= £6 - £0.90$$

$$= £5.10$$

Method 2

$$SP = CP - \frac{15}{100} CP$$

$$= \frac{85}{100} CP$$

$$= CP \times \frac{85}{100}$$

$$= £6 \times \frac{85}{100}$$

$$= £5.10$$

In general terms, if the loss is $L\%$

$$SP = CP \times \frac{(100-L)}{100}$$

For example if $CP = £36$ and loss is 45%

$$SP = £36 \times \frac{(100-45)}{100}$$

$$= £36 \times \frac{55}{100}$$

$$= £19.80$$

EXAMPLE 4 When a radio cassette recorder is sold for £33.60 the shopkeeper makes a profit of 40%. Find the cost price.

Method 1 The percentage profit (or loss) is always on the cost price.

$$\text{Since } SP = CP \times \frac{(100+P)}{100}$$

$$£33.60 = CP \times \frac{(100+40)}{100}$$

$$= CP \times \frac{140}{100}$$

i.e. $£33.60 \times \frac{100}{140} = CP$ $\left(\text{multiplying each side by } \frac{100}{140}\right)$

or $\quad CP = £33.60 \times \dfrac{100}{140}$

$$= £24$$

Method 2   If the cost price is 100 p, the selling price will be

$$100 \times \frac{140}{100}\text{p} = 140\,\text{p}$$

i.e. the cost price is $\dfrac{100}{140}$ of the selling price

$$\therefore \quad CP = £33.60 \times \frac{100}{140}$$

$$= £24$$

EXAMPLE 5   A second hand car dealer sells a car for £1840. If this means that he has suffered a loss of 8%, how much did he pay for it?

Method 1

$$SP = CP \times \frac{(100 - L)}{100}$$

i.e. $\quad £1840 = CP \times \dfrac{(100 - 8)}{100}$

$$= CP \times \frac{92}{100}$$

i.e. $\quad CP = £1840 \times \dfrac{100}{92}$

$$= £2000$$

Method 2   If the cost price is £100, the selling price will be

$$£100 \times \frac{92}{100} = £92$$

i.e. the cost price is $\dfrac{100}{92}$ of the selling price

$$\therefore \quad CP = £1840 \times \frac{100}{92}$$

$$= £2000$$

EXAMPLE 6

John Baker buys eight packs of towels at £35 per pack, each pack containing 25 towels. He is able to sell the towels at £1.96 each. Calculate (a) the total profit, (b) the percentage profit.

Cost of 8 packs at £35 per pack $= £8 \times 35$

$$= £280$$

Number of towels bought $= 8 \times 25$

$$= 200$$

Amount received by selling 200 towels at £1.96 each

$$= £1.96 \times 200$$

$$= £392$$

$\therefore$ Profit $= SP - CP$

$$= £392 - £280$$

$$= £112$$

% Profit $= \dfrac{\text{Profit}}{\text{CP}} \times 100$

$$= \dfrac{£112}{£280} \times 100$$

i.e. Profit $= 40\%$

EXERCISE 50

In each of the following write down the factor by which the cost price must be multiplied to give the selling price:

1. Profit 20%
2. Profit 50%
3. Profit 45%
4. Profit $33\frac{1}{3}\%$
5. Loss 20%
6. Loss 60%
7. Loss 75%
8. Loss $66\frac{2}{3}\%$
9. Profit 5%
10. Loss 12%.

In each of the following find the selling price:

11. CP £2, profit 20%
12. CP £10, loss 10%
13. CP £10, loss 25%
14. CP £16, profit 50%
15. CP £15, profit 30%
16. CP £300, profit 8%
17. CP £120, loss 60%
18. CP £7.50, loss 80%
19. CP £4.96, profit $12\frac{1}{2}\%$
20. CP £639, loss $33\frac{1}{3}\%$.

In each of the following write down the factor by which the selling price must be multiplied to give the cost price:

21. Profit 20%

22. Profit 50%

23. Profit 75%

24. Profit $66\frac{2}{3}$%

25. Loss 60%

26. Loss 10%

27. Loss 50%

28. Profit $12\frac{1}{2}$%

29. Loss $37\frac{1}{2}$%

30. Loss 15%.

In each of the following find the cost price:

31. SP £126, profit 5%

32. SP £80, profit 100%

33. SP £2.04, loss 40%

34. SP 18 p, loss $33\frac{1}{3}$%

35. SP £2.20, profit 10%

36. SP 63 p, loss 30%

37. SP £17.28, profit 60%

38. SP £7.69, loss 60%

39. SP £17, loss 15%

40. SP £336, profit 180%.

In each of the following find the percentage profit or loss:

41. CP £4, profit 60 p

42. CP £60, profit £12

43. CP £350, loss £42

44. CP £60, loss £15

45. CP £105, profit £63

46. CP £5.60, SP £7

47. CP £7.30, SP £9.49

48. CP £60, SP £102

49. CP £14.90, SP £26.82

50. CP £480, SP £540.

EXERCISE 51   MISCELLANEOUS EXAMPLES

1. A calculator is bought for £5 and sold at a loss of 40%. Find the selling price.

2. A bookseller buys a book for £8.50 and sells it for £15.30. Find the percentage profit.

3. A house bought for £48 000 is sold at a profit of 12%. Find the selling price.

4. Imported bicycles cost a dealer £110 and are sold at 35% profit. Find the selling price.

5. Six months after paying £8000 for a car the owner is forced to sell for £6560. Find the percentage loss.

6. Record albums sold at £9.80 result in a loss of 30% for the shop-keeper. How much did he pay for them?

7. A box of paints bought for £12 is sold at a profit of $22\frac{1}{2}\%$. Find the selling price.

8. Ray George made a loss of $16\frac{2}{3}\%$ by selling some potatoes for £6. How much did they cost him?

9. A silversmith sells silver for £264, thereby making 120% profit. How much did the silver cost him?

10. An art dealer bought a picture for £3500 and sold it at a profit of 80%. Find the selling price.

11. A discount store bought a suite of furniture for £1260 and sold it at a profit of $66\frac{2}{3}\%$. How much did they sell it for?

12. Ernie Pugh buys a greyhound for £360 and sells it at a loss of $12\frac{1}{2}\%$. How much does he lose?

13. A greengrocer buys a box of 150 Seville oranges for £13.50 and sells them at 14 p each. Find his percentage profit.

14. A scrap metal dealer buys lead for £72 and sells it for £132. Find his percentage profit.

15. By selling a picture for £2160 an antique dealer makes a profit of 80%. What did she pay for it?

16. By selling a quantity of gold for £11 340 a bullion dealer makes a profit of 110%. What did he pay for it?

17. Jane bought a necklace for £7.50 and sold it at a loss of 36%. How much did she lose?

18. If a second hand car dealer buys a car for £4600 and sells it at a loss of 15%, how much does he sell it for?

19. Dried fruit bought at £44 per 50 kg bag is sold at £1.21 per kilogram. Find the percentage profit.

20. Eggs are bought at the farm for £1.50 per tray and sold at 90 p per dozen. If a tray holds 36 eggs, find the percentage profit.

21. A retailer buys 100 articles for £180 and sells them at £2.40 each. Find the percentage profit.

22. A shopkeeper buys 300 articles for £1200 and sells them at £3.50 each. Find his percentage loss.

23. A shopkeeper buys an article and 'marks it up' so that he makes 80% profit on the cost price. If he allows 5% off the marked price for cash, find the cost price of an article he sells for £8.55 cash.

24. A garage allows 12% off the list price of a car when no car is offered in part-exchange. If the list price is calculated by adding 60% to the cost price, how much profit does the dealer make on a car costing him £12 000?

25. A herb bought at £25 per kilogram is sold at 3 p per gram. Find the percentage profit.

26. A builders' merchant allows a discount of $2\frac{1}{2}$% if payment is made within seven days. How much would I save by paying a bill totalling £768 immediately?

27. A small business made a profit of £8909 this year. If this was an increase of 18% over last year, how much profit was made last year?

28. The population of Bernshire increased by 5% last year but had decreased by 2% the previous year. If the population is 12 348 now, what was it (a) last year, (b) 2 years ago?

29. The local team's score was standing at 180 for 9 wickets when the last pair came together. If these two increased the total by 35%, find:
    (a) how many runs they put on for the last wicket
    (b) the innings score.

30. A tailor 'marks up' his suits to give a profit of 55%. In a sale he reduces all his prices by 10% which means that Joe Bloggs is able to save £18.60 on the suit he buys. Find:
    (a) the original marked price of the suit
    (b) the tailor's actual profit on the suit.

12
AREA AND VOLUME

AREA

The *area* of a plane figure is the amount of surface enclosed within its boundary lines. The total length of these boundary lines is called its *perimeter*.

In the metric system we have the metre as the standard unit of length, from which several other units follow. In the same way the square metre, which is the area contained within a square of side one metre, is the standard unit of area. The particular unit used depends on the amount of area we are measuring. Thus we might measure the area of the head of a screw in square millimetres (mm^2), the area of a page of this book in square centimetres (cm^2), the area of a roof in square metres (m^2) and the area of a country in square kilometres (km^2).

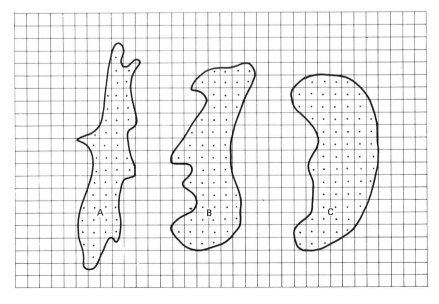

The diagrams given on page 135 show three imaginary islands which have been drawn on squared paper. We can compare their areas by counting squares.

By counting squares the approximate area of A is 49 squares. We include a square if more than half of it is within the area, but neglect it if more than half is outside. Similarly the area of B is 59 squares and the area of C is 68 squares. It follows that C has the largest area and A the smallest.

The value of any area may be found by counting squares, but it would simplify things considerably if we could build up areas from basic shapes, which we measured in acceptable units. The simplest area to consider is the square.

THE SQUARE

The area of a square of side 3 cm is $3 \times 3\, \text{cm}^2 = 9\, \text{cm}^2$, i.e. 9 squares, each of side 1 cm are required to cover completely a square of side 3 cm.

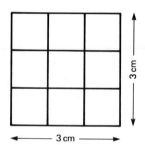

Similarly we can show that the area of a square of side x units is x^2 square units.

The perimeter of a square is the sum of the lengths of the four equal sides. Thus the perimeter (P) of a square of side x units is given by:

$$P = 4x \text{ units}$$

THE RECTANGLE

The number of squares of side 1 cm required to cover completely a rectangle which is 4 cm long and 3 cm wide is $4 \times 3 = 12$, i.e. the area of a rectangle measuring 4 cm by 3 cm is $12\, \text{cm}^2$.

Similarly, if a rectangle measures L units by B units, the number of unit squares required to cover it will be given by B rows, each row containing L squares, i.e. $L \times B$ squares.

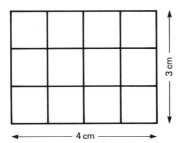

Thus the area (A) of a rectangle which is L units long and B units wide is given by:

$$A = L \times B \text{ square units}$$

The perimeter of this rectangle is the sum of the lengths of the four sides, two of length L units and two of length B units.

i.e.
$$\text{Perimeter } (P) = 2L + 2B \text{ units}$$
$$= 2(L + B) \text{ units}$$

EXAMPLE 1 Find (a) the perimeter, (b) the area of the given figure. All dimensions are in centimetres.

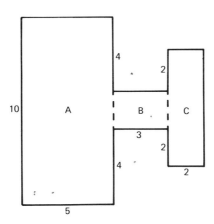

(a) Beginning at the top left hand corner of the diagram and moving clockwise, the perimeter of the figure is given by $P = 5 + 4 + 3 + 2 + 2 + 6 + 2 + 2 + 3 + 4 + 5 + 10 \text{ cm} = 48 \text{ cm}$.

(b) Dividing the given figure into three rectangles A, B and C:

$$\text{Area of A} = 10 \times 5 \text{ cm}^2 = 50 \text{ cm}^2$$
$$\text{Area of B} = 3 \times 2 \text{ cm}^2 = 6 \text{ cm}^2$$
$$\text{Area of C} = 6 \times 2 \text{ cm}^2 = 12 \text{ cm}^2$$
$$\therefore \quad \text{Total area of figure} = 68 \text{ cm}^2$$

137

EXAMPLE 2 The area of a rectangle, which is 9 m long, is $72 \, \text{m}^2$. Find (a) its breadth, (b) its perimeter.

(a) Since $A = L \times B$

$$72 = 9 \times B$$

i.e.

$$\text{Breadth} = \frac{72}{9} \, \text{cm} = 8 \, \text{cm}$$

∴ the rectangle is 8 cm in breadth.

(b) Perimeter $= 2(L + B)$ units

$$= 2(9 + 8) \, \text{cm}$$

$$= 2 \times 17 \, \text{cm}$$

i.e.   Perimeter $= 34 \, \text{cm}$

EXAMPLE 3 The floor of a hall measuring 30 m by 22 m is to be covered with square floor tiles of side 50 cm. How many tiles are required? If the tiles are sold only in complete boxes containing 50 tiles, how much will it cost to tile the floor at £8.46 per box?

Method 1

Laying one row of tiles against the long wall requires $30 \, \text{m} \div \frac{1}{2} \, \text{m} = 60$ tiles,

and laying one row of tiles against the short wall requires $22 \, \text{m} \div \frac{1}{2} \, \text{m} = 44$ tiles.

∴ Number of tiles required $= 60 \times 44 = 2640$.

Method 2

Area of floor to be covered $= 30 \times 22 \, \text{m}^2$

Area of one tile $= \frac{1}{2} \times \frac{1}{2} \, \text{m}^2$

$$\text{Number of tiles required} = \frac{\text{area of floor}}{\text{area of one tile}}$$

$$= \frac{30 \times 22 \, \text{m}^2}{\frac{1}{2} \times \frac{1}{2} \, \text{m}^2}$$

$$= 30 \times 22 \times 2 \times 2$$

$$= 2640$$

Method 3

Area of floor $= 3000 \times 2200 \, \text{cm}^2$

Area of one tile $= 50 \times 50 \, \text{cm}^2$

$$\text{Number of tiles required} = \frac{3000 \times 2200 \, \text{cm}^2}{50 \times 50 \, \text{cm}^2}$$

$$= 2640$$

$$\text{Number of boxes of tiles required} = \frac{2640}{50} = 52\tfrac{4}{5}$$

∴ 53 boxes must be purchased

Cost of 53 boxes at £8.46 per box $= £8.46 \times 53$

$$= £448.38$$

EXAMPLE 4

A rectangular vegetable garden measuring 18.5 m by 14 m is surrounded by a path of uniform width 1 m. Find (a) the area of the path, (b) the total perimeter of the path.

(a) If the path is 1 m wide the large rectangle measures 20.5 m by 16 m and therefore has an area of $20.5 \times 16 \, \text{m}^2 = 328 \, \text{m}^2$

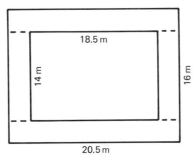

Area of small rectangle (the vegetable garden)

$$= 18.5 \times 14 \, \text{m}^2 = 259 \, \text{m}^2$$

$$\therefore \quad \text{Area of path} = 328 - 259 \, \text{m}^2$$

$$= 69 \, \text{m}^2$$

The area may also be found by dividing the path into four rectangles, as shown in the diagram.

Then Area of path $= (20.5 + 14 + 20.5 + 14) \, \text{m}^2$

$$= 69 \, \text{m}^2$$

(b) External perimeter of path $= 2(20.5 + 16) \, \text{m}$

$$= 73 \, \text{m}$$

Internal perimeter of path $= 2(18.5 + 14) \, \text{m}$

$$= 65 \, \text{m}$$

∴ Total perimeter $= (73 + 65) = 138 \, \text{m}$

139

EXERCISE 52

By counting squares determine which is (a) the largest, (b) the smallest, in each of the following:

1.

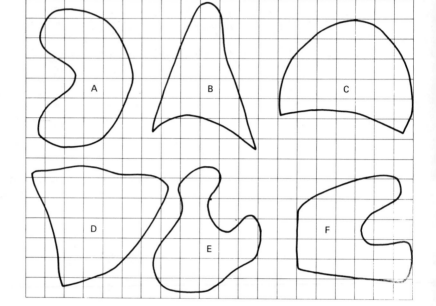

2.

Find (a) the perimeter, (b) the area, for each of the following figures (all measurements are in centimetres):

3.

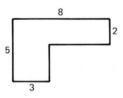

4.

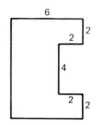

5.

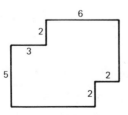

6.

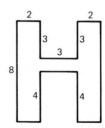

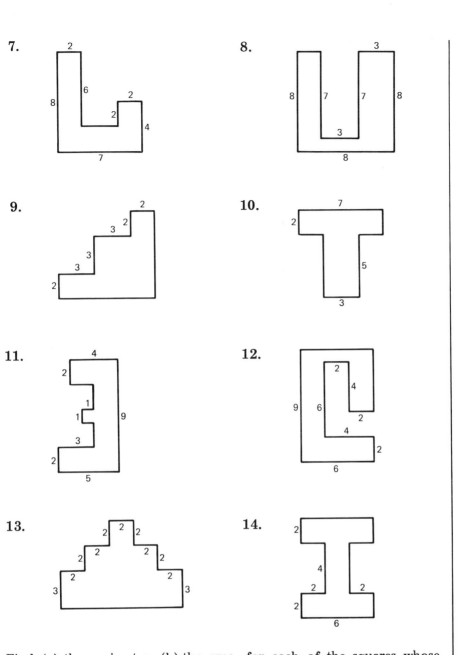

7. **8.** **9.** **10.** **11.** **12.** **13.** **14.**

Find (a) the perimeter, (b) the area, for each of the squares whose sides are:

15. 2 cm   **16.** 3 km   **17.** 5 m   **18.** 7 mm

19. 0.5 cm   **20.** 0.75 km   **21.** 1.2 cm   **22.** 0.4 km.

Find (a) the perimeter, (b) the area, of rectangles measuring:

23. 4 cm by 3 cm   **24.** 12 mm by 8 mm

25. 7 m by 5 m   **26.** 10 m by 80 m.

Find the area of each of the following rectangles, giving your answer
in the units given in brackets.

	LENGTH	BREADTH	
27.	5 cm	5 mm	(mm^2)
28.	1 m	40 cm	(cm^2)
29.	26 m	5 m	(m^2)
30.	1.5 km	750 m	(km^2)
31.	360 m	450 m	(hectares)

32. Fill in the blanks in the following table which gives data for
various rectangles:

	LENGTH	BREADTH	AREA	PERIMETER
(a)	5 cm		20 cm^2	
(b)		10 m		50 m
(c)	3.4 cm		8.84 cm^2	
(d)	18 mm			60 mm
(e)	1.5 m		1.125 m^2	

33. A lounge measuring 3.5 m by 3 m is to be covered with square
carpet tiles each of side 50 cm. How many tiles are required?

34. How many rectangular tiles measuring 16 cm by 8 cm are required
to tile a wall 2 m long and 2.88 m high? If they are sold only in
complete boxes containing 25 tiles, at £9.50 a box, find the cost
of this tiling.

35. A rectangular building plot is 30 m long and 8.5 m wide. Find:
(a) the perimeter of the plot
(b) its area in m^2.

36. John Price has a greenhouse which measures 9.5 m by 3.5 m, and
wishes to use it for plants each of which will require an area of
2500 cm^2. How many plants should he buy?

37. Find the length of the side of a square which has an area equal to
the area of a rectangle measuring (a) 9 m by 4 m, (b) 24 cm by
60 mm, (c) 45 cm by 20 cm.

38. Peter Evans buys 86 square paving stones, each of side 50 cm, with
a view to paving his yard which is rectangular and measures 6.5 m
by 3.5 m. What area is unpaved when he has laid all his paving
stones? How many more are required to complete the job?

39. The diagram shows a flag, all dimensions being in centimetres. Find (a) the unshaded area, (b) the shaded area.

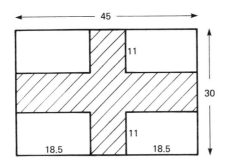

40. Greengrass fertiliser costs £14.20 for a 10 kg bag. If it is to be used at the rate of 30 g per square metre, find:
   (a) the cost of fertilising a rectangular lawn measuring 15.5 m by 12 m
   (b) the quantity of fertiliser remaining.

41. A rectangular lawn measuring 12 m by 10.5 m is to be bordered on two adjacent sides by a path 0.75 m wide. Find the area of this path.

42. An open-air rectangular swimming pool measuring 20 m by 15 m is surrounded by a path 1 m wide. If the path is made of square paving stones of side 50 cm, how many stones are required?

43. A rectangular table top is 1.5 m long and 80 cm wide. A rectangular cloth is to be made which will cover the table and have an over-hang of 10 cm. Find:
   (a) the area of the table cloth in square metres
   (b) the area of the overhang in square metres.

44. A rectangular carpet is laid in a rectangular room measuring 4.2 m by 3.6 m so that there is a uniform uncarpeted border 60 cm wide surrounding the carpet. Calculate:
   (a) the perimeter of the carpet
   (b) the area which is uncarpeted.

45. The page of a dictionary measures 24 cm by 17 cm with the text set out in two columns separated by a 5 mm margin. At the edge of the page is a border which is 1.5 cm wide except at the bottom of the page where it is only 1 cm wide. Find the total area of text if the dictionary has 1640 similar pages.

143

THE PARALLELOGRAM

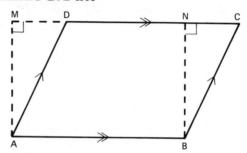

ABCD is a parallelogram with AB parallel to DC and AD parallel to BC. BN is the perpendicular from B to CD, and AM is the perpendicular from A to CD produced. Simple geometry tells us that the area of triangle AMD is equal to the area of triangle BNC. It follows that the area of the parallelogram ABCD is equal to the area of the rectangle ABNM.

Since   Area of the rectangle $= AB \times BN$

then   Area of the parallelogram ABCD $= AB \times BN$

i.e.   Area of parallelogram $=$ base $\times$ height

THE TRIANGLE

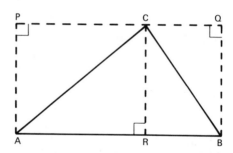

If AP and BQ are the perpendiculars from A and B in triangle ABC to the line through C parallel to AB, and R is the foot of the perpendicular from C to AB, then ABQP is a rectangle with area $AB \times BQ$. But $BQ = CR$. Therefore area of rectangle $= AB \times CR$, where CR is the perpendicular height of the triangle.

simple geometry gives:

$$\triangle CBQ = \triangle CBR \qquad \text{and} \qquad \triangle CPA = \triangle CRA$$

i.e. the area of the triangle ABC is half the area of the rectangle ABQP.

$\therefore$ Area of triangle ABC $= \frac{1}{2} AB \times CR$

More generally:

Area of a triangle $= \frac{1}{2}$ base $\times$ perpendicular height

THE TRAPEZIUM

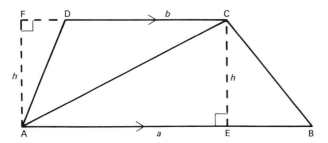

The diagonal AC divides the trapezium into two triangles.

$$\triangle ABC = \tfrac{1}{2} AB \times CE = \tfrac{1}{2} ah$$

and $$\triangle ADC = \tfrac{1}{2} DC \times AF = \tfrac{1}{2} bh$$

$\therefore$ $$\text{Area of trapezium} = \tfrac{1}{2} ah + \tfrac{1}{2} bh$$

$$= \left(\frac{a+b}{2} \right) h$$

i.e. Half the sum of the parallel sides $\times$ the perpendicular distance between them

EXERCISE 53

Questions 1 to 6 refer to the following diagram:

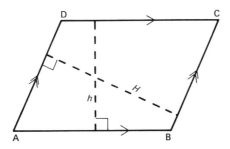

ABCD is a parallelogram with h the distance between AB and DC, and H the distance between BC and AD.

1. If $AB = 12$ cm, $AD = 8$ cm and $h = 6.5$ cm, find (a) the area of the parallelogram, (b) the value of H.

2. If $AB = 8$ cm, $h = 7$ cm and $H = 5$ cm, find (a) the area of the parallelogram, (b) the length of AD.

3. If $DC = 14$ cm, $AD = 10$ cm and $H = 10\tfrac{1}{2}$ cm, find (a) the area of the parallelogram, (b) the value of h.

4. If the area of the parallelogram is $48 \, cm^2$, and $H = 2h = 8 \, cm$, find the lengths of AB and BC.

5. If the area of the parallelogram is $72 \, cm^2$, $AB = 18 \, cm$ and $AD = 12 \, cm$, find h and H.

6. If the area of the parallelogram is $108 \, cm^2$, $h = 9 \, cm$ and $3AB = 4AD$, find (a) AB, (b) AD, (c) H.

Questions 7 to 13 refer to the following diagram:

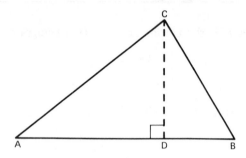

Find the area of triangle ABC if:

7. $AB = 12 \, cm$, $CD = 8 \, cm$

8. $AB = 20 \, cm$, $CD = 13 \, cm$

9. $AB = 8.4 \, cm$, $CD = 5.2 \, cm$

10. $AB = 2.25 \, cm$, $CD = 5\frac{1}{3} \, cm$.

11. Find CD if the area of the triangle is $48 \, cm^2$ and $AB = 12 \, cm$.

12. Find AB if the area of the triangle is $13.65 \, cm^2$ and $CD = 4.2 \, cm$.

13. Find CD if the area of the triangle is $14.04 \, cm^2$ and $AB = 5.2 \, cm$.

Questions 14 to 19 refer to the following diagram:

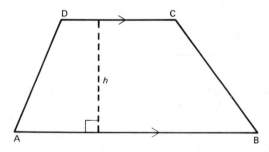

Find the area of trapezium ABCD if:

14. $AB = 12 \, cm$, $DC = 8 \, cm$ and $h = 8 \, cm$.

15. $AB = 18.7 \, cm$, $DC = 11.3 \, cm$ and $h = 5.5 \, cm$.

16. $AB = 7.7 \, cm$, $DC = 4.3 \, cm$ and $h = 3.7 \, cm$.

17. Find h if the area of the trapezium is $77\,\text{cm}^2$ and the parallel sides have lengths $14\,\text{cm}$ and $8\,\text{cm}$.

18. Find AB if the area of the trapezium is $200\,\text{cm}^2$, $DC = 24\,\text{cm}$ and $h = 10\,\text{cm}$.

19. Find the lengths of the parallel sides AB and CD, given that the area of the trapezium is $60\,\text{cm}^2$, the distance between the parallel sides is $6\,\text{cm}$ and $2AB = 3CD$.

20. Find the distance between the parallel sides of a trapezium with area $117.3\,\text{cm}^2$ if the parallel sides are respectively of length $15.4\,\text{cm}$ and $12.2\,\text{cm}$.

VOLUME

The volume of a solid is the amount of space it occupies. The volume of an irregular solid may be found by measuring the amount of water displaced from a full container when the solid is totally submerged in the water. We measure volume in cubic units, thus $1\,\text{m}^3$ is the volume occupied by a cube of side one metre. The units chosen vary according to what is being measured and what is considered most suitable. Thus the volume of a small object such as a half-penny may be measured in cubic millimetres (mm^3), the volume of a typical book in cubic centimetres (cm^3) and the volume of a room in cubic metres (m^3).

The simplest solid to give a general expression for its volume is the rectangular block or cuboid. The volume of a wooden block measuring $4\,\text{cm}$ by $3\,\text{cm}$ by $2\,\text{cm}$ would be $24\,\text{cm}^3$, because 12 cubes of side $1\,\text{cm}$ would be required to cover the area on which the block stands, together with another 12 blocks to bring the height or thickness up to $2\,\text{cm}$.

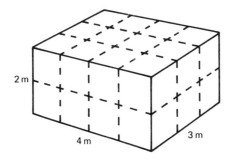

i.e. Volume of block $(V) = 4 \times 3 \times 2\,\text{cm}^3$

i.e. $V = 24\,\text{cm}^3$

It is only a short step to generalise this result so that we can say that the volume (V) of a cuboid L units long, B units wide and H units in height is given by:

$$V = L \times B \times H \text{ cubic units}$$

Care must be taken to check that all dimensions are given in the same units.

The metric units of volume in common use are related as follows:

$$1\,cm^3 = 10^3\,mm^3 = 1000\,mm^3$$
$$1\,m^3 = 100^3\,cm^3 = 1\,000\,000\,cm^3$$

The internal volume of a container, such as a milk bottle or a water tank is called its *capacity*, i.e. the capacity of a container is the volume inside it. We usually measure capacity in litres, where:

$$1\,litre = 1000\,cm^3$$
$$\therefore \quad 1000\,litres = 1\,m^3$$

When the capacity is small, the millilitre (ml) is used; e.g. a 5 ml spoon is often used for measuring medicines.

$$1000\,ml = 1\,litre$$
$$\therefore \quad 1\,ml = 1\,cm^3$$

EXAMPLE 5 Find the volume of a concrete block measuring 30 cm by 20 cm by 10 cm, giving your answer in (a) cubic centimetres, (b) cubic metres.

(a) Volume $= L \times B \times H$

$$= 30 \times 20 \times 10 \text{ cm}^3$$

$$= 6000 \text{ cm}^3$$

(b) If we work in metres

Volume $= 0.3 \times 0.2 \times 0.1 \text{ m}^3$

$$= 0.006 \text{ m}^3$$

This result may also be obtained by dividing the result for (a) by 100^3.

EXAMPLE 6 An open mould for making concrete blocks is shown in the diagram on page 149. The external dimensions of the mould, which is everywhere 3 cm thick, are 42 cm by 24 cm by 12 cm. Calculate (a) the volume of a concrete block, (b) the volume of material used in making the mould.

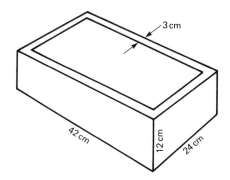

(a) The internal dimensions of the mould will be:

Length: $(42-6)\,cm = 36\,cm$

Breadth: $(24-6)\,cm = 18\,cm$

Depth: $(12-3)\,cm = 9\,cm$

∴   Volume of a concrete block

$= 36 \times 18 \times 9\,cm^3$

$= 5832\,cm^3$

(b) Volume of the external cuboid

$= 42 \times 24 \times 12\,cm^3$

$= 12\,096\,cm^3$

∴ Amount of material used in making the block

$= (12\,096 - 5832)\,cm^3$

$= 6264\,cm^3$

EXAMPLE 7   The diagram on page 150 shows the cross-section of a girder 4.5 m long, all dimensions on the diagram being in centimetres. Find:

(a) the area of cross-section in square centimetres,

(b) the volume of the girder in (i) cubic centimetres, (ii) cubic metres,

(c) the mass of the girder if $1\,cm^3$ of the metal used has a mass of 7.8 g. Give your answer correct to the nearest kilogram.

149

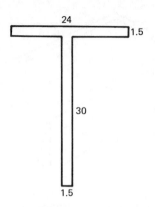

(a) Consider the area of cross-section as two rectangles:

Area of cross-section $= (24 \times 1.5 + 30 \times 1.5)\,\text{cm}^2$

$$= (36 + 45)\,\text{cm}^2$$

$$= 81\,\text{cm}^2$$

(b) Volume of girder $=$ area of cross-section $\times$ length

$$= 81 \times 450\,\text{cm}^3$$

$$= 36\,450\,\text{cm}^3$$

Since $100^3\,\text{cm}^3 = 1\,\text{m}^3$:

$$\text{Volume of girder} = \frac{36\,450}{100 \times 100 \times 100}\,\text{m}^3$$

$$= 0.036\,45\,\text{m}^3$$

(c) Mass of girder $=$ volume in $\text{cm}^3 \times 7.8\,\text{g}$

$$= 36\,450 \times 7.8\,\text{g}$$

$$= 284\,310\,\text{g}$$

$$= 284.31\,\text{kg}$$

$$= 284\,\text{kg correct to the nearest kilogram}$$

EXERCISE 54

1. Find the volume of a cube with side:
   (a) 8 cm   (b) 4 mm   (c) 5 m   (d) 2.3 cm
   (e) 0.6 km   (f) $\frac{3}{5}$ m.

Use the data below to find the volumes of the following rectangular solids:

	LENGTH	BREADTH	HEIGHT
2.	5 cm	4 cm	3 cm
3.	12 m	8 m	7 m
4.	10 cm	4.3 cm	3.5 cm
5.	5 km	2.4 km	1.5 km
6.	1.5 km	0.75 km	0.5 km

7. Find the side of a cube if its volume is:

(a) 216 mm^3 (b) 0.125 m^3 (c) $\dfrac{8}{27} \text{ cm}^3$.

Find the missing quantity for rectangular solids with the data below:

	LENGTH	BREADTH	HEIGHT	VOLUME
8.	12 cm	8 cm		576 cm^3
9.		9 mm	8 mm	792 mm^3
10.	1 m	23 cm		$18\,400 \text{ cm}^3$
11.		1.4 mm	0.5 mm	3.5 mm^3
12.	2.5 cm		0.6 cm	1.2 cm^3
13.	1.5 m		0.5 m	$\frac{9}{16} \text{ m}^3$

14. Find the volume of a rectangular room measuring 10 m by 6 m by 3 m. If 4.5 m^3 of airspace is required for each person, what is the maximum number of people who may use the room at the same time?

15. A classroom measuring 8 m by 6 m is to be used for a form of 32 pupils. If 5 m^3 of airspace is allowed for each pupil, how high should the ceiling be?

16. How many litres of water can be stored in a rectangular tank measuring 1.2 m by 80 cm by 50 cm?

17. Find the cost of a rectangular piece of timber measuring 20 cm by 8 cm which is 4 m long, if the price of the timber is £55 per cubic metre.

18. Find the mass of a metal bar measuring 3 m by 8 cm by 4 cm if 1 cm^3 of the metal has a mass of 9.4 g. Give your answer (a) in grams, (b) in kilograms.

19. How many rectangular packets of tea measuring 12 cm by 4 cm by 4 cm may be packed in a cardboard box measuring 48 cm by 24 cm by 16 cm?

20. If the total surface area of a cube is 150 cm^2, find its volume.

21. A rectangular tank measuring 1.3 m by 80 cm by 80 cm is full of water. If 400 litres of water is drawn off into another tank 1 m long and 80 cm wide, find the depth of water in each tank.

22. The page of a book measuring 20 cm by 12 cm is 0.05 mm thick. Find the volume of a page in cubic centimetres. Hence find the volume of the book if it has 220 pages.

23. A rectangular block of lead measuring 15 cm by 9 cm by 6 cm is melted down and recast, without any loss of volume, into cubes of side 3 cm. How many cubes are produced?

24. The external dimensions of a closed rectangular box are 12 cm by 10 cm by 9 cm. If the wood is everywhere 5 mm thick, find:
    (a) the volume of the interior of the box
    (b) the volume of wood used in its construction.

25. An open rectangular tank has internal dimensions 1.2 m by 75 cm by 60 cm. If the metal is everywhere 2.5 mm thick, find:
    (a) the number of litres of water which the tank will hold
    (b) the volume of metal used in its construction.

26. The diagram shows the cross-section of a girder which is 4 m long. All measurements are in centimetres. Find the volume of the girder in (a) cubic centimetres, (b) cubic metres.

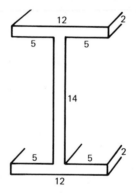

27. The diagram shows the cross-section of a hollow metal girder 6 m long which is everywhere 7.5 mm thick. Find the volume of metal in the girder in (a) cubic centimetres, (b) cubic metres.

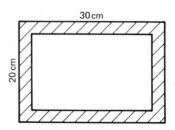

28. The diagram shows the cross-section of a girder 5.5 m long. All dimensions are in centimetres. Calculate:
   (a) the volume of the girder in cubic centimetres
   (b) the mass of the girder in kilograms if 1 cm³ of the girder has a mass of 8 g.

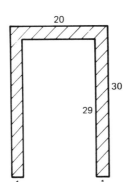

29. A 10 litre can of washing-up liquid has a rectangular cross-section measuring 25 cm by 10 cm. How tall is the can?

30. How many concrete blocks measuring 50 cm by 25 cm by 12.5 cm may be cast from 1 m³ of concrete?

31. A 3 m length of timber has a uniform cross-section in the form of a rhombus of area 4.5 cm². Find its volume in cubic centimetres.

32. The area of cross-section of a 16 cm bar of chocolate is in the form of an equilateral triangle of area 4.5 cm². Find the volume of chocolate in the bar.

33. The diagram shows the cross-section of a horse trough which is everywhere a trapezium, the parallel sides of which have lengths 30 cm and 24 cm. If the trough is 30 cm deep and 2.5 m long, find the volume of water it will hold when full, giving your answer in cubic metres correct to three significant figures.

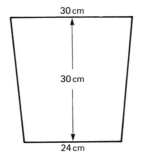

34. The diagram shows the cross-section of a water channel which is 10 m long. How many litres of water will it hold when full?

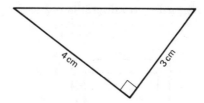

35. The diagram shows the cross-section of a uniform metal bar which is 3.5 m long. Find:
   (a) its cross-sectional area in square centimetres
   (b) its volume in cubic centimetres correct to three significant figures
   (c) its mass, correct to the nearest kilogram, if $1\,cm^3$ of the metal has a mass of 8.2 g.

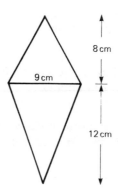

REVISION PAPERS
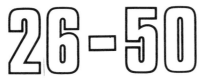

PAPER 26

1. How many bars of chocolate costing 45 p each may be bought for £10 and how much change is there?

2. A car uses 22 litres of petrol for a journey of 594 km. How many litres are required for a journey of 351 km?

3. Divide £8.55 between Anne and David in the ratio 7 : 12.

4. An article is bought for £1.80. Find its selling price if it is sold (a) at a gain of 10%, (b) at a loss of 10%.

5. George Waters earns £800 per month. He receives a rise of 12%, but income tax is deducted from his gross pay at 18%, together with a further deduction of 14% of gross pay for national insurance and pension contribution. Calculate his net monthly pay after he has received his rise.

PAPER 27

1. (a) Express $\dfrac{13}{20}$ and $\dfrac{7}{4}$ as percentages.

   (b) Express 45% and 320% as fractions in their lowest terms.

2. A factory worker is paid £2.76 per hour for a $37\frac{1}{2}$ hour week. If deductions for national insurance and income tax amount to £18.56, calculate her 'take-home' pay.

3. Simplify $\left(\dfrac{3}{7} \times \dfrac{5}{9}\right) \div \left(6\dfrac{1}{4} - 5\dfrac{4}{15}\right)$.

155

4. A lounge measures 4.5 m by 3.5 m and has a ceiling 2.6 m high. Calculate the number of rolls of wallpaper, each 10 m long and 52 cm wide, required to paper the walls of this room. Allow 7.5 m^2 for doors and windows and add 10% to allow for matching the pattern.

5. A school hall measures 21 m by 12 m. How many square tiles of side 25 cm are required to cover the floor? If they can only be bought in complete boxes containing 25 tiles, how many boxes are required?

PAPER 28

1. Divide £35.84 between George, Harold and Idris in the ratio 5 : 4 : 7.

2. Find (a) $10 - 7.364 + 0.243 + 1.64$, (b) $0.0492 \div 0.123$.

3. What number when increased by 15% becomes 207?

4. An auctioneer arranges the transfer of a piece of furniture from Mr Martin's house to the saleroom at a cost of £26.50. At auction the piece is sold for £755. If the auctioneer's commission is 12% of the selling price, how much could Mr Martin expect to receive from the sale?

5. If 46 rolls of cloth each 100 m in length may be bought for £8464, how many 50 m rolls of a similar quality cloth may be bought for £6808?

PAPER 29

1. Simplify $\dfrac{1\frac{3}{8} + 1\frac{5}{7}}{2\frac{6}{7} + 1\frac{3}{4}}$.

2. The representative fraction of a map is 1 : 50 000. Calculate the distance in kilometres between two points which are 5.4 cm apart on the map.

3. Simplify (a) $\dfrac{(-12) \times 3 \times (-8)}{4 \times (-16)}$, (b) $\dfrac{(-4)^2 \times (-3) \times (-6)}{-36}$.

4. A sum of money was divided between four girls. The first received $\frac{1}{3}$ of it, the second $\frac{2}{5}$, the third $\frac{1}{6}$ and the fourth £1.86. Calculate (a) the sum of money, (b) the amount received by the first girl.

5. A house cost £23 000 to build on a site costing £5600. What weekly rent must the owner charge to have a return of 10% on his investment after paying $\frac{1}{3}$ of the rent for rates and repairs?

PAPER 30

1. Find $\frac{4}{7}$ of £164.29.

2. A drum contains 36 litres of oil. If $8\frac{1}{3}\%$ leaks out, how much remains?

3. Evaluate $51.6 \div 2.45$ giving your answer correct to (a) the nearest whole number, (b) three significant figures, (c) two decimal places.

4. A shopkeeper allows a discount of $2\frac{1}{2}\%$ for cash. Find the cash price of an article marked £244.

5. During a school charity week £2475 was collected. If the proceeds were divided between five charities A, B, C, D and E in the ratio $3:4:5:6:7$. how much more would charity E receive than charity A?

PAPER 31

1. What percentage is (a) 294 of 840, (b) 150 g of 2 kg, (c) 655 m of 2 km?

2. Simplify $\left(2\dfrac{1}{8} - \dfrac{1}{5}\right) \div \left(1\dfrac{1}{10} + 2\dfrac{4}{5}\right)$.

3. A grocer bought 850 cans of tomatoes at 21 p each and sold them at $23\frac{1}{2}$ p. Find the profit.

4. An oil-fired boiler consumes 15 litres of oil a day. If the tank which supplies the boiler with oil contains sufficient oil to last 21 days, how many days would the oil supply last if cold weather caused the consumption to rise to 18 litres per day?

5. A photograph measuring 24 cm by 18 cm is mounted on a rectangular piece of card so that it has a 3.5 cm border all round. Calculate the area of card visible.

PAPER 32

1. (a) Multiply £3.49 by 27. (b) Divide £50.35 by 19.

2. Ken is 21 years old, Len 23 and Morgan 18. Divide £21 700 between them in the ratio of their ages.

3. If the coach fare for an 86 mile journey is £6.45, what is the coach fare for a journey of 125 miles? How far could you travel for £5?

4. A square has a side of length 8 cm. Find the percentage change in area if:
    (a) the length of each side is increased by 25%
    (b) the length of each side is decreased by 25%.

5. A dealer buys a number of tins of paint for £206.58. By selling them at £4.20 each he makes a profit of £70.62. How many tins did he buy?

PAPER 33

1. Simplify $\left(2\dfrac{1}{3} + 3\dfrac{1}{4}\right) \div \left(1\dfrac{1}{4} + 5\dfrac{5}{12}\right)$.

2. In a sale five articles may be bought for the price of four. What percentage reduction is this?

3. A man saved £750 in a year. The next year his savings were 10% greater than the first year, and the following year his savings were 5% greater than his savings the second year. How much did he save during the three years?

4. In a certain factory 116 workers are required to produce 6612 articles in a week. How many workers would be required to produce 7638 articles in a week, assuming that they all work at the same rate?

5. The diagram shows an L-shaped lounge. How many floor tiles, each measuring 25 cm by 25 cm, are required to tile the floor? If they are sold only in complete boxes, 12 to a box, how many boxes must be purchased and how many tiles are left over?

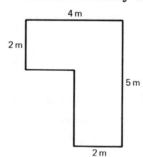

PAPER 34

1. Find the HCF of 4284 and 5355. What is the smallest number by which 4284 must be multiplied to make it a perfect square?

2. Write down the next two numbers in the sequence 3, 22, 59, 120, ...

3. Working in the binary system only, find (a) $1101101 + 11110$. (b) $10000 - 1010$, (c) 1011×111, (d) $1001000 \div 1100$.

4. If £10.54 is divided into equal numbers of 2 p, 10 p and 50 p coins, how many of each are there?

5. A lawn measuring 42 m by 25 m requires fertiliser at the rate of 56 g per square metre. How many 10 kg bags of fertiliser must be purchased?

PAPER 35

1. Simplify (a) $(-16) \times (-2) \times (-3)^2$, (b) $[60 \div (-12)] \times (-5)$.

2. What must be added to $\left(\dfrac{2}{3} - \dfrac{4}{7}\right) \div \dfrac{1}{2}$ to make it equal to $\dfrac{1}{2} \div \left(\dfrac{2}{3} - \dfrac{4}{7}\right)$?

3. Divide 23.474 by 0.97 and multiply your result by 17.5.

4. If it takes 24 men 18 days to paint a bridge, how long would it take 9 men to paint the same bridge, assuming that they all work at the same rate?

5. A retailer bought 45 garden seats for £5058. How much should each be sold for to make a profit of 35%?

PAPER 36

1. Simplify $2\dfrac{3}{4}$ of $5\dfrac{1}{8} \div \left(2\dfrac{3}{4} + 5\dfrac{1}{2}\right)$.

2. Find the percentage increase if 155 is increased to 186.

3. How many glasses, each of which will hold 50 ml, may be filled to $\frac{2}{3}$ full from a 1 litre bottle?

4. If a train journey of 216 km costs £10.80, find the fare for a journey of 376 km. How far could I expect to travel for £10?

5. Find the cost of:

        12 kg of potatoes at 36 p per kg
        34 plants at 17 p each
        3 lengths of fencing at £12.49 per length
        8 bags of fertiliser at £14.28 each.

PAPER 37

1. (a) Express 440 g as a decimal of 2.75 kg.

    (b) Express $\frac{7}{45}$ as a decimal correct to two decimal places.

2. A sum of money is divided between three girls. Wendy receives $\frac{1}{9}$ of it, Tracey three times as much as Wendy, and Susan receives £4.95. How much does Tracey receive?

3. A bucket of water when full has a mass of 16.5 kg. If its mass when half-full is 9 kg, calculate the mass of the bucket.

4. An oak beam is 12 m long, 10 cm wide and 15 cm deep. If 1 m³ of oak has a mass of 800 kg, calculate the mass of the beam.

5. Seats in a cinema were sold at £3, £2.50 and £2. If the numbers of people who bought seats at these prices were in the ratio 3 : 4 : 5, find the size of the audience if the total receipts amounted to £1914. How many bought the cheapest seats?

PAPER 38

1. Simplify (a) $9 \times (-2)^2 \div (-8)$, (b) $(-24) \div [(-3) \times 4]$.

2. (a) Express (i) 743 as a binary number, (ii) 1 1 0 0 1 1 1 as a denary number.

    (b) Find (i) $23_5 + 24_5$, (ii) $232_5 - 34_5$.

3. A carpet measuring 4 m by 3.5 m costs £210. How much will a similar carpet cost which measures 4.5 m by 5 m?

4. A company agrees to take on 37 new workers if the existing work-force agree to a reduction in the working week from 42 to 40 hours. By doing this the company saves £428 if the hourly rate is £2. How many were employed at the factory before the extra staff were taken on?

5. A shipping company advertise a 15 day 4286 mile cruise at £1500. Calculate the cost per mile correct to the nearest penny. Is this cheaper or dearer per mile than the local bus service where a particular $1\frac{4}{5}$ mile journey costs 70 p?

PAPER 39

1. Find $1\frac{5}{7}$ of $\frac{1}{2} \div 3\frac{3}{7}$.

2. What is the cost of 96 boxes of soap at £1.46 each?

3. Of what sum of money is £4.93 equal to $14\frac{1}{2}\%$?

4. A comprehensive school is on two sites. In the lower school, which is on one site, there are 240 boys, and in the middle and upper schools, which are on a separate site, there are 477 boys. If boys form 48% of lower school but 53% of middle and upper school, how many girls are there in the whole school? What percentage of the whole school are girls?

5. An open rectangular box with external dimensions 10 cm by 8 cm by 6 cm is made from wood 5 mm thick. Calculate (a) its capacity, (b) the volume of wood used to make it.

PAPER 40

1. Simplify (a) 0.043×3.72, (b) $2.394 \div 0.456$.

2. (a) Change 24_5, 42_6 and 32_4 into denary numbers.
   (b) Calculate (i) 10101×1101, (ii) $101010 \div 110$.

3. A hot water tank is $\frac{5}{8}$ full. If 36.5 litres is drawn off for a bath, it is $\frac{19}{45}$ full. How many litres does the tank hold when full?

4. David Peters left $\frac{2}{5}$ of his assets to his wife, $\frac{1}{3}$ to his son, with the remainder to be divided equally between eight charities. If each charity received £2564, how much did his wife get?

5. For a concert 500 seats are on sale at £12, 260 at £9 and 488 at £7.50. If the most expensive seats are $\frac{3}{4}$ taken, the £9 seats $\frac{12}{13}$ taken and the cheapest seats $\frac{7}{8}$ taken, find the total takings for the concert. How much more would they have taken had all the seats been sold?

PAPER 41

1. Simplify $\left(1\frac{3}{5} + 2\frac{2}{3}\right) \div \left(6\frac{19}{24} - 1\frac{1}{4}\right)$.

2. How long would a boy take to walk 2.5 km to school if he takes seventy 85 cm paces each minute? Give your answer correct to the nearest minute.

3. When $8\frac{1}{2}\%$ of the pupils in a school are absent, 1098 pupils are present. How many pupils are there in the school?

4. Find the cost of 23 m² of carpeting at £11.86 per square metre.

5. A greenhouse stands on an area measuring 12 m by 6 m. It is to be used for growing tomato plants, each plant requiring $\frac{2}{3}$ m^2. How many plants will the greenhouse take?

PAPER 42

1. Divide the sum of $2\frac{1}{2}$ and $3\frac{2}{5}$ by the difference between $5\frac{2}{3}$ and $4\frac{1}{6}$.

2. What is the least length of planking 15 cm wide which will be required to cover a floor 5 m long and 3 m wide?

3. Express:
   (a) 450 cm^3 as a percentage of 2.5 litres
   (b) $\dfrac{2730}{4368}$ as a fraction in its lowest terms.

4. Twelve sets of the same stamps cost £13.20. There are four stamps in each set, the values of three of them being $\frac{2}{3}$, $\frac{5}{9}$ and $\frac{5}{6}$ of the value of the most expensive stamp. Find the value of each stamp in one set.

5. A wine merchant bought a 50 litre cask of sherry for £127.70. Some leaked out, but he sold what remained at £3.56 per litre thereby making a profit of £41.40. How many litres leaked out?

PAPER 43

1. Simplify $\dfrac{12\frac{1}{6} + 5\frac{1}{4}}{8\frac{3}{4} - 3\frac{1}{2}}$.

2. Of what mass in kilograms is 234 g equal to $9\frac{3}{4}$%?

3. Find the cost of wallpaper per square metre if a roll 10 m long and 52 cm wide costs £7.54.

4. Find the total area, in square metres, of sheet metal used to make an open rectangular water tank 1.5 m long, 1.1 m wide and 90 cm high. What volume of water, in cubic metres, does this hold? Find the mass of this water in kilograms if 1 m^3 of water has a mass of 1 t.

5. To send a message costs 5 p a word plus an initial charge of 30 p. How much will it cost to send a message with 12 words? How many words are there in a message costing £1.10?

PAPER 44

1. My father was born in December 1952. How old was he in June 1983?

2. Divide the product of $2\frac{2}{3}$ and $1\frac{7}{8}$ by the difference between $5\frac{3}{7}$ and $3\frac{4}{5}$.

3. A passenger liner steaming at 22 knots takes 14 days to travel between two ports. By how much must it increase its speed to cut 3 days off the voyage?

4. Find the cost of 4.75 t of coal at £136 per tonne.

5. A given mass of sheet copper is sufficient to cover an area measuring 5 m by 4 m when it is 5 mm thick. What area could be covered with the same mass of copper using a sheet 3 mm thick?

PAPER 45

1. Arrange in descending order: $\dfrac{9}{16}, \dfrac{5}{8}, \dfrac{11}{20}, \dfrac{16}{30}$.

2. When the price of petrol was £1.86 per gallon a motorist's monthly petrol bill was £52.08. What was the increase in his monthly bill when petrol rose to £2.05 per gallon?

3. A guitar is marked at a price which gives the seller a profit of 45%, but a discount of 10% is given for cash. Find the net percentage profit. Find the cost price of such a guitar which, with discount, sells at £143.55.

4. George Foster is paid £2.54 per hour for a $38\frac{1}{2}$ hour week. Find his gross wage.

5. The external dimensions of a closed wooden rectangular box are 18 cm × 12 cm × 8 cm. If the wood is everywhere 4 mm thick, find:
   (a) the volume of space within the box
   (b) the volume of wood used to make the box.

PAPER 46

1. Simplify $\dfrac{2\frac{1}{4} - \frac{2}{3} \times 1\frac{5}{6}}{\frac{1}{5} \times 3\frac{1}{3} + \frac{13}{36}}$.

2. The smaller of two numbers is 14.6 and their sum is 38.4. Find their product.

3. Five men on a trek across the desert have sufficient water for 15 days. How long would the water last three of them?

4. A car does 38 miles per gallon on a 306 mile trip. How many complete gallons must be purchased for the journey? Find the cost of this petrol at £2.14 per gallon.

5. By selling a chair for £110.40 a shopkeeper loses 8%. What percentage must he gain on a similar chair to give him a gain of 10% on the two?

PAPER 47

1. If eight articles cost £27.68, find the cost of five.

2. Divide £784 between four brothers in the ratio $2:3:4:5$.

3. In a sale a shopkeeper reduced the price of everything in the shop by 15p in the £. What was the original price of an article which has a sale price of £53.04?

4. Find the cost per square metre, correct to the nearest pound, of an Indian carpet measuring 4 m 20 cm by 3 m 45 cm, which sells for £1565.

5. The total mass of three parcels is 8.1 kg. If one of these parcels is 1.2 kg heavier than each of the other two, find the masses of the three parcels.

PAPER 48

1. Simplify $\dfrac{1\frac{1}{4} + 2\frac{11}{12}}{4\frac{1}{3} - 3\frac{1}{6}} \times 2\frac{1}{4} \div 3\frac{1}{8}$.

2. Convert the following into denary numbers:
   (a) 1210_3 (b) 1231_4 (c) 2054_8.

3. The population of Oakdale is 2970. Last year the population increased by 8%, and the previous year it increased by 10%. What was its population 2 years ago?

4. A boy is 16 years old now while his father is 44. Calculate the ratio of their ages (a) now, (b) 4 years ago, (c) in 12 years' time.

5. A second hand car dealer buys two similar cars for £1500 each. He sells the first at a loss of 6%. What percentage profit must he make on the second car in order to make a profit of 8% on the two?

PAPER 49

1. If $\dfrac{1}{3} + \dfrac{1}{4} + \dfrac{1}{5}$ of a sum of money is £22.09, find $\dfrac{23}{47}$ of it.

2. What length of paper 52 cm wide is required to paper the walls of a room 4 m 14 cm long, 3 m, 14 cm wide and 2 m 80 cm in height? If each roll is 10 m long, how many rolls must be bought? What will they cost at £4.56 per roll?

3. If a machine can fill and seal 225 tins with beans in 3 minutes, how many tins could be filled and sealed in half an hour?

4. In a year Peter Eschle spends 63% of his income on household expenses, 18% on his car, 12% on incidental expenses, and saves the remainder. If he saves £987, calculate his annual income.

5. A closed rectangular box measures 12 cm by 8 cm by 6 cm and is made from wood 5 mm thick. Find the volume of wood used in cubic centimetres. If a second box which is twice as long, twice as wide and twice as high is to be made from wood of the same thickness, calculate the volume of wood required for this second box, in cubic centimetres.

PAPER 50

1. Simplify $\dfrac{2 - \dfrac{1}{1 + \frac{1}{3}}}{4 + \dfrac{1}{2 + \frac{3}{4}}}$

2. A woman of mass 220 kg goes on a diet which claims that over 6 months she should lose 10% of her mass at the beginning of that time. What can she expect her mass to be 2 years later? Give your answer correct to the nearest kilogram.

3. If 1 m^3 of water has a mass of 1 t and mercury is 13.6 times as heavy as water, find the volume of 0.25 t of mercury in cubic metres, correct to three significant figures.

4. A photograph measuring 12 cm by 8 cm, which is surrounded by a border 3 cm wide, is increased so that its length becomes 27 cm. What does its width become if it is increased in the same ratio? Find the ratio in which the area is increased. If the *width* of the border is unchanged, find its new area?

5. The external dimensions of a lidless wooden box are: length 18.5 cm, breadth 12.8 cm, depth 9.6 cm. If the timber used to make the sides is 8 mm thick but the base is only 6 mm thick, calculate:
    (a) the internal volume of the box in cubic centimetres
    (b) the volume of wood used in its manufacture.

PART
B

13

SIMPLE GRAPHS

The object of graphs is to represent data clearly so that it may be understood easily and quickly. To plot a graph we require two lines at right angles, called *axes*. One axis is usually drawn across the page, at the foot of the area where the graph will be drawn, while the other is drawn on the left hand side of the page. The number of units represented by a unit length along an axis is called the *scale* of that axis, thus 1 cm could represent 1 hour on a horizontal time-axis while representing 20 km on a vertical distance-axis.

EXAMPLE 1   Draw a rough graph to show the takings in a small shop for a week. Attempt to draw some conclusions from your graph.

A typical graph is shown below:

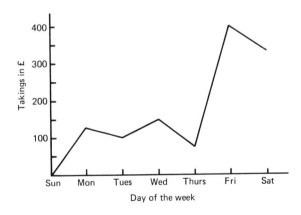

This shows that:

(a) the shop is closed on Sunday and probably opens only for half the day on Thursday;

167

(b) Friday is the best day, with Saturday a close second;

(c) Tuesday is the quietest whole day.

EXAMPLE 2

The graph shows two brothers' distance from home on a Saturday when they went for a walk.

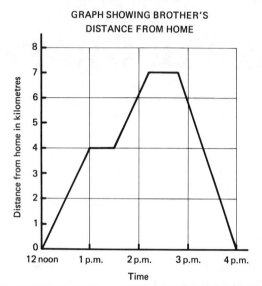

GRAPH SHOWING BROTHER'S
DISTANCE FROM HOME

It is fairly easy to conclude from the graph that:

(a) They walked 4 km in the first hour and then rested for half an hour.

(b) They continued their journey until they were 7 km from home.

(c) They rested for another half an hour before returning home without a stop, arriving home at 4 p.m.

(d) The total distance they walked was 14 km.

(e) The total time they were away from home was 4 hours.

EXAMPLE 3

Given that 80 French francs (f.) are equivalent to 18 US dollars ($), draw a conversion graph which will convert sums up to $50.

Use your graph to express (a) $45 in francs, (b) $27 in francs, (c) 150 f. in dollars, (d) 76 f. in dollars.

Choose a suitable scale for each axis.

Plot two points, e.g. 80 f. ≡ $18 and 160 f. ≡ $36, apart from the origin.

Draw a straight line to pass through the three points.

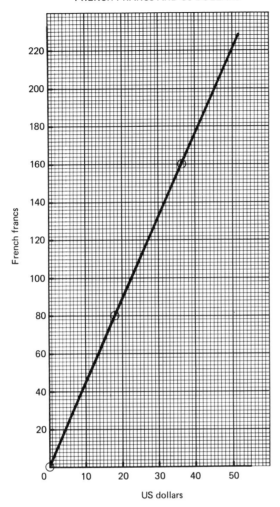

CONVERSION GRAPH:
FRENCH FRANCS AND US DOLLARS

French francs

US dollars

From the graph:
(a) $45 = 200 f.
(b) $27 = 120 f.
(c) 150 f. = $34
(d) 76 f. = $17

EXERCISE 55

Draw rough graphs to illustrate questions 1 to 7.

1. School attendance for a calendar year.

2. The number of central heating systems installed in houses in the
   United Kingdom over the past 20 years.

3. The amount of money a boy has in his pocket each day of the
    week assuming that he receives his pocket money on a Thursday.

4. A journey of 120 miles in a car driven at a constant 40 mph except
    for two stops, each of 20 minutes at roadside cafes.

5. The time you spend eating during the 24 hours of an average day.

6. Your English marks for the last five examinations.

7. The number of hours of daylight each day over a period of 1 year.

8. Given that 50 miles ≡ 80 km, draw a conversion graph that will
    convert distances up to 100 miles into kilometres. Use your graph
    to convert:
    (a) 64 miles into kilometres
    (b) 135 km into miles
    (c) 46 km/h into miles per hour
    (d) 62 mph into kilometres per hour.

9. Given that 10 kg ≡ 22 lb, draw a conversion graph that will convert
    masses up to 130 lb into kilograms. Use your graph to convert:
    (a) 100 lb into kilograms
    (b) 32 kg into pounds.

10. Draw a graph for converting temperatures measured in degrees
    Fahrenheit (°F) into degrees centigrade (°C) given that 0°C is
    equivalent to 32°F and 100°C is equivalent to 212°F.

    Use your graph to find:
    (a) 60°F and 160°F in degrees centigrade
    (b) 50°C and 80°C in degrees Fahrenheit.

11. Draw a graph for converting temperatures in degrees Fahrenheit
    (°F) into degrees Réaumur (°R) given that 32°F is equivalent to
    0°R and 212°F is equivalent to 80°R. Use your graph to express:
    (a) 45°R in degrees Fahrenheit,
    (b) 80°F in degrees Réaumur.

12. Draw a graph for converting pounds into dollars, given that
    £100 = $178, for values up to £150. Use your graph to find:
    (a) the number of dollars in £135
    (b) the number of pounds in $220.

13. Draw a graph for converting petrol measured in litres into gallons,
    given that 10 gallons = 45.5 litres. Your graph should be able to
    convert volumes up to 20 gallons.

    Use your graph to find:
    (a) 44 litres in gallons
    (b) $5\frac{1}{2}$ gallons in litres.

14. The graph below shows the 'A' level results for Stanley Comprehensive School since it was formed in 1976. Use the graph to
answer the following questions:
(a) What is the general trend in:
    (i) the total number of 'A' level passes,
    (ii) the total number of candidates,
    (iii) the total number obtaining three 'A' level passes?
(b) Excluding the first year, which year would the results be
considered (i) best, (ii) poorest?
(c) How many 'A' level passes were secured by candidates who
had fewer than three 'A' level passes in (i) 1978, (ii) 1982?

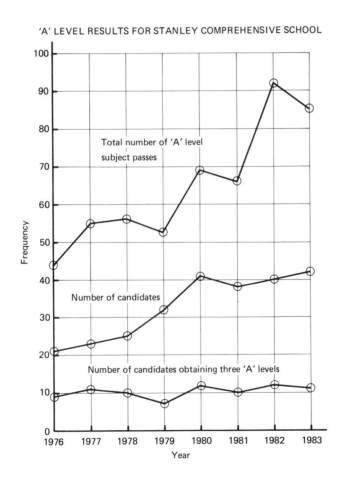

'A' LEVEL RESULTS FOR STANLEY COMPREHENSIVE SCHOOL

15. The following graph shows the relationship between the area of a
circle and its radius. Use this graph to find:
(a) the area of a circle with radius (i) 4.5 cm, (ii) 7.3 cm
(b) the radius of a circle with area (i) $100\,cm^2$, (ii) $180\,cm^2$.

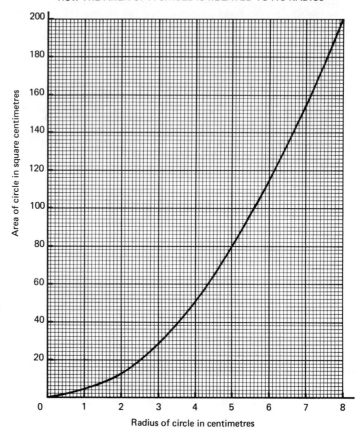

Radius of circle in centimetres

TRAVEL GRAPHS

EXAMPLE 4 The travel graph on p. 173 shows the journeys of two motorists. The first leaves town A at 12 noon and travels to town B, while the second travels from town B to town A. Use the graph to determine:

(a) the first motorist's time of arrival at B,

(b) the speed of the first motorist for (i) the first part of the journey, (ii) the whole journey,

(c) the second motorist's average speed,

(d) when and where the two pass.

(a) Since 10 small squares represent 1 hour on the time-axis, each small square represents $\frac{60}{10} = 6$ minutes. Therefore the first motorist arrives at B at 3.54 p.m. (i.e. the travel graph passes through B 1 small squares to the left of the line representing 4 p.m.).

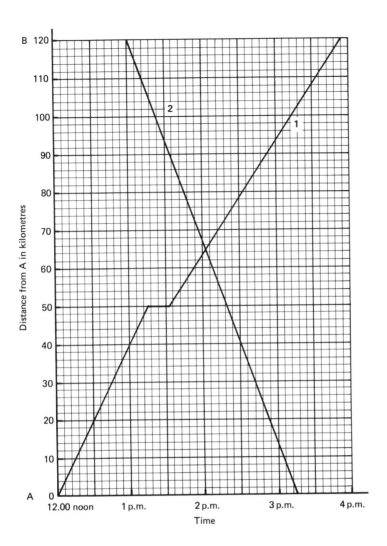

(b) (i) Average speed for the first 50 km $= \dfrac{50 \text{ km}}{1\frac{1}{4}\text{h}}$

$= \dfrac{50}{5} \times 4 \text{ km/h} = 40 \text{ km/h}$

(ii) Average speed for the whole journey

$= \dfrac{\text{total distance}}{\text{total time}}$

$= \dfrac{120 \text{ km}}{3 \text{ h } 54 \text{ min}}$

$= \dfrac{120}{3.9} \text{ km/h}$

$= 30.77 \text{ km/h}$

(c) Second motorist's average speed

$$= \frac{120}{2\frac{1}{4}} \text{ km/h} = \frac{120}{9} \times 4 \text{ km/h}$$

$$= 53\frac{1}{3} \text{ km/h}$$

(d) The two motorists pass at the point where the two travel graphs intersect, i.e. 65 km from A at 2.03 p.m.

EXERCISE 56

1. A slow train leaves Paddington at 0200 and travels west at a steady 52.5 km/h. A faster train leaves Paddington at 0336 and travels at a steady 110 km/h along a parallel line. Draw travel graphs for the two journeys taking $4 \text{ cm} \equiv 1 \text{ h}$ on the time-axis and $1 \text{ cm} \equiv 10 \text{ km}$ on the distance-axis. From your graph find:
    (a) how far the slow train is from Paddington when the other train starts its journey
    (b) when and where the two trains pass
    (c) the distance between the trains at 0530.

2. A motorist leaves Caxton at 1016 to travel north to Dewchurch which is 160 km away. He is able to travel at a steady 60 km/h and completes the journey without a stop. A second motorist leaves Eastwood, which is 40 km north of Dewchurch, at 1040 to drive to Caxton. He travels to Dewchurch at a steady 60 km/h where he stops for 10 minutes before continuing his journey to Caxton, arriving there at 1240.

    Taking $6 \text{ cm} \equiv 1 \text{ h}$ and $1 \text{ cm} \equiv 10 \text{ km}$, draw travel graphs for these two journeys.

    Use your graphs to find:
    (a) the time the first motorist arrives at Dewchurch
    (b) the average speed of the second motorist between Dewchurch and Caxton
    (c) where and when the two pass
    (d) the second motorist's average speed for the whole journey.

3. A, B and C are three stations on a railway line such that A is 45 miles south of B, and C is 60 miles north of it. A train leaves A at 8 a.m. and travels to B at a constant speed of 60 mph where it stops until 9 a.m. It then continues its journey to C arriving there

at 10.12 a.m. A second train leaves C at 8.52 a.m. and travels non-stop to A at a steady speed of 55 mph.

Draw graphs to represent these journeys using 2 cm to represent 10 miles on the distance-axis, and 6 cm to represent 1 h on the time-axis. Use your graphs to determine:
(a) the time of arrival of the first train at B
(b) the average speed of the first train between B and C
(c) when and where the two trains pass
(d) the time of arrival of the second train at A.

4. Peter and David are two school friends who live in Elmwood and Oakwood, two towns which are 18 km apart. On the first Monday of the summer holiday Peter leaves Elmwood at 9.12 a.m. and walks at a steady pace of 7 km/h directly to Oakwood.

David's father leaves Oakwood at 9.40 a.m. and cycles towards Elmwood. He travels for the first 20 minutes at a steady speed of 21 km/h, but then has a small problem with his bicycle which causes him to reduce his speed, finally arriving in Elmwood at 10.44 a.m.

Taking 6 cm to represent 1 h on the time-axis, and 1 cm to represent 1 km on the distance-axis, draw travel graphs to represent the two journeys. Use your graphs to find:
(a) Peter's time of arrival at Oakwood
(b) David's father's average speed for the slower part of his journey
(c) when and where they pass
(d) their distance apart at 10.20 a.m.

5. A salesman leaves his home (H) at 9 a.m. to visit four businesses A, B, C and D, which lie at distances 36 km, 50 km, 92 km and 110 km respectively, along a motorway from his home. His log for the journey shows that:

he arrived at A at 9.54 a.m. and stayed for 15 minutes,
he arrived at B at 10.33 a.m. and left at 10.54 a.m.,
he arrived at C at 11.45 a.m.,
he arrived at D at 12.39 a.m., having travelled from C at a very slow 36 km/h.

Draw a travel graph to represent his journey, taking 2 cm to represent 10 km on the distance-axis and half-an-hour on the time-axis.

Use your graph to find:
(a) his average speed between his home and A
(b) the time he left C
(c) the total time he was actually travelling
(d) his average speed for the whole journey (including stops).

6. A coach leaves A at noon to travel to B, a town 95 miles away. It travels the first 40 miles at an average speed of 40 mph and, without stopping, completes the journey to B arriving there at 2.30 p.m.

   A second coach leaves B and travels at 60 mph, arriving at A at 2.44 p.m.

   Taking 2 cm to represent 10 miles on the one axis and 20 minutes on the other, draw travel graphs for the two journeys and use them to determine:
   (a) the starting time for the second coach
   (b) when and where they pass
   (c) the average speed of the first coach for the whole journey.

7. Dick leaves the village of Axeter at 12.06 p.m. to walk to the neighbouring village of Botlow $9\frac{1}{2}$ miles away. He walks at a steady 4 mph but after walking for 5 miles he gets a lift in a friend's car which takes him the remainder of the journey at a steady speed of 30 mph. At 12.16 p.m. his brother George leaves Axeter and jogs to Botlow at a steady 6 mph.

   Draw travel graphs for the two journeys taking 2 cm to represent 1 mile and 6 cm to represent 1 h.

   Use your graphs to find:
   (a) which of the brothers arrives at Botlow first, and how long he must wait for his brother
   (b) when and where they pass
   (c) how long George is ahead of Dick.

8. A and B are two service stations on a motorway 120 miles apart. Mrs Brown leaves A at noon to travel to B. She covers the first 40 miles in 1 h, then rests for 45 minutes before proceeding to B at a steady 70 mph. At 12.27 p.m. Mrs White leaves B at a steady 60 mph. After 1 h she takes a 15 minute rest before proceeding to A at a steady 50 mph.

   Draw travel graphs to represent these journeys taking $4\,\text{cm} \equiv 1\,\text{h}$ and $2\,\text{cm} \equiv 10$ miles. Use your graph to determine:
   (a) when and where they pass
   (b) which woman arrives at her destination first.
   (c) their distance apart at 1.31 p.m.

9. John sets out at noon from his home village of Atley, to call at Bentham which is 16 km away, before going on to Cottle, a village which is 9 km beyond Bentham. He walks for 1 h at 6 km/h, then rests for 20 minutes before running the remaining distance to his cousin's home at Bentham at 10 km/h. Here he chats for 4 minutes before leaving on a borrowed bicycle, cycling to Cottle at an average speed of 16 km/h.

Draw a travel graph to represent John's journey taking $6\,cm \equiv 1\,h$ and $4\,cm \equiv 5\,km$. Use your graph to find his time of arrival at Cottle.

In the mean time his friend Tim leaves Cottle at 12.40 p.m. and cycles leisurely to Atley at a steady $12\,km/h$. Show this on the same graph and hence find:
(a) when and where the two pass
(b) Tim's time of arrival at Atley
(c) their distance apart at 1.34 p.m.

10. (Assume all speeds are uniform.) A, B and C are three towns on a straight road such that B is 35 miles from A, and C is 86 miles from A.
   (a) A motorist sets out from A at 12 noon and drives to C without stopping, arriving there at 2.18 p.m. Draw a travel graph to represent this journey using $2\,cm \equiv 10$ miles and $2\,cm \equiv 20$ minutes. From your graph determine the motorist's average speed.
   (b) A second motorist leaves C at 12.10 p.m. and drives to B at 47 mph. He stops at B until 1.56 p.m. when he continues his journey to C, arriving there at 2.30 p.m. On the same axes draw a travel graph to represent this journey and use your graph to determine:
      (i) the second motorist's time of arrival at B
      (ii) the second motorist's average speed for the journey between B and A.
   (c) A third motorist leaves C at 12.40 p.m. and travels directly to A, arriving there at 2.36 p.m.

      On the same axes draw a travel graph for this journey, and from your graphs determine:
      (i) the average speed of the third car
      (ii) when and where the third motorist passes the other two
      (iii) which motorist is nearest to A at 1.12 p.m.

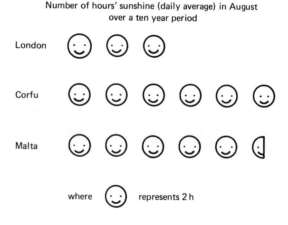

14
STATISTICS

PICTOGRAPHS

A *pictograph* (or *pictogram*) is an eye-catching way of presenting data by using pictures. Magazines and newspapers frequently use pictures of cars to compare the numbers of different types of cars sold, or matchstick people to compare the number of empoyees in various industries. Data is presented in this way because it is easy for most people to understand, and takes far less time to get information over than laboriously presenting masses of figures.

Consider the pictograph given below:

Number of hours' sunshine (daily average) in August
over a ten year period

This shows that:

(a) Corfu has the most sunshine and London the least

(b) London has 6 h, Corfu 12 h and Malta 11 h.

EXERCISE 57

1. Study the following pictograph:

Daily number of hours' sunshine in July

(a) How many hours' sunshine did each place have?
(b) Which place has the most sunshine?
(c) Which place has the least sunshine?

2. Study the following pictograph:

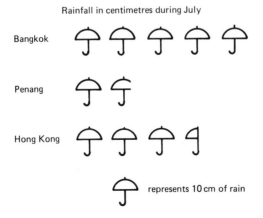

Rainfall in centimetres during July

(a) How much rain does each place have during July?
(b) Which is the wettest place?

3. Study the following pictograph:

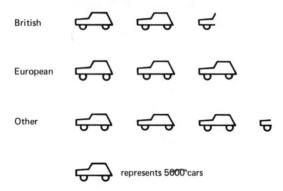

Number of registrations of new cars in Great Britain
during the last week of March

<table>
<tr><td>British</td></tr>
<tr><td>European</td></tr>
<tr><td>Other</td></tr>
</table>

represents 5000 cars

(a) How many cars belonging to each category were sold?
(b) What was the total number of cars sold during the week?

4. The average number of hours of sunshine per day at four holiday regions during the month of April was: London 6 h, Costa Brava 8 h, Algarve 9 h and Dalmatian Coast 6 h. Draw a pictograph to illustrate this information using 😊 to represent 2 h of sunshine.

5. A local council spent the following amounts last year on various services:

   housing £700 000; refuse collection and disposal £800 000; environmental health £600 000; recreation and amenities £1 200 000; industrial and commercial development £600 000; planning and development £400 000; interest payments £300 000.

   Draw a pictograph to represent this data using 👜 to represent £200 000.

Pie Charts

Another way of illustrating data so that it is fairly easy to understand is using a *pie chart*. A pie chart is a circle which is divided into sectors which are shaded or coloured in various ways. Frequently they are used by national and local government to show how money has been raised or spent.

The following pie chart shows how £9 000 000 was raised in rates by a local council.

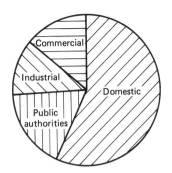

To read a pie chart, the angle at the centre for each sector must be measured. For the above diagram the angles are:

domestic ratepayers	$205°$
industrial ratepayers	$43°$
commercial ratepayers	$50°$
public authorities	$62°$

The amount contributed by each section is therefore as follows:

domestic ratepayers: £9 million $\times \dfrac{205°}{360°}$

$\quad = £5\,125\,000$

industrial ratepayers: £9 million $\times \dfrac{43°}{360°}$

$\quad = £1\,075\,000$

commercial ratepayers: £9 million $\times \dfrac{50°}{360°}$

$\quad = £1\,250\,000$

public authorities: £9 million $\times \dfrac{62°}{360°}$

$\quad = £1\,550\,000$

EXAMPLE 1   The makes of 50 cars in a car park were observed to be as follows: Ford 10, Vauxhall 5, BL 12, Japanese 10, European 8, Other 5. Illustrate this information on a pie chart.

Since there are 50 cars, each car subtends an angle of $\dfrac{360°}{50} = 7.2°$ at the centre.

∴   Angle required at centre for Ford $= 7.2° \times 10$

$$= 72°$$

Angle required at centre for Vauxhall

$$= 7.2° \times 5 = 36°$$

Angle required at centre for BL $= 7.2° \times 12$

$$= 86°$$

Angle required at centre for Japanese

$$= 7.2° \times 10 = 72°$$

Angle required at centre for European

$$= 7.2° \times 8 = 58°$$

Angle required at centre for Other $= 7.2° \times 5$

$$= 36°$$

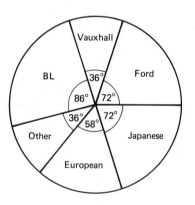

EXERCISE 58

Draw pie charts to illustrate the following information:

1. The shoe sizes of 40 pupils in a class are as follows:
   Size 4 4,   Size 5 5,   Size 6 10,   Size 7 8,
   Size 8 12,   Size 9 1.

2. A family spends £100 as follows:
   food £60, clothes £10, heat and light £15, pleasure £10, other £5.

3. The subject preferences of 36 pupils in a form were:
   languages 2, science 9, mathematics 8, craft subjects 5,
   English 10, other 2.

4. The ages of 24 boys in a youth club were:
   14 years 6,   15 years 4,   16 years 12,
   17 years 2.

5. Every £1 spent by a local authority is divided as follows:

> housing 15 p, refuse 16 p, highways 8 p, health 12 p,
> leisure 25 p, planning and development 18 p, other 6 p.

6. Every £1 income for a particular local authority originates as follows:

> government grants 38 p, rents 40 p, charges 12 p,
> ratepayers 10 p.

7. One hundred fourth-form pupils choose as follows from an option group with four subjects:

> history 45, chemistry 15, German 12, art 28.

8. In the following pie chart measure the angles to determine the percentage of shares in Goldmine Ltd that are held by each of the given groups:

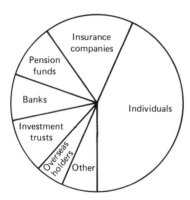

9. The following pie chart shows the amount saved by various groups or bodies. If the total saved is £20 000 m., calculate the amount saved by each group.

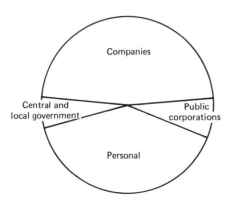

10. A first former spent 2 h one evening revising for end of term examinations. The pie chart shows how he divided up his time. How much time was spent revising:

(a) history   (b) geography   (c) French?

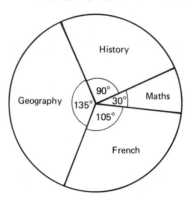

BAR CHARTS OR BAR GRAPHS

The pictographs and pie charts already considered have disadvantages: they take a long time to draw well, and they are difficult to read accurately — 'bits' of pictures have to be converted into numbers, or angles have to be read to an exact number of degrees.

If instead we draw columns or *bars*, we can get over these difficulties.

Consider Example 1 which gave the makes of 50 cars in a car park. The information could be represented as follows:

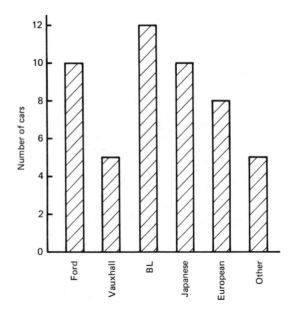

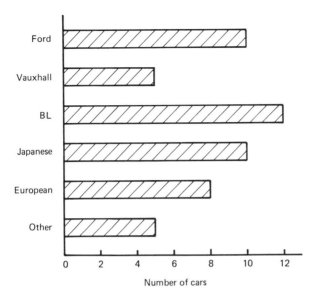

Both diagrams illustrate the information clearly. At a glance we can determine the most popular and least popular makes. As the two diagrams show, it makes little difference whether we draw the bars vertically or horizontally.

EXERCISE 59

1.

AREAS OF THE OCEANS OF THE WORLD

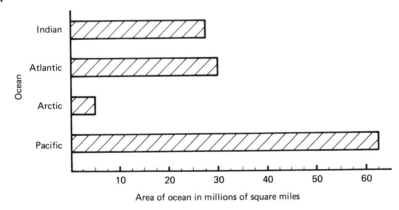

(a) Which is the largest ocean?
(b) Which is the smallest ocean?
(c) What is the total area of the three principal oceans?

2.

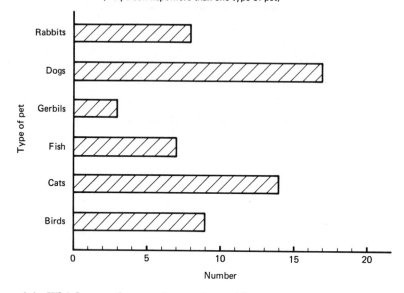

PETS KEPT BY MEMBERS OF A YOUTH CLUB
(No person kept more than one type of pet)

(a) Which was the most popular pet?
(b) How many more kept cats than rabbits?
(c) How many members kept a pet?
(d) List the pets in numerical order, starting with the most popular.

3. NUMBER OF LUNCHES SERVED AT SOUTHSTOCK SCHOOL DURING A CERTAIN WEEK

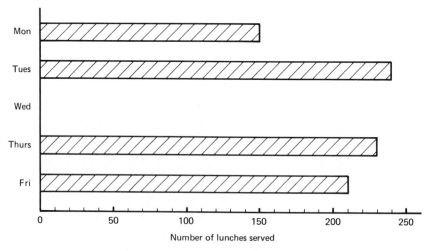

(a) On which day were the most lunches served?
(b) How many lunches were served in the week?
(c) What do you think happened on Wednesday?
(d) How many more lunches were served on Thursday than Monday?

4.

PETER SMITH'S MONTHLY DISTANCE RECORD FOR A YEAR

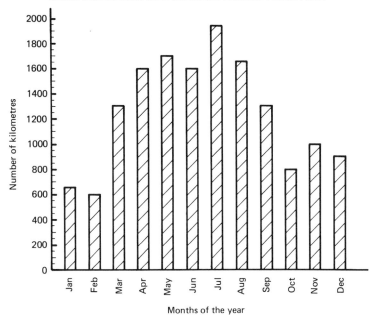

Months of the year

The bar chart shows the number of kilometres travelled by Peter Smith each month in his car.

(a) In which month did he (i) travel furthest, (ii) travel least?
(b) In which two consecutive months did he travel furthest?
(c) How many more kilometres did he travel in the summer months of June, July and August than in the winter months of December, January and February?
(d) How far did he travel in the year?
(e) In which months did he travel exactly the same distance?

5.

ROAD USERS PASSING MY HOUSE

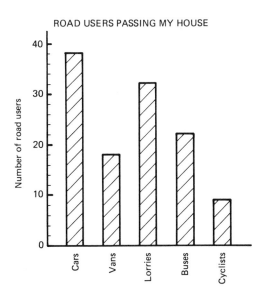

187

The bar chart shows the number of road users passing my house between 10 a.m. and 11 a.m. on a particular day. Use the chart to find:

(a) the number of lorries passing
(b) the number of buses passing
(c) how many more vans than cyclists passed
(d) the least used means of transport.

HISTOGRAMS

One of the clearest ways of representing a large number of observations graphically is to use a bar chart called a *histogram*. A histogram uses rectangles of the same width above each different category or class interval. The area of each rectangle is proportional to the number of observations or frequency within each interval.

Given below is a histogram which shows the number of goals scored by a first division club during the first half of the season.

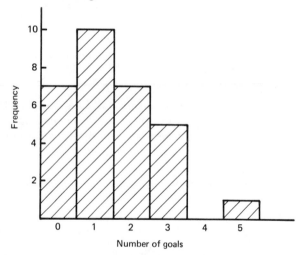

We can see from this histogram that:

$$\text{Number of goals scored} = 1 \times 10 + 2 \times 7 + 3 \times 5 + 5 \times 1$$
$$= 10 + 14 + 15 + 5$$
$$= 44$$

$$\text{Number of matches played} = 7 + 10 + 7 + 5 + 1$$
$$= 30$$

Number of times the team scored more than two goals $= 5 + 1 = 6$

Number of times the team failed to score $= 7$

The most likely score was 1 goal.

1. The frequency table below shows the shoe sizes for the pupils in a class:

Shoe size	2	3	4	5	6	7	8	9
Frequency	1	0	4	9	6	5	1	2

Draw a histogram to represent this data.
(a) How many pupils are there in the class?
(b) What is the most popular shoe size?
(c) How many pupils take a size 6 or larger?

2. The frequency table below shows the number of loaves of bread delivered on one day to the houses in Coronation Street:

Number of loaves delivered	0	1	2	3	4	5
Frequency	16	31	14	9	1	2

Draw a histogram to represent this data.
(a) How many houses are there in the street?
(b) How many houses received a delivery of bread?
(c) How many loaves of bread were delivered in Coronation Street?

3. The frequency table below shows the number of goals scored by the home teams in first division matches one Saturday:

Number of goals	0	1	2	3	4	5
Frequency	4	6	4	4	2	1

Draw a histogram to represent this data and hence find:
(a) how many matches were played
(b) how many goals were scored
(c) how many home teams scored more than one goal.

4. The frequency table below shows the number of marks scored in a maths test by the 34 children in a class:

Number of marks	0	1	2	3	4	5	6	7	8
Frequency	1	3	2	4	8	6	5	3	2

Draw a histogram to represent this data.
(a) What is the most common score?
(b) How many scored more than half marks?
(c) Find the total marks awarded.

5. The number of words in each line of a page in a novel are given below:

```
11   8 13 10 10   2 10   9 12 14
 8   9  6 11   9 10 12   8 10   9
 9 10  9 12   9   8 12 12   9 11
12   4 12 10 13 11 10   9   7   2
12   3
```

Draw a histogram to represent this data.
(a) How many lines are there on the page?
(b) How many lines have more than 11 words?
(c) How many words are there on the page?
(d) What is the most likely number of words in a line?

Data may be more easily understood if it is tabulated in an orderly fashion. It is often useful to have a single number which represents the *average* for the group. In statistics three different 'averages' are used, each of which will be considered in turn.

MEAN

In a terminal examination Anne scored 59, 48, 64, 72 and 52 in her five optional subjects, while her friend Carol scored 73, 40, 38, 54 and 80. Anne's *mean mark* is found by adding all her marks together and dividing by the number of subjects, thus:

$$\text{Anne's mean mark} = \frac{59 + 48 + 64 + 72 + 52}{5}$$

$$= \frac{295}{5} = 59$$

Similarly: $$\text{Carol's mean mark} = \frac{73 + 40 + 38 + 54 + 80}{5}$$

$$= \frac{285}{5} = 57$$

We can therefore use a single mark to justify the statement that while Carol had two marks that were higher than Anne's best mark, Anne's results were, on the whole, better than Carol's. We are using a single mark for Carol (her mean mark) to compare her performance with Anne's (her mean mark).

Similarly if Peter and John played four rounds of golf together and Peter's scores were 84, 79, 89 and 84 while John's were 76, 87, 80 and 85, we can calculate their mean scores and compare them as golfers.

$$\text{Peter's mean score} = \frac{84 + 79 + 89 + 84}{4}$$

$$= \frac{336}{4} = 84$$

$$\text{John's mean score} = \frac{76 + 87 + 80 + 85}{4}$$

$$= \frac{328}{4} = 82$$

On the basis of these scores, John is a slightly better golfer than Peter even though Peter had the better score on two occasions.

MEDIAN

Sometimes the mean does not represent a set of data as well as we would like. Suppose Jane's marks in her five optional subjects were 62, 65, 5, 60, 58.

$$\text{The mean of these marks} = \frac{62 + 65 + 5 + 60 + 58}{5}$$

$$= \frac{250}{5}$$

$$= 50$$

The very poor mark of 5 brings her mean mark down in relation to her marks in the other four subjects. If we arrange the marks in *ascending order* they are 5, 58, 60, 62 and 65. The middle mark is 60 and as a single mark it is a much better representation of the whole than is the mean.

The *median* is defined as the value of the middle number if they have been placed in ascending order, provided that there is an odd number of numbers. When the total number of numbers is even, the median is taken as the mean of the two middle numbers, assuming that they have first been placed in ascending order.

EXAMPLE 2   Find the median of the following boys' heights, which are given correct to the nearest centimetre:

168, 149, 172, 153, 159, 164, 166.

Arranging these heights in ascending order:

149, 153, 159, 164, 166, 168, 172

Then the median height is 164 cm.

EXAMPLE 3   Find the median of the following girls' heights which are given to the nearest centimetre:

155, 152, 160, 167, 165, 146, 159, 148.

Arranging the heights in ascending order:

146, 148, 152, 155, 159, 160, 165, 167

Since the number of heights is even, we take the median height as the mean of the two middle ones, thus:

$$\text{Median} = \frac{155 + 159}{2} \text{ cm} = 157 \text{ cm}$$

MODE

The *mode* of a set of numbers is the number that occurs most frequently.

EXAMPLE 4   Find the mode of the following golf scores:

72, 70, 69, 72, 67, 69, 76, 72, 76.

The score which occurs most frequently, i.e. the mode, is 72.

EXAMPLE 5   Give the mean, median and mode of the following boys' masses, which are given to the nearest kilogram:

60, 54, 63, 73, 66, 60, 58.

$$\text{Mean} = \frac{60 + 54 + 63 + 73 + 66 + 60 + 58}{7} \text{ kg}$$

$$= \frac{434}{7} \text{ kg} = 62 \text{ kg}$$

The median is the middle value of 54, 58, 60, 60, 63, 66, 73, thus:

Median mass = 60 kg

Modal mass or mode = 60 kg

EXERCISE 61

Find the mean, median and mode of each of the following sets of numbers:

1. 20, 16, 11, 16, 14, 27, 22

2. 29, 28, 32, 29, 30, 34, 29, 29

3. 71, 75, 73, 86, 74, 70, 85, 70, 71

4. 14, 12, 8, 8, 6, 8, 8, 14, 10, 8, 14, 10

5. 31, 33, 33, 34, 35, 30, 37, 35, 31, 31

6. 12, 83, 31, 92, 12, 62, 15, 27, 44.

7. The heights of seven girls (to the nearest centimetre) are 169, 162, 171, 166, 179, 169, 167. Calculate (a) the mean height, (b) the median height, (c) the modal height.

8. Find the mean, median and mode of seven successive rounds for a golfer whose scores were:

    71, 84, 70, 70, 85, 70, 75.

9. The number of goals scored by a league team in ten consecutive matches were:

    1, 1, 4, 0, 0, 2, 5, 0, 2, 0

    Find the mean score, the median score and the modal score.

10. The heights (to the nearest centimetre) of a group of boys are:

    160, 164, 162, 158, 160, 156, 165, 155, 157, 163

    What is (a) the mean height, (b) the median height, (c) the modal height?

11. The hourly rates of pay of five factory workers are:

    £1.80, £1.65, £1.76, £2.00, £1.73

    What is (a) the median hourly rate, (b) the mean hourly rate?

12. The hourly rates of pay for a group of workers were:

    £2.10, £2.65, £1.85, £2.05, £2.10, £2.43, £2.16, £2.10, £2.10, £2.16

    Find:
    (a) the mean hourly rate
    (b) the median hourly rate
    (c) the modal hourly rate.

13. The recorded rainfall, in millimetres, falling on Manchester during a particular week was:

    34, 18, 0, 0, 21, 22, 24

    Find:
    (a) the mean rainfall for the week
    (b) the median rainfall for the week.

14. The marks of a form in a mathematics test were as follows:

Mark	0	1	2	3	4	5	6	7	8	9	10
Number of pupils	0	0	3	1	1	8	8	7	2	2	2

Find (a) the mean mark, (b) the median mark, (c) the modal mark.

15. The table below shows the distribution of the marks out of 10 obtained in a test given to the whole of the first-year pupils in a school:

Mark	0	1	2	3	4	5	6	7	8	9	10
Number of boys	3	4	5	8	10	12	24	28	21	16	5
Number of girls	2	2	2	3	2	11	30	34	26	23	6

Calculate the mean, median and modal marks for: (a) the boys, (b) the girls, (c) all first-year pupils. Give any answers that are not exact correct to one decimal place.

EXAMPLE 6

Find the mean, median and mode of the following numbers: 10, 4, 13, 23, 16, 10, 8.

$$\text{Mean } = \frac{10 + 4 + 13 + 23 + 16 + 10 + 8}{7} = \frac{84}{7}$$

$$= 12$$

Median of 4, 8, 10, 10, 13, 16 and 23 is 10.

The mode is 10.

Comparing these results with Example 5 we see that each of the results is 50 less than the corresponding answers in Example 5. This would suggest that when the numbers in a set are fairly close together we can add or subtract the same quantity from all the given values to simplify the numbers for our calculations. The number we subtract from all the values is called *the working origin*. The following example illustrates how much easier the calculations become.

EXAMPLE 7

Use a working origin to find the mean and median of the following numbers:

157, 151, 171, 159, 159, 158, 165.

Subtracting 150 from each, these figures become:

7, 1, 21, 9, 9, 8, 15

$$\text{Mean of these } = \frac{70}{7} = 10$$

Median of 1, 7, 8, 9, 9, 15, 21 is 9.

The mode is also 9.

If we now add the working origin to each, we have a mean of 160, a median of 159 and a mode of 159.

There is nothing special about choosing 150 as the working origin. Had we chosen 160, the reduced numbers would have been $-3, -9, 11, -1, -1, -2, 5$.

$$\text{Mean of these} = \frac{-3-9+11-1-1-2+5}{7}$$

$$= \frac{16-16}{7} = 0$$

Median of $-9, -3, -2, -1, -1, 5, 11$ is -1.

The mode is -1.

If we add the working average of 160, we have a mean of 160, a median of 159 and a mode of 159, i.e. the results are the same as when a working origin of 150 was used.

EXERCISE 62

Use a working origin to find the mean for each of the following:

1. 84, 79, 89, 86, 84, 82
2. 116, 111, 116, 120, 122, 127, 114
3. 492, 496, 505, 494, 492, 491, 506, 491, 497
4. 229, 232, 230, 228, 234, 229, 231, 227
5. 112, 106, 108, 114, 108, 114, 108, 110, 108, 110, 108, 114.

PROBABILITY

If we toss a coin it is equally likely to come down heads or tails. There are two possible outcomes: the chance of a head being one in two, and the chance of a tail also being one in two. We say that the probability of a head is $\frac{1}{2}$, and the probability of a tail is also $\frac{1}{2}$.

Similarly if we toss two coins the possibilities are:

HH HT TH TT

i.e. there are four possible outcomes, all being equally likely.

If we want two heads, only one of the four possible outcomes is acceptable. The chance of this is one in four, i.e. the probability is $\frac{1}{4}$. However, the chance of one head and one tail is two out of four, i.e. the probability is $\frac{2}{4}$ or $\frac{1}{2}$. Thus:

The probability of two heads is $\dfrac{1}{4}$

The probability of one head and one tail is $\dfrac{1}{2}$

The probability of two tails is $\dfrac{1}{4}$

The sum of all these probabilities is $\dfrac{1}{4} + \dfrac{1}{2} + \dfrac{1}{4} = 1$.

The sum of all the possible probabilities is always 1. The probability of an event that is certain is 1; e.g. the probability that the sun will rise tomorrow is 1. The probability of an event that is certain *not* to happen is 0; e.g. the probability that you will grow to a height of 6 m is 0.

The probability that a particular event will occur

$$= \frac{\text{number of favourable outcomes}}{\text{number of possible outcomes}}$$

EXAMPLE 8   A card is drawn at random from an ordinary pack of 52 cards. What is the probability that it is (a) a black card, (b) a deuce, (c) the two of diamonds?

(a)   The probability of drawing a black card is $\dfrac{26}{52} = \dfrac{1}{2}$.

(b)   The probability of drawing a deuce $= \dfrac{4}{52}$

$= \dfrac{1}{13}$, since there are four twos in a pack.

(c)   The probability of drawing the two of diamonds is $\dfrac{1}{52}$, since there is only one such card in the pack.

EXAMPLE 9   If a die is thrown, what is the probability of (a) a 5, (b) a number greater than 2?

(a)   There are six possible outcomes, only one of which is the 5.

$\therefore$ Probability of a 5 $= \dfrac{1}{6}$

(b) There are four sides with a number greater than 2.

∴ Probability of a number greater than $2 = \dfrac{4}{6}$

$= \dfrac{2}{3}.$

EXAMPLE 10   A bag contains 12 marbles — 5 are red, 4 green and 3 are black. What is the probability that the first marble drawn is (a) red, (b) not red, (c) white, (d) either red or black?

(a) Number of favourable outcomes $= 5$

Number of possible outcomes $= 12$

∴ Probability of drawing a red $= \dfrac{5}{12}.$

(b) Number of favourable outcomes $= 7$

Number of possible outcomes $= 12$

∴ Probability of not drawing a red $= \dfrac{7}{12}.$

Note that the sum of the two probabilities for (a) and (b) is 1. The first marble drawn must fall into one of the categories 'red' or 'not red'.

(c) Number of favourable outcomes $= 0$

Number of possible outcomes $= 12$

∴ Probability of drawing a white $= \dfrac{0}{12} = 0.$

(d) Number of favourable outcomes $= 5 + 3 = 8.$

Number of possible outcomes $= 12$

∴ Probability of drawing a red or a black

$= \dfrac{8}{12} = \dfrac{2}{3}.$

EXERCISE 63

1. If we have an ordinary pack of 52 playing cards, what is the probability of drawing: (a) an ace, (b) the ace of hearts, (c) a heart, (d) a red card, (e) a card higher than a ten?

2. If all the court cards (Jacks, Queens and Kings) are removed from an ordinary pack of cards, what is the probability of drawing (a) a five, (b) a black card, (c) a card higher than a five?

3. Assuming that all the months of the year have the same number of days, what is the probability of Peter having his birthday in the winter, i.e. during December, January or February?

4. If a letter is taken at random from the word SCIENTIST, what is the probability that it is (a) a vowel, (b) a consonant, (c) the letter T?

5. Assuming that the hundred houses in a particular street are numbered consecutively from 1 to 100, what is the probability that the house you stop outside has a number that is (a) odd, (b) a multiple of 3, (c) ending in a 7?

6. Three coins are tossed together. What is the probability of: (a) three heads, (b) two heads and one tail, (c) at least one head?

7. In a car park there are 100 cars. If 35 of them are Fords, 20 BL, 30 Japanese and the remainder European, what is the probability that the first car to leave is (a) a Ford, (b) Japanese, (c) not European?

8. Two dice are thrown together. What is the probability that the total score will be (a) 1, (b) 2, (c) 12, (d) more than 4?

9. Six red discs, 3 black discs and 1 white disc are placed in a bag. If 1 disc is selected from the bag, what is the probability that it will be (a) black, (b) a colour other than red?

10. A letter is chosen at random from the word MINIMUM. What is the probability that it is (a) an M, (b) not an I, (c) a consonant?

11. In a class there are 16 boys and 12 girls. What is the probability that a pupil chosen at random is (a) a girl, (b) a boy?

12. A bag contains 12 black discs and 8 white discs. What is the probability that the first disc drawn from the bag is white?

13. Two coins are tossed together. What is the probability of (a) at least one head, (b) no heads?

14. Three coins are tossed together. What is the probability of (a) no tails, (b) at least two heads?

15. If a letter is taken at random from the word MATHEMATICS, what is the probability that it is (a) a vowel, (b) a consonant, (c) the letter M?

16. Mary's birthday is in June. What is the probability that:
    (a) the date will divide exactly by 5
    (b) it is an even date
    (c) the date is not divisible by 3?

17. Two dice are thrown together. What is the probability that:
    (a) the total score is 3
    (b) the total score is 6?

18. A single die is cast on the table. What is the probability that the uppermost face shows (a) a 6, (b) an even number, (c) a prime number?

19. A girl is chosen at random from the whole population. What is the probability that her birthday this year is (a) on a Tuesday, (b) in the month of May, (c) on the 12th of the month?
    (Assume for this question that each month has 30 days.)

20. Four boys, Arthur, Bernard, Clive and Don, are to compete in the final of the school's 100 m and 200 m. The probabilities that each will win are given in the following table:

	A	B	C	D
100 m	$\frac{1}{12}$	$\frac{1}{6}$	$\frac{1}{4}$	$\frac{1}{2}$
200 m	$\frac{1}{8}$	$\frac{1}{8}$	$\frac{3}{8}$	$\frac{3}{8}$

(a) Which boy is considered the best overall sprinter?
(b) What is the probability that Arthur will win both races?
(c) What is the probability that Don will not win the 200 m?

15

CALCULATORS AND TABLES

As long as people have needed to calculate, they have been looking for easier, quicker and more accurate ways of reaching their answers.

In the early 17th century, John Napier devised a system which turned multiplication and division into addition and subtraction. His system of logarithms was later improved by Henry Briggs, resulting in the tables still in use today (and in more recent times adapted to the slide rule, a device which was very popular with engineers and scientists).

In recent years, another great leap forward has been the development and widespread use of electronic calculators, ranging from the relatively simple to the more complex 'programmable' types which have 'memories'. Most examination boards now permit the use of calculators for some or all of their examinations. This chapter and those that follow leave it to the reader as to which method of computation is used.

SQUARES

The square of any number is the number obtained by multiplying the number by itself, e.g. $4^2 = 4 \times 4 = 16$, $20^2 = 20 \times 20 = 400$.

The table of squares enables you to find the square of any number to four figures. Slight errors occur in the fourth figure on occasions, but the results correct to three significant figures would be the same as results obtained with a calculator. In most cases this degree of accuracy is sufficient. The one thing the table will not give is the position of the decimal point. This must be found by the user.

It is essential to find an approximate answer first, particularly if a calculator is to be used.

EXAMPLE 1   Find 8.726^2.

Approximate answer $= 9 \times 9 = 81$.

From tables

$8.726^2 = 76.15$

The value obtained using a calculator is 76.143 076. Correct to four significant figures this gives 76.14. The fourth significant figure thus differs by 1 from the value obtained from the table of squares.

EXAMPLE 2   Find $0.076\ 53^2$.

Approximate answer: $0.08^2 = 0.0064$.

From tables

$0.076\ 53^2 = 0.005\ 857$

(the same value, correct to four significant figures, as a calculator gives).

NOTE: The square of any number greater than unity is greater than the given number, but the square of any number smaller than unity is smaller than the given number. This is a very important fact.

EXERCISE 64

Use a calculator or tables to find the squares of:

1. 1.4	2. 7.3	3. 9.2	4. 3.7
5. 5.2	6. 6.9	7. 8.5	8. 4.3
9. 7.8	10. 0.73	11. 0.92	12. 0.32
13. 0.66	14. 0.54	15. 0.69	16. 43
17. 32	18. 56	19. 73	20. 82
21. 29	22. 0.055	23. 0.034	24. 0.076
25. 2.44	26. 5.92	27. 8.74	28. 0.724
29. 0.928	30. 0.546	31. 37.2	32. 59.3
33. 88.7	34. 0.0876	35. 0.0534	36. 0.0216
37. 573	38. 844	39. 304	40. 5.926
41. 3.142	42. 7.643	43. 8.924	44. 1.537

45. 4.259	46. 0.5566	47. 0.2493	48. 0.7646
49. 0.043 72	50. 0.012 64	51. 0.093 74	52. 14.37
53. 26.59	54. 62.64	55. 53.97	56. 72.43
57. 39.26	58. 497.2	59. 173.8	60. 256.4
61. 5.267	62. 0.09	63. 0.3334	64. 37.92
65. 453.4	66. 5926	67. 0.5372	68. 0.004 36
69. 0.1264	70. 1438	71. 53.45	72. 43.28
73. 0.078 56	74. 0.002 493	75. 34 920.	

SQUARE ROOTS

The square root of a number N is the number which when multiplied by itself gives N, e.g. since $4 \times 4 = 16$, the square root of 16 is 4. The square root is denoted by the symbol $\sqrt{}$. $\sqrt{81}$ is therefore asking the question: What number multiplied by itself gives 81? It follows that $\sqrt{81} = 9$. Using index notation the square root is denoted by the index $\frac{1}{2}$, e.g. $36^{\frac{1}{2}} = \sqrt{36} = 6$. Every number will have two square roots which are equal in magnitude but opposite in sign, e.g. $\sqrt{36} = +6$ or -6. In this section we concern ourselves only with the positive root.

EXAMPLE 3   Find $\sqrt{76.43}$.

It is necessary to determine the first figure of your answer *before* you go to the tables. This is an easy example. Since $8^2 = 64$ and $9^2 = 81$ it follows that $\sqrt{76.43}$ must lie between 8 and 9. Now go to the table.

$$\therefore \sqrt{76.43} = 8.743$$

(A calculator gives a value of 8.742.)

EXAMPLE 4   Find $\sqrt{0.000\,853\,6}$.

When the number is smaller than 1, mark off in pairs from the point as far as the first non-zero pair

i.e.   0.00'08'536

The first pair from the decimal point contains two zeros. In the answer this accounts for a single zero immediately following the decimal point.

The second pair contains a non-zero number, namely 8. Now ask the question: What is the largest whole number, which when squared, is equal to 8 or less than it? The largest number satisfying this is 2. We therefore know that our square root begins 0.02.

$$\therefore \sqrt{0.000\,853\,6} = 0.029\,22$$

EXERCISE 65

Use a calculator or tables to find the square root of each of the following numbers:

1. 6.9	2. 3.7	3. 4.6	4. 9.5
5. 8.3	6. 2.4	7. 94	8. 67
9. 54	10. 31	11. 19	12. 74
13. 0.92	14. 0.53	15. 0.31	16. 0.82
17. 0.44	18. 0.76	19. 5.93	20. 2.47
21. 6.16	22. 8.24	23. 9.17	24. 7.23
25. 15.2	26. 29.3	27. 59.4	28. 35.9
29. 63.8	30. 90.2	31. 0.554	32. 0.393
33. 0.727	34. 0.849	35. 0.615	36. 0.888
37. 427	38. 392	39. 536	40. 794
41. 827	42. 694	43. 8.342	44. 6.197
45. 3.142	46. 9.892	47. 7.645	48. 4.241
49. 68.64	50. 73.92	51. 27.49	52. 58.26
53. 40.04	54. 13.27	55. 483.6	56. 590.1
57. 243.7	58. 892.8	59. 343.4	60. 727.2
61. 0.5949	62. 0.7264	63. 0.9887	64. 0.2739
65. 0.3924	66. 0.8339	67. 0.002 14	68. 0.0536
69. 0.000 629	70. 0.0214	71. 0.007 93	72. 0.000 052
73. 0.072 61	74. 0.003 345	75. 0.000 647	76. 4264

77. 8287	78. 9361	79. 5937
80. 3492	81. 4437	82. 0.8136
83. 0.002 497	84. 0.000 008 4	85. 7 264 000
86. 83 290	87. 12 340 000	88. 16 200
89. 4 539 000	90. 620 000	91. 54.27
92. 0.3174	93. 39.2	94. 0.001 43
95. 0.0009	96. 0.000 537 2	97. 4.926
98. 56 730	99. 0.1243	100. 99.37.

Find the following:

101. $\sqrt{5.2^2 + 4.3^2}$

102. $\sqrt{9.24^2 + 15.3^2}$

103. $\sqrt{34.2^2 + 16.4^2}$

104. $\sqrt{83.9^2 + 56.4^2}$

105. $\sqrt{6.342^2 + 9.641^2}$

106. $\sqrt{3.142^2 + 2.413^2}$

107. $\sqrt{0.372^2 + 0.593^2}$

108. $\sqrt{0.5926^2 + 0.4455^2}$

109. $\sqrt{0.071\,45^2 + 0.8264^2}$

110. $\sqrt{0.1253^2 + 0.4537^2}$

111. $(\sqrt{36.4} + \sqrt{49.7})^2$

112. $(\sqrt{15.9} + \sqrt{40.1})^2$

113. $(\sqrt{63.1} + \sqrt{54.7})^2$

114. $(\sqrt{1.73} + \sqrt{5.92})^2$

115. $(\sqrt{4.143} + \sqrt{20.92})^2$

116. $(\sqrt{240} + \sqrt{739})^2$

117. $(\sqrt{592.6} + \sqrt{849.2})^2$

118. $(\sqrt{3.726} + \sqrt{10.17})^2$

119. $(\sqrt{0.92} + \sqrt{0.44})^2$

120. $(\sqrt{0.042\,64} + \sqrt{0.072\,35})^2$.

PYTHAGORAS' THEOREM

The knowledge we have just acquired has very many uses, none more important than the application of Pythagoras' theorem.

Pythagoras' theorem states that: The square on the hypotenuse of a right-angled triangle is equal to the sum of the squares on the other two sides.

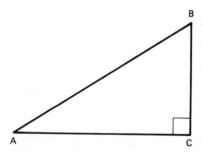

In the diagram above $AB^2 = AC^2 + BC^2$.

This result has very wide applications, some of which are referred to in the following examples.

EXAMPLE 5　　A rectangular lawn measures 4.5 m by 7.2 m. How far is it between opposite corners?

If the length of the required diagonal is x m:

$$x^2 = 4.5^2 + 7.2^2$$
$$= 20.25 + 51.84$$

i.e. $x^2 = 72.09$

$\therefore \quad x = \sqrt{72.09} = 8.490$

$\therefore$ Distance between opposite corners is 8.490 m.

EXAMPLE 6   An open rectangular box has internal measurements
12 cm by 10 cm by 8 cm. Find the length of the
longest straight stick which would fit into the box.

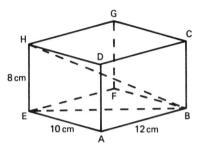

The longest stick would be the length HB.

In right-angled triangle EBH:

$HB^2 = HE^2 + EB^2$

and in right-angled triangle ABE:

$EB^2 = EA^2 + AB^2$

$\qquad = 10^2 + 12^2$

$\therefore \quad EB^2 = 100 + 144 = 244$

But $HB^2 = HE^2 + EB^2$

$\therefore \quad HB^2 = 8^2 + 244$

$\qquad\qquad = 64 + 244$

$HB^2 = 308$

i.e. $HB = 17.55$

$\therefore$ The longest stick that would fit into the box has
length 17.55 cm.

EXERCISE 66

Find the hypotenuse of a right-angled triangle if the other two sides
are:

1. 7.63 cm and 4.92 cm

2. 16.4 cm and 23.9 cm

3. 42.6 cm and 27.9 cm

4. 1.823 m and 2.641 m

5. 0.926 m and 0.534 m

6. 297 mm and 502 mm.

205

Find the third side of a right-angled triangle in which:

7. One side is 15.7 cm and the hypotenuse is 26.5 cm

8. One side is 4.92 m and the hypotenuse is 9.67 m

9. One side is 82.3 cm and the hypotenuse is 112.5 cm.

10. A ladder 7.6 m long leans against a vertical wall, its base being 2.4 m from the base of the wall. How far up the wall does it reach?

11. A ladder 6.4 m long just reaches a window sill 5.1 m above the ground. How far is the foot of the ladder from the base of the vertical wall containing the window sill?

12. The main room of a house measures 4.4 m by 3.7 m and the ceiling is 2.8 m high. Calculate the distance from a corner of the floor to the opposite corner of the ceiling.

13. The diagonal of a rectangle is 40.8 cm and one side is 5.43 cm. Find its perimeter.

14. The area of an isosceles triangle is 28 cm^2, the length of its base being 4.5 cm. Find the length of one of the equal sides.

15. A man makes a rectangular window frame measuring 1.43 m by 1.12 m. He tests to see that it is 'square' by measuring its diagonals. What lengths should they be?

16.

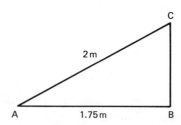

A builder wants to use plastic sheets, 2 m in length, to roof a lean-to shed 1.75 m wide. Find the height of the top end of the sheet C above the level AB.

17. A vertical pole AB, of length 10 m is supported by two wires CF and DE as shown on p. 207. C is 1.5 m from the top of the pole, and D is 7 m from its base. If the points of attachment, E and F, at ground level are respectively 1.75 m and 2 m from the base B, calculate the total length of supporting wire used, in metres, giving your answer correct to one decimal place.

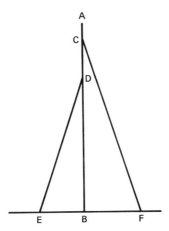

18. The pendulum of a clock is 100 cm long and swings to and fro so that the horizontal distance between its extreme positions is 12 cm. Find the height through which the tip of the pendulum rises, correct to one decimal place.

19. Find the length of the longest straight line that could be marked out on a soccer pitch measuring 29 m by 31 m.

20. The diagonal of a picture frame is 25 cm and its length is twice its width. Find the dimensions of the frame.

RECIPROCALS

If two numbers are such that their product is 1, the one number is said to be the reciprocal of the other, e.g. 4 and $\frac{1}{4}$, $\frac{5}{3}$ and $\frac{3}{5}$, 5.26 and $\frac{1}{5.26}$ are pairs of reciprocals.

Reciprocal tables usually give the reciprocals of all numbers between 1 and 10. From these we may find the reciprocal of any number.

EXAMPLE 7   Find the reciprocal of 4.926.

In reciprocal tables look down the left hand column as far as 4.9, then across to the column headed 2. This gives 0.2033 in the table. Continue along this line to the number in the column headed 6. The number appearing here, 2, is *subtracted* from 2033 giving 2031. Thus:

$$\frac{1}{4.926} = 0.2031$$

Since the number is between 1 and 10 the position of the decimal point in the answer is given.

EXAMPLE 8

Find $\dfrac{1}{536.4}$.

Use the reciprocal tables as above but disregard the decimal point in the given number and in the table.

From the table we have 1865 (remember to subtract the difference). The final question is: Where do we position the decimal point?

Write the given number correct to the first figure, in this case 500. Then:

$$\frac{1}{500} = 0.002 \qquad\qquad 500)\overline{1.000}^{\,0.002}$$

i.e. our answer is to be as near 0.002 as we can get. It will in fact be smaller, since 526.4 is greater than 500.

$$\therefore \quad \frac{1}{536.4} = 0.001\,865$$

EXAMPLE 9

Find $\dfrac{1}{0.002\,436}$.

From tables, if we look up 2436 as in the previous examples, we have 4105.

Next write $\dfrac{1}{0.002\,436}$ with the denominator correct to the first figure i.e. $\dfrac{1}{0.002}$.

Now multiply top and bottom to make the denominator a whole number

i.e. $\quad \dfrac{1}{0.002} = \dfrac{1000}{2} = 500$

Our answer is therefore to be as near 500 as we can arrange it

i.e. $\quad \dfrac{1}{0.002\,436} = 410.5$

EXERCISE 67

Use a calculator or tables to find the following reciprocals:

1. $\dfrac{1}{71.4}$ 2. $\dfrac{1}{74}$ 3. $\dfrac{1}{0.74}$ 4. $\dfrac{1}{740}$

5. $\dfrac{1}{12.6}$ 6. $\dfrac{1}{1260}$ 7. $\dfrac{1}{0.126}$ 8. $\dfrac{1}{0.001\,26}$

9 $\dfrac{1}{64.27}$ 10. $\dfrac{1}{0.064\,27}$ 11. $\dfrac{1}{6457}$ 12. $\dfrac{1}{5923}$

13. $\dfrac{1}{0.3629}$ 14. $\dfrac{1}{0.019\,34}$ 15. $\dfrac{1}{0.005\,415}$ 16. $\dfrac{1}{0.091\,64}$

17. $\dfrac{1}{4371}$ 18. $\dfrac{1}{639.2}$ 19. $\dfrac{1}{84.31}$ 20. $\dfrac{1}{1234}$

21. $\dfrac{1}{92.14}$ 22. $\dfrac{1}{737.4}$ 23. $\dfrac{1}{5152}$ 24. $\dfrac{1}{0.2453}$

25. $\dfrac{1}{0.5734}$ 26. $\dfrac{1}{16.21}$ 27. $\dfrac{1}{59.34}$ 28. $\dfrac{1}{0.004\,217}$

29. $\dfrac{1}{7856}$ 30. $\dfrac{1}{1.004}$.

Find the following, giving your answers correct to three significant figures:

31. $\dfrac{5}{33.49}$ 32. $\dfrac{1}{126.2}$ 33. $\dfrac{2}{0.1625}$ 34. $\dfrac{3}{8264}$

35. $\dfrac{6}{47.34}$ 36. $\dfrac{7}{692.7}$ 37. $\dfrac{3}{0.2456}$ 38. $\dfrac{4}{0.043\,61}$

39. $\dfrac{5}{0.009\,264}$ 40. $\sqrt{\dfrac{5}{19.36}}$ 41. $\sqrt{\dfrac{30}{492.3}}$ 42. $\dfrac{2}{\sqrt{0.9653}}$

43. $\sqrt{\dfrac{6}{0.4536}}$ 44. $\dfrac{4}{\sqrt{54.26}}$ 45. $\dfrac{7}{\sqrt{6924}}$

46. $\dfrac{3}{(1.264)^2}$ 47. $\left(\dfrac{6}{3.954}\right)^2$ 48. $\left(\dfrac{5}{7.291}\right)^2$

49. $\dfrac{1}{32.64}+\dfrac{1}{44.93}$ 50. $\sqrt{\dfrac{1}{5.26}-\dfrac{1}{9.87}}$.

16
LOGARITHMS

INDICES

In an earlier chapter we saw that we could abbreviate $2 \times 2 \times 2 \times 2$ to 2^4. We called the 4 the *power* or *index* to which the number 2 was raised.

Thus $\qquad\qquad 3^3 = 3 \times 3 \times 3 = 27$

and $\qquad\qquad 5^5 = 5 \times 5 \times 5 \times 5 \times 5 = 3125$

In general terms, for any number N the following facts apply when a and b are positive integers:

$$N^a \times N^b = N^{a+b} \qquad\qquad\qquad\qquad \text{(i)}$$

$$N^a \div N^b = N^{a-b} \qquad (a \text{ greater than } b) \qquad \text{(ii)}$$

$$(N^a)^b = N^{ab} \qquad\qquad\qquad\qquad \text{(iii)}$$

Numerical examples would be:

$$2^4 \times 2^5 = 2^{4+5} = 2^9$$

$$3^7 \div 3^4 = 3^{7-4} = 3^3$$

and $\qquad\qquad (5^2)^3 = 5^{2 \times 3} = 5^6$

It would be quite natural to ask next: Is there any meaning for 6^0, 4^{-2} or $12^{\frac{1}{2}}$, i.e. can we have zero, negative or fractional values in the index?

ZERO INDEX

Consider $6^2 \times 6^0$.

If we observe the rule given in equation (i), the value of $6^2 \times 6^0$ would be 6^2, i.e. we can multiply 6^2 by 6^0 to give an answer of 6^2. The only quantity we can multiply a number by which leaves the number unchanged is 1, and therefore the meaning we can give to 6^0 is that its value is unity.

Similarly for any non-zero value of N we can write $N^0 = 1$.

NEGATIVE INDEX

If we put $b = -a$ in equation (i), it will read:

$$N^a \times N^{-a} = N^{a-a} = N^0 = 1 \quad \text{(from above)}$$

N^{-a} is therefore a quantity which when multiplied with N^a gives an answer of 1, i.e. N^{-a} is the reciprocal of N^a

$$\therefore \qquad\qquad N^{-a} = \frac{1}{N^a}$$

FRACTIONAL INDEX

In equation (i) put $a = b = \dfrac{1}{2}$, then:

$$N^{\frac{1}{2}} \times N^{\frac{1}{2}} = N^{\frac{1}{2} + \frac{1}{2}} = N^1 = N$$

i.e. $N^{\frac{1}{2}}$ multiplied by itself gives N. The obvious meaning for $N^{\frac{1}{2}}$ is therefore the square root of N (as we saw on p. 202).

Thus
$$9^{\frac{1}{2}} = \sqrt{9} = 3$$

and
$$\left(\frac{25}{4}\right)^{\frac{1}{2}} = \sqrt{\frac{25}{4}} = \frac{5}{2}$$

Similarly
$$N^{\frac{1}{3}} \times N^{\frac{1}{3}} = N^{\frac{2}{3}}$$

$$\therefore \qquad N^{\frac{1}{3}} \times N^{\frac{1}{3}} \times N^{\frac{1}{3}} = N^{\frac{2}{3}} \times N^{\frac{1}{3}} = N^1 = N$$

$$\therefore \qquad N^{\frac{1}{3}} \text{ is the cube root of } N \text{ or } \sqrt[3]{N}$$

It is only a short step to generalise and say that $N^{\frac{a}{b}}$ is the bth root of N to the power a

i.e.
$$N^{\frac{2}{3}} = \sqrt[3]{N^2} \qquad \text{or} \qquad (\sqrt[3]{N})^2$$

and
$$N^{\frac{5}{4}} = \sqrt[4]{N^5} \qquad \text{or} \qquad (\sqrt[4]{N})^5$$

Numerically
$$32^{\frac{3}{5}} = \text{(the 5th root of 32)}^{\text{cubed}}$$
$$= 2^3 = 8$$

EXERCISE 68

Find the following:

1. 2^2 2. 3^3 3. 5^2 4. $\left(\dfrac{1}{2}\right)^2$

5. $\left(\dfrac{1}{3}\right)^3$ 6. $9^{\frac{1}{2}}$ 7. $16^{\frac{1}{2}}$ 8. $8^{\frac{1}{3}}$

9. $8^{\frac{2}{3}}$ 10. $27^{\frac{2}{3}}$ 11. 5^0 12. 8^0

13. 10^0 14. 2^{-2} 15. 3^{-4} 16. 5^{-3}

17. $36^{\frac{3}{2}}$ 18. 36^0 19. $\left(\dfrac{1}{2}\right)^{-3}$ 20. $\left(\dfrac{4}{3}\right)^{-2}$

THE GRAPH OF $y = 10^x$

From our work on indices we can find y for various values of x given that $y = 10^x$. For example:

if $\qquad x = 0, \ y = 10^0 = 1$

if $\qquad x = \dfrac{1}{2}, \ y = 10^{\frac{1}{2}} = \sqrt{10} = 3.162$

if $\qquad x = \dfrac{1}{4}, \ y = (10^{\frac{1}{2}})^{\frac{1}{2}} = \sqrt{10^{\frac{1}{2}}} = \sqrt{3.162} = 1.778$

if $\qquad x = \dfrac{1}{8}, \ y = (10^{\frac{1}{4}})^{\frac{1}{2}} = \sqrt{10^{\frac{1}{4}}} = \sqrt{1.778} = 1.334$

if $\qquad x = \dfrac{3}{8}, \ y = 10^{\frac{1}{4}+\frac{1}{8}} = 10^{\frac{1}{4}} \times 10^{\frac{1}{8}} = 1.778 \times 1.334$

$\qquad\qquad\qquad = 2.372$

if $\qquad x = \dfrac{3}{4}, \ y = 10^{\frac{1}{2}+\frac{1}{4}} = 10^{\frac{1}{2}} \times 10^{\frac{1}{4}} = 3.162 \times 1.778$

$\qquad\qquad\qquad = 5.622$

if $\qquad x = \dfrac{5}{8}, \ y = 10^{\frac{1}{2}+\frac{1}{8}} = 10^{\frac{1}{2}} \times 10^{\frac{1}{8}} = 3.162 \times 1.334$

$\qquad\qquad\qquad = 4.218$

if $\qquad x = \dfrac{7}{8}, \ y = 10^{\frac{3}{4}+\frac{1}{8}} = 10^{\frac{3}{4}} \times 10^{\frac{1}{8}} = 5.622 \times 1.334$

$\qquad\qquad\qquad = 7.500$

if $\qquad x = 1, \ y = 10^1 = 10$

We can now gather this information in a table, giving each value of 10^x correct to two decimal places, and draw the graph of $y = 10^x$ between the given values.

x	0	$\dfrac{1}{8}$	$\dfrac{1}{4}$	$\dfrac{3}{8}$	$\dfrac{1}{2}$	$\dfrac{5}{8}$	$\dfrac{3}{4}$	$\dfrac{7}{8}$	1
Value of 10^x	1	1.33	1.78	2.37	3.16	4.22	5.62	7.50	10

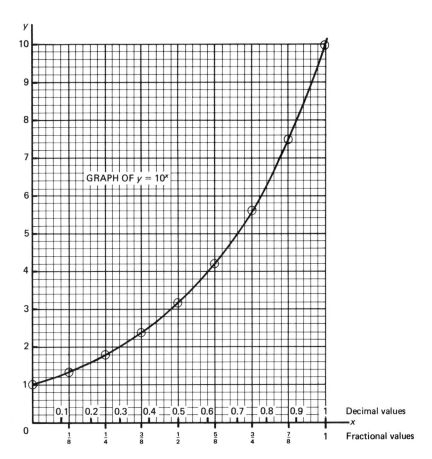

GRAPH OF $y = 10^x$

This graph may now be used to find the value of 10^x for any value of x between 0 and 1. For example:

if $\qquad\qquad x = 0.15,\ 10^x = 1.4$ (approximately)

if $\qquad\qquad x = 0.65,\ 10^x = 4.5$ (approximately)

Conversely, if we give a value for 10^x, we can find the corresponding value of x. For example:

if $\qquad\qquad 10^x = 4,\ x = 0.60$ (approximately)

if $\qquad\qquad 10^x = 7,\ x = 0.85$ (approximately)

213

Suppose we want to multiply 1.7 by 4.3. From the graph:

$$1.7 = 10^{0.23}$$

and

$$4.3 = 10^{0.63}$$

Then

$$1.7 \times 4.3 = 10^{0.23} \times 10^{0.63}$$
$$= 10^{0.23 + 0.63}$$
$$= 10^{0.86}$$
$$= 7.3 \quad \text{(approximately from graph)}$$

It follows that we could multiply any two numbers which lie between 1 and 10, and whose product lies between 1 and 10, using the above idea in conjunction with the graph of $y = 10^x$. The more accurate our graph, the more accurate our result.

LOGARITHMS

We are now in a position to provide a definition. We define the *common logarithm* of a number as *the power, or index, to which 10 is raised to obtain the number.*

For example:

$$\log 3.162 = 0.5 \quad \text{since } 10^{0.5} = 3.162$$

and

$$\log 1.334 = 0.125 \quad \text{since } 10^{0.125} = 1.334$$

From the graph of $y = 10^x$ we are able to find the value of the logarithm of any number between 1 and 10. More accurately these values have been found correct to four decimal places, and are listed in tables headed 'Common Logarithms'.

To find the logarithm of a number bigger than 10, consider:

$$31.62 = 10 \times 3.162$$
$$= 10^1 \times 10^{0.5}$$
$$= 10^{1.5}$$

i.e. it follows that $\log 31.62 = 1.5$.

Similarly since

$$133.4 = 100 \times 1.334$$
$$= 10^2 \times 10^{0.125}$$
$$= 10^{2.125}$$
$$\log 133.4 = 2.125$$

EXAMPLE 1　Use logarithm tables to express the following as powers of 10: (a) 4, (b) 5.3, (c) 6.74, (d) 8.884.

(a) Go down the left hand column of the tables as far as 40. Read the first number following it. This gives the decimal part of the power. From the graph of $y = 10^x$ we have already seen that the number in front of the decimal point is 0.

$$\therefore \quad 4 = 10^{0.6021}$$

Similarly:

(b) $5.3 = 10^{0.7243}$

(c) $6.74 = 10^{0.8287}$

(Down to 67, then across to the column headed 4)

(d) $8.884 = 10^{0.9486}$

(Down to 88, across to the column headed 8, then add the number in the same line found under the 4 in the column on the extreme right)

Another way of writing the four results given above would be:

$$\log 4 = 0.6021, \quad \log 5.3 = 0.7243,$$
$$\log 6.74 = 0.8287, \quad \log 8.884 = 0.9486$$

The part of a logarithm that follows the decimal point is called the *mantissa*; the part that is in front of the decimal point, i.e. the integral part, is called the *characteristic*. For any number between 1 and 10 the characteristic of the logarithm is 0.

Given that $\log 5.3 = 0.7243$, we could ask a different question. Instead of asking: What is the logarithm of 5.3? we could ask: What number has a logarithm of 0.7243? This question could be answered by finding the position of .7243 within the logarithm tables. This gives 530, the position of the decimal point being determined by the characteristic, which is 0. If the characteristic is 0 the number lies between 1 and 10,

i.e.　　　　　　the number whose logarithm is 0.7243 is 5.30

We can shorten this to:

antilogarithm 0.7243 = 5.3

or simply:

antilog 0.7243 = 5.3

In order to save finding the position of the numbers within the logarithm tables, *antilogarithm tables* have been constructed.

To find the antilog of 0.7243 from these tables, consider only the digits after the decimal point. Go down to .72 and across to 4. This gives 5297. Continue in the same line to the column on the extreme right, headed 3, add this number, 4, to 5297 to give 5301. The placing of the decimal point has already been referred to. Thus:

$$\text{antilog}\,0.7243 = 5.301$$

EXAMPLE 2   Antilog 2.4561 = 285.9

Antilog 1.9256 = 84.26

Antilog 3.7364 = 5450

EXAMPLE 3   Find 32.64×8.926.

$$32.64 \times 8.926 = 10^{1.5137} \times 10^{0.9507}$$
$$= 10^{2.4644}$$
$$= 291.4$$

EXAMPLE 4   Find $116.4 \div 82.94$.

$$\frac{116.4}{82.94} = \frac{10^{2.0660}}{10^{1.9188}}$$
$$= 10^{2.0660 - 1.9188}$$
$$= 10^{0.1472}$$
$$= 1.404$$

EXERCISE 69

Express the following numbers as powers of 10:

1. 6	2. 8	3. 4.2	4. 5.7
5. 8.24	6. 4.36	7. 1.29	8. 6.74
9. 5.214	10. 7.396	11. 2.457	12. 3.229
13. 7.341	14. 6.458	15. 9.264	16. 1.292
17. 4.727	18. 8.437	19. 6.394	20. 3.514.

Find the values of:

21. $10^{0.6435}$	22. $10^{0.8129}$	23. $10^{0.8774}$	24. $10^{0.4456}$
25. $10^{0.9499}$	26. $10^{0.2345}$	27. $10^{0.7436}$	28. $10^{0.5173}$
29. $10^{0.2926}$	30. $10^{0.8284}$		

Find the numbers whose logarithms are:

31. 0.8451	32. 0.5682	33. 0.7520	34. 0.2923
35. 0.4271.			

Find the antilogarithms of:

36. 0.7439 **37.** 0.8735 **38.** 0.9214 **39.** 0.7675

40. 0.3107.

Find the value of each of the following using the method given in the text:

41. 4.2×1.96 **42.** 3.4×2.17 **43.** 1.54×3.72

44. 2.887×1.073 **45.** 5.246×1.641 **46.** 7.3÷4.6

47. 8.27÷5.42 **48.** 9.264÷3.142 **49.** 6.737÷2.641

50. 8.541÷2.354.

It will be found more convenient for adding and subtracting the logarithms in this type of question if a table is used. Example 3 could then be set out as follows:

Number	Logarithm
32.64	1.5137
8.926	0.9507
291.4	2.4644

The answer is always the last entry in the left hand or number column.

EXAMPLE 5   Evaluate 15.64 × 4.926 × 23.92.

Number	Logarithm
15.64	1.1942
4.926	0.6925
23.92	1.3788
1843	3.2655

EXAMPLE 6   Evaluate $\dfrac{3.592 \times 126.4}{83.91}$.

Number	Logarithm
3.592	0.5553
126.4	2.1018
	2.6571
83.91	1.9239
5.411	0.7332

EXAMPLE 7 $\sqrt{\dfrac{7.364 \times 537.9}{34.26 \times 49.17}}$.

Number	Logarithm	
7.364	0.8671	
537.9	2.7307	
	3.5978	←
34.26	1.5348	Subtract
49.17	1.6917	
	3.2265	⌐
	0.3713	÷ 2
1.534	0.1857	

EXERCISE 70

Use logarithms or a calculator to find:

1. 7.42×5.91
2. 3.37×9.21
3. 9.26×33.4
4. 18.7×4.36
5. 54.2×16.3
6. 38.5×24.2
7. 8.294×3.142
8. 59.73×4.454
9. 65.92×13.61
10. 27.24×82.31
11. 104×4.242
12. 260×8.142
13. 34.26×810.5
14. 527.3×18.61
15. 4300×7.364
16. 1.276×7360
17. $4.364 \times 5.27 \times 13.8$
18. $9.273 \times 15.92 \times 27.93$
19. $14.9 \times 16.72 \times 7.364$
20. $81.62 \times 17.92 \times 6.423$
21. $9.36 \div 4.17$
22. $8.92 \div 6.43$
23. $34.7 \div 16.5$
24. $56.9 \div 33.4$
25. $7.364 \div 2.93$
26. $6.143 \div 4.72$
27. $15.64 \div 9.17$
28. $73.95 \div 8.43$
29. $50.27 \div 19.78$
30. $93.14 \div 14.61$
31. $72.36 \div 45.61$
32. $55.92 \div 47.36$
33. $214.4 \div 93.7$
34. $652.9 \div 127$
35. $901 \div 45.12$
36. $354 \div 174.9$

37. $463.4 \div 92.73$

38. $172.4 \div 88.62$

39. $7214 \div 436.2$

40. $3419 \div 76.47$

41. $\dfrac{25.2 \times 37.3}{50.4}$

42. $\dfrac{9.72 \times 28.8}{40.3}$

43. $\dfrac{73.7 \times 16.4}{45.9}$

44. $\dfrac{58.9 \times 51.6}{124}$

45. $\dfrac{53.14 \times 26.24}{82.97}$

46. $\dfrac{73.28 \times 16.92}{34.45}$

47. $\dfrac{327.4 \times 50.24}{98.56}$

48. $\dfrac{16.42 \times 593.7}{246.2}$

49. $\dfrac{73.2 \times 42.6}{13.9 \times 54.7}$

50. $\dfrac{29.2 \times 83.9}{54.7 \times 33.2}$

51. $\dfrac{31.26 \times 14.93}{8.726 \times 42.43}$

52. $\dfrac{56.14 \times 27.36}{75.29 \times 5.634}$

53. $\dfrac{21.46 \times 8.72 \times 33.74}{53.98 \times 7.462}$

54. $\dfrac{74.21 \times 6.927 \times 39.26}{42.71 \times 57.42}$

55. $\dfrac{38.72 \times 51.26 \times 73.92}{102.4 \times 7.31 \times 21.97}$

56. $\left(\dfrac{42.4 \times 18.6}{59.77}\right)^2$

57. $\left(\dfrac{7.243 \times 92.61}{124.2}\right)^2$

58. $\sqrt{\dfrac{206 \times 87.53}{16.24 \times 73.92}}$

59. $\left(\dfrac{1043 \times 6.243}{529.2 \times 10.66}\right)^3$

60. $\sqrt[3]{\dfrac{65.72 \times 8.943}{49.21 \times 1.521}}.$

NUMBERS LESS THAN 1

In a similar way, 0.45 may be written as a power of 10 as follows:

$$
\begin{aligned}
0.45 &= \frac{4.5}{10} = \frac{1}{10} \times 4.5 \\
&= 10^{-1} \times 4.5 \\
&= 10^{-1} \times 10^{0.6532} \\
&= 10^{-1 + 0.6532} \\
&= 10^{\bar{1}.6532}
\end{aligned}
$$

where we write the minus sign above the 1 and read it as 'bar one'. This is necessary because it is convenient to keep the part after the decimal point positive.

It follows that $\log 0.45 = \bar{1}.6532$.

Similarly:

$$0.0672 = \frac{6.72}{100} = \frac{6.72}{10^2}$$
$$= 10^{-2} \times 10^{0.8274}$$
$$= 10^{\bar{2}.8274}$$

i.e. $\log 0.0672 = \bar{2}.8274$

and $\log 0.006\,72 = \bar{3}.8274$

Thus for any number between 0 and 1 the characteristic is *negative*. Its value is found by counting the number of places between the position of the decimal point and where it would be if the number were in standard form.

Thus for $\log 0.5'6$ the characteristic is $\bar{1}$.

and for $\log 0.000\,05'6$ the characteristic is $\bar{5}$.

(The oblique stroke indicates where the decimal point would be if the number were in standard form.)

EXAMPLE 8   Find the logarithms of (a) 0.0724, (b) 0.4364, (c) 0.000 005 463.

(a) $\log 0.0724 = \bar{2}.8597$
(b) $\log 0.4364 = \bar{1}.6399$
(c) $\log 0.000\,005\,463 = \bar{6}.7374$

EXAMPLE 9   Find the numbers whose logarithms are:
(a) $\bar{1}.4436$, (b) $\bar{3}.7924$, (c) $\bar{5}.2143$.

(a) The number whose logarithm is $\bar{1}.4436$ is 0.2777
   or antilog $\bar{1}.4436 = 0.2777$
(b) Antilog $\bar{3}.3724 = 0.006\,200$
(c) Antilog $\bar{5}.2143 = 0.000\,016\,38$

Frequently we need to be able to apply the four rules to logarithms involving negative characteristics. Examples for each are as follows.

ADDITION

EXAMPLE 10   Find (a) $3.4 + \bar{2}.6$, (b) $\bar{2}.6 + \bar{4}.7$.

(a) $\begin{array}{r} 3.4 \\ \bar{2}.6 \\ \hline 2.0 \end{array}$ i.e. $4 + 6 = 10$, 0 down carry 1, 1 and -2 is -1, added to 3 gives 2.

(b) $\overline{2}.6$ i.e. $6 + 7 = 13$, 3 down carry 1, 1 and
$\underline{\overline{4}.7}$ -4 is -3, added to -2 gives -5
$\overline{5}.3$

SUBTRACTION

EXAMPLE 11   Find (a) $\overline{3}.6 - 2.4$, (b) $\overline{3}.6 - \overline{2}.9$.

(a) $\overline{3}.6$ i.e. 4 from 6 is 2, 2 from -3 (i.e.
$\underline{2.4}$ $-3 - 2$) is -5.
$\overline{5}.2$

(b) $\overline{3}.6$ i.e. 16 take away 9 gives 7, carry 1, -2
$\underline{\overline{2}.9}$ and 1 is -1, which is subtracted from
$\overline{2}.7$ -3, i.e. $-3 - (-1) = -3 + 1 = -2$.

Or write $\overline{3}$ as $\overline{4} + 1$. Then 9 from 16
gives 7, and $\overline{2}$ from $\overline{4} = -4 - (-2)$
$= -4 + 2 = -2$.

MULTIPLICATION

EXAMPLE 12   Find (a) $\overline{2}.7 \times 3$, (b) $\overline{3}.7 \times 5$.

(a) $\overline{2}.7 \times 3 = \overline{4}.1$ i.e. $7 \times 3 = 21$, 1 down carry
2, $3 \times (-2)$ is -6, -6 and 2
is -4.

(b) $\overline{3}.7 \times 5 = \overline{12}.5$ i.e. $7 \times 5 = 35$, 5 down carry
3, 5 times -3 is -15, -15
and 3 is -12.

DIVISION

EXAMPLE 13   Find (a) $\overline{4}.1 \div 3$, (b) $\overline{12} \div 5$, (c) $\overline{6}.56 \div 4$.

(a) Always express the negative characteristic so
that the negative part is exactly divisible by the
number you are dividing by. Thus, since we are
dividing $\overline{4}.1$ or $-4 + 0.1$ by 3 we write it as:
$(-6 + 2.1) \div 3 = -2 + 0.7 = \overline{2}.7$

(b) $\overline{12} \div 5 = -12 \div 5 = (-15 + 3) \div 5 = -3 + 0.6$
$= \overline{3}.6$

(c) $\overline{6}.56 \div 4 = (-6 + .56) \div 4 = (-8 + 2.56) \div 4$
$= -2 + .64 = \overline{2}.64$

We are now in a position to proceed to more difficult examples.

EXAMPLE 14   Find 12.06 × 0.0872.

Approximate answer = 12 × 0.1 = 1.2

Number	Logarithm
12.06	1.0813
0.0872	$\bar{2}$.9405
1.052	0.0218

EXAMPLE 15   Find 0.562 × 0.092 61 × 0.007 21.

Approximate answer = 0.6 × 0.1 × 0.007

= 0.000 42

Number	Logarithm
0.562	$\bar{1}$.7497
0.092 61	$\bar{2}$.9666
0.007 21	$\bar{3}$.8579
0.000 375 2	$\bar{4}$.5742

EXAMPLE 16   Find $\dfrac{78.2}{0.004\ 54}$.

Approximate answer = 80 ÷ 0.005 = 16 000

Number	Logarithm	
78.2	1.8932	
0.004 54	$\bar{3}$.6571	
17 220	4.2361	[1 − (−3) = 4]

EXAMPLE 17   Find $\dfrac{0.4732}{12.96}$.

Approximate answer = 0.5 ÷ 13 ≈ 0.04

Number	Logarithm	
0.4732	$\bar{1}$.6751	
12.96	1.1126	
0.036 52	$\bar{2}$.5625	[−1 − 1 = −2]

EXAMPLE 18   Find $(0.2468)^4$.

Approximate answer $= 0.2 \times 0.2 \times 0.2 \times 0.2$

$= 0.0016$

Number	Logarithm	
0.2468	$\bar{1}.3923$	$\times 4$
0.003 709	$\bar{3}.5692$	$[\bar{1} \times 4 + 1 = \bar{3}]$

EXAMPLE 19   Find $\sqrt[5]{0.6435^3}$.

Number	Logarithm	
0.6435	$\bar{1}.8085$	$\times 3$
	$\bar{1}.4255$	$\div 5$ [Write $\bar{1}$ as $\bar{5} + 4$]
0.7676	$\bar{1}.8851$	

EXAMPLE 20   Find $\dfrac{\sqrt[3]{0.6345}}{51.42 \times 0.84^2}$.

Number	Logarithm		
0.6345	$\bar{1}.8024 \div 3$	$\bar{1}.9341$	←
51.42		1.7112	
0.84	$\bar{1}.9243 \times 2$	$\bar{1}.8486$	
		1.5598	Subtract
0.023 68		$\bar{2}.3743$	

EXAMPLE 21   Find $\sqrt[3]{0.085\,16}$.

Number	Logarithm	
0.085 16	$\bar{2}.9302$	$\div 3$ [Write $\bar{2}$ as $\bar{3} + 1$]
0.4399	$\bar{1}.6434$	

Check: Approximate value of $0.4399^3 = 0.4^3$

$= 0.064$.

EXERCISE 71

Find the logarithms of:

1. 0.84   2. 0.026   3. 0.0057

4. 0.0007   5. 0.009 24   6. 0.000 086

7. 0.4436   **8.** 0.000 941 6   **9.** 0.022 43

10. 0.6492   **11.** 0.051 61   **12.** 0.000 008 172.

Find the numbers whose logarithms are (i.e. find the antilogarithms of):

13. $\bar{1}$.7300   **14.** $\bar{2}$.4530   **15.** $\bar{4}$.7260   **16.** $\bar{2}$.5473

17. $\bar{5}$.9271   **18.** $\bar{4}$.4372   **19.** $\bar{7}$.9000   **20.** $\bar{1}$.5416

21. $\bar{3}$.2454   **22.** $\bar{2}$.5617   **23.** $\bar{5}$.4736   **24.** $\bar{2}$.7856.

Find the following so that the part after the decimal point is positive:

25. $\bar{1}$.6 + $\bar{3}$.4   **26.** $\bar{2}$.1 + $\bar{3}$.7   **27.** $\bar{5}$.4 + 1.6

28. $\bar{5}$.7 + $\bar{3}$.9   **29.** $\bar{2}$.7 − $\bar{1}$.4   **30.** $\bar{5}$.6 − $\bar{2}$.8

31. $\bar{3}$.1 − 2.8   **32.** $\bar{1}$.4 − 3.9   **33.** $\bar{2}$.5 × 5

34. $\bar{1}$.6 × 4   **35.** $\bar{3}$.7 × 3   **36.** $\bar{1}$.85 × 2

37. $\bar{1}$.2 ÷ 2   **38.** $\bar{5}$.5 ÷ 3   **39.** $\bar{1}$.0 ÷ 5

40. $\bar{4}$.1 ÷ 3   **41.** $\bar{8}$.0 ÷ 6   **42.** $\overline{11}$.6 ÷ 4

43. $\bar{4}$.8 ÷ 8   **44.** $\overline{13}$.2 ÷ 2.

Use a calculator or tables to evaluate the following:

45. 12 × 0.76   **46.** 0.425 × 6.4

47. 0.724 × 36.1   **48.** 0.514 × 0.267

49. 0.897 × 0.43   **50.** 0.7421 × 0.0827

51. 0.000 296 7 × 534   **52.** 0.003 472 × 82.6

53. 192.7 × 0.004 135   **54.** 47 ÷ 0.926

55. 78.4 ÷ 0.0453   **56.** 237.4 ÷ 0.7474

57. 0.743 ÷ 36.2   **58.** 0.0916 ÷ 81.4

59. 0.000 73 ÷ 47.5   **60.** 0.517 ÷ 0.0243

61. 0.2714 ÷ 0.000 92   **62.** 0.081 ÷ 0.0072

63. 0.349 ÷ 0.924   **64.** 0.005 43 ÷ 0.713

65. 0.084 31 ÷ 0.4862   **66.** $(0.74)^2$

67. $(0.5624)^2$ **68.** $(0.0088)^2$

69. $(0.516)^3$ **70.** $(0.3142)^4$

71. $(0.0934)^5$ **72.** $\sqrt{0.0426}$

73. $\sqrt[3]{0.8743}$ **74.** $\sqrt[4]{0.074\,12}$

75. $\sqrt[5]{0.000\,86}$ **76.** $\sqrt[3]{0.000\,433\,4}$

77. $\sqrt[4]{0.005\,917}$

78. $\sqrt[6]{0.7241}$

79. $\sqrt{(0.2643)^3}$

80. $\sqrt[3]{(0.096\,43)^2}$

81. $\dfrac{83.41 \times 0.026\,43}{50.63}$

82. $\dfrac{14.9 \times 0.6751}{42.64}$

83. $\dfrac{7.643}{0.0042 \times 237.1}$

84. $\dfrac{0.7264}{13.61 \times 0.0563}$

85. $\dfrac{15.61}{0.2435 \times 0.0916}$

86. $\dfrac{5}{0.6243 \times 0.0927}$

87. $\dfrac{243.7}{34.12 \times 0.004\,653}$

88. $\dfrac{0.043\,61 \times 82.14}{7.361 \times 0.0095}$

89. $\dfrac{0.72 \times 0.086}{40.26 \times 0.225}$

90. $\dfrac{\sqrt[3]{67.21}}{0.9624}$

91. $\dfrac{13.71}{0.8261^3}$

92. $\dfrac{15.43}{0.926^3 + 1.264}$

93. $\sqrt[3]{2.417} + 1.292^3$

94. $\sqrt[3]{16.42 + 2.347^3}$

95. $\dfrac{\sqrt{24.71}}{0.92} - \dfrac{4.273^2}{28.55}$

Find the value of:

96. $V = \dfrac{4}{3}\pi R^3$ if $\pi = 3.142$ and $R = 0.4734$

97. $A = 2\pi r(r + h)$ if $\pi = 3.142$, $r = 0.5731$ and $h = 0.9264$

98. $\dfrac{m_1 - m_2}{1 + m_1 m_2}$ if $m_1 = 0.2614$ and $m_2 = 0.7345$

99. $\dfrac{4\pi}{T}\sqrt{a^2 - x^2}$ if $\pi = 3.142$, $T = 2$, $a = 1.242$ and $x = 0.643$

100. $\dfrac{a}{\sqrt{b^2 - c^2}}$ if $a = 18.21$, $b = 2.726$ and $c = 0.846$.

17

FURTHER AREAS AND VOLUMES

THE PRISM

Any solid that has a uniform cross-section is called a *prism*. While any shape is possible for the cross-section, the most common are triangles, quadrilaterals and regular polygons. If the cross-section is in the form of a circle or ellipse, the solid is called a *cylinder*.

The volume V of any solid of length L which has a uniform cross-section is given by:

$$V = \text{area of cross-section} \times \text{length}$$

EXAMPLE 1   The diagram shows the section through a plastic ruler of length 31.5 cm. Find the volume of material used.

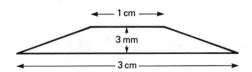

Area of cross-section $= \dfrac{1}{2}$ (sum of the parallel sides) $\times$ the distance between them

$$= \frac{1}{2}(3+1) \times 0.3 \text{ cm}^2$$

$$= 0.6 \text{ cm}^2$$

$$\therefore \text{ Volume of ruler} = \text{area of cross-section} \times \text{length}$$
$$= 0.6 \times 31.5 \text{ cm}^3$$
$$= 18.9 \text{ cm}^3$$

EXAMPLE 2

The diagram shows the cross-section of a barn 11 m wide and 25 m long. The barn is 12.5 m high at the ridge and 9.9 m at its sides. Calculate the volume of hay that may be stored in it.

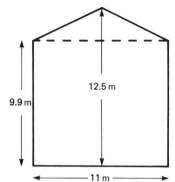

Area of cross-section = area of rectangle + area of triangle

$$= (11 \times 9.9) + \frac{1}{2}(11 \times 2.6) \text{ m}^2$$
$$= (11 \times 9.9) + (11 \times 1.3) \text{ m}^2$$
$$= 11 \times 11.2 \text{ m}^2$$
$$= 123.2 \text{ m}^2$$

Volume of hay = area of cross-section × length
$$= 123.2 \times 25 \text{ m}^3$$
$$= 3080 \text{ m}^3$$

EXERCISE 72

Reminders:

Length
$$10 \text{ mm} = 1 \text{ cm}$$
$$100 \text{ cm} = 1 \text{ m}$$

Area
$$100 \text{ mm}^2 = 1 \text{ cm}^2$$
$$10\,000 \text{ cm}^2 = 1 \text{ m}^2$$

Volume
$$1000 \text{ mm}^3 = 1 \text{ cm}^3$$
$$1\,000\,000 \text{ cm}^3 = 1 \text{ m}^3$$

$$1 \text{ litre} = 1000 \text{ cm}^3$$
$$1 \text{ ml} = 1 \text{ cm}^3$$

You should take care to see that you are working in the same units, i.e. if the cross-section is given in cm^2 but the length in m, the length should be changed into cm if the volume is to be given in cm^3, or the area of the cross-section changed to m^2 if the volume is to be given in m^3.

Find the volumes of the following prisms:

1. Length 4 m, cross-sectional area 54 cm^2

2. Length 32 mm, cross-sectional area 2.74 cm^2

3. Length 5.9 cm, cross-sectional area 39.2 cm^2

4. Length 2.5 m with a rectangular cross-section measuring 4 cm by 5 cm

5. Length 70 cm with a triangular cross-section, the triangle having sides 3 cm, 4 cm and 5 cm.

6. The cross-section of a trough is in the form of a trapezium with the parallel sides of lengths 80 cm and 50 cm. If the trough is 2 m long and 25 cm deep, find its volume.

7. The cross-section of a trough 1.8 m long is a triangle whose sides are 30 cm, 40 cm and 50 cm. How many litres of water will it hold?

8. The depth of a swimming pool increases uniformly from 1 m at the shallow end to 2.5 m at the deep end. If the pool is 35 m long and 12 m wide, how many litres of water are required to fill it?

9. The diagram shows the cross-section through a trench 12 m long which a gardener has prepared for planting his kidney beans. Calculate the volume of the soil removed.

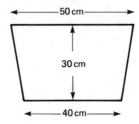

10. The next diagram shows a lean-to greenhouse 3 m long. The heights of the back and front walls are respectively 1.8 m and 2.2 m. If the greenhouse is 2 m wide, find its volume.

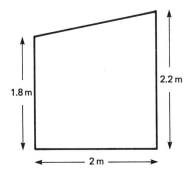

11. A metal bar 1.5 m long has an hexagonal cross-section of side 1 cm. Find the distance between parallel faces and calculate the volume of the bar. Hence find its mass in kilograms if 1 cm^3 has a mass of 7 g.

12. A block of chocolate is in the form of a prism 20 cm long with its cross-section an equilateral triangle of side 3.5 cm. Find the volume of chocolate in the bar.

13. The diagram shows the cross-section of a kerb-stone 1 m long. Calculate its volume in cubic metres.

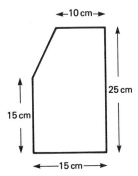

14. A wedge of cheese has a cross-section in the form of an isosceles triangle with equal sides 13 cm and base 10 cm. If the cheese is 5.5 cm wide, calculate its volume.

15. The diagram shows the cross-section of a piece of wooden channelling used for sliding glass doors in a kitchen wall cupboard. Calculate the volume of wood in a 2 m length, expressing your answer in cubic centimetres.

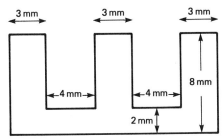

229

16. The diagram shows the cross-section of concrete ends for a park seat. If the structures are 6 cm thick, calculate the volume of concrete used in the manufacture of one seat.

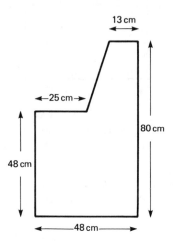

17. A foam cushion for a fireside chair is in the form of the letter T with dimensions as shown in the diagram. If the cushion is 8 cm thick, find the volume of foam used.

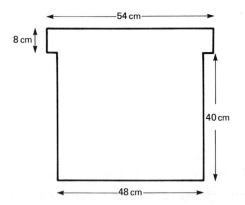

18. The depth of water in a swimming pool increases uniformly from 1 m at the shallow end to 3 m at the deep end. If the pool is 25 m long and 9 m wide, calculate the volume of water (in cubic metres) in the pool when full. If it takes 8 h to empty the pool completely, how long will it take until half the area of the floor of the pool is visible?

19. A capital letter E is cut from plywood 2 cm thick. Calculate (a) its cross-sectional area, (b) its volume.

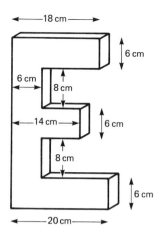

20. The diagram below shows the cross-section through a domestic central heating radiator. The centre section is 50 cm high and 0.75 cm thick; at the top and bottom is a square of side 2.5 cm. Calculate the area of cross-section and hence find the volume of water, in litres, inside a radiator 2 m long.

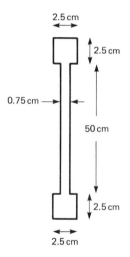

THE PYRAMID

The diagram on the next page shows a typical pyramid. Its base may be a polygon with any number of sides. If the vertices of the polygon are joined to a point V outside the plane of the polygon, V is called the *vertex* of the pyramid. If V is equidistant from all the vertices of the polygon, the pyramid is a *right pyramid*. The line from V to any corner of the polygon is called a *slant edge*, and the perpendicular distance from V to the base is the *height* of the pyramid.

The volume of any pyramid $= \dfrac{1}{3} \times$ base area

$\times$ perpendicular height

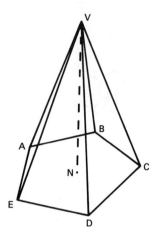

EXAMPLE 3

VABCD is a right pyramid with a rectangular base measuring 8 cm by 6 cm. If each slant edge is 10 cm in length, calculate the volume of the pyramid and the area of one of the smaller sloping faces.

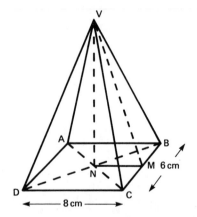

Let the diagonals of the rectangle ABCD intersect in N and let M be the midpoint of BC. Then BM = 3 cm. Using Pythagoras' theorem for triangle VBM:

$$VB^2 = VM^2 + MB^2$$

i.e. $VM^2 = VB^2 - MB^2$

$$= 10^2 - 3^2 \, \text{cm}^2$$

$\therefore VM^2 = 91 \, \text{cm}^2$

i.e. $VM = 9.539 \, \text{cm}$

Similarly for triangle VNM:

$$VM^2 = VN^2 + NM^2$$

$$VN^2 = VM^2 - NM^2$$

$$= 91 - 16 \text{ cm}^2 \quad \text{since} \quad NM = 4 \text{ cm}$$

$$\therefore VN^2 = 75 \text{ cm}^2$$

i.e. $VN = 8.660$ cm

$$\text{Volume of pyramid} = \frac{1}{3} \text{ area ABCD} \times VN$$

$$= \frac{1}{3} \times 8 \times 6 \times 8.660 \text{ cm}^3$$

$$= 138.56 \text{ cm}^3$$

$$= 139 \text{ cm}^3$$

$$\text{Area } \triangle VBC = \frac{1}{2} BC \times VM$$

$$= \frac{1}{2} \times 6 \times 9.539 \text{ cm}^2$$

$$= 28.617 \text{ cm}^2$$

$\therefore$ Area of one of the smaller sloping faces $= 28.6 \text{ cm}^2$.

EXERCISE 73

Find the volume of a pyramid with:

1. Height 10 cm, base area 30 cm^2

2. Height 18 cm, base area 45 cm^2

3. Height 8 cm, base a square of side 5 cm

4. Height 4.5 cm, base a rectangle measuring 9 cm by 6 cm.

5. Find the height of a pyramid which has a volume of 600 cm^3 if the area of its base is 25 cm^2.

6. Find the height of a pyramid which has a volume of 96 cm^3 if its base is a square of side 6 cm.

7. Find the volume of a right pyramid which has a square base of side 8 cm and slant height 12 cm.

8. Find the volume of a right pyramid which has a rectangular base measuring 12 cm by 10 cm, and a slant height of 15 cm.

9. The volume of a right pyramid with a rectangular base measuring 8 cm by 6 cm is 160 cm^3. Find the length of a slant edge.

10. The volume of a right pyramid with a square base of side 5 cm is $100 \, \text{cm}^3$. Find (a) its height, (b) the length of one of its slant edges.

11. A right pyramid has a square base and is of height 15 cm. If its volume is $245 \, \text{cm}^3$, calculate the length of a side of its base.

12. A right pyramid has a rectangular base whose length is twice its width. If the volume of the pyramid is $256 \, \text{cm}^3$ and its height is 6 cm, calculate the dimensions of its base.

13. Find the total surface area of a right pyramid with a square base of side 8 cm and slant edge 10 cm.

14. The rectangular base of a right pyramid measures 15 cm by 10 cm. If its height is 20 cm, calculate (a) its volume, (b) the total area of its sloping faces.

15. A right pyramid of height 10 cm has an hexagonal base of side 4 cm. Calculate its volume and the area of one of the sloping sides.

THE CIRCLE

Careful measurement will show that when the circumference or perimeter of a circle is divided by its diameter the answer is approximately 3.14. You can check this by drawing a circle of radius 5 cm, setting your dividers or compasses at 1 cm and 'walking' them around the circumference until you are back at the starting point. Even more accurate will be the value obtained by wrapping a piece of string around a drum with circular cross-section and dividing this value by the diameter of the drum.

The ratio $\dfrac{\text{Circumference of circle}}{\text{Diameter of circle}}$ is denoted by the Greek letter π (pronounced 'pie'). While its exact value cannot be expressed as a common fraction, a good approximation is given by $\frac{22}{7}$. Apart from fairly simple questions it is more usual to use 3.142 which is the value of π correct to three decimal places.

It follows that if C denotes the circumference of a circle with diameter D, then:

$$\frac{C}{D} = \pi \quad \text{i.e.} \quad C = \pi D$$

If the radius of this circle is R, then $D = 2R$ giving $C = 2\pi R$. This formula should be learnt because it is extremely important.

EXAMPLE 4   Find the circumference of a circle of radius 35 cm. Take $\pi = \frac{22}{7}$.

$C = 2\pi R$

$\qquad = 2 \times \dfrac{22}{7} \times 35$

i.e. Circumference $= 220$ cm

EXAMPLE 5   Find the circumference of a circle of radius 9 cm. Take $\pi = 3.142$ and give your answer correct to three significant figures.

$C = 2\pi R$

$\qquad = 2 \times 3.142 \times 9$

$\qquad = 56.556$

i.e. Circumference $= 56.6$ cm

EXAMPLE 6   Find the radius of a circle whose circumference is 10 cm. Take $\pi = \frac{22}{7}$, and give your answer correct to two decimal places.

$C = 2\pi R$

i.e. $10 = 2 \times \dfrac{22}{7} \times R$ where R is the radius in cm

i.e. $44R = 70$

$\therefore R = \dfrac{70}{44}$

$\qquad = 1.591$

i.e. Radius $= 1.59$ cm

EXAMPLE 7   The diameter of the wheel of a car is 77 cm. How many revolutions will the wheel make when the car travels 20 km? (Take $\pi = \frac{22}{7}$)

Circumference of wheel is given by $2\pi R$

$\qquad = 2 \times \dfrac{22}{7} \times \dfrac{77}{2}$ cm

$\qquad = 242$ cm

$\qquad = 2.42$ m

$\therefore$ In one revolution of the wheel the car travels 2.42 m.

∴ Number of revolutions of the wheel in travelling 20 km or 20 000 metres is:

$$\frac{20\,000\ m}{2.42\ m} = 8264$$

(correct to the nearest whole number)

EXERCISE 74

Give all answers that are not exact correct to three significant figures. Take $\pi = \frac{22}{7}$ unless stated otherwise.

Find the circumference of a circle with:

1. Radius 7 cm
2. Radius 21 cm
3. Radius 4.9 m
4. Diameter 42 cm
5. Diameter 11.2 cm
6. Diameter 67.2 cm
7. Radius 84 m
8. Diameter 7.56 m
9. Radius 0.63 km.

Take $\pi = 3.142$ in questions 10 to 15. Find the circumference of a circle with:

10. Radius 5 cm
11. Radius 0.8 m
12. Radius 2.5 cm
13. Diameter 3.5 m
14. Diameter 300 cm
15. Diameter 6 km.

Find the radius of a circle whose circumference is:

16. 308 cm
17. 5.28 m
18. 572 cm
19. 1144 m
20. 70.4 cm
21. 40.48 m.

Find the perimeters of the following figures. The curved lines represent the whole, three-quarters, half, or a quarter of the circumference of a circle.

22.

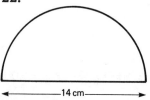

—14 cm—

23.

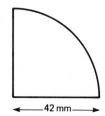

—42 mm—

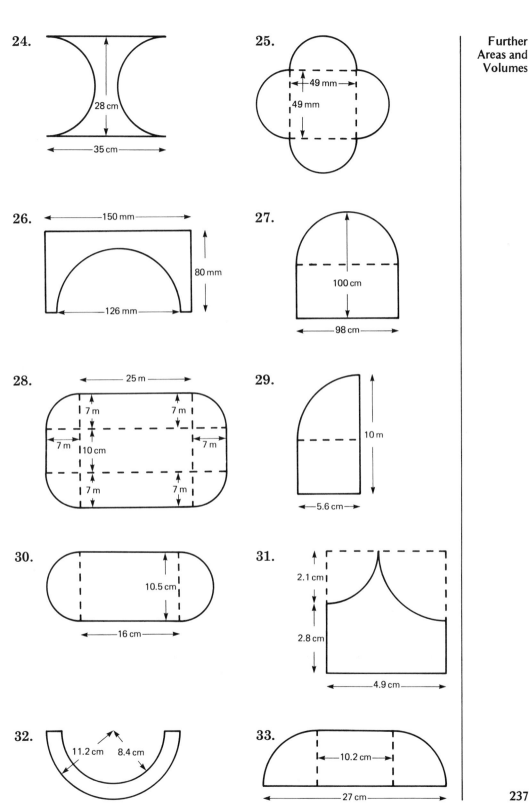

24. 28 cm, 35 cm

25. 49 mm, 49 mm

26. 150 mm, 80 mm, 126 mm

27. 100 cm, 98 cm

28. 25 m, 7 m, 7 m, 7 m, 7 m, 10 cm, 7 m, 7 m

29. 10 m, 5.6 cm

30. 10.5 cm, 16 cm

31. 2.1 cm, 2.8 cm, 4.9 cm

32. 11.2 cm, 8.4 cm

33. 10.2 cm, 27 cm

34.

35.

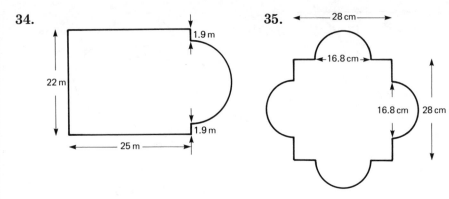

36.

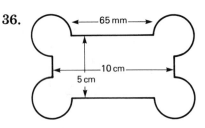

37. The diameter of a circular running track is 126 m. Find the length of its circumference.

38. A bicycle wheel is 66 cm in diameter. How many revolutions does it make per kilometre? Give your answer correct to the nearest whole number.

39. The total distance around a circular pond is 330 m. Find its radius.

40. A circular running track with an inner radius of 98 m is 7 m wide. How much further is it around the outer edge of the track than the inner?

41. The diameter of a 10 p piece is 28 mm. Find its circumference.

42. If the diameter of a penny is 20 mm, find its circumference correct to the nearest millimetre.

43. A quadrant of radius 3.5 cm is cut away from each corner of a square of side 10 cm. Find the perimeter of the resulting figure.

44. A rope may be wound 35 times around a metal drum of radius 30 cm. How long is the rope?

45. A circular Scalextric track allows one car to move in a circle of radius 77 cm while the other car moves in a circle of radius 70 cm. How much further does a car on the outer track move than one on the inner track if both cars complete 10 circuits?

46. In a training session an athlete makes 25 circuits of a circular track of radius 56 m. How far has she run?

47. The minute hand of the town clock is 1.4 m long while the hour hand is 0.91 m long. How far does the tip of each hand move in one hour?

48. A goat is tethered by a rope 5.6 m long to the corner of a rectangular field. Find the length of the perimeter of the area of grass from which the goat may eat.

49. A circular tablecloth is to be made for a circular table of radius 60 cm. If the overhang is to be everywhere 12 cm, find the circumference of the tablecloth. Take $\pi = 3.142$ and give your answer correct to the nearest whole number.

50. The diameter of a long-playing record is 30 cm and it revolves at $33\frac{1}{3}$ revolutions per minute. Find the speed of a point:
    (a) at the centre of the record
    (b) at a point on its rim
    (c) at a point half-way along a radius. (Take $\pi = 3.142$.)

51. A rope which is 99 m long can be wound exactly 25 times around a circular drum. Find the diameter of the drum.

52. A length of copper wire 66 cm long is cut into two pieces each of which is bent into a circle. If the diameter of the larger circle is twice that of the smaller, find the two diameters.

53. A metal spring, made from wire 1 mm thick, is 40 cm long and has a circular cross-section of radius 14 mm. Find the length of wire required to make the spring, giving your answer correct to the nearest metre.

54. A cylinder lawn mower is 35 cm wide and has a diameter of 21 cm. Assuming that when it is used the cylinder revolves without slipping, calculate:
    (a) the distance moved forward by the mower for each revolution of the wheel
    (b) the number of complete revolutions required to mow a straight run of 99 m.

55. An artist in a china factory paints a gold line, 0.5 cm from the edge, on saucers of diameter 12 cm, on plates of diameter 15 cm, and also on the tops of cylindrical cups of diameter 7 cm. Calculate the total length of gold line painted on a half-dozen teaset. Take $\pi = 3.142$, and give your answer correct to three significant figures.

AREA OF A CIRCLE AND AN ANNULUS

The formula for the area A of a circle of radius R may be shown to be given by $A = \pi R^2$. The proof is a little beyond our present level, but drawing a circle of any radius (5 cm is convenient) on squared paper, and counting the squares to give its area will show that the ratio $\dfrac{\text{Area of circle}}{\text{Square of radius}}$ is approximately equal to 3.14 or π.

i.e.
$$\frac{A}{R^2} = \pi \quad \text{or} \quad A = \pi R^2$$

It is only a small step from the area of a circle to the area of an *annulus* or *ring*, which is bounded by two concentric circles. If the inner radius is denoted by r and the outer one by R, then the area within the circle of radius R is πR^2 and the area within the circle of radius r is πr^2.

Hence the area of the annulus (which is shaded in the diagram) is given by:

$$A = \pi R^2 - \pi r^2$$
$$= \pi(R^2 - r^2)$$
i.e.
$$A = \pi(R + r)(R - r)$$

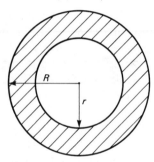

EXAMPLE 8   Find the area of a circle of radius 4.2 cm. ($\pi = 3\frac{1}{7}$)

$$A = \pi R^2$$

$$\text{Area} = \frac{22}{7} \times 4.2 \times 4.2 \text{ cm}^2$$

i.e. Area $= 55.44 \text{ cm}^2$

EXAMPLE 9   If the diameter of a 10 p coin is 2.8 cm, find the area of one side. ($\pi = 3\frac{1}{7}$)

$$A = \pi R^2$$

$$\text{Area of one side} = \frac{22}{7} \times 1.4 \times 1.4 \text{ cm}^2$$

i.e. Area $= 6.16 \text{ cm}^2$

EXAMPLE 10   The diagram below shows a metal washer in the form of an annulus with internal and external radii 0.6 cm and 1.5 cm respectively. Find the shaded area. $(\pi = 3\frac{1}{7})$

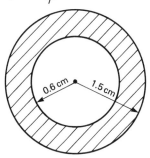

$$A = \pi(R+r)(R-r)$$

where R and r are the external and internal radii.

$$\therefore \text{ Area } = \frac{22}{7}(1.5+0.6)(1.5-0.6) \text{ cm}^2$$

$$= \frac{22}{7} \times 2.1 \times 0.9 \text{ cm}^2$$

i.e. Area $= 5.94 \text{ cm}^2$

Arc Length and Area of a Sector of a Circle

Starting with the radius OA, suppose we draw radii from O, the centre of the circle, at $1°$ intervals to cut the circumference of the circle. Since the sum of all the $1°$ angles at O is $360°$, two consecutive radii cut off an arc length on the circumference which is $\dfrac{1}{360}$ of the circumference of the circle. It follows that if $\angle AOB = \theta°$ (Greek letter θ pronounced 'theta'), then the arc length AB is $\dfrac{\theta}{360}$ of the circumference of the circle

i.e. $$\text{Arc length AB} = 2\pi R \times \frac{\theta}{360}$$

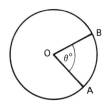

Similar reasoning leads to the result that:

$$\text{The area of the sector OAB} = \pi R^2 \times \frac{\theta}{360}$$

EXAMPLE 11   Find the arc length of a circle of radius 10 cm that subtends an angle of $147°$ at its centre. What is the area of the sector so formed? (Take $\pi = 3\frac{1}{7}$)

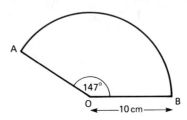

$$\text{Arc length} = 2\pi R \times \frac{\theta}{360}$$

$$\therefore \text{Arc length AB} = 2 \times \frac{22}{7} \times 10 \times \frac{147}{360} \text{ cm}$$

$$= \frac{77}{3} \text{ cm}$$

$$= 25\frac{2}{3} \text{ cm}$$

$$\text{Area of sector OAB} = \pi R^2 \times \frac{\theta}{360}$$

$$= \frac{22}{7} \times 100 \times \frac{147}{360} \text{ cm}^2$$

$$= \frac{770}{6} \text{ cm}^2$$

$$= 128\frac{1}{3} \text{ cm}^2$$

EXERCISE 75

Take $\pi = 3\frac{1}{7}$ unless stated otherwise.

1. Find the area of a circle with:
   (a) radius 14 mm,
   (b) diameter 8.4 cm,
   (c) radius 0.21 cm,
   (d) radius 4 m,
   (e) diameter 10 m,
   (f) diameter 25 cm.

2. Find the radius of a circle with area (a) 154 cm², (b) 6.16 m², (c) 124.74 m².

3-17. Find the area of each of the figures given in questions 22 to 36 of Exercise 74.

18. Two circles have radii 2 cm and 3 cm. Find the ratio of their areas.

19. Two circles have radii 4 cm and 5 cm. Find the ratio of (a) their diameters, (b) their perimeters, (c) their areas.

20. The areas of two circles are 20 cm^2 and 45 cm^2. Find the ratio of their radii.

21. The ratio of the areas of two circles is $36:49$. Find the ratio of their radii.

22. A circle of radius 3.5 cm is cut from a square piece of paper of side 10 cm. Find the area remaining.

23. The area of a circular pond is 1386 m^2. Find its perimeter.

24. From a thin square metal plate of side 20 cm, four quadrants of a circle, each of radius 7 cm, are cut away at the corners. Find (a) the area cut away, (b) the area remaining.

25. A circular pond is 98 m in diameter. A fisherman, who is able to fish from anywhere along the edge of the pond, hopes to catch any fish coming within 14 m of the edge. Find the area of water for which:
    (a) the fish are outside the fisherman's range
    (b) the fisherman can expect to catch something.

26. Find the area of a circular running track 3.5 m wide if the inner radius is 100 m.

27. Find the radius of a circle whose area is equal to the sum of the areas of two circles with radii respectively 3 cm and 4 cm.

28. Find the radius of a circle whose area is equal to the difference in the areas of two circles with respective radii 13 cm and 12 cm.

29. A piece of lace is to be crocheted to edge a plain white circular tablecloth with a radius of 56 cm. If the edging is to be 7 cm wide all the way round, calculate the area of lace to be crocheted.

30. A copper pipe has a bore of 21 mm and an external diameter of 25 mm. Find its cross-sectional area.

THE CYLINDER

A solid, such as a length of wire or a pencil, whose cross-section is circular and uniform, is called a *circular cylinder*. The radius of the circular cross-section is called the radius of the cylinder, and the straight line which passes through the centre of all the cross-sections is called the axis of the cylinder. The length of this axis is called the *length* of the cylinder—as in the case of a jam roll or a piece of dowelling. However, it may be referred to as the *height*, as in the case of a can or jug with circular cross-section, or the *thickness*, as in the case of a circular disc or coin, or even as the *width*, as in the case of a roll of wallpaper or garden roller. The word chosen depends on the position of the axis of the cylinder, i.e. whether it is horizontal or vertical, and the relative proportions.

If you look at a cylindrical metal can you will usually find a seam where the metal forming the curved part has been joined. Carefully remove the circular top and bottom, and cut the curved part along the length of the seam. The curved part will open out into a flat surface in the shape of a rectangle. The diagrams show the three areas which make up the surface of the cylinder.

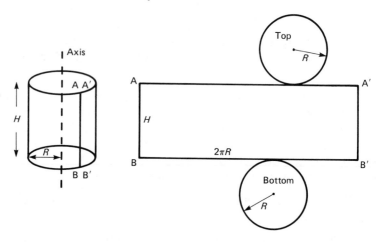

The distance AA′ which represents the length of the rectangle is exactly the same as the perimeter of the circular top. Similarly for BB′. The area of the curved surface of the cylinder is therefore equal to the circumference of any circle of cross-section multiplied by the height of the cylinder.

If the radius of the cylinder is R units and the height H units, the curved surface area A is given by:

$$A = 2\pi RH \text{ square units}$$

The area of each circular end will be πR^2 square units.

∴   The total surface area
of a *solid* or *closed* $= 2\pi R^2 + 2\pi RH$ square units
cylinder $= 2\pi R(R + H)$ square units

and   The total external
surface area of an $= \pi R^2 + 2\pi RH$ square units
open cylinder $= \pi R(R + 2H)$ square units

(e.g. a cylindrical mug or drinking glass).

Particular care must be taken with *units*, because it is not uncommon for the radius and height (or length) to be given in different units (e.g. the radius in centimetres but the length in metres).

EXAMPLE 12   Calculate the total surface area, correct to three significant figures, of a closed cylindrical can of radius 6.3 cm and height 20 cm. $(\pi = 3\frac{1}{7})$

$$\text{Surface area} = 2\pi R (R + H)$$
$$= 2 \times \frac{22}{7} \times 6.3 \times (6.3 + 20) \text{ cm}^2$$
$$= 44 \times 0.9 \times 26.3 \text{ cm}^2$$
$$= 1041.48 \text{ cm}^2$$
$$= 1040 \text{ cm}^2$$

EXERCISE 76

Take $\pi = 3\frac{1}{7}$ unless stated otherwise.

Find (a) the curved surface area, (b) the total surface area of a solid circular cylinder with:

1. Radius 2.1 cm, height 4 cm

2. Radius 30 cm, length 1.4 m

3. Diameter 1.54 m, length 2.5 m

4. Diameter 3.5 cm, height 11 cm

5. Radius 6.3 cm, thickness 4 mm.

6. Fill in the blanks in the following table:

DESCRIPTION OF CYLINDER	RADIUS	HEIGHT OR LENGTH	EXTERNAL SURFACE AREA
Open	7 cm	20 cm	
Open	10 cm		1100 cm^2
Open		8 m	330 m^2
Closed	12 mm	9 mm	
Closed		6 cm	704 cm^2
Closed	11 mm		2904 mm^2

7. A garden roller has a radius of 35 cm and is 60 cm wide. Find the area rolled, in square metres, during 100 revolutions of the roller.

    How many revolutions are necessary to roll an area of 800 m^2? Give your answer correct to the nearest whole number.

8. A cylindrical can containing mineral water is 10 cm high and has a diameter of 7 cm. Find the total area of sheet metal used in its manufacture.

9. A cylindrical can of soup has radius 3.5 cm and is 15 cm high. The curved area is completely covered by the label. Calculate the area of this label.

10. A cylindrical breakfast cup has a radius of 4 cm and is 8 cm high. Find the surface area of the cup in contact with tea when it is filled to within 0.5 cm of the top. Neglect the thickness of the cup.

11. A cylindrical sherry glass has a diameter of 3.5 cm and is 6 cm high. Find the area of the glass in contact with sherry when it is filled to within 2 mm of the rim.

12. A cylindrical pillar-box is 1.5 m high and has a diameter of 63 cm. Find the area that requires painting.

13. A cylindrical summerhouse is 2.5 m high and has a radius of 2 m. It has a flat roof and is glazed from a height of 0.75 m above the ground, to the roof. Calculate the glazed area. ($\pi = 3.14$)

14. A kitchen table has four cylindrical legs, each of length 0.75 m and diameter 5 cm. If they are to be painted, find the amount of paint required if 1 litre covers $12\,\mathrm{m}^2$.

15. Calculate the total surface area of a coin with diameter 2.5 cm which is 1.5 mm thick. Take $\pi = 3.14$ and give your answer in square centimetres.

VOLUME OF A CIRCULAR CYLINDER

The volume of any solid with a uniform cross-section is equal to the area of cross-section multiplied by its length (or height).

Therefore the volume V of a cylinder of radius R units and height H units is given by:

$$V = \pi R^2 \times H$$

i.e. $\qquad V = \pi R^2 H$ cubic units

EXAMPLE 13 A cylindrical metal can has a base radius of 4.2 cm and is 20 cm high. Calculate the volume of liquid it will hold, giving your answer correct to three significant figures. ($\pi = 3\frac{1}{7}$)

$$V = \pi R^2 H$$

Required volume $= \dfrac{22}{7} \times 4.2 \times 4.2 \times 20 \,\mathrm{cm}^3$

$$= 1108.8\,\mathrm{cm}^3$$

$$= 1110\,\mathrm{cm}^3$$

EXAMPLE 14   Find the base area of a cylinder which has a volume of $300 \, \text{cm}^3$ and is $8.5 \, \text{cm}$ high. Give your answer correct to three significant figures. ($\log \pi = 0.4972$)

Let the radius of the base be R cm. Then using $V = \pi R^2 H$:

$$300 = \pi R^2 \times 8.5$$

i.e. $R^2 = \dfrac{300}{8.5\pi}$ *Logs*

                                                2.4771

$\therefore R = \sqrt{\dfrac{300}{8.5\pi}}$ 0.9294
                                            0.4972
                                            ‾‾‾‾‾‾
                                            1.4266   1.4266
                                                     ‾‾‾‾‾‾
$\quad = 3.352$ 1.0505 ÷ 2

i.e. Radius $= 3.35 \, \text{cm}$ 0.5253

EXERCISE 77

Give all answers that are not exact correct to three significant figures. Take $\pi = 3.142$ or $\log \pi = 0.4972$, whichever is the more convenient.

1. Find the volume of a cylinder of radius $12 \, \text{cm}$ and height $15 \, \text{cm}$.

2. Find the volume of a cylinder of radius $8 \, \text{cm}$ and height $10 \, \text{cm}$.

3. Find the volume of a cylinder of radius $5.4 \, \text{cm}$ and height $12.4 \, \text{cm}$.

4. Find the volume of a cylindrical can of diameter $18 \, \text{cm}$ and height $18 \, \text{cm}$. How much waste space is there if this can is placed inside a box which is in the form of a cube of side $18 \, \text{cm}$?

5. Find the radius of a 5 litre cylindrical can if it is $24 \, \text{cm}$ high.

6. Find the radius of a 20 litre cylindrical drum if it is $40 \, \text{cm}$ high.

7. Find the height of a 10 litre cylindrical can if it has a radius of $14.6 \, \text{cm}$.

8. Find the height of a 50 litre cylindrical drum if it has a radius of $24.5 \, \text{cm}$.

9. A cylindrical milk bottle has a capacity of $568 \, \text{cm}^3$. If it has an $8 \, \text{cm}$ diameter, find its height.

10. Find the volume of a can of baked beans which has a radius of $3.5 \, \text{cm}$ and is $11 \, \text{cm}$ high.

11. A cylindrical jug which is full of water has a radius of $6 \, \text{cm}$ and is $20 \, \text{cm}$ tall. Water from it is poured into cylindrical glasses of diameter $6 \, \text{cm}$ and height $10 \, \text{cm}$. How many such glasses may be filled?

12. A Coronation crown has a diameter of 3.8 cm and is 2.6 mm thick. Find the volume in cubic centimetres of a pack of 25 such coins.

13. A Victorian half-sovereign is 0.8 mm thick and contains 0.23 cm³ of gold. Calculate its diameter, giving your answer correct to the nearest millimetre.

14. A 1797 George III cartwheel penny is 3.2 mm thick and has a diameter of 3.5 cm. Find its volume. If a modern penny is 1.2 mm thick and 2.0 cm in diameter, how many are required to have the same volume as one cartwheel penny? Give your answer correct to the nearest whole number.

15. A one dollar coin is 2.15 mm thick and has a diameter of 3.75 cm. Find the volume of metal used.

16. A solid cube of lead of side 4.2 cm is melted down and recast, without any change in volume, into a circular cylinder whose height is equal to its diameter. Find its height correct to three significant figures.

17. A solid cylindrical block of lead with radius 4 cm and height 8 cm is recast, without any change in volume, into two similar cylinders, one of which has a volume equal to twice the other. In each case the height of the new cylinder is the same as its diameter. Find the dimensions of the two new solids.

18. A 5 m length of copper pipe has an external diameter of 25 mm and is made from copper 1 mm thick. Find the volume of copper used. If a second copper pipe is manufactured with the same external diameter but with the thickness of the metal reduced by 0.1 mm, find:
    (a) the volume of copper saved compared with the original pipe
    (b) the increased amount of water which the pipe will hold.

19. The diagram below shows a semi-circular railway tunnel 1400 m long which has been driven through a mountain. If the height of the tunnel is 5 m, find the volume, in cubic metres, of material which has been removed in its construction, giving your answer correct to three significant figures.

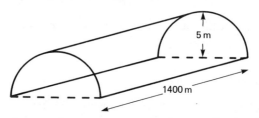

20. Water flows through a cylindrical pipe of diameter 2 cm at 8 m/s. How long will it take to fill a tank of capacity 1000 litres?

21. A cylindrical container whose height is four times its base radius will hold 1 litre. Find its dimensions.

22. A cylindrical petrol can is to contain 5 litres. If its height is equal to the diameter of its base, find its dimensions.

23. A cylindrical jam jar has a volume of $600 \, \text{cm}^3$. If its height is twice its diameter, calculate its dimensions.

24. A cylindrical pencil, with a diameter of 8 mm, needs resharpening. If the pencil is 0.5 cm shorter after sharpening, find the volume of pencil removed.

25. Wooden dowelling with a diameter of 1 cm is made from lengths of timber with a square cross-section of side 1.2 cm. Find the percentage of wood wasted.

26. A 4 m length of tubular metal, external diameter 2 cm and 1.5 mm thick, is required to manufacture a school desk. Calculate the volume of metal used.

27. Copper wire is circular in cross-section with radius 0.4 mm. Find the volume of copper in cubic centimetres used in a 100 m length. If the mass of each cubic centimetre of copper is 8.9 g, find the total mass in kilograms.

28. The diagram shows the section through a cylindrical bottle top which is everywhere 1.5 mm thick. If its external diameter is 16 mm and its external height 16 mm, calculate the volume of material used in its manufacture.

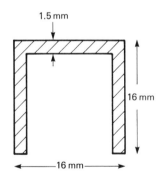

1.5 mm

16 mm

16 mm

29. An 8 m length of guttering along the front of a house has a semi-circular cross-section of diameter 11.5 cm. If there are stoppers at each end, calculate the maximum volume of water in cubic metres that the guttering will hold at any one time.

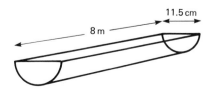

11.5 cm

8 m

30. The diagram shows a horse trough with semi-circular cross-section. The trough, which is full of water, is 2.5 m long and 35 cm wide. If 124 litres of water is consumed by animals, how much remains?

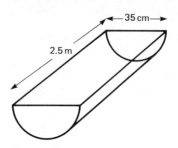

THE RIGHT CIRCULAR CONE

If a sector of a circle is folded so that the bounding radii are joined, the resulting surface is called a right circular cone. Conversely, a right circular cone may be cut along any straight line from a point A on its circular base to its vertex V, and opened out. The resulting shape is a sector of a circle, radius VA.

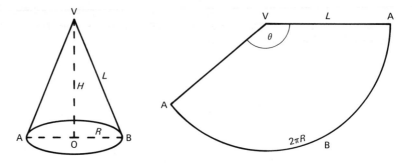

If the angle subtended by the arc length ABA at the centre V is θ, then from previous work $L\theta = 2\pi R$

i.e.
$$\theta = \frac{2\pi R}{L}$$

But area of sector $= \frac{1}{2}(\text{radius})^2 \times \theta$

$\therefore$
$$\text{Area of sector } = \frac{1}{2}L^2 \times \frac{2\pi R}{L} = \pi R L$$

i.e. the curved surface area of a cone, base radius R, slant height L is $\pi R L$.

If O is the centre of the circular base of the cone, VO is defined as the height H of the cone.

Since the cone may be considered as a pyramid, and the volume of a pyramid $= \frac{1}{3}$ base area $\times$ perpendicular height:

$$\text{Volume of cone} \;=\; \frac{1}{3}\pi R^2 H$$

NOTE: $\angle VOA = 90°$, therefore R, H and L are connected by Pythagoras' theorem, i.e. $R^2 + H^2 = L^2$.

EXAMPLE 15 Find the curved surface area and volume of a right circular cone of base radius 12 cm and height 20 cm. Give your answers as multiples of π.

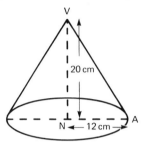

If N is the foot of the perpendicular from the vertex V to the base of the cone with base radius NA, then:

$$VA^2 \;=\; 12^2 + 20^2 \text{ cm}^2$$
$$=\; 144 + 400 \text{ cm}^2$$
$$=\; 544 \text{ cm}^2$$

$$\therefore \; VA \;=\; 23.32 \text{ cm}$$

$$\begin{aligned}
\text{Curved surface area of cone} &= \pi R L \\
&= \pi \times 12 \times 23.2 \text{ cm}^2 \\
&= 278.4\pi \text{ cm}^2
\end{aligned}$$

$$\begin{aligned}
\text{Volume of cone} &= \frac{1}{3}\,\text{base area} \times \text{height} \\
&= \frac{1}{3} \times \pi \times 12^2 \times 20 \text{ cm}^3 \\
&= 960\pi \text{ cm}^3
\end{aligned}$$

EXERCISE 78

Take $\pi = 3.142$ or $\log \pi = 0.4972$, whichever is the more convenient. Give all answers correct to three significant figures.

Find the volumes of the following right circular cones:

1. Height 10 cm, base area 30 cm^2
2. Height 12 cm, base area 42 cm^2

3. Height 6.45 cm, base area 36.93 cm^2

4. Height 23.4 cm, base area 98.64 cm^2

5. Height 12 cm, base radius 5 cm

6. Height 7 cm, base radius 8 cm

7. Height 14.2 cm, base radius 7.5 cm

8. Height 6.34 cm, base radius 4.96 cm

9. Height 4 cm, slant height 5 cm

10. Height 1.6 cm, slant height 2 cm

11. Height 6 cm, slant height 8 cm

12. Base radius 1.2 cm, slant height 1.5 cm

13. Height 5 cm, slant height 13 cm

14. Base radius 7 cm, slant height 12 cm

15. Height 4 cm, perimeter of base 10 cm

16. Height 6 cm, perimeter of base 12 cm.

In questions 17 to 20, find the curved surface areas of the right circular cones with the given dimensions:

17. Slant height 12 cm, base radius 6 cm

18. Slant height 15 cm, base radius 8.5 cm

19. Height 12 cm, base radius 9 cm

20. Height 3.6 cm, base radius 2.7 cm.

21. Find the height of a cone of volume 100 cm^3 if its base radius is 3.75 cm.

22. Find the base radius of a cone of volume 500 cm^3 if its height is 6.5 cm.

23. A conical tent is 2.5 m high and has a base radius of 2 m. Find the area of canvas used.

24. The volume of a cone is 100 cm^3 and its height is 60% more than its base radius. Find its height.

25. Two similar right circular cones are such that the volume of one is three times that of the other. Find the ratio of their radii.

26. A conical tent is 3 m high and the radius of its base is 2.5 m. Find:
     (a) the ground area on which it stands
     (b) its volume.

27. The depth of a conical wine glass is 7 cm and the diameter of its top is 5 cm. Calculate the volume of liquid it holds when it is (a) full, (b) filled to half-way.

28. The diagrams show a salt cellar and pepper pot, each in the form of a right circular cone of base diameter 4 cm and height 9 cm. Find the volume of salt in the salt cellar when it is 4 cm deep, and the volume of pepper in the pepper pot when it is 5 cm deep.

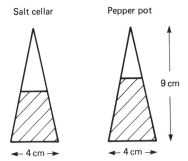

29. A solid wooden cone of base radius r and height h is cut into two pieces by a plane parallel to its base and $\dfrac{h}{3}$ from it. Find the ratio of the volumes of the two parts.

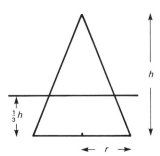

30. The diagram shows a rectangular block of ice-cream measuring 6 cm × 4 cm × 1.5 cm which rests in a cone of base radius 2.5 cm and depth 10 cm. If the ice-cream melts and flows into the cone without any change in volume, find the depth of ice-cream in the cone.

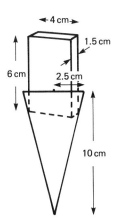

THE SPHERE

One of the most commonly occurring shapes in everyday life is the sphere. It is the shape that contains the largest volume for a given surface area, and will withstand high internal or external pressures.

It can be shown that for a sphere of radius R:

$$\text{Surface area} = 4\pi R^2$$

and

$$\text{Volume} = \frac{4}{3}\pi R^3$$

EXAMPLE 16 Find the volume of a sphere of radius 4.75 cm. Take $\pi = 3.142$.

$$V = \frac{4}{3}\pi R^3$$

$$= 1.333\pi \times 4.75^3 \text{ cm}^3$$

$$= 449 \text{ cm}^3$$

	Logs
	0.1248
	0.4972
0.6767×3	2.0301
	2.6521

EXAMPLE 17 Find the radius of a sphere which has a volume of 1500 cm^3. Take $\pi = 3.142$

$$V = \frac{4}{3}\pi R^3$$

$$\therefore \ 1500 = \frac{4}{3}\pi R^3$$

i.e. $R^3 = \dfrac{4500}{4\pi} \text{ cm}^3$

i.e. $R = \sqrt[3]{\dfrac{1125}{\pi}} \text{ cm}$

Logs
3.0512
0.4972
2.5540 ÷ 3
0.8513

$$= 7.101 \text{ cm}$$

i.e. $R = 7.10$ cm correct to three significant figures.

EXERCISE 79

Give all answers correct to three significant figures. Take $\pi = 3.142$.

Find the surface area and volume of a sphere of:

1. Radius 5 cm
2. Radius 4.26 cm
3. Radius 9.73 cm
4. Diameter 14.62 cm
5. Diameter 2.93 cm
6. Diameter 32.64 cm.

Find the radius and surface area of a sphere with volume:

7. $1000 \, \text{cm}^3$

8. $520 \, \text{cm}^3$

9. $264 \, \text{cm}^3$

10. $0.4164 \, \text{cm}^3$.

Find the volume of a sphere given that its surface area is:

11. $300 \, \text{cm}^2$

12. $724 \, \text{cm}^2$.

13. Find the volume of metal required to produce 50 solid metal spheres each of diameter 6.4 cm.

14. Find the volume of gas contained within a spherical balloon 7.46 m in diameter.

15. Find the volume of china contained in a hemispherical lid of external diameter 8.4 cm, which has a uniform thickness of 3 mm.

16. Calculate the number of lead shot, of diameter 2 mm, that it would be possible to make from a sphere of lead 4 cm in radius.

17. Find the mass of a hollow metal ball, of external diameter 9 cm and thickness 5 mm, if each cubic centimetre of the metal has a mass of 8.9 g.

18. A hollow metal sphere of uniform thickness requires $88 \, \text{cm}^3$ of metal for its manufacture. If its external diameter is 12 cm, find its thickness.

19. Considering the Earth as a sphere of radius 4×10^4 km, calculate (a) its surface area, (b) its volume, giving each answer in standard form.

20. The external diameter of a sphere which is made from metal 2 mm thick is 8 cm. Calculate:
    (a) the volume of metal used
    (b) its mass if each cubic centimetre of the metal has a mass of 8.9 g.

FLOW OF LIQUID IN A PIPE

The amount of liquid that flows through a pipe in a given time depends on two factors: (a) the area of cross-section of the pipe, (b) the speed at which the liquid flows.

EXAMPLE 18   Find the number of litres of water per second issuing through a circular pipe of internal radius 3.5 cm if the water flows at 5 m/s. ($\pi = \frac{22}{7}$)

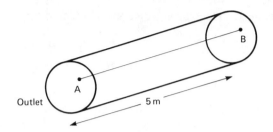

Outlet   A   5 m   B

Consider a particle of water A issuing from the outlet. One second earlier it would have been at B, a distance of 5 m from the outlet, i.e. in one second a cylindrical volume of water with cross-sectional area equal to the area of cross-section of the pipe, and of length 5 m will leave the pipe.

$\therefore$ Volume of water
issuing per second $= \pi \times \text{radius}^2 \times \text{length AB}$

$$= \frac{\overset{11}{\cancel{22}}}{\cancel{7}} \times \frac{\cancel{7}}{\cancel{2}} \times \frac{7}{\cancel{2}} \times \overset{250}{\cancel{500}} \, \text{cm}^3$$

$$= \frac{77 \times 250}{1000} \, \text{litres}$$

$$= \frac{77}{4} \, \text{litres}$$

$$= 19\tfrac{1}{4} \, \text{litres}$$

EXAMPLE 19   Water flows at 8 m/s through a copper pipe of radius 2.5 cm. Find (a) the area of cross-section of the pipe, (b) the amount of water, correct to the nearest litre, flowing through the pipe per minute, (c) the time taken, correct to the nearest minute, to fill a pool which will hold 100 000 litres. ($\pi = 3.142$)

(a) Area of
cross-section $= \pi r^2$

$$= \pi \times 2.5 \times 2.5 \, \text{cm}^2$$
$$= 6.25\pi \, \text{cm}^2$$
$$= 19.64 \, \text{cm}^2$$

Logs

0.7959
0.4972
‾‾‾‾‾‾
1.2931

(b) Amount of water
flowing per second $= 19.64 \times 800 \, \text{cm}^3$

$$= \frac{19.64 \times 800}{1000} \, \text{litres}$$

$$= 15.712 \, \text{litres}$$

$$\therefore \text{ Amount flowing per minute} = 15.712 \times 60 \text{ litres}$$

$$= 942.72 \text{ litres}$$

$$= 943 \text{ litres correct to the nearest litre}$$

(c) Time taken to fill pool $= \dfrac{\text{volume of pool}}{\text{volume entering per minute}}$

$$= \dfrac{100\,000}{943} \text{ minutes}$$

$$= 106 \text{ minutes correct to the nearest minute}$$

EXERCISE 80

1. Find the number of litres of water per second flowing through a pipe of diameter 14 cm if the water flows at 6 m/s. $(\pi = \frac{22}{7})$

2. Find the volume of water per minute flowing through a pipe of radius 21 cm if the water flows at 3.5 m/s. $(\pi = \frac{22}{7})$

3. Water flows at 6.5 m/s in a pipe of diameter 4 cm. What volume will leave the pipe per hour? How long would it take to fill a tank of volume 1000 litres? $(\pi = 3.142)$

4. Water flows from a pipe with diameter 8 cm at 8.4 m/s. Find, in litres, the volume of water leaving the pipe per hour, giving your answer correct to three significant figures. $(\pi = 3.142)$

5. Find the number of gallons of water per minute flowing through a pipe of circular cross-section, radius 5 cm, if the speed of the water is 8 m/s. $(\pi = 3.142, \ 1 \text{ gallon} = 4.546 \text{ litres})$

6. Oil flows along a pipeline at 5 m/s. If the pipe is 28 cm in diameter, find the number of litres flowing through the pipe per hour. $(\pi = \frac{22}{7})$

7. Water flows through an iron pipe with a square cross-section of side 7.5 cm. If the speed of the water is 8 m/s, how long would it take to empty a tank holding 15 000 gallons? Give your answer correct to the nearest minute. $(1 \text{ gallon} = 4.546 \text{ litres})$

8. A pipe with circular cross-section of diameter 8 cm is used to supply the water required for a swimming pool. The water flows in at a steady 6 m/s and it takes exactly half an hour before it is full. Find the total volume of water in the pool when full, giving your answer in gallons correct to three significant figures. $(\pi = 3.142, \ 1 \text{ gallon} = 4.546 \text{ litres})$

9. Water flows at 5.5 m/s through a cylindrical pipe which has a radius of 10 cm. Calculate:
   (a) its area of cross-section
   (b) the volume of water, in litres, issuing from the pipe per minute
   (c) how long it would take to empty a full rectangular tank measuring 8 m by 6 m by 3 m. Give your answers correct to three significant figures. ($\pi = 3.142$)

10. A 1500 km pipeline connects an oil-producing area with a refinery. The cylindrical pipe has a diameter of 35 cm and oil flows along it at a steady speed of 3 m/s. If the oilfield produces 60 000 barrels of oil a day, how long would it take to pump this oil from the oilfield to the refinery, assuming that the whole pipeline is full at the beginning and end of the operation? (1 barrel = 35 gallons, 1 gallon = 4.546 litres, $\pi = \frac{22}{7}$)

SIMILAR SHAPES

AREAS

Consider the three squares shown below which have sides in the ratio $1:2:3$.

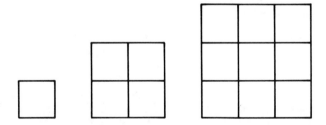

The first square is required four times to cover the same area as the second, and nine times to cover the same area as the third.

i.e.   The ratio of the areas is $1:4:9$

or $1^2:2^2:3^2$

This idea may be extended into any shape and illustrates that *the ratio of the areas of similar shapes is equal to the ratio of the squares of their corresponding linear dimensions.*

If two triangles are similar and the ratio of their corresponding sides is $5:8$, then the ratio of their areas is $5^2:8^2$ or $25:64$.

If two rectangular photographs have been printed from the same negative and the ratio of their widths is $3:4$, then the ratio of their areas will be $3^2:4^2$ or $9:16$.

VOLUMES

Similarly, consider the cubes shown below. The ratio of their sides is $1:2:3:4$.

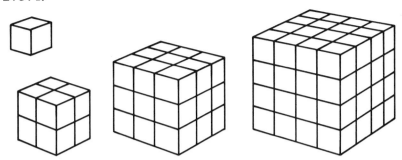

If we take the first cube as the unit cube, 8 of these (2 walls, each with 4 cubes) are required to fill the same space as the second cube, 27 (3 walls, each with 9 cubes) to fill the same space as the third cube, and 64 (4 walls, each with 16 cubes) to fill the same space as the fourth cube.

The ratio of their volumes is therefore $1:8:27:64$

i.e. $\qquad 1^3:2^3:3^3:4^3$

This idea may be extended into any shape and illustrates that *the ratio of the volumes of similar solids is the same as the ratio of the cubes of their corresponding linear dimensions.*

If the radii of two spheres are in the ratio of $2:5$, then the ratio of their volumes will be $2^3:5^3$, i.e. $8:125$.

If the heights of two similar jars of jam are in the ratio $4:5$, the ratio of their volumes will be $4^3:5^3$ or $64:125$.

EXAMPLE 20
A wax figure stands 30 cm high, has a surface area of $400 \, \text{cm}^2$ and a mass of 2 kg. The modeller wants to make a similar wax figure which is twelve times as high. Find, for the new figure (a) its height, (b) its surface area, (c) its mass.

(a) Height of new figure $=$ height of original figure $\times 12$

$\qquad = 30 \times 12 \, \text{cm}$

$\qquad = 360 \, \text{cm}$

(b) $\dfrac{\text{Surface area of new figure}}{\text{Surface area of original figure}} = \dfrac{12^2}{1^2} = \dfrac{144}{1}$

$\therefore$ Surface area of new figure $= 400 \times 144 \, \text{cm}^2$

$\qquad = 57\,600 \, \text{cm}^2$

$\qquad = 5.76 \, \text{m}^2$

(c) $\dfrac{\text{Volume of new figure}}{\text{Volume of original figure}} = \dfrac{12^3}{1^3} = \dfrac{1728}{1}$

$\begin{array}{l}\text{Volume of}\\ \text{new figure}\end{array}$ = volume of original figure $\times 1728$

Since the two models are made from the same material it follows that:

$\begin{array}{l}\text{Mass of}\\ \text{new figure}\end{array}$ = mass of original figure $\times 1728$

$= 2 \times 1728 \text{ kg}$

$= 3456 \text{ kg}$

EXAMPLE 21   The model produced by an art student is considered to be so good that she decides to make a much larger version. The original model is 20 cm long, 12 cm high, has a mass of 2 kg and requires 125 cm^3 of paint to decorate it. If the new model is to be 96 cm high, calculate: (a) its length, (b) the quantity of paint required to decorate it, (c) its mass.

(a) Ratio of heights, of new model to original model, is 96 : 12, i.e. 8 : 1.

$\dfrac{\text{Length of new model}}{\text{Length of original}} = \dfrac{8}{1}$

$\therefore \begin{array}{l}\text{Length of}\\ \text{new model}\end{array}$ = length of original model $\times 8$

$= 20 \times 8 \text{ cm}$

$= 160 \text{ cm}$

(b) $\dfrac{\text{Surface area of new model}}{\text{Surface area of original}} = \dfrac{8^2}{1^2} = \dfrac{64}{1}$

$\therefore \begin{array}{l}\text{Surface area of}\\ \text{new model}\end{array}$ = surface area of original $\times 64$

If 125 cm^3 is required to paint the original model:

$125 \times 64 \text{ cm}^3 = \dfrac{125 \times 64}{1000} \text{ litres}$

$= 8$ litres is required to paint the new model

(c) $\dfrac{\text{Volume of new model}}{\text{Volume of original}} = \dfrac{8^3}{1^3} = \dfrac{512}{1}$

Volume of new model = volume of original $\times 512$

Since they are to be made from the same material:

$$\text{Mass of new model} = \text{mass of original} \times 512$$
$$= 2 \times 512 \text{ kg}$$
$$= 1024 \text{ kg}$$

EXERCISE 81

1. Fill in the blanks in the following table which gives certain data for similar solids. (Some of the ratios are not in their simplest form.)

RATIO OF LENGTHS	RATIO OF SURFACE AREAS	RATIO OF VOLUMES
1:2	1:4	1:8
3:4		
5:2		
2:7		
	49:81	
	100:1	
	9:4	
		125:8
		125:27
		1000:27
		32:108

2. A set of three jugs have similar shapes. The largest jug is 14 cm high, the smallest 10 cm high and the third jug 12 cm. If the volume of the largest jug is 1372 cm^3, find the volumes of the other two.

3. A set of three similar jugs have volumes 256 cm^3, 500 cm^3 and 864 cm^3. If the smallest jug is 8 cm tall, find the heights of the other two.

4. Three cups belonging to a set have similar shapes. The breakfast cup is 8 cm high, the tea cup 7 cm high and the coffee cup 6 cm high. If the volume of the tea cup is 343 cm^3, find the volume of (a) the breakfast cup, (b) the coffee cup.

5. Three similar jars of pickle, produced by a leading manufacturer, have heights 10 cm, 15 cm and 18 cm. If the largest jar holds 729 g, how much will each of the other jars hold? Give your answers correct to the nearest gram.

6. If the peel of an orange, which has a diameter of 10 cm, is 1 cm thick, find the ratio of the edible part to the part which must be thrown away.

7. A motor manufacturer produces a range of three (mathematically) similar cars with engine capacities $1000\,\text{cm}^3$, $1331\,\text{cm}^3$ and $1728\,\text{cm}^3$. If the smallest car is 3.5 m long and has an 8 gallon tank, find the corresponding values for the other two cars, giving your answers correct to three significant figures.

8. A boy makes a model of his home, each linear dimension being $\dfrac{1}{50}$ of the actual dimension.
   (a) If the volume of the actual lounge is $50\,\text{m}^3$, find its volume, in cubic centimetres, in the model.
   (b) If the volume of the main bedroom in the model is $300\,\text{cm}^3$, find its actual volume in cubic metres.

9. A boy makes a model aeroplane with which he is very pleased. It is 20 cm long, has a wing span of 30 cm and a mass of 40 g. He decides to make another similar aeroplane using the same materials but increasing all linear dimensions in the ratio 3:2. Calculate for the new model:
   (a) its wing span
   (b) the ratio by which its wing surface area has increased
   (c) its mass.

10. A DIY supermarket sells screws by mass, a given mass costing £5. Three particular boxes each with the same mass, contain similar screws of lengths 2.5 cm, 5 cm and 7.5 cm respectively. If the box containing the 7.5 cm screws contains 40 of them, how many screws should there be in a box containing (a) 2.5 cm screws, (b) 5 cm screws?

EXERCISE 82 MISCELLANEOUS EXAMPLES

Take $\pi = 3.142$. Give your answers correct to three significant figures.

1. A cube of lead, side 10 cm, is melted down and recast into a sphere. Find its radius.

2. A sphere of lead, radius 5 cm, is melted down and recast into a cube. Find the length of a side of the cube.

3. A lead sphere, radius 4 cm, is melted down and recast into a right circular cylinder with base radius equal to its height. Find the dimensions of the cylinder.

4. A cylindrical beaker, radius 4 cm and height 10 cm, is full of water. How many hemispherical glasses of radius 4 cm may be filled from the beaker?

5. A lead sphere, radius 5 cm, is melted down and recast as lead shot; each shot must have a radius of 1 mm. How many shot may be cast from this sphere?

6. One thousand lead shot, each of radius 1 mm, are melted down and recast into a cylinder whose base diameter is equal to its height. Find this height.

7. A cylindrical bottle, radius 4 cm and height 16 cm, is full of liquid. How many conical glasses, radius 2 cm and depth 6 cm, may be filled from this bottle?

8.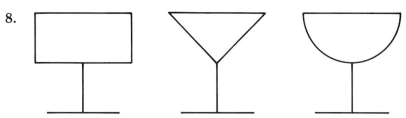

Three wine glasses are in the form of a cylinder, a cone and a hemisphere. When viewed from above, all three are circles of radius r cm. If the three glasses have the same depth, find the ratio of their volumes.

9. A cylindrical bottle of orange squash is of radius 3.5 cm and height 20 cm. It is used to provide glasses of squash for a party by diluting with water in the ratio 1:3. If the cylindrical glasses have a diameter of 6 cm and are 10 cm tall, how many full glasses of diluted squash, correct to the nearest whole number, may be dispensed from one bottle of squash?

10. A rectangular bag of sugar measures 9 cm by 6 cm by 14 cm. How many times may a hemispherical sugar basin of diameter 8 cm be filled from one bag of sugar?

11. A cylindrical measuring glass has a radius of 3 cm and is half full of water. When a metal sphere is dropped into the cylinder the water level rises by 2.5 cm. Find the radius of the sphere.

12. The diagram below shows a metal drinking vessel consisting of a circular base of radius 3 cm and thickness 2 mm, on which stands a cylindrical stem 5 cm tall and 5 mm thick, which supports a hemispherical bowl of external diameter 7 cm and uniform thickness 2 mm. Find:
    (a) the visible outside surface area which would need to be polished
    (b) the volume of metal used.

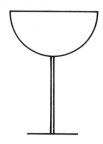

13. A right circular cylinder, base radius 8 cm and height 12 cm, is half-full of water. A solid metal cube of side 10 cm is placed in the water. How much does the water level rise?

14. Two solid metal spheres, each with diameter 18 cm, are placed in a rectangular tank measuring 50 cm by 20 cm which is 30 cm deep and two-thirds full of water. Find the distance by which the water level rises.

15. A wooden sphere has the same volume as the combined volumes of a right circular cylinder and a right circular cone, each of which has a base radius of 5 cm and is of height 12 cm. Find the radius of the sphere.

16. A solid cone, base radius 7 cm and height 14 cm, and a solid sphere, diameter 14 cm, are placed in a cylinder of base radius 7 cm which is 28 cm high. Calculate the volume of the unfilled space in the cylinder and express this as a percentage of the total volume of the cylinder.

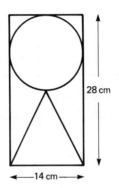

28 cm

←—14 cm—→

17. A cylindrical tin of drinking chocolate has a base diameter of 7 cm and a height of 12 cm. A hemispherical spoon with radius 1.5 cm is provided, and it is suggested that two *heaped* neatly rounded measures are required to make an evening drink. How many such drinks may be made from one tin of drinking chocolate?

18. A factory produces 5000 cans of peas per day. If each can contains 250 g of peas, how many kilograms of peas are required each day?

The cans are cylindrical with a base diameter of 7 cm and a height of 10 cm. Allowing 5 cm^2 for wastage in the manufacture of each tin, calculate the area of sheet metal required to produce the total number of cans used in a day, giving your answer in (a) cm^2, (b) m^2. ($\pi = \frac{22}{7}$)

19. A tin of shoe polish which has a circular cross-section holds 91 millilitres of polish. If the polish is 1.5 cm deep, calculate the diameter of the tin.

20. A child's football has an external diameter of 22 cm and an internal diameter of 21.5 cm. Calculate the volume of material used to make the ball.

21. A salt cellar is in the form of a cylinder, diameter 3 cm and height 3 cm, topped by a hemisphere. It contains salt to a depth of 2.5 cm and is inverted with its outlet covered. Find the distance from the new level of the salt (assumed horizontal) to the flat base of the salt cellar.

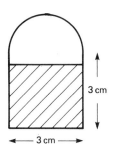

22. The diagram illustrates a milk saucepan which is everywhere circular in horizontal cross-section. The *curved part* has been formed by cutting a cone with base radius 5 cm, from a cone with base radius 7 cm which is 28 cm high. The curved part is welded to a circular metal plate of diameter 10 cm to complete the saucepan. Calculate:
(a) the depth of the saucepan
(b) the area of sheet metal used in the manufacture of the saucepan (neglect its thickness)
(c) the volume of milk, in cm^3, it will hold when full
(d) the volume of milk poured off if the milk level falls to half-way.

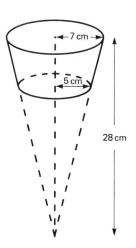

23. A small cylindrical flower vase, of diameter 2 cm and depth 12 cm, is completely filled with water. Three flowers, each with cylindrical stems 3.5 mm in diameter are now placed in the vase so that the stems touch the bottom. Find:
    (a) the amount of water which overflows from the vase
    (b) the amount remaining within it.

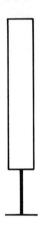

24. Water flowing in a pipe arrives at a junction A where it separates, part flowing in a pipe of diameter 2 cm, and the remainder in a pipe of diameter 1.5 cm. If the cross-sectional area of the pipe (a circle of radius R) bringing the water to the junction is equal to the sum of the cross-sectional areas of the pipes taking the water away from the junction, find R.

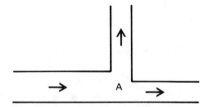

25. The next diagram shows a cylindrical container of diameter 6 cm and height 14 cm, with a cylindrical neck of diameter 3 cm and height 2 cm. The container is closed by means of a metal cap of diameter 3.25 cm and depth 1.5 cm. Calculate:
    (a) the area of sheet metal used to make the container and cap
    (b) the volume of liquid held by the container if it is filled to a level half-way up the neck
    (c) the depth of liquid in the container if $300 \, \text{cm}^3$ of liquid is poured off.

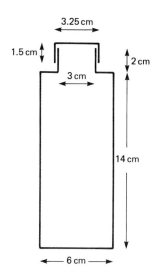

18
TAXES

INCOME TAX

Income tax is a tax on a person's income derived from any source. It was introduced by William Pitt in 1798 as a temporary tax to meet war expenses and, apart from the period 1816-42, has been with us ever since. In arriving at the taxable income, the Inland Revenue allows certain deductions from the gross income for such things as expenses, pension contributions and personal allowances. The gross income after deductions is called the taxable income which is taxed on a graduated scale. The first £12 000 may be taxed at 30% — this is called the *basic rate*; the next £2000 at 40%, the next £4000 at 45%, and so on, at increasing rates until an upper value of taxable income is reached at, say, £30 000. Everything in excess of this figure is taxed at the top rate which may be 60%. The Chancellor of the Exchequer is likely to vary these rates, and the bands to which they apply, according to the financial needs of the country.

While self-employed people pay their income tax in a small number of equal payments, most people have the tax deducted under what is termed *Pay as You Earn* (PAYE). The tax is deducted from their pay each week or month before they receive it. Both the tax payer and the employer receive a Notice of Coding which shows the allowances to which the person is entitled and gives his or her code number. The employer also receives tax tables from the Inland Revenue which show the tax deductions to be made for each code number.

The PAYE code is normally a number followed by a letter. The number is the amount of your total allowances without the last figure. There are several letters which can appear after the number: L for a single person, H for a married man, P, V, T, etc.

A typical Notice of Coding is shown below:

Your Allowances		£
Expenses		80
Loan, etc. interest		–
Personal		3000
Wife's earned income		1500
Dependent relative		200
Total Allowances		**4780**
Less:		
Untaxed interest	360	
Occupational pensions	–	
National Insurance benefits	–	
		360
Net Allowances		**4420**
Less:		
Tax unpaid for earlier years. Equivalent to a deduction of	430	
		430
Allowances given against pay		**3990**
Your code for the year is 399H		

EXAMPLE 1 John Miles earns £10 000 per annum (p.a.) and his allowances amount to £4560. Calculate his annual income tax payments if the basic rate is 30%.

Taxable income $=$ £10 000 $-$ £4560

$\qquad\qquad\quad = $ £5440

Tax on £5440 at 30% $=$ £5440 $\times \dfrac{30}{100}$

$\qquad\qquad\qquad\quad = $ £1632

$\therefore$ Income tax due for the year $=$ £1632

EXAMPLE 2 David Carpenter earns £942 per calendar month. If his total allowances for the year amount to £3470, calculate his monthly income tax deduction if the basic rate is 30%.

Gross annual income $=$ £942 $\times$ 12

$\qquad\qquad\qquad = $ £11 304

Yearly allowance $=$ £3470

$\therefore$ Taxable income $=$ £7834

$$\text{Income tax due for the year} = \text{£}7834 \times \frac{30}{100}$$

$$= \text{£}2350.20$$

$$\therefore \text{ Income tax due each calendar month} = \frac{\text{£}2350.20}{12}$$

$$\therefore \text{ Monthly tax deduction} = \text{£}195.85$$

EXAMPLE 3

Joan Eastwood earns £22 000 p.a. and has allowances of £4800. Her taxable income is taxed as follows:

the first £12 000 of taxable income	30%
the next £2000	40%
balance	45%

Calculate her tax bill and express this as a percentage of her income, giving your answer correct to the nearest whole number.

$$\text{Taxable income} = \text{£}22\,000 - \text{£}4800 = \text{£}17\,200$$

$$\text{Tax on £12 000 at 30\%} = \text{£}12\,000 \times \frac{30}{100} = \text{£}3600$$

$$\text{Tax on £2000 at 40\%} = \text{£}2000 \times \frac{40}{100} = \text{£}800$$

$$\text{Tax on £3200 at 45\%} = \text{£}3200 \times \frac{45}{100} = \text{£}1440$$

$$\therefore \text{ Total tax due} = \text{£}5840$$

$$\% \text{ paid in tax} = \frac{\text{tax paid}}{\text{gross income}} \times 100$$

$$= \frac{5840}{22\,000} \times 100 \text{ i.e. tax paid} = 27\%$$

EXERCISE 83

Calculate the amount of income tax per annum due on each of the following taxable incomes at the basic rate of tax 30%:

1. £10 000
2. £8000
3. £5000
4. £4500
5. £3700
6. £12 000
7. £20 000
8. £50 000
9. £60 000
10. £75 500.

Calculate the amount of income tax due per annum in each of the following for the details given:

	TAXABLE INCOME	BASIC TAX RATE
11.	£7500	35%
12.	£9200	28%
13.	£3400	33%
14.	£17 300	35%
15.	£14 600	27%

Calculate the annual amount of income tax due in each of the following at the given basic rate:

	GROSS INCOME	ALLOWANCES	BASIC TAX RATE
16.	£8000	£2000	30%
17.	£5000	£1500	30%
18.	£6300	£1800	30%
19.	£10 000	£2400	30%
20.	£7500	£2175	30%
21.	£9550	£1920	30%
22.	£8640	£1734	30%
23.	£12 570	£2650	30%
24.	£5420	£2155	30%
25.	£7736	£1876	30%
26.	£8800	£2100	33%
27.	£9260	£1560	32%
28.	£6430	£1810	28%
29.	£10 249	£2114	35%
30.	£11 530	£2654	34%

Calculate the monthly income tax which is due for each of the following:

	GROSS ANNUAL INCOME	TOTAL ANNUAL ALLOWANCES	BASIC TAX RATE
31.	£8400	£1790	30%
32.	£7960	£2430	30%
33.	£6555	£3245	30%
34.	£9276	£1936	33%
35.	£6548	£2841	35%

Calculate, correct to the nearest penny, the weekly income tax that is due for each of the following:

	GROSS ANNUAL INCOME	TOTAL ANNUAL ALLOWANCES	BASIC TAX RATE
36.	£7680	£1820	30%
37.	£8295	£2245	30%
38.	£12 470	£2197	30%
39.	£9354	£3562	32%
40.	£16 735	£4372	28%

The rates of tax and bands of taxable income for the year are:

			£
Basic rate	30%		14 000
Higher rates	40%		14 001–16 000
	45%		16 001–18 000
	50%		18 001–23 000
	55%		23 001–30 000
	60%		over 30 000

Use this information to calculate the total income tax due on a taxable income of:

41. £17 500   42. £22 000   43. £26 500

44. £44 000   45. £72 000   46. £90 000

47. £230 000   48. £460 000.

49. Mr Wright receives a gross salary of £1450 per month. His allowances per annum are: £2800 as a married man, £100 for a dependent relative, 6% of his gross salary for his pension fund, £1800 home improvement loan interest. Calculate for the year:
   (a) his total allowances
   (b) his taxable income
   (c) the tax he must pay if the tax rate is 30%.

50. Miss Anderson receives a gross wage of £470 per week for a 52 week year. Her allowances per annum are as follows:
   Single person £1550
   Pension fund 8% of gross wage
   Home improvement loan interest 14% of £14 000.

   Calculate for the year:
   (a) Miss Anderson's total allowances
   (b) her taxable income
   (c) the income tax due at the basic rate of 33%.

VALUE ADDED TAX (VAT)

If you have an income which is above a certain figure, you must, by law, pay income tax; if you live in a house or flat you must pay local taxes in the form of rates; but with value added tax (VAT) you can be said to have some choice as to whether or not you pay it. Value added tax is a tax on the value added to an article or service, a tax which the last in a line of buying and selling pays in full. It is payable on virtually everything except most foods, fuel, exports and certain children's needs such as clothes and footwear. The only way you can avoid paying VAT is by keeping your money in your pocket. If you buy furniture, go to a concert, go out for a meal, or even buy a few sweets, you will pay VAT.

The Chancellor of the Exchequer may vary the rate of VAT from time to time.

EXAMPLE 4   A married couple buy a set of kitchen units, price £1200 + VAT. How much will they pay for the units if the VAT rate is 15%?

$$\text{VAT due is 15\% of £1200} = £1200 \times \frac{15}{100}$$

$$= £180$$

∴ Total cost of units $= £1200 + £180 = £1380$

EXAMPLE 5   Jane pays £9.52 for an LP record. If this price includes VAT at 12%, what was the price of the record before VAT was added?

Method 1   If the price of the record exclusive of VAT is £A, then the VAT to be added is £$A \times \dfrac{12}{100}$

i.e. the price inclusive of VAT is

$$£A + \frac{12A}{100} = £\frac{112}{100}A$$

But this price is £9.52

$$∴ £\frac{112}{100}A = £9.52$$

i.e. $A = £\dfrac{9.52 \times 100}{112} = £8.50$

Method 2   Let 100% be the price of the record *exclusive* of VAT, then 112% of this price will be the price of the record *inclusive* of VAT

i.e. 112% of this price $= £9.52$

273

$$\therefore \ 1\% = £\frac{9.52}{112}$$

$$\therefore \ \text{Price exclusive of VAT} = 100\% = £\frac{9.52}{112} \times 100$$

$$= £8.50$$

EXERCISE 84

In questions 1 to 25 the rate of VAT is 15%. Use this value to calculate the cash price of:

1. A set of woodworking tools priced £85 + VAT

2. A record priced £5 + VAT

3. A suite of furniture costing £600 + VAT

4. A bucket costing £2.25 + VAT

5. A pair of shoes costing £27 + VAT

6. A tyre costing £32 + VAT

7. A book marked at £12.50 + VAT

8. A china teaset priced £35.50 + VAT

9. Half a kilogram of sweets priced £1.80 + VAT

10. Ten rolls of wallpaper marked £5.50 per roll + VAT

11. A cut-glass vase marked £85 + VAT

12. Three fountain pens each marked £5.30 + VAT

13. A ticket for a concert marked £7.50 + VAT

14. An electric fire marked £26.40 + VAT

15. A food mixer marked £64.30 + VAT

16. Two bicycle wheels marked £7.60 each + VAT

17. Glass costing £12 + VAT per square metre

18. Bed and breakfast for two costing £42 + VAT

19. A three-course meal costing £4.40 + VAT

20. A load of sand costing £25.50 + VAT

21. Light-fittings marked £16.60 + VAT

22. A hammer marked £9.55 + VAT

23. Motorcycle helmets costing £38 + VAT

24. A pine table costing £176.50 + VAT

25. A clock marked £227.50 + VAT.

26. If a pair of walking shoes costs £40.25 including VAT at 15%, find the price before the tax was added.

27. The selling price of a carpet is £483 including VAT at 15%. Calculate its price before the VAT was added.

28. A customer pays £328.90 for a washing machine. If this price includes VAT at 15%, find the price of the machine if VAT is reduced to 10%.

29. When VAT is 15%, the price of a pressure cooker to the customer is £34.50. Find its new price if VAT is reduced to 12%.

30. When VAT is 10%, the price of an LP record is £8.25. What will it cost if the VAT is increased to 15%?

31. A wheel-barrow costs £15.68 including VAT at 12%. If the VAT is increased to 15%, find the new price of the wheel-barrow.

32. A fur coat costs £1080 including VAT at $12\frac{1}{2}$%. Find the increase in the price if the rate of VAT rises to 25%.

33. The purchase price of a gold necklace falls by £7.20 when VAT is reduced from 16% to 12%. Find its original purchase price.

34. The purchase price of a diamond ring increases by £22.50 when VAT is increased from 15% to 20%. Find the original purchase price of the ring.

35. The purchase price of a dining table and chairs increases by £44.10 when VAT rises from 8% to 15%. Find the new price of the table and chairs.

CAPITAL GAINS TAX (CGT)

Capital gains tax was introduced in April 1965 as a tax on capital gained by any UK resident. The normal rate is the same as the basic rate of income tax, several thousand pounds each year being exempt from the tax. The tax applies to gains from buying and selling property (except your own home), as well as to stocks and shares. If an investor buys some shares which show a good profit but others which show a loss, the losses may be set against the gains before the tax is calculated. The allowances and rate of capital gains tax may change from time to time.

EXAMPLE 6

Mr Freeman buys a property for £25 000 and sells it six years later for £78 000. If the capital gains tax rate is 30% and the first £5000 of the gain is exempt, find the total capital gains tax which Mr Freeman will have to pay.

Capital gain on the property $=$ £78 000 $-$ £25 000

$=$ £53 000

Since the first £5000 is exempt, the CGT is due on:

£53 000 $-$ £5000 $=$ £48 000

Tax on this at 30% $=$ £48 000 $\times \dfrac{30}{100}$

$=$ £14 400

$\therefore$ Capital gains tax due is £14 400

EXERCISE 85

Find the capital gains tax due in each of the following:

	CAPITAL GAIN	AMOUNT EXEMPT	RATE
1.	£12 000	£5000	30%
2.	£26 000	£5000	30%
3.	£14 000	£5000	32%
4.	£21 000	£5000	33%
5.	£36 000	£5500	30%
6.	£17 600	£6000	30%
7.	£48 000	£6000	32%
8.	£28 000	£5000	25%
9.	£167 000	£7500	35%
10.	£4 300 000	£8000	30%

Calculate the total capital gain in each of the following:

	TOTAL CGT PAID	AMOUNT EXEMPT	RATE
11.	£8100	£5000	30%
12.	£4800	£5000	30%
13.	£1960	£5000	35%
14.	£6880	£5500	32%
15.	£169 200	£6000	30%

CAPITAL TRANSFER TAX (CTT)

Capital transfer tax was introduced to tax capital which is given by one person to another during the lifetime of the donor, or which passes to a beneficiary at the donor's death. (The tax replaced Estate Duty.) Only the donor or trustees of an estate need to declare such transfers. Two rates of capital transfer tax are in use: one for gifts or transfers during the donor's lifetime, and a higher rate for transfers as a result of death. The rates given below were set in 1982 and will change each year according to the change in the Retail Price Index.

£000's	PERCENTAGE RATE (DEATH)	PERCENTAGE RATE (LIFETIME)
0–55	nil	nil
55–75	30	15
75–100	35	$17\frac{1}{2}$
100–130	40	20
130–167	45	$22\frac{1}{2}$
167–200	50	25
200–250	55	30
250–650	60	35
650–1250	65	40
1250–2500	70	45
Over 2500	75	50

EXAMPLE 7   A father gives his son £85 000. Calculate the capital transfer tax due on the transfer.

Capital transfer tax due on first £55 000 is nil

Capital transfer tax due on next £20 000 at a rate of 15%:

$$£20\,000 \times \frac{15}{100} = £3000$$

Capital transfer tax due on the balance of £10 000 at a rate of 17.5%:

$$£10\,000 \times \frac{17.5}{100} = £1750$$

∴ Total CTT due = £3000 + £1750 = £4750

EXAMPLE 8 A parent dies leaving £145 000 equally between four children. How much will each child receive?

Capital transfer tax is due as follows (the cumulative amount taxed is given in brackets):

First £55 000 (£55 000) nil

$$\text{Next £20 000 (£75 000) at 30\%} = £20\,000 \times \frac{30}{100}$$

$$= £6000$$

$$\text{Next £25 000 (£100 000) at 35\%} = £25\,000 \times \frac{35}{100}$$

$$= £8750$$

$$\text{Next £30 000 (£130 000) at 40\%} = £30\,000 \times \frac{40}{100}$$

$$= £12\,000$$

$$\text{Balance of £15 000 (£145 000) at 45\%} = £15\,000 \times \frac{45}{100} = £6750$$

$$\therefore \text{ Total CTT due} = £6000 + £8750 + £12\,000 + £6750$$

$$= £33\,500$$

$$\text{i.e. Amount received by each child} = £\frac{145\,000 - 33\,500}{4}$$

$$= £\frac{111\,500}{4}$$

$$= £27\,875$$

EXERCISE 86

Use the rates and bands for capital transfer tax given in the text.

Calculate the total capital transfer tax due on each of the following gifts made during the lifetime of the donor:

1. £40 000   2. £60 000   3. £70 000

4. £95 000   5. £182 000   6. £136 000

7. £59 000   8. £2 434 000   9. £604 000.

Calculate the total capital transfer tax due on each of the following transfers at the time of death:

10. £70 000   11. £50 000   12. £93 000

13. £76 000	14. £43 500	15. £130 000	Taxes
16. £82 500	17. £434 000	18. £733 000.	

19. A man died leaving £260 000 between his five children. How much would each receive after capital transfer tax had been paid?

20. Lord Gatwick died leaving an estate of £450 000. After capital transfer tax had been paid, the balance was divided equally between his eight children. How much did each receive?

19
INCOME

The amount of pay you receive will depend on such factors as how long and how hard you work, your qualifications and abilities, and possibly on how well you get on with other people and whether or not you can get the best out of them. The type of work you will do usually determines the manner in which your earnings will be calculated.

Most people are paid a *fixed sum of money for each hour* worked, up to an agreed number of hours each week. Additional hours may be paid at a higher rate. Others are paid by the number of articles they produce or the number of tasks they perform — this method is called *piecework*. Salesmen frequently receive a relatively low basic wage but get paid *commission* at an agreed percentage of the value of the goods they sell. This percentage may vary according to the product they are selling. For example a salesman selling earth-moving machines at thousands of pounds each will hardly expect the same rate of commission as another salesman selling children's toys. A further group of people, including civil servants, college lecturers, teachers and most office workers, receive a *salary*. A salary is a fixed sum for a year's work. Salaried workers do not generally receive overtime or bonus payments. This annual sum is divided into twelve equal amounts which are paid at regular monthly intervals.

HOURLY PAY

If you are paid at an *hourly rate* you are paid a fixed amount for each hour you work up to an agreed number of hours each week. This is called the *basic working week*. Any time worked in excess of the basic week is usually paid at a higher rate. Such things as the number of hours in a basic week, and the rates of pay, including overtime and unsocial hours payments, are agreed between the employers and the employees, often after negotiations through a trade union. In some industries the rates of pay and conditions of work are agreed nationally, in others, locally. It is a fact of life that it may be far more expensive to live in one part of the country than another: hourly pay rates sometimes reflect this difference.

EXAMPLE 1

William Andrews works 48 hours in a given week, 10 hours of which is overtime which is paid at time-and-a-half. If the basic rate is £3.40 per hour, calculate his gross wage for the week.

Basic wage for 38 hours at £3.40 per hour $= £3.40 \times 38 = £129.20$

Overtime rate at time-and-a-half is

£3.40 + £1.70 $= £5.10$ per hour

Overtime payment for 10 hours at £5.10 per hour $= £5.10 \times 10 = £51$

$\therefore$ Gross wage for the week $= £129.20 + £51$

$= £180.20$

EXAMPLE 2

Clive Lloyd worked 54 hours in a given week, 9 hours of which was overtime paid at time-and-a-half and 5 hours of which was at double-time. If the basic hourly rate is £3.60, find his gross wage for the week.

Overtime at time-and-a-half is paying for $1\frac{1}{2}$ hours at the basic rate for each hour worked, while overtime at double-time is paying for 2 hours at the basic rate for each hour worked.

Therefore payment for 9 hours at time-and-a-half is equivalent to $9 \times 1\frac{1}{2}$ i.e. $13\frac{1}{2}$ hours at basic rate, and 5 hours at double-time is equivalent to 10 hours at the basic rate.

Therefore total number of hours to be paid for at the basic rate is:

$(40 + 13\frac{1}{2} + 10)$ hours $= 63\frac{1}{2}$ hours

Then

Gross basic wage $= £3.60 \times 63\frac{1}{2}$

$= £228.60$

EXAMPLE 3   Fred Manson's time-sheet for a week is shown below:

Name: Fred Manson
Works Number: 1098
Week Ending: 17 April 198—

DAY	CLOCKED IN AT	CLOCKED OUT AT
Mon	07.00	16.00
Tues	07.00	16.00
Wed	07.15	18.15
Thurs	07.00	16.00
Fri	07.00	16.00

(a) What seems to be the time at which Fred is due to start work?

(b) What is the length of his normal working day?

(c) Assuming that he has 1 hour for lunch each day (unpaid), how many hours make up his basic week?

(d) How many hours of overtime has he worked?

(e) Calculate his basic pay at £2.84 per hour.

(f) If the overtime rate is time-and-a-quarter, how much did he earn above the basic wage in that week?

(a) He starts work at 07.00 or 7.00 a.m. but was 15 minutes late on Wednesday.

(b) The normal day is from 07.00 to 16.00, i.e. 9 hours but with 1 hour off for lunch.

(c) He is paid for 8 hours each day at the basic hourly rate. The basic week is therefore $5 \times 8 = 40$ hours.

(d) The only overtime worked was on Wednesday. He worked for 11 hours, had 1 hour for lunch leaving 10 hours of paid work. Since the basic day is 8 hours, he works 2 hours of overtime.

(e) Basic pay for 40 hours at £2.84 $= £2.84 \times 40$
$$= £113.60$$

(f) Overtime rate is time-and-a-quarter

i.e. $£2.84 \times \dfrac{5}{4} = £3.55$

$\therefore$ Payment for 2 hours of overtime $= £7.10$

EXERCISE 87

1. George Smith earns £1.75 per hour for a 40 hour week. Calculate his gross weekly wage.

2. Alma Higgins earns £2.25 per hour for a 35 hour week. Calculate her gross weekly wage.

3. Barry Crooks works a basic week of $37\frac{1}{2}$ hours and is paid £2.50 per hour. Calculate his gross weekly wage.

4. Penny Brown works a basic week of 35 hours and is paid £2.15 per hour. Calculate her gross weekly wage.

5. John Giles works a basic week of 40 hours and is paid £1.95 per hour. Calculate John's weekly wage.

6. Colin Vincent works a basic week of 35 hours. Overtime is paid at time-and-a-quarter. If the basic hourly rate is £2.20, how much does he earn in a week when he puts in 41 hours?

7. Peggy.Wright works in a factory where the basic week is 38 hours. Overtime is paid at time-and-a-half. How much will she earn in a week when she works for 48 hours if the basic rate is £1.86 per hour?

8. Rodney Hill works for a builder who pays £2.30 per hour for a basic week of 36 hours. Overtime is paid at time-and-a-half. How much will Rodney earn in a week when he works for 52 hours?

9. Beryl Parr works in a factory where the basic rate of pay is £1.76 per hour for a basic week of 36 hours. Overtime on weekdays is paid at time-and-a-half, but on Saturdays it is paid at double-time. How much will Beryl earn in a week when she works for 50 hours including 5 hours on Saturday?

10. Mr Gifford's time-sheet showed that he worked the required basic week of $37\frac{1}{2}$ hours. He also worked 7 hours of overtime at time-and-a-quarter and 5 hours on Saturday at time-and-a-half. If the basic hourly rate is £2.20, calculate his wage for the week.

11. Sally Prescott's work-card showed that she worked $8\frac{1}{2}$ hours each day, Monday to Friday. If the basic day was 7 hours and overtime was paid at time-and-a-half, calculate her weekly wage when the basic rate was £1.90 per hour. How much would her pay increase if the basic hourly rate rose by 10 p per hour?

12. Mrs Black's time-sheet for each day in a week shows that she worked as follows: Monday $7\frac{1}{2}$ hours, Tuesday 9 hours, Wednesday 10 hours, Thursday $7\frac{1}{2}$ hours, Friday $8\frac{1}{2}$ hours and Saturday 3 hours. Her basic hourly payment is £2.80 but she is paid at time-and-a-half for any hours worked in excess of 7 on any one day, and double-time for Saturday working. Calculate her gross wage for the week.

13. Trevor Cook's work-card for each day in a week shows that he worked as follows: Monday 10 hours, Tuesday 10 hours, Wednesday 4 hours, Thursday 10 hours, Friday 10 hours and Saturday 3 hours. Trevor is paid at a basic hourly rate of £3.10 but works 'flexitime', i.e. he may work when he pleases provided he works the required number of hours. The basic week is 40 hours and any overtime is paid at time-and-a-quarter. Calculate Trevor's gross wage for the week.

14. Jack Burley's work-card for a week gave the following 'clocking in' and 'clocking out' times:

	IN	OUT
Mon	7.30 a.m.	3.30 p.m.
Tues	7.30 a.m.	5.15 p.m.
Wed	7.30 a.m.	3.30 p.m.
Thurs	7.30 a.m.	5.15 p.m.
Fri	8.30 a.m.	3.30 p.m.
Sat	7.30 a.m.	12.30 p.m.

(a) If he only works overtime on certain days, what is the length of the basic working day?
(b) How many hours of overtime does he work, excluding Saturday morning?
(c) The basic rate of payment is £2.64 per hour, with time-and-a-half for overtime and double-time for Saturday morning. Calculate his gross wage for the week.

15. Richard Baldwin's time-sheet for a week shows that he worked as follows:

	IN	OUT
Mon	7.58 a.m.	4.28 p.m.
Tues	8.00 a.m.	4.30 p.m.
Wed	8.04 a.m.	4.31 p.m.
Thurs	8.12 a.m.	5.45 p.m.
Fri	7.59 a.m.	6.15 p.m.
Sat	8.05 a.m.	12 noon

Richard is due to start work each day at 8.00 a.m. and to finish at 4.30 p.m. He is not paid for arriving early but loses 15 minutes any day he is more than 5 minutes late. He also loses 15 minutes if he leaves before 4.30 p.m. but is paid at time-and-a-half for each complete 15 minutes he works overtime — any work on Saturday being counted as overtime. If the basic hourly rate is £2.40, calculate his wage for the week.

PIECEWORK

If you are paid at piecework rates you are paid for the amount of work you do irrespective of the time it takes you. A person who is able to produce 300 articles in a shift is thus able to earn more than a work-mate who produces 250 articles in the same time. Casual workers, picking fruit or potatoes, or laying hedges, are often paid for what they do rather than by the hour. In the factory situation there is usually a guaranteed minimum wage per shift plus piecework payments which are dependent on the number of articles produced.

EXAMPLE 4   A casual labourer receives 45 p for each bag of potatoes he picks. How much will he earn if he picks 38 bags on Monday, 26 on Tuesday, 32 on Wednesday and 36 on Thursday?

Total number of bags picked $= 38 + 26 + 32 + 36$
$$= 132$$

$\therefore$ Total payment at 45 p per bag $= 132 \times 45$ p
$$= £59.40$$

EXAMPLE 5   During a particular week a factory worker making parts for motor cars produces the following numbers each day:

Mon	Tues	Wed	Thurs	Fri
164	140	182	171	121

Apart from his guaranteed weekly wage of £80 he is paid 15 p for every part above 140 he produces on a given day. Calculate his wage for the week.

His production in excess of 140 parts per day is:

24 on Monday, 42 on Wednesday and 31 on Thursday, i.e. a total of 97.

$\therefore$ Bonus payment $= 97 \times 15$ p $= £14.55$

$\therefore$ Wage for the week $= £80 + £14.55 = £94.55$

EXERCISE 88

1. Dilys and Enid go fruit picking and are paid 14 p for each kilogram of fruit they pick. During the first week they pick the following quantities:

	Mon	Tues	Wed	Thurs	Fri
Dilys	70 kg	63 kg	65 kg	73 kg	78 kg
Enid	64 kg	73 kg	60 kg	75 kg	73 kg

Calculate their pay for the week.

2. Graham Scott gets paid 8 p for each article he completes up to 150 a day. For every article over this number he receives 10 p. Calculate how much he will earn in a week if his production figures are as follows:

Mon	Tues	Wed	Thurs	Fri
184	221	264	266	205

3. David Elston wants to earn £25 to buy a second-hand bicycle. He decides to wash cars at 35 p a time. How many cars must he wash to raise the money?

4. A window cleaner charges 8 p per square metre to clean your windows. If your house has fourteen rectangular windows, each 1 m by 1.5 m, how much will it cost to have your windows cleaned on the outside?

5. A son agrees with his father that for every 5 concrete blocks he moves from the front gate to the rear garden he will receive 8 p payment. How much will the son earn if he moves 190 blocks?

6. The following table shows the number of articles produced by four factory workers each day for a week. If each person is paid 8 p for each article up to 200 per day and 12 p for each article above 200 per day, calculate each worker's earnings for the week.

	Mon	Tues	Wed	Thurs	Fri	Sat
Mr Hollands	296	202	264	276	243	—
Miss Bennett	284	198	273	—	176	234
Mrs Hogan	217	254	244	175	269	—
Mr Hyde	273	284	180	233	245	—

7. Barry Price gets paid 5 p for every article he produces above 600 in a week. In addition he receives a guaranteed wage of £85. The following table shows the number of articles produced each day for a week:

Mon	Tues	Wed	Thurs	Fri
164	173	154	182	176

Calculate his earnings.

8. Philip Haddon works with nine colleagues in a team producing headlamps for cars. For each headlamp they produce in a day up to 250 the team receives a bonus payment of 15 p; above this figure they receive 25 p per headlamp. If the bonus payments are shared equally between all the members of the team, and the numbers of lamps produced each day for a week are given below, calculate the bonus received by each member of the team.

Mon	Tues	Wed	Thurs	Fri
452	375	520	584	440

9. Workers in a factory receive a basic wage of £85 per week plus 32p for each complete box of the parts they are making. Joy Eden produces 7921 parts in a week, and when packed each box contains 80 of these parts. Calculate Joy's wage for the week.

10. A team of ten workers in a factory produce brakes for lorries. Apart from a basic weekly wage of £98 each member of the team gets paid 15p for each complete set of four brakes. Calculate the weekly wage of one of the team in a week when the team produces 2420 sets of brakes.

COMMISSION

Salesmen frequently receive a low basic wage, which is independent of the number of hours they work, plus commission on the value of the goods they sell, at an agreed rate.

EXAMPLE 6   Mike Pugh sells period furniture. He receives a basic weekly wage of £35 plus commission at $1\frac{1}{2}\%$ on all sales over £7500. Calculate his gross pay in a week when he sells furniture to the value of £16 800.

Basic weekly wage $=$ £35

Commission on £16 800 $-$ £7500 $=$ £9300 at $1\frac{1}{2}\%$ is:

$$£9300 \times \frac{1.5}{100} = £139.50$$

$\therefore$ Gross wage for the week $=$ £35 $+$ £139.50

$$= £174.50$$

EXERCISE 89

1. Calculate the commission earned on sales of £3500 at $2\frac{1}{2}\%$.

2. Calculate the commission earned on sales of £48 000 at $1\frac{1}{4}\%$.

3. A salesman receives a basic wage of £20 per week plus commission at $2\frac{1}{2}\%$ of the value of the goods he sells. Calculate his gross annual earnings in a year when he sells goods to the value of £450 000.

4. Carl Humphreys receives a basic monthly wage of £225 together with commission at 2% of the value of his sales. Calculate his gross annual earnings in a year when he sells goods to the value of £275 000.

5. An office machines salesman receives a basic wage of £150 per month plus commission. His commission is calculated as follows:

On the first £10 000 of sales   nil

On the next £20 000 $1\frac{1}{2}\%$

On the remainder   2%

Calculate his income in a month when he sells machines to the value of £34 600.

6. A salesman selling earth-moving machines is paid a basic wage of £120 per month plus commission. His commission is calculated as follows:

On the first £12 000 of sales   nil

On the next £12 000   1%

On the next £12 000 $1\frac{1}{2}\%$

On the remainder   2%

Calculate his income in a month when he sells goods to the value of (a) £30 000, (b) £54 000.

7. An ice-cream seller receives a basic wage of £40 per week plus commission at 15% on weekly sales over £60. Calculate his wage in a week when his takings amount to £440.

8. Mr Potter sells newspapers. Apart from his basic weekly wage of £30 he receives commission at 12% on sales over £35. Find his wage for a week when he sells newspapers to the value of £640.

9. In a large department store a salesman is employed to promote coffee percolators. He receives a weekly wage of £85 plus commission at $2\frac{1}{2}\%$ of the value of his sales over £200. Find his earnings in a month when he sells 106 percolators each selling at £36.50.

10. Two brothers George and Henry Patterson both work as salesmen for the same company, but in different sections. Each receives a basic monthly wage of £130 plus commission as follows:

George: 2% on all sales above £10 000 each month

Henry: $1\frac{1}{2}\%$ on all sales above £2000 each week

During a four week month their respective sales figures were:

George: £7420, £8680, £12 000, £9450

Henry: £4930, £1950, £15 170, £11 000

Which brother has the better month and by how much?

SALARIES

Many jobs pay a salary rather than a wage. Instead of your pay being calculated each week by taking into account the exact number of hours you have worked, you agree to work for a year for a given sum of money. This annual amount is called your *salary* and is usually paid in twelve equal monthly instalments. Local government office staff, bank employees and senior staff in industry are a few of the groups paid in this way. A glance at your local newspaper will give the salary scales for many different occupations. Overtime is not generally taken into account — it is assumed that the salary includes payment for any extra work which may be found necessary. Consider the mining engineer spending 12 hours underground repairing a power failure, the teacher attending a school function in the evening, or the bank manager delayed after hours with a client — none of these gets paid extra for their extra work, it is all part of the job.

EXERCISE 90

In each of the following, calculate the employee's monthly salary:

	EMPLOYEE	ANNUAL SALARY
1.	Mr Guy	£12 000
2.	Mr Borrow	£8064
3.	Miss Collins	£36 600
4.	Mrs Reynolds	£9072
5.	Mrs Hodson	£15 168
6.	Mr Cox	£18 432
7.	Mrs Ambler	£25 680
8.	Mr Andrews	£45 840
9.	Mrs Holmes	£8000
10.	Mr Comerford	£10 000.

In each of the following, calculate the employee's annual salary:

	EMPLOYEE	MONTHLY SALARY
11.	Mrs Moore	£800
12.	Mr Paterson	£1200
13.	Mrs Aveling	£963
14.	Miss Giles	£874
15.	Mr Hammond	£1040
16.	Mr Chinn	£644
17.	Miss Davis	£536
18.	Mrs Grant	£3720
19.	Mr Warwick	£2485
20.	Mr Lewis	£5350.

21. Mr Norman is paid a gross monthly salary of £736 while Mr Manners receives a gross annual salary of £9750. Which is the better off and by how much?

22. Mrs Deakin is paid a gross salary of £920 per calender month while her husband earns a gross weekly wage of £264. Which is the better off and by how much each year?

23. Walter Grant's take-home pay is £576 per calendar month. If his deductions from gross pay amount to 40%, find his gross annual salary.

24. When deductions amounting to 38% of gross salary are subtracted from Janet Hutchinson's gross monthly salary her take-home pay is £484.25. Calculate her gross annual salary.

25. Jill and David Edge each receive salaries. Jill earns £756 per calendar month and David £10 400 p.a. If Jill's take-home pay is 65% of her gross pay, and David's take-home pay is 68% of his gross pay, which is the better off, and by how much?

GROSS AND NET WAGES/SALARIES

The amount of money you earn in a week, or a month, or a year is called your *gross* wage or salary. In practice your 'take-home' pay is always considerably less. Certain payments, such as income tax and national insurance contributions, must be deducted from your earnings. In addition other deductions may be made for such things as an employees' pension scheme, union fees, sports club fees or private medical/hospital insurance. When all the agreed deductions have been subtracted from your gross pay you have what is called your *net pay* or *take-home pay*.

By far the largest deduction is for income tax. This has already been dealt with in detail in Chapter 18. The other two most important deductions are national insurance and pension contributions.

NATIONAL INSURANCE

National insurance contributions are paid by all employees and their employers. When you are working your contributions are deducted from your pay by your employer. The employer adds a contribution on your behalf, and pays the combined amount to the State. The main benefits of the scheme are:

(a) Sickness benefits when you are unable to work,

(b) Unemployment benefits when you are out of work,

(c) Free hospital treatment and care,

(d) The provision of doctors, dentists and opticians whose services are made available at less than cost,

(e) Retirement and other pensions.

All self-employed people must also pay national insurance contributions, but at a different rate and consequently with different benefits.

The rates of contributions may be varied from time to time by the Chancellor of the Exchequer. In calculating employees' contributions they are divided into two categories: those who have an acceptable staff pension scheme, and those who do not. These two groups are respectively known as those who are *contracted out* and those who are *not contracted out*.

Employees not contracted out pay 9% of their gross weekly income for all their income up to £235.

Employees contracted out pay 9% of their gross weekly income up to £32.50 plus 6.85% of their income between this figure and £235 per week.

EXAMPLE 7
An employee earning £7488 p.a. is not contracted out. Calculate his weekly national insurance (NI) contribution.

$$\text{Weekly pay} = \frac{£7488}{52} = £144$$

$$\text{NI contribution at 9\%} = £144 \times \frac{9}{100}$$

$$= £12.96$$

∴ Weekly NI contribution is £12.96

EXAMPLE 8
Calculate the weekly NI deductions of a woman earning £14 280 p.a. if she is contracted out. If other deductions amount to 6% of her gross salary, find the total weekly deductions and express this as a percentage of her gross salary.

$$\text{Salary} = \frac{£14\,820}{52} = £285 \text{ per week}$$

NI contributions are therefore due as follows:

$$£32.50 \text{ at } 9\% = £32.50 \times \frac{9}{100} = £2.93$$

$$£235 - £32.50 = £202.50 \text{ at } 6.85\%$$

$$= £202.50 \times \frac{6.85}{100}$$

$$= £13.87$$

$$\therefore \text{ Total weekly NI contribution } = £2.93 + £13.87$$
$$= £16.80$$

$$\text{Other deductions } = £285 \times \frac{6}{100} = £17.10$$

$$\therefore \text{ Total deductions } = £16.80 + £17.10$$
$$= £33.90$$

$$\text{Percentage deductions } = \frac{£33.90}{£285} \times 100$$

$$\text{i.e. Deductions } = 11.9\% \text{ correct to three}$$
$$\text{significant figures}$$

EXERCISE 91

Calculate the weekly national insurance contributions due in each of the following, assuming that the people concerned have not been contracted out. Give your answers correct to the nearest penny.

1. Weekly wage £75

2. Weekly wage £98

3. Weekly wage £160

4. Weekly wage £230

5. Weekly wage £398

6. Annual salary £4836

7. Annual salary £6448

8. Annual salary £8580

9. Annual salary £10 920

10. Annual salary £17 680.

In each of the following calculate the weekly national insurance contributions assuming that the employee has been contracted out. Give your answers correct to the nearest penny.

11. Weekly wage £85

12. Weekly wage £124

13. Weekly wage £150

14. Weekly wage £195

15. Weekly wage £220

16. Annual salary £3952

17. Annual salary £8008

18. Annual salary £9672

19. Annual salary £10 400

20. Annual salary £20 800.

PENSION SCHEMES

More and more people today belong to company pension schemes. Money is deducted from their pay, usually at a fixed percentage of gross salary, and invested in property or stocks and shares, so that it will provide a pension for the contributors when they retire. The size of the pension will depend on the contributor's final salary, and the number of years for which contributions have been paid. Frequently there is also a substantial lump sum which is paid on retirement. The government pension schemes deduct a percentage of salary but do not invest it, the pension payments being made out of current government income.

EXAMPLE 9 Nurse Brown earns £8196 p.a. If pension scheme deductions are made at 6%, how much does she pay each month towards her pension?

Monthly salary $= \dfrac{£8196}{12} = £683$

Monthly pension contribution at 6% $= £683 \times \dfrac{6}{100}$

$= £40.98$

EXAMPLE 10 John Miles earns £9672 p.a. and makes pension contribution payments at $7\frac{1}{2}$%. How much does this work out to each week?

Weekly wage $= \dfrac{£9672}{52} = £186$

Weekly pension contribution $= £186 \times \dfrac{7.5}{100}$

$= £13.95$

EXAMPLE 11 John West worked for his company for 35 years and was earning £14 240 p.a. when he retired. The benefits from his company's scheme were:

(i) a lump sum payment equal to $\dfrac{3X}{80}$ of his final annual salary, where X is the number of years he worked for them,

(ii) an annual pension equal to $\dfrac{X}{80}$ of his final annual salary. Calculate (a) his lump sum payment, (b) his annual pension.

(a) Lump sum $= £\dfrac{3 \times 35}{80} \times 14\,240 = £18\,690$

(b) Annual pension $= £\dfrac{35}{80} \times 14\,240 = £6230$

EXERCISE 92

In each of the following calculate the monthly pension scheme deductions at the given rates:

	ANNUAL SALARY	PENSION CONTRIBUTION RATE
1.	£6240	6%
2.	£5760	6%
3.	£9240	8%
4.	£15 600	8%
5.	£10 440	$7\frac{1}{2}$%.

In each of the following calculate the weekly pension scheme deductions at the given rates:

6. Annual salary £4472, pension contribution rate 6%

7. Monthly salary £376, pension contribution rate 7%

8. Monthly salary £672, pension contribution rate 8%

9. Weekly salary £210, pension contribution rate 6%

10. Weekly salary £120, pension contribution rate $7\frac{1}{2}$%.

11. The benefits of a pension scheme are a lump sum payment on retirement equal to $\dfrac{3X}{80}$ of the annual salary, together with an

annual pension equal to $\frac{X}{80}$ of the annual salary, where X is the number of years worked. Calculate the lump sum and annual pension due to an employee who retires after 37 years' service when earning £10 240 p.a.

12. If the employee referred to in Question 11 had only worked for 33 years, but had retired on an annual salary of £10 800, would he have received a greater or smaller annual pension?

13. The benefits of a pension scheme are a lump sum payment equal to $\frac{X}{20}$ of the annual salary, together with an annual pension equal to $\frac{X}{60}$ of the annual salary, where X is the number of years the employee has belonged to the scheme. Paul Drake has paid into the scheme for 35 years and retires on an annual salary of £14 640. Calculate (a) his lump sum payment, (b) his annual pension.

14. Rework Question 13 for Judy Marshall who is earning a salary of £1120 per month when she retires after 40 years' service.

15. Employees of Sebco Ltd pay 6% of their salary into the firm's pension fund. The benefits paid on retirement are as follows:
(a) a lump payment equal to the final year's salary
(b) an annual pension equal to $\frac{X}{75}$ of the final year's salary, where X is the number of years the employee has worked, provided that X is greater than 10.

Peter Reynolds retires from the firm after 8 years when he is earning £9640, while his brother Eric retires with a final year's salary of £10 725 after 35 years' service. Calculate, for each brother, his lump sum payment and annual pension.

SOCIAL BENEFITS

One of the biggest spenders of all the government departments is the Department of Health and Social Security (DHSS). This department is responsible for helping you when you are unemployed, sick or retired. They will help you if you are disabled, if you are unfortunate enough to suffer an industrial injury or contract an industrial disease, or if you become an invalid. They also subsidise medical prescriptions and dental treatment, and pay maternity benefits, supplementary benefits (for those with special needs), disability and widows' pensions, and death grants.

The workings of the DHSS are vast and often seem complicated; rates of benefits and people's eligibility for them are likely to change from year to year. The object here is simply to outline the subject.

The following Exercise is a collection of questions which bring out some of the most common social benefits.

EXERCISE 93

1. If the weekly rate of unemployment benefit is (a) £25, (b) £28.50, (c) £32.75, (d) £37.40, (e) £52.70, calculate, in each case, the annual income from this source.

2. If the annual rate of unemployment benefit is (a) £1518.40, (b) £1804.40, calculate the corresponding weekly rate.

3. If the child benefit is £5.85 per week for each child, calculate the amount received from this source by a family with five children in (a) a week, (b) a year.

4. If the child benefit is £6.15 per week for each child, find the yearly income from this source for a family with four children. If the benefit is increased by 35 p per week for each child, find the yearly increase in income.

5. A family receives £31.05 per week in child benefit when the weekly rate is £6.21. How many children are there? If the weekly rate increases by 12%, find the rise in the family's weekly income, giving your answer correct to the nearest penny.

6. A family with four children receives £25.48 each week in child benefits. How much would another family receive each week if they had (a) one child, (b) seven children?

7. A family with three children receives £28.35 each week in child benefits. How much would another family receive if they had (a) one child, (b) five children?

8. The following table shows the pension position of Mr and Mrs Average:

	AGE AT WHICH PENSION BECOMES DUE	LIFE EXPECTANCY	AMOUNT OF RETIREMENT PENSION PER WEEK
Mr Average	65	67	£33
Mrs Average	60	72	£33

Using this information, calculate how much more in total Mrs Average can expect to receive than Mr Average.

9. Repeat Question 8 on the assumption that the weekly rate of retirement pension is increased to £41.80.

10. The basic rate of retirement pension is £32.85 per week, with a further £19.70 for a married woman who does not qualify in her own right. Find the joint income of a husband and wife in a year.

Compare this figure with their income if they were to receive two basic pensions.

11. The basic weekly retirement pension is £38.60. Calculate, correct to the nearest penny, the basic pension (a) next year, (b) the year after, assuming that it is increased by 10% for next year and by a further 8% for the following year.

EARNINGS RULES — RETIREMENT PENSIONS

If a man under 70 or a woman under 65 earns more than £57 a week, the basic pension will be reduced as follows:

> Earnings between £57 and £61 — 5 p deducted for each 10 p earned over £57,
>
> Earnings over £61 — as above, then 5 p deducted for each 5 p earned over £61.

Assume that the weekly pension is £32.85.

Using this information calculate the retirement pension due in each of the following cases:

12. A 68-year-old man earning £60 per week

13. A 64-year-old woman earning £58 per week

14. A 72-year-old man earning £60 per week

15. A 69-year-old woman earning £60 per week

16. A 67-year-old man earning £70 per week

17. A 64-year-old woman earning £65 per week

18. A 70-year-old man earning £70 per week

19. A 70-year-old woman earning £75 per week

20. An 80-year-old man earning £100 per week.

REVISION PAPERS
51-75

PAPER 51

1. Give 246.717 correct to (a) the nearest 10, (b) three significant figures, (c) one decimal place. Express the answer to (a) in standard form.

2. Find (a) $\sqrt{573.4}$, (b) $\sqrt{0.057\,34}$, (c) $\dfrac{1}{573.4}$.

3. Elizabeth buys a clock which is marked £15.70 + VAT. How much will she pay if the rate of VAT is 15%?

4. A garage charges £10 per hour for work on my car. How much would a job taking 96 minutes cost if the price of materials is £35.60?

5. The diagram shows a cuboid ABCDEFGH measuring 12 cm by 8 cm by 5 cm. Calculate:
   (a) its total surface area
   (b) its volume
   (c) the side of a cube which would have a volume equal to that of the given cuboid
   (d) the length of FD
   (e) the length of AH.

   Give any answers which are not exact correct to three significant figures.

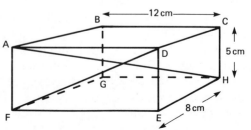

PAPER 52

1. Find (a) $5 - 0.154 + 1.246$, (b) 0.7×0.6, (c) $8.4 \div 0.6$.

2. Evaluate 0.6216^2, 31.42^2, $\dfrac{1}{0.4597}$.

3. A train 23 m long is travelling at 132 km/h. If it enters a tunnel 340 m in length, how long after the engine enters the tunnel does the last carriage leave the tunnel?

4. When a sum of money is divided between three sisters, Lesley, Lynne and Lorna, in the ratio $5:7:9$, Lynne receives £12.95. How much more will Lorna receive than Lesley?

5. A department store allows a discount of $2\frac{1}{2}\%$ for a cash sale. Calculate the cash price for a dining table and six chairs if the marked price of the table is £426.50 and the marked price of each chair is £67.25.

PAPER 53

1. Simplify $\left(4\dfrac{1}{3} - 3\dfrac{5}{9}\right) \times \left(2\dfrac{1}{8} + 4\dfrac{5}{8}\right)$.

2. Evaluate (a) 15.12×0.94, (b) $\dfrac{37.64 \times 14.82}{83.92}$.

3. Peter pays £59.80 for a set of headlamps, the price including VAT at 15%. How much did he pay in VAT? Express this as a percentage of the price Peter paid.

4. In an election Mr Roberts received $\frac{2}{7}$ of the votes cast, Mrs Peters $\frac{1}{4}$, and Miss Hulton $\frac{2}{5}$. If the votes cast for the remaining candidates totalled 1762 and 83 voting papers were spoilt, calculate:
   (a) the total number of votes cast
   (b) Miss Hulton's winning margin.

5. In a dishwashing machine the container for the powder is in the shape of a *quarter* of a sphere of diameter 7 cm. The powder is bought in cylindrical drums, with radius 8.75 cm and height 22 cm, which are 90% full. How many times may the powder container be filled from one drum of powder? If a drum costs £5, find the weekly cost of powder, assuming that the machine runs once each day.

PAPER 54

1. Express 24 696 in prime factors in index form. Hence find the smallest whole number by which 24 696 must be multiplied to make it (a) a perfect square, (b) a perfect cube.

2. Evaluate $\sqrt{\dfrac{57.3 \times 6.543}{138.9}}$ and $\left(\dfrac{0.8264}{1.374}\right)^2$.

3. When the rate of VAT rose from 8% to 15% the cost of a chair increased by £11.20. Find the new price of the chair.

4. Peter Embry earns £18 000 p.a. and his tax-free allowances amount to £3650. He must pay income tax on his taxable income at the rate of 30% on the first £12 000 and at 40% on the balance. Calculate his tax bill for the year, and express it as a percentage of his gross income, giving your answer correct to the nearest whole number.

5. A sphere of radius R cm has exactly the same volume as a cube of side 8 cm. Find R correct to three significant figures. Take $\pi = 3.142$.

PAPER 55

1. Simplify (a) $(-16) - (-34)$, (b) $(-8) \times (-2) \div (-4)$.

2. Divide £7497 between three sisters, Pearl, Mary and Nance, in the ratio $5:7:9$. How much more will Nance receive than Pearl?

3. If a shopkeeper sells a camera at £78, he makes a loss of 35%. What would it have to be sold for to make a profit of 35%?

4. A train passes through A at a steady speed of 180 km/h but when it reaches B it is forced to reduce its speed uniformly until it reaches C. After passing through C it accelerates uniformly until it reaches D. It completes the journey to E at a steady speed. If this journey is illustrated by the travel graph opposite, use it to find:
   (a) the distance travelled from A to B
   (b) the acceleration in km/h^2 between C and D
   (c) the total distance travelled between A and E.

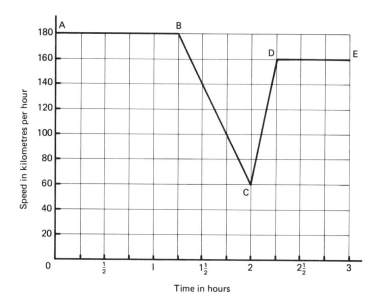

5. In a micro-bore central heating system water is carried from the boiler in a cylindrical pipe of internal diameter 2 cm. At the junction A it divides into six equal cylindrical pipes, each of radius R mm. Assuming that the area of cross-section of the inflow pipe is equal to the sum of the areas of the cross-sections of the six outflow pipes, find R in millimetres correct to two decimal places.

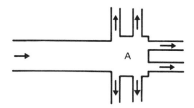

PAPER 56

1. When the price of a cut-glass salad bowl is reduced by 30% it sells at £26.25. Calculate its original price.

2. A caravan site owner charges a rent of £1.55 per night or £9 per week. How much is saved during a four week holiday by paying at the weekly rather than the nightly rate?

3. The pocket money given by a father to his three daughters, Audrey, Olive and Sue, is in the ratio $4:7:11$. If Olive receives £6.30, how much will Sue receive?

4. If $\log 0.7264 = \bar{1}.8611$, find the logarithm of $(0.7264)^2$ and of $\sqrt{0.7264}$.

5. A, B, C and D are four service stations on a motorway. A motorist
    leaves A at noon and travels to D which is 160 miles away. He
    arrives at B (50 miles from A) at 1.30 p.m. and rests there for 15
    minutes, before continuing to C (a further 90 miles on from B) at
    an average speed of 55 mph. At C he stops until 4.45 p.m. He then
    continues his journey to D, arriving there at 5.30 p.m.

    Taking 2 cm to represent 30 minutes on the time-axis and 20 miles
    on the distance-axis, draw a graph to represent this journey. Use
    your graph to determine:
    (a) the motorist's time of arrival at C
    (b) the average speed for the whole trip from A to D.

    A second motorist leaves D at 1.30 p.m. and travels non-stop at a
    uniform speed to A, arriving there are 5 p.m. Draw, on the same
    axes, a graph to represent this journey. From your graph find:
    (c) when and where the two motorists pass
    (d) their distance apart at 3.30 p.m.

PAPER 57

1. (a) Express (i) $\dfrac{2}{5}$ as a percentage, (ii) 65% as a fraction in its
    lowest terms.
    (b) What is the next prime number after 19?

2. If 350 g of sugar costs 14 p, find the cost of 2.25 kg.

3. A woman drives the 20 km from home to the station at an average
    speed of 30 km/h and immediately catches the train to London,
    which is 100 km away. If the train travels at an average speed of
    200 km/h, calculate the woman's average speed from home to
    London, giving your answer correct to the nearest whole number.

4. A bag contains 12 identically shaped discs, 8 of which are red and
    the remainder blue. What is the probability of picking out (a) a
    red disc, (b) a blue disc, (c) a white disc?

5. The base of a bedside lamp (shown on the next page) is turned
    from a cylindrical block of wood 10 cm in diameter and of length
    11.5 cm. It consists of an inverted hemisphere of radius 4.5 cm,
    topped by a sphere of diameter 7 cm. Calculate:
    (a) the volume, in cubic centimetres, of wood used in the lamp
    (b) its mass if each cubic centimetre of the wood has a mass of
        0.8 g
    (c) the percentage of the original wood which was wasted. ($\pi = \frac{22}{7}$)

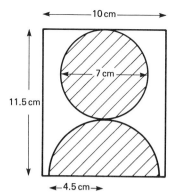

PAPER 58

1. Express each of the following base 8 numbers in base 5 (a) 34_8, (b) 57_8.

2. Find (a) $\sqrt{0.25}$, (b) $\dfrac{1}{0.025}$, (c) 0.5×0.25.

3. Simplify:

   (a) $5\dfrac{1}{8} - 2\dfrac{7}{24} + 1\dfrac{1}{2}$

   (b) $\left(3\dfrac{3}{8} - 1\dfrac{1}{2}\right) \times 2\dfrac{2}{3}$

   (c) $3\dfrac{1}{3} \times 1\dfrac{1}{2} \div 1\dfrac{1}{4}$.

4. In Spain I buy a leather bag for 2556 pesetas. If £1 ≡ 180 pesetas, find the equivalent cost in pounds.

5. Steven Arnold orders a new car believing that its price will be £9800. When the car arrives its price has increased by 9%, but the retailer agrees to allow him a discount of 10%. How much more (or less) must he pay for the car?

PAPER 59

1. Express:

   (a) $\dfrac{7}{20}$ as a percentage

   (b) 0.48 as a percentage

   (c) 55% as a fraction in its lowest terms.

2. Find (a) $\sqrt{654.2}$, (b) $\dfrac{1}{654.2}$, (c) 0.6542^2.

3. Express:
    (a) 543.6 in standard form
    (b) 7.64×10^{-3} as a decimal
    (c) 643.9 correct to the nearest hundred.

4. A earns 30% more than B.
    (a) If B earns £80, how much does A earn?
    (b) If A earns £156, how much does B earn?

5. Ten years ago it cost £45 to produce a bookcase. This cost was made up of materials, labour, and other expenses in the ratio $5:8:2$. By last year the cost of materials had increased three times, the cost of labour five times, and other expenses had doubled. Calculate:
    (a) the cost of labour ten years ago
    (b) the cost of materials last year
    (c) the total cost of the bookcase last year.

Paper 60

1. Find the value of $4\dfrac{5}{16} - 2\dfrac{1}{8} + 2\dfrac{9}{32}$.

2. A boy sets out on a 30 km journey from A to C via B. He cycles the 10 km from A to B at an average speed of 20 km/h and then walks the 20 km from B to C at an average speed of 10 km/h. Calculate his average speed for the whole journey.

3. Express:
    (a) 52_8 as (i) a denary number, (ii) a binary number
    (b) 100101_2 as (i) a denary number, (ii) a number in base 8.

4. David and Jill Brown are left £1080 between them in the ratio $4:5$. Jill decides to divide her share between herself and her three children in the ratio $10:7:5:2$. Calculate the amount received by the child who gets (a) the largest share, (b) the smallest share.

5. A pepper pot is in the form of a cylinder of diameter 4 cm and height 3 cm, topped by a right circular cone of height 4 cm. When it contains pepper to a depth of 2.5 cm, it is turned upside down. Find the new depth of the pepper if its surface is assumed horizontal.

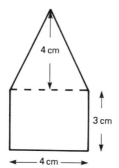

PAPER 61

1. Assuming that sound travels at 335 m/s, how far away, in kilometres, is a thunderclap heard 8 seconds after the flash of lightning is seen? Assume that the flash may be seen immediately it has occurred.

2. A car is travelling at 30 m/s. Express this speed in kilometres per hour.

3. (a) Find (i) 0.0427^2, (ii) $\dfrac{1}{\sqrt{0.04275}}$.

    Give each answer correct to three significant figures.
    (b) Express your answer to (a) (i) in standard form.

4. A builders' merchant's terms are:

    $6\frac{1}{2}\%$ discount for immediate cash payment,

    $2\frac{1}{2}\%$ discount if paid within 7 days,

    otherwise strictly net.

    If a builder buys goods to the value of £770, how much discount would be allowed if he paid (a) immediately, (b) on the fifth day?

5. A group of walkers leave their coach at A at noon, to walk to the summit of a hill which is 12 miles away. They walk uphill at a steady 4 mph and when they reach the summit take a well-earned 21 minute rest, before proceeding down the other side to their pick-up point B. B is 8 miles from the summit and they are able to walk this downhill section of the journey at 6 mph.

    Taking 4 cm ≡ 1 hour on the time-axis and 5 miles on the distance-axis, draw a travel graph to illustrate this journey.

    A second group leaves B at 12.30 p.m. to walk the same route in reverse. They walk to the summit at 4 mph and proceed downhill to A without a break, arriving there at 4.12 p.m. On the same axes draw the travel graph of this journey.

Use your graphs to find:
(a) the time of arrival of the first group at (i) the summit, (ii) B
(b) the average speed of the first group for the whole walk
(c) when and where the two groups pass
(d) the distance between the groups at 2 p.m.

PAPER 62

1. Evaluate $\sqrt{4.273^2 + 3.147^2}$ giving your answer correct to three significant figures.

2. Rain falls on an area of $5\,km^2$ to a uniform depth of 16 mm. If 20% of this rain finds its way into a reservoir, calculate the increase in volume of water in the reservoir.

3. Calculate the distance in metres travelled in 2.5×10^{-5} seconds by a particle moving at 5.64×10^8 cm/s.

4. A man receives a gross annual salary of £12 192. He pays $8\frac{1}{2}$% in national insurance contributions, 8% to a pension fund, and 20% is deducted for income tax, all percentages being based on his gross salary. Assuming that his net salary is paid in equal amounts, calculate his net monthly pay.

5. Circular tablets of diameter 1 cm are 3 mm thick. If a cylindrical container 3 cm in diameter and of height 4 cm contains 100 tablets, find the percentage of unused space within the container.

PAPER 63

1. Calculate:
   (a) $3\frac{1}{3} + 1\frac{1}{2}$ (b) $3\frac{1}{3} - 1\frac{1}{2}$
   (c) $3\frac{1}{3} \times 1\frac{1}{2}$ (d) $3\frac{1}{3} \div 1\frac{1}{2}$.

2. A video recorder is marked £427 + VAT. If the rate of VAT is 15%, how much will the recorder cost me? How much would I save if I were given an 8% discount on the marked price?

3. Express:
   (a) 0.005 64 km in centimetres
   (b) 726 000 cm^2 in square metres
   (c) 24 300 cm^3 in litres.

4. (a) Express:
   (i) 284 as a binary number
   (ii) 1111100_2 as a denary number.
   (b) Working in base 6, find (i) $521_6 + 35_6$ (ii) $123_6 \times 42_6$.

5. The speedometer of a car gives a correct reading when tyres of radius 28 cm are fitted. If oversize tyres of radius 30 cm are fitted, what will be the true length of a journey if the recorded distance is 100 km? Give your answer correct to three significant figures.

PAPER 64

1. (a) Express:
   (i) 1308 kg as a decimal fraction of 5.45 kg
   (ii) $\frac{32}{47}$ as a decimal fraction correct to three decimal places.
   (b) Of what sum of money is £9.66 21%?

2. Write down the next two numbers in each of the following sequences
   (a) $9, 27, 81, \ldots$, (b) $2, 6\frac{1}{2}, 11, \ldots$.

3. A school hall is 30 m long, 12 m wide and the walls are 6 m high. In each of the long walls there are four rectangular windows each 3.5 m high and 2 m wide. Calculate:
   (a) the floor area of the hall
   (b) the volume of the hall
   (c) the area of wall available for painting
   (d) the quantity of paint required if the walls are to be given two coats. Assume that 1 litre of paint covers 8 m².

4. The average height of 12 girls in a class is 1.44 m, while the average height of the 15 boys is 1.53 m. Find the average height of the class. If the average height of the class falls to 1.48 m when one boy leaves, find his height.

5. The diagram shows the cross-section of an hexagonal pencil of side 4 mm through which runs a cylindrical 'lead' of diameter 2 mm. Calculate the volume of wood used to make a pencil which is 18 cm long.

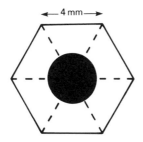

$\leftarrow$ 4 mm $\rightarrow$

PAPER 65

1. Evaluate:
   (a) $26.43 \times 8.08 \times 1.732$
   (b) $44.26 \times 76.41 \div 246.3$.

2. A man bought a car for £1550 and sold it for £1800. Find his percentage profit.

3. The ratio of boys to girls in a year group is $5:4$. If 15 boys leave and 10 girls arrive, the ratio becomes $1:1$. How many boys were there?

4. A woman buys a property for £28 000 and sells it after one year for £38 000. How much would she have to pay in capital gains tax if the tax rate was 30% and the first £5000 gain was exempt?

5. The diagram below represents the cross-section through a swimming pool which is 18 m wide. All dimensions in the diagram are in metres. Calculate:
   (a) the area of cross-section of the pool
   (b) the volume of water in the pool, in litres, when full
   (c) the volume of water in the pool, in litres, when exactly half of the *sloping floor* of the pool is visible.

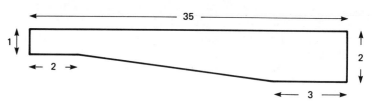

PAPER 66

1. Find, without using calculators or tables:

   (a) 0.8^2 (b) 0.12^2 (c) $\sqrt{0.16}$ (d) $\dfrac{7.2 \times 0.12}{1.44}$.

2. State the number of significant figures in each of the following
   (a) 1.04, (b) 0.014, (c) 1040.

3. A reference book with 1246 pages is 5.26 cm thick excluding its covers. Calculate the thickness of a single page, giving your answer in millimetres correct to three decimal places.

4. A farmer wants to rear 945 laying hens. Experience has shown that he can expect 70% of the eggs he incubates to hatch, and 10% of the chicks which hatch to die. Assuming that there are equal numbers of hens and cockerels at each stage, how many eggs should he place in the incubator?

5. Rainwater from a flat rectangular roof measuring 10 m by 8 m runs into a covered water butt in the form of a circular cylinder of diameter 1 m. How much would the water level in the butt rise if a storm gives a rainfall of 8.5 mm on the roof? ($\pi = 3.142$)

PAPER 67

1. Find (a) $\dfrac{3}{5}$ of £7.25, (b) 12% of 9 kilograms.

2. (a) Evaluate (i) 0.54×0.4, (ii) $0.72 \div 0.09$.

   (b) Given that $\dfrac{42 \times 35}{30} = 49$, write down without using any calculating aids, the value of:

   (i) $\dfrac{4.2 \times 3.5}{30}$ (ii) $(42 \times 35) - (49 \times 30)$

   (iii) $\dfrac{0.42 \times 3.5}{0.049}$.

3. If cabbages are planted 30 cm apart, how many, correct to two significant figures, could be planted in 1 hectare?

4. A shopkeeper buys a set of china for £54 and adds 55% to give a profit. VAT at 15% is then added to this total to give the selling price. Find the selling price.

5. A factory worker is paid £5.50 per hour with time-and-a-half for overtime and double-time for Sunday work, the normal working week being $7\frac{1}{2}$ hours each day from Monday to Friday. During a certain week his work-card shows that he has worked as follows:

Mon	Tues	Wed	Thurs	Fri	Sat	Sun
10	8	$10\frac{1}{2}$	$11\frac{1}{2}$	8	0	4

   (a) How many hours form his basic working week?
   (b) How much would he get paid for working a basic week?
   (c) How much overtime does he work?
   (d) Calculate his total wage for the week before any deductions are made.

PAPER 68

1. Evaluate (a) $\dfrac{5}{8} - \dfrac{3}{5}$, (b) $5\dfrac{4}{7} \div 6\dfrac{1}{2}$, (c) $605.5 \div 7$, (d) 0.14×0.6.

2. The ratio of men to women at a squash club is $5:3$. If the club has 42 female members, how many men are there? If the annual subscription is £85 for men and £75 for women, find the club's annual subscription income.

3. In eight consecutive completed innings a batsman's scores were 42, 18, 64, 137, 8, 54, 95 and 38. Find his average score. In his next innings he scores 88 not out. What is his new average?

4. Divide £6.21 into two parts so that:
    (a) one part is £0.87 more than the other
    (b) one part is 30% more than the other.

5. The cash price of a set of garden tools is £85.10, including VAT at 15%. Calculate the price before the VAT was added. What would be the selling price if the VAT rate was reduced to 12%?

PAPER 69

1. The weekly rental for a television set is £11.36. For how many weeks could the set be hired for £150? How much would be left over?

2. The cash price of some kitchen units, including VAT at 15%, is £977.50. How much would they cost if the rate of VAT rose to 18%?

3. A has 30% more money than B, and B has 20% more money than C. If B has £90, how much more does A have than C?

4. Jennifer Bird left $\frac{2}{5}$ of her assets to her husband, $\frac{1}{7}$ to each of her two children, the balance to be equally divided between her six grandchildren. If each grandchild received £1386, how much did her husband receive?

5. The exterior diameter of the dome of St Paul's Cathedral is approximately 44 m. Calculate:
    (a) the external area of the dome in square metres
    (b) the volume of rain in cubic metres which falls on the dome during a storm producing a rainfall of 12 mm. Give your answers correct to three significant figures.

PAPER 70

1. If $a = 2.4 \times 10^5$ and $b = 6 \times 10^3$, find (a) $a + b$, (b) $a - b$, expressing each answer in standard form.

2. Give 59.8165 correct to (a) the nearest hundred, (b) two decimal places, (c) four significant figures.

3. Evaluate (a) 5.264^3, (b) $\sqrt[3]{0.4436}$.

4. A shopkeeper buys an article for a certain sum of money. He adds 60% to the cost price to give the selling price, and VAT at 15% is added to this total. If the customer must now pay £13.80 for the article, how much did it cost the shopkeeper?

5. A, B and C are three towns connected by a railway line. The distance from A to B is 60 miles, and from B to C 50 miles. A train leaves B at noon and travels to C at 34 mph. Draw a graph of this journey using 2 cm to represent 10 miles on the distance-axis, and 6 cm to represent 1 hour on the time-axis.

   A second train leaves C at noon and travels to B, passing the first train at 12.32 p.m. It stops at B with a fault, but sets off from B at 1.30 p.m., on the remainder of its journey to A, arriving there at 2.40 p.m.

   Draw, on the same page, the travel graph of these journeys. Use your graphs to find:
   (a) the average speed of the second train between C and B, and the time it arrived at B
   (b) how far the first train was from B when they passed
   (c) the length of time that the second train waited at B
   (d) the average speed of the second train between B and A.

PAPER 71

1. Simplify:
   (a) $(-12) \times (-4) \div 3$
   (b) $(-12) \div (-4 + 3)$
   (c) $12 \div (-2 - 4)$.

2. A motorist travels the first 60 km of a journey at an average speed of 80 km/h, the next 150 km at an average speed of 100 km/h and the final 15 km at an average speed of 60 km/h. Calculate the average speed for the whole journey.

3. The age categories of 1000 students in a school are given in the following table:

Age group	11+	12+	13+	14+	15+	16+
Frequency	154	176	182	x	168	132

Use this information to:
(a) find the value of x
(b) draw a histogram to represent the data
(c) find the age group in which the median lies
(d) state the modal group
(e) state the probability that a pupil chosen at random has had his or her fifteenth birthday.

4. Three coins are tossed simultaneously. Calculate the probability of (a) three heads, (b) exactly two heads, (c) more than one head.

5. A jar of cream containing 45 g costs £1.35. Calculate the cost of the cream per kilogram.

PAPER 72

1. Find the total cost of:

   8 rolls of wallpaper at £6.50 per roll
   2 packets of paste at 85 p per packet
   3 litres of paint at £5.63 per litre
   3 brushes at 90 p each.

2. Which of the symbols $>$, $=$, $<$ may correctly be placed between the following?
   (a) 0.3^2 0.9
   (b) $\sqrt{0.16}$ 0.4
   (c) $\dfrac{1}{2} - \dfrac{1}{6}$ $\dfrac{1}{3}$
   (d) $7^2 - 2^2$ 5^2.

3. A photograph measuring 12 cm by 10 cm is to be enlarged such that all linear dimensions increase in the ratio 2:3. Find the area of the enlargement.

4. The table shows the number of peas found in 50 pea pods from a particular variety:

Number of peas per pod	2	3	4	5	6	7	8
Frequency	1	7	9	13	15	4	1

   Find:
   (a) the median number of peas
   (b) the modal number of peas
   (c) the mean number of peas per pod.

5. The diagram shows a shed roof, each of the two sloping sides measuring 10 m by 5 m. If the ridge of the roof is 3 m above the eaves, calculate the amount of water which falls on the roof during a storm when 15 mm of rain falls vertically. If the rain is collected in a cylindrical water butt of diameter 0.8 m, calculate the amount by which the water level in the butt will rise. Give your answer correct to three significant figures.

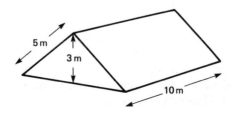

PAPER 73

1. Without using calculating aids, find (a) $\sqrt{400}$, (b) $\sqrt{0.16}$, (c) $\sqrt{0.0081}$, (d) 0.11^2, (e) 0.03^3.

2. Convert (a) $7436\,cm$ into metres, (b) $0.45\,km$ into metres, (c) $31\,740\,cm^2$ into square metres, (d) $2624\,g$ into kilograms.

3. An aeroplane is travelling at $1296\,km/h$. How far, in metres, does it travel in 15 seconds?

4. A garden centre buys seats of two different types, paying the manufacturer £40 for one type of seat and £60 for the other. The garden centre sells the cheaper seat at a profit of 40% and the dearer seat at a profit of $33\frac{1}{3}\%$. Calculate the total profit after selling 25 of the cheaper seats and 10 of the dearer.

   When the manufacturer increases all his prices by $12\frac{1}{2}\%$, the centre raises the selling price of the cheaper seat to £67.50 and the dearer seat to £87.75. Find the percentage profit on each type of seat after the price rise.

5. The volume of a cube is $100\,cm^3$. Find its total surface area, giving your answer correct to three significant figures.

PAPER 74

1. Evaluate (a) $\dfrac{15.92 \times 56.37}{721.4}$, (b) 13.74^3.

2. If a litre of paint will cover $14\,m^2$, how much paint would be required to cover a wall measuring $33\,m$ by $4\,m$ if two coats of paint are required? Give your answer correct to the nearest litre.

3. An office worker who works flexihours is paid at the rate of £4.50 per hour for the first $37\frac{1}{2}$ hours in any given week. Time worked in excess of this is paid at time-and-a-half, except for hours worked on a Sunday when the rate is double-time. In a certain week the recorded hours worked were:

Mon	Tues	Wed	Thurs	Fri	Sat	Sun
8	$9\frac{1}{2}$	8	$10\frac{1}{2}$	7	0	4

   Calculate:
   (a) the total number of hours worked in the week
   (b) the gross wage.

4. A shopkeeper buys an article and marks up a selling price which will give a profit of 30% on the cost price. When the cost price of the article rises by 10%, he continues to sell at the same price. What percentage profit on the cost price is he then making?

5. A suit is reduced in a sale from £84 to £60. If another suit is offered in the sale for £125, how much was its original price if both reductions are in the same ratio?

PAPER 75

1. (a) Consider the number 503.52. What is the difference in the value of the two 5 digits?

   (b) Given that $1 \text{ km} = \dfrac{5}{8} \text{ mile}$, express (i) 260 miles in kilometres, (ii) 560 km in miles, (iii) 5 square miles in square kilometres.

2. Find the average of 7.35, 0.4, 5.5, 3.75, 0.84 and 9.52.

3. A shopkeeper sells goods so as to make a profit of 40% on the cost price. Use this information to complete the following table:

COST PRICE	PROFIT	SELLING PRICE
£50		
	£24	
		£105

4. Peter Walker's gross weekly wage is £175. If he pays income tax at 30% except on the first £40 he earns each week, and other weekly deductions amount to £19.40, calculate his net weekly wage.

5. Snow falls on a flat rectangular roof, measuring 5 m by 8 m, to a depth of 1 m. When the thaw sets in, 10 cm^3 of snow melts into 1 cm^3 of water. Calculate:
   (a) the volume of water which runs off the roof
   (b) the mass of snow in kilograms supported by each square metre of the roof.

20

SIMPLE AND COMPOUND INTEREST

SIMPLE INTEREST

Everything has its price. We are all familiar with the price of a loaf of bread, a bottle of milk, a pop record, a gallon of petrol, a new motorcycle or a house; but often we do not appreciate that money too has its price. If you think of borrowing or hiring things for a day or a month there is a charge. Perhaps you need to hire a concrete mixer in order to build a garage, or a smart car for some special occasion, or a video recorder or carpet cleaner. Borrowing or hiring any of these costs money, i.e. has a price, the cost depending on the value of the article and the period of time for which it is hired. The most common thing to borrow is money. You may borrow money from a parent, brother or sister to buy something you particularly want, promising to pay them back, but usually only exactly the amount you have borrowed! When you want to borrow larger sums of money for such things as a motorcycle, a car or a house you have to go outside your family circle. This means going to a bank, the local council, a building society or a finance company or similar institution. In normal circumstances they will lend you the money but only at a price. The more money you want to borrow and the longer the period of the loan, the higher the price. The price or cost is called *interest*.

The price of most things depends on 'supply and demand'. The more available an article is, the cheaper it tends to be, and vice versa. If we have severe weather in December the price of Brussels sprouts will rise. In the same way, if a bank has little spare cash (it can only lend money which it has earned or which has been deposited with it) and very many people wish to borrow it, its price will be high. The price, or interest rate, therefore varies according to the supply of and demand for money.

Any money borrowed or lent is called the *principal* and is usually denoted by P. The price of the money is called the *interest* which is the rate per cent per annum on the money borrowed. Thus if the rate of interest is 20% per annum, this means that £100 borrowed for 1 year will cost 20% of £100 i.e. $£100 \times \dfrac{20}{100} = £20$. Similarly if the rate of interest is $37\frac{1}{2}\%$, the cost of borrowing £100 for 1 year will be $£100 \times \dfrac{37\frac{1}{2}}{100} = £37.50$. In general terms we call the rate of interest R per cent per annum, or $R\%$ for short.

We pay our rent, rates, electricity bills, etc., at regular intervals, and the cost of money is also charged at regular intervals, which may be yearly, half-yearly or even monthly.

The cost of borrowing is directly related to the time for which the money is borrowed, e.g. if we borrow for 2 years it costs exactly twice as much as for 1 year. Since the interest is the rate per cent *per annum* it is always necessary to give the time in years, time usually being denoted by T.

While the above has been written about borrowing money, remember that you cannot borrow unless someone else is prepared to lend. Many people have more than enough money to cover their normal expenses; other people will economise and save some money regularly, so that they can meet unexpected expenses. Lenders are said to *invest* money when they buy National Savings Certificates, or put it in a building society or bank deposit account. They receive payment for the loans, and the more they get for each £100 invested, the better they consider the investment.

Suppose a sum of £P is invested for T years at $R\%$ simple interest. The interest may be calculated as follows:

> £100 invested for 1 year at 1% gives £1 simple interest
>
> £100 invested for 1 year at 4% gives £4 simple interest
>
> £100 invested for 1 year at 10% gives £10 simple interest
>
> £100 invested for 1 year at $R\%$ gives £R simple interest

If we now double the time for which this sum is invested, we double the interest

i.e.   £100 invested for 2 years at $R\%$ gives £$2R$ simple interest

Similarly: £100 invested for 3 years at $R\%$ gives £$3R$ simple interest

£100 invested for 8 years at $R\%$ gives £$8R$ simple interest

£100 invested for T years at $R\%$ gives £TR or £RT simple interest

If next we double the sum invested, the interest will double i.e. £200 invested for T years at $R\%$ gives £$2RT$ simple interest and £P invested for T years at $R\%$ gives £$\dfrac{P}{100} \times RT$ simple interest i.e. the simple interest, £I, on £P invested for T years at $R\%$ is given by:

$$£I = £\frac{PRT}{100}$$

Although this has been calculated using pounds, the expression is true whatever the currency

i.e.
$$I = \frac{PRT}{100}$$

In practice today simple interest usually means interest calculated on a principal over a period of twelve months or less. If we add the principal P and interest I together, we have what is called the *amount*. This is denoted by A. Hence:

$$A = P + I$$

EXAMPLE 1 Find the simple interest on £500 invested for 2 years at 26%.

$$I = \frac{PRT}{100}$$

$$= \frac{£500 \times 26 \times 2}{100}$$

$\therefore$ Interest $= £260$

EXAMPLE 2 Find the simple interest on £750 invested for 3 years at 16%.

$$I = \frac{PRT}{100}$$

$$= \frac{£750 \times 16 \times 3}{100}$$

$\therefore$ Interest $= £360$

EXAMPLE 3   Find the simple interest on £240 invested for 8 months at 12%.

$$I = \frac{PRT}{100} \quad \left(\frac{PRT}{100} \text{ is exactly the same as } \frac{P}{100} \times R \times T\right)$$

$$= £\frac{240}{100} \times 12 \times \frac{8}{12}$$

$\therefore$ Interest = £19.20

EXAMPLE 4   Find the simple interest on £726 invested for 4 years at 14%.

$$I = \frac{PRT}{100}$$

$$= \frac{£726 \times 14 \times 4}{100} \quad \text{(Keep the 100 in the denominator unless it can be 'used' completely)}$$

$$= \frac{£40\,656}{100}$$

$\therefore$ Interest = £406.56

EXAMPLE 5   Find the amount of £350 invested for 5 years at 16% simple interest.

$$I = \frac{PRT}{100}$$

$$= \frac{£350 \times 16 \times 5}{100}$$

$\therefore$ Interest = £280

Amount $A = P + I = £350 + £280 = £630$

EXAMPLE 6   Find the simple interest on, and the amount at simple interest of, £255 on 120 days at 17%, giving your answer correct to the nearest penny.

$$I = \frac{PRT}{100}$$

Remember that the time must be given in years.

$$\therefore T = \frac{120}{365} \text{ years}$$

$$\text{i.e. } I = \pounds\frac{255}{100} \times 17 \times \frac{120}{365}$$

$$I = \pounds 14.25$$

$$\text{Amount } A = P + I$$
$$= \pounds 255 + \pounds 14.25$$
$$= \pounds 269.25$$

EXERCISE 94

Find the simple interest on:

1. £100 for 1 year at 18%

2. £100 for 1 year at 24%

3. £100 for 1 year at $16\frac{1}{2}$%

4. £100 for 4 years at 15%

5. £100 for 3 years at 12%

6. £100 for 5 years at 8%

7. £100 for $\frac{1}{2}$ year at 20%

8. £100 for 6 months at 19%

9. £100 for 9 months at 16%

10. £100 for 4 months at 21%

11. £200 for 2 years at 12%

12. £200 for 7 years at 15%

13. £500 for 4 years at 8%

14. £300 for 2 years at 9%

15. £400 for 5 years at 24%

16. £600 for 6 years at 7%

17. £800 for 6 months at 11%

18. £500 for 15 months at 18%

19. £300 for $1\frac{1}{2}$ years at 15%

20. £450 for $5\frac{1}{2}$ years at 12%.

Find the amount at simple interest of:

21. £100 for 1 year at 14%

22. £100 for 1 year at 30%

23. £100 for 1 year at 25%

24. £100 for 1 year at 11%

25. £100 for 1 year at $5\frac{1}{2}$%

26. £200 for 2 years at 12%

27. £500 for 3 years at 18%

28. £300 for 5 years at $7\frac{1}{2}$%

29. £700 for 8 years at 13%

30. £800 for 10 months at 16%.

Find the simple interest on, and the amount at simple interest of:

31. £250 for 2 years at 12%

32. £370 for 2 years at 18%

33. £430 for 3 years at $3\frac{1}{3}$%

34. £820 for 5 years at 7%

35. £550 for 8 years at 22%

36. £640 for 7 years at $7\frac{1}{4}$%

37. £95 for 4 years at 19%

38. £372 for $2\frac{1}{2}$ years at 18%

39. £425 for 15 months at 15%

40. £124 for $3\frac{1}{4}$ years at 16%.

Find the simple interest on each of the following, giving any answers which are not exact, correct to the nearest penny:

41. £220 for 5 years at $8\frac{1}{2}$%

42. £92 for 4 years at $12\frac{1}{2}$%

43. £163 for $3\frac{1}{2}$ years at 15%

44. £513 for $1\frac{3}{4}$ years at 16%

45. £476 for 7 years at 24%

46. £1020 for $5\frac{1}{2}$ years at 18%

47. £3422 for 7 months at $5\frac{3}{4}$%

48. £90.50 for 13 months at $9\frac{1}{2}$%

49. £258.70 for 3 years at 32%

50. £162.30 for 18 months at $16\frac{1}{2}$%.

INVERSE PROBLEMS ON SIMPLE INTEREST

Frequently questions arise where the simple interest I or the amount A is known while P or R or T is a quantity which we are asked to find. The basic formula to remember is still:

$$I = \frac{PRT}{100}$$

From which it follows that $PRT = 100I$

i.e.
$$P = \frac{100I}{RT} \quad \text{or} \quad R = \frac{100I}{PT} \quad \text{or} \quad T = \frac{100I}{PR}$$

EXAMPLE 7   At what rate per cent will £200 give £72 simple interest in 3 years?

Method 1 $I = \dfrac{PRT}{100}$

$\therefore \ 72 = \dfrac{200 \times R \times 3}{100}$

i.e. $72 = 6R$

$\therefore$ Rate $= 12\%$

Method 2 $R = \dfrac{100I}{PT}$ from above

$\therefore$ Rate $= \dfrac{100 \times 72}{200 \times 3}\% = 12\%$

EXAMPLE 8   What sum of money will give £150 simple interest if invested for 4 years at 15%?

Method 1 $I = \dfrac{PRT}{100}$

$\therefore \ 150 = \dfrac{P \times 15 \times 4}{100}$

i.e. $15\,000 = P \times 60$

$\therefore \ P = \dfrac{15\,000}{60} = 250$

$\therefore$ £250 is invested

Method 2 $\quad P = \dfrac{100I}{RT} = \dfrac{100 \times 150}{15 \times 4} = 250$

i.e. £250 is invested.

EXAMPLE 9

What sum of money amounts to £800.80 when invested for 3 years at 18%?

$$I = \frac{P \times 18 \times 3}{100} = \frac{54}{100}P$$

and $A = P + I = P + \dfrac{54}{100}P = \dfrac{154}{100}P$

$\therefore \ 800.80 = \dfrac{154}{100}P$

i.e. $P = \dfrac{800.80 \times 100}{154} = 520$

i.e. £520 is the sum invested.

EXAMPLE 10

If £192 amounts to £204 in 5 months, to what will it amount in 2 years at the same rate of interest?

Interest $I = £204 - £192 = £12$

Then since $I = \dfrac{PRT}{100}$, we have:

$$12 = \frac{192}{100} \times R \times \frac{5}{12}$$

i.e. $14\,400 = 192 \times 5 \times R$

i.e. $R = \dfrac{14\,400}{192 \times 5} = 15$

$\therefore$ Rate of interest is 15%

Using $I = \dfrac{PRT}{100}$ again, with $T = 2$:

$$I = \frac{192 \times 15 \times 2}{100} = 57.60$$

i.e. Simple interest is £57.60

$\therefore$ Amount after 2 years $= £192 + £57.60$

$\hspace{4.5cm} = £249.60$

EXERCISE 95

1. Copy and complete the following table:

PRINCIPAL IN £	RATE %	TIME IN YEARS	SIMPLE INTEREST IN £	AMOUNT IN £
150		2	36	
240		5		420
320	18			492.80
720		4		1411.20
	8	$2\frac{1}{2}$	81	
356	11		146.85	
534	13			$574.49\frac{1}{2}$
890		$\frac{3}{4}$	$113.47\frac{1}{2}$	

2. Mr Brown obtained a bank loan of £2200 when the rate of interest was 14% p.a. If he is able to repay the loan plus interest after 9 months, how much will it cost him?

3. If £360 amounts to £398.40 in 8 months, to what will it amount in 1 year at the same rate of interest?

4. To pay for new equipment a garage owner borrows £16 500 from his bank. If the rate of interest is 14%, what sum must he pay at the end of the year to repay the loan plus interest?

5. My bank pays 12% p.a. interest on money I have in a deposit account. How much do I have in the bank if the interest for 9 months is £46.80?

6. If the bank increases its interest from 12% p.a. to 13% p.a., the interest I receive from money in my deposit account increases by £60 over a 6 month period. Find the amount in the account.

7. The interest I receive on £2400 increases by £36 when the interest rate rises by 2% p.a. For how long is the sum invested?

8. Peter put £8500 into his deposit account in the bank when the interest rate paid was $6\frac{1}{2}$%. When he received his first statement the interest received was £110.50. How many days had the money been on deposit?

9. A woman borrowed £146 at 15% p.a. and when she repaid it the interest due was £9.60. For how many days did she borrow the money?

10. When a firm borrowed a substantial sum of money the interest rate was 14%, the interest to be paid monthly. After 5 months the interest rate dropped by $1\frac{1}{2}$% thereby decreasing the monthly interest due by £18.75. Find the sum of money borrowed.

COMPOUND INTEREST

Most loans or investments are for periods of more than a year. Many investors prefer not to take their interest when it becomes due but to leave it untouched so that their savings or capital grows. In this way their capital increases so that the following year interest is paid on a larger principal, i.e. on the old principal plus the interest for the year. This type of interest is called *compound interest*. It is nothing more than simple interest, but taking each year separately. Exactly how this works is shown by some examples.

EXAMPLE 11 Find the compound interest on £320 invested for 2 years at 12%.

	£
Principal at beginning of 1st year	320.00
Interest for 1st year at 12%	38.40
Principal at beginning of 2nd year	358.40
Interest for 2nd year at 12%	43.008
Principal at end of second year	401.408
Original sum	320.00
∴ Compound interest	81.408

i.e. £81.41 correct to the nearest penny

NOTES: (1) Multiply the £320 by 12 but write down the result two decimal places to the right i.e. instead of 3840 write £38.40. This has the effect of dividing by 100 since 12% of £320 is $£320 \times \dfrac{12}{100}$.

(2) Take great care to keep the decimal points one beneath the other in succeeding lines. A vertical line indicating the point position is often an advantage.

(3) The horizontal lines are drawn after each year's interest has been calculated.

(4) The interest payment in any year should always be slightly more than the corresponding value for the previous year.

Example 11 could also be set out as follows:

Principal at beginning of 1st year $= £320$

Simple interest on £320 for 1 year at 12% $= \dfrac{PRT}{100}$

$$= £\dfrac{320 \times 12 \times 1}{100} = £38.40$$

∴ Principal at beginning of 2nd year $= £320 + £38.40$
$$= £358.40$$

Simple interest on £358.40 for 1 year at 12%
$$= £\dfrac{358.40 \times 12 \times 1}{100} = £43.008$$

∴ Principal at end of 2nd year $= £358.40 + £43.008$
$$= £401.408$$

i.e. Total compound interest $= £401.408 - £320$
$$= £81.408$$
$$= £81.41 \text{ correct to the}$$
nearest penny

EXAMPLE 12   Find the compound interest on £164 invested for 2 years at 13%, giving your answer correct to the nearest penny.

	£
Principal at beginning of 1st year	164.00
Interest for 1st year at 10%	16.40
Interest for 1st year at 3%	4.92
Principal at beginning of 2nd year	185.32
Interest for 2nd year at 10%	18.532
Interest for 2nd year at 3%	5.5596
Principal at end of 2nd year	209.4116
Original sum	164.00
Compound interest	45.4116

i.e. Compound interest $= £45.41$

If you are able to calculate the compound interest for 2 years, the interest for longer periods of time is found by continuing the process a little further. In some cases the interest may be due or payable in shorter periods of time than 1 year, e.g. half-yearly or quarterly (see Example 13), or if money has been borrowed, repayments may be due at regular intervals of less than 1 year.

EXAMPLE 13   Find the compound interest on £145 for 2 years at 10% p.a. if interest is payable six-monthly.

A rate of 10% p.a. payable six-monthly means that 5% is due for one six month period, and 5% of the new sum will be due for the second six month period.

Thus:

	£
Principal at beginning of 1st 6-month period	145.00
Interest for 1st 6-month period at 5%	7.25
Principal at beginning of 2nd 6-month period	152.25
Interest for 2nd period at 5%	7.6125
Principal at beginning of 3rd 6-month period	159.8625
Interest for 3rd period at 5%	7.9930
Principal at beginning of 4th 6-month period	167.8555
Interest for 4th period at 5%	8.3930
Principal at end of 4th 6-month period	176.2485
Original sum	145.0000
∴ Compound interest	31.2485

i.e. Compound interest = £31.25 to the nearest penny

EXERCISE 96

Find the compound interest payable yearly, giving your answers correct to the nearest penny, on:

1. £240 invested for 2 years at 10%

2. £500 invested for 2 years at 8%

3. £700 invested for 2 years at 12%

4. £900 invested for 2 years at 6%

5. £470 invested for 2 years at 9%

6. £520 invested for 2 years at 7%

7. £670 invested for 2 years at 11%

8. £370 invested for 2 years at 14%

9. £180 invested for 2 years at $9\frac{1}{2}$%

10. £350 invested for 2 years at $11\frac{1}{2}$%

11. £600 invested for 2 years at $8\frac{3}{4}$%

12. £900 invested for 2 years at $12\frac{3}{4}$%

13. £840 invested for 2 years at $7\frac{3}{4}$%

14. £330 invested for 2 years at $15\frac{1}{4}$%

15. £960 invested for 2 years at $14\frac{1}{4}$%

16. £472 invested for 2 years at $7\frac{1}{4}$%

17. £533 invested for 2 years at $13\frac{3}{4}$%

18. £400 invested for 3 years at 8%

19. £800 invested for 3 years at 12%

20. £740 invested for 3 years at 7%

21. £920 invested for 3 years at 9%

22. £700 invested for 3 years at $13\frac{1}{2}$%

23. £300 invested for 3 years at $12\frac{1}{2}$%

24. £420 invested for 3 years at $10\frac{1}{4}$%

25. £270 invested for 3 years at $7\frac{1}{4}$%

26. £515 invested for 3 years at $6\frac{3}{4}$%

27. £642 invested for 3 years at $14\frac{3}{4}$%.

Find the compound interest, payable half-yearly, on:

28. £500 invested for 1 year at 8%

29. £600 invested for 2 years at 10%

30. £400 invested for 2 years at 12%

31. £750 invested for $1\frac{1}{2}$ years at 14%

32. £240 invested for 2 years at 18%.

33. A man borrows £8000 at 12% compound interest and agrees to pay £2000 off the loan at the end of each year. How much does he owe after 3 years?

34. A company borrows £14 000 at 16% compound interest and agrees to repay £3500 at the end of each year. How much is still owed after 2 years?

35. A couple buy a car by borrowing £2000 from a credit company. They agree to repay £60 each month, compound interest to be 24% p.a. payable monthly. What is their debt after six monthly payments?

36. A couple want to borrow £1000 for a year. The bank offers to lend the money at 16% compound interest payable yearly, while a finance company offers to lend at 2% per month payable monthly. Compare the total due to the bank with that due to the finance company by the end of the year.

37. A small company borrows £10 000 at 14% and agrees to pay half the amount due after 1 year at the end of that year, and the remainder at the end of the following year. How much more do they pay at the end of the second year than at the end of the first?

38. A woman borrowed £3500. She agreed to repay £1000 after 1 year, a further £2000 after 2 years and the balance at the end of the third year. If compound interest was agreed at 18% payable yearly, how much was repaid at the end of the third year to clear the debt?

39. A school borrows £5000 at 15% compound interest towards the cost of a minibus. They repay £2000 after 1 year, together with a further £2000 at the end of the second year. How much must they find at the end of the third year to clear the debt?

40. A motorist owns a car valued at £1000 and has £8000 cash in a building society. He debates whether or not to spend his cash on a new car costing £9000. If he leaves his money in the building society it will earn compound interest at 8%. On the other hand any car he owns depreciates by 20% p.a. of its value at the beginning of any year. Compare his financial position after 4 years if he buys the new car, with his position if he does not.

COMPOUND INTEREST TABLE

The following table gives the amount to which £1 will grow at various rates of compound interest for the number of years stated.

RATE OF INTEREST	NUMBER OF YEARS									
	1	2	3	4	5	6	7	8	9	10
9%	1.090	1.1881	1.2950	1.4116	1.5386	1.6771	1.8280	1.9926	2.1719	2.3674
$9\frac{1}{2}$%	1.095	1.1990	1.3129	1.4377	1.5742	1.7238	1.8876	2.0669	2.2632	2.4782
10%	1.100	1.2100	1.3310	1.4641	1.6105	1.7716	1.9487	2.1436	2.3579	2.5937
$10\frac{1}{2}$%	1.105	1.2210	1.3492	1.4909	1.6474	1.8204	2.0116	2.2228	2.4562	2.7141
11%	1.110	1.2321	1.3676	1.5181	1.6851	1.8704	2.0762	2.3045	2.5580	2.8394
$11\frac{1}{2}$%	1.115	1.2432	1.3862	1.5456	1.7234	1.9215	2.1425	2.3890	2.6636	2.9699
12%	1.120	1.2544	1.4049	1.5735	1.7623	1.9738	2.2107	2.4760	2.7701	3.1058
$12\frac{1}{2}$%	1.125	1.2656	1.4238	1.6018	1.8020	2.0273	2.2807	2.5658	2.8865	3.2473
13%	1.130	1.2769	1.4429	1.6305	1.8424	2.0820	2.3526	2.6584	3.0040	3.3946
$13\frac{1}{2}$%	1.135	1.2882	1.4621	1.6595	1.8836	2.1378	2.4264	2.7540	3.1258	3.5478
14%	1.140	1.2996	1.4815	1.6890	1.9254	2.1950	2.5023	2.8526	3.2519	3.7072
$14\frac{1}{2}$%	1.145	1.3110	1.5011	1.7188	1.9680	2.2543	2.5801	2.9542	3.3826	3.8731
15%	1.150	1.3225	1.5209	1.7490	2.0114	2.3131	2.6600	3.0590	3.5179	4.0456

EXAMPLE 14

Use the table above to find:

(a) The compound interest obtained if £50 is invested for 1 year at 14%.

(b) The amount to which £800 will grow if invested at 9% p.a. compound interest for 10 years.

(c) The sum, which when invested for 6 years at $12\frac{1}{2}$% p.a. compound interest will grow to £2432.76.

(d) How many years £5000 needs to be invested at 13% p.a. compound interest to yield interest of £8292.

(a) From the table £1 invested for 1 year at 14% compound interest grows to £1.14.

∴ £50 invested for 1 year at 14% grows to:

£50 × 1.14 = £57

∴ compound interest on £50 for 1 year at 14% is £7.

(b) £1 invested for 10 years at 9% p.a. compound interest grows to £2.3674.

∴ £800 invested for 10 years at 9% p.a. compound interest grows to:

£800 × 2.3674 = £1893.92

(c) £1 invested for 6 years at $12\frac{1}{2}$% compound interest p.a. grows to £2.0273, or £2.0273 is what £1 will grow to in 6 years at $12\frac{1}{2}$% compound interest.

∴ £2432.76 is what £$\dfrac{2432.76}{2.0273}$ = £1200 will

grow to in 6 years at $12\frac{1}{2}$% compound interest

(d) £5000 when invested at 13% compound interest for a certain number of years yields £8292 interest.

i.e. it grows to £5000 + £8292 = £13 292

If £5000 grows to £13 292 at the given rate, then £1 grows to:

£$\dfrac{13\,292}{5000}$ = £2.6584

Looking along the 13% row in the table we see that £1 grows to £2.6584 in 8 years.

∴ £5000 will yield £8292 compound interest at 13% in 8 years

EXERCISE 97

Use the compound interest table given in the text to answer the following questions:

1. What interest is obtained when £10 is invested for 1 year at $12\frac{1}{2}$% p.a.?

2. What interest is obtained when £200 is invested for 5 years at $9\frac{1}{2}$% p.a.?

3. What interest is obtained when £1000 is invested for 8 years at 14% p.a.?

4. What interest is obtained when £3000 is invested for 10 years at 11% p.a.?

5. What will £500 grow to in 3 years at 11% p.a. compound interest?

6. What will £2000 grow to in 8 years at 14% p.a. compound interest?

7. What will £800 grow to in 6 years at $10\frac{1}{2}$% p.a. compound interest?

8. What will £30 000 grow to in 5 years at 10% p.a. compound interest?

9. What sum of money when invested for 4 years at 9% p.a. compound interest will grow to £2823.20?

10. What sum of money when invested for 7 years at $13\frac{1}{2}$% p.a. will grow to £12 132?

11. What sum of money when invested for 2 years at 12% p.a. will grow to £10 035.20?

12. What sum of money, invested for 5 years at 10% p.a. compound interest, yields £305.25 interest?

13. What sum of money, invested for 3 years at $12\frac{1}{2}$% p.a. compound interest, yields £2542.80 interest?

14. What sum of money, invested for 8 years at 14% p.a. compound interest, yields £2778.90 interest?

15. When £1000 is invested for 4 years at a certain rate of compound interest it amounts to £1689. What rate of compound interest p.a. is being paid?

16. When £12 000 is invested for 6 years at a certain rate of compound interest it amounts to £24 984. Find the rate of interest.

17. When £20 000 is invested at 12% p.a. compound interest for a certain number of years it amounts to £49 520. What is the period of the investment?

18. When £6000 was invested at $10\frac{1}{2}$% compound interest p.a. for a certain number of years it amounted to £7326. What was the period of the investment?

19. Peter Snow has £10 000 invested at $11\frac{1}{2}\%$ compound interest p.a. He decides to switch his investment to give 14% compound interest p.a. How much better off is he 5 years later?

20. David Hillins has £20 000 invested at $12\frac{1}{2}\%$ p.a. compound interest. He decides to switch to another investment but as things turn out the new investment only gives a return of $11\frac{1}{2}\%$ p.a. compound interest. How much does he lose as a result of the switch over an 8 year period?

COMPOUND INTEREST FORMULA

The interest on £P invested for 1 year at $R\%$ is £$\dfrac{PR}{100}$. Since the amount A is the sum of the principal P and the interest for the year $\dfrac{PR}{100}$:

$$A = P + \frac{PR}{100} = P\left(1 + \frac{R}{100}\right)$$

Compound interest means that the amount at the *end* of 1 year becomes the *principal* at the *beginning* of the next. The above formula shows that the amount at the end of a year is found by multiplying the principal at the beginning of the year by $\left(1 + \dfrac{R}{100}\right)$. If $A_1, A_2, A_3, \ldots$, denote the amounts at the end of the first year, the second year, the third year, etc., then:

$$A_1 = P\left(1 + \frac{R}{100}\right)$$

$$A_2 = A_1\left(1 + \frac{R}{100}\right) = P\left(1 + \frac{R}{100}\right)\left(1 + \frac{R}{100}\right)$$

$$= P\left(1 + \frac{R}{100}\right)^2$$

$$A_3 = A_2\left(1 + \frac{R}{100}\right) = P\left(1 + \frac{R}{100}\right)^2\left(1 + \frac{R}{100}\right)$$

$$= P\left(1 + \frac{R}{100}\right)^3$$

It follows that the amount after n years is given by:

$$A_n = P\left(1 + \frac{R}{100}\right)^n$$

331

This is the *compound interest formula* and it applies to any quantity which increases or decreases so that the amount at the end of each period of constant length is in a constant ratio to the amount at the beginning of that period. When used in questions on *depreciation* (i.e. the drop in value of such things as cars and machinery over a period of time) it is called the *decay factor*, but when used for things which usually *appreciate* (i.e. rise in value, such as populations and property values) it is called the *growth* factor.

Questions using the compound interest formula require us to evaluate expressions such as 1.1^{10}. It is a good idea to practise some of these before considering compound interest questions.

EXAMPLE 15

Find 1.1^{10}.

Let $x = 1.1^{10}$, then:

$$\log x = 10 \times \log 1.1$$
$$= 10 \times 0.0414$$
$$= 0.414$$
$$\therefore x = 2.594$$
$$\therefore 1.1^{10} = 2.594$$

The fourth figure is not always reliable (in this example it is), but the degree of accuracy is usually considered satisfactory.

EXAMPLE 16

Find 0.95^{20}.

Let $x = 0.95^{20}$, then:

$$\log x = 20 \times \log 0.95$$
$$= 20 \times \bar{1}.9777$$
$$= 20 \times (-0.0223)$$
$$= -0.446$$
$$= \bar{1}.554$$
$$\therefore x = 0.95^{20} = 0.3581$$

EXAMPLE 17

Find the compound interest on £570 invested for 12 years at 12%.

$$A = P\left(1 + \frac{R}{100}\right)^n$$

$$= 570\left(1 + \frac{12}{100}\right)^{12}$$

$$= 570(1.12)^{12}$$

$$= 2220$$

$$\begin{array}{r} 0.0492 \times 12 \\ \hline 0.5904 \\ 2.7559 \\ \hline 3.3463 \end{array}$$

$$\therefore \text{ Compound interest} = £2220 - £570$$
$$= £1650$$

EXAMPLE 18

At what rate per cent p.a. will £1000 amount to £2000 in 5 years at compound interest? Give your answer correct to the nearest whole number.

$$A = P\left(1 + \frac{R}{100}\right)^n$$

$$\therefore 2000 = 1000\left(1 + \frac{R}{100}\right)^5$$

$$\therefore 2 = \left(1 + \frac{R}{100}\right)^5$$

i.e. $1 + \dfrac{R}{100} = 2^{\frac{1}{5}}$

$0.3010 \div 5$

0.0602

$$= 1.149$$

$$\therefore \frac{R}{100} = 0.149$$

i.e. $R = 14.9$

∴ Rate of interest is 15% correct to the nearest whole number

EXAMPLE 19

In what time will a sum of money treble itself at 9% compound interest?

$$A = P\left(1 + \frac{R}{100}\right)^n$$

$$3P = P\left(1 + \frac{9}{100}\right)^n$$

$$3 = 1.09^n$$

i.e. $1.09^n = 3$

$\therefore n \log 1.09 = \log 3$

$\bar{1}.6786$

$\bar{2}.5729$

$$\therefore n = \frac{0.4771}{0.0374}$$

1.1057

$$= 12.76$$

∴ The time is approximately 12.76 years

333

INCREASE IN VALUE — APPRECIATION

EXAMPLE 20

A couple bought a house 20 years ago for £5000. If its value appreciated by 12% each year, what is its value today? Give your answer correct to the nearest £1000.

$$A = P\left(1 + \frac{R}{100}\right)^n$$

$$= £5000\left(1 + \frac{12}{100}\right)^{20}$$

$$= £5000\,(1.12)^{20}$$

$$= £5000 \times 9.638$$

$$= £48\,190$$

0.0492 × 20
0.9840

∴ Today's value is £48 000

DECREASE IN VALUE — DEPRECIATION

EXAMPLE 21

A company buys a machine for £60 000. In any year it depreciates by 16% of its value at the beginning of the year. How much will it be worth after 10 years?

$$A = P\left(1 + \frac{R}{100}\right)^n$$

Since it is *losing* value, R is -16

$$\therefore A = £60\,000\left(1 - \frac{16}{100}\right)^{10}$$

$$= £60\,000\,(0.84)^{10}$$

$$= £60\,000 \times 0.1750$$

$$= £10\,500$$

$\bar{1}.9243 \times 10$
$\bar{1}.2430$

∴ Value when machine is 10 years old is £10 500

EXERCISE 98

Find the following giving your answers to four significant figures:

1. 1.2^{10}	2. 1.3^{20}	3. 1.25^8	4. 1.08^7
5. 1.09^5	6. 1.42^6	7. 1.24^{12}	8. 1.05^4
9. 0.95^{10}	10. 0.87^{20}	11. 0.83^5	12. 0.75^8.

Find the approximate amounts of the given sums, invested at compound interest for the given times at the given rates:

13. £200, 10 years, 15%

14. £6000, 8 years, 12%

15. £1000, 12 years, 23%

16. £5000, 30 years, 18%

17. £8000, 20 years, $14\frac{1}{2}$%

18. £5400, 5 years, 36%

19. £8600, 17 years, $8\frac{1}{2}$%

20. £43, 34 years, $16\frac{1}{2}$%.

In the remaining questions, give your answers which do not work out exactly correct to three significant figures.

21. At what rate per cent p.a. will £100 amount to £200 in 5 years at compound interest?

22. At what rate per cent p.a. will £400 amount to £700 in 5 years at compound interest?

23. At what rate per cent p.a. will £5000 amount to £15 000 in 8 years at compound interest?

24. In what time will £1000 double itself at $12\frac{1}{2}$% compound interest?

25. In what time will a sum of money treble itself at 14% compound interest?

26. In what time will £500 amount to £750 at $15\frac{1}{2}$% compound interest?

27. What sum of money will amount to £1771 if invested at 10% compound interest for 6 years?

28. What sum of money will amount to £274 if invested at 18% compound interest for 20 years?

29. In what time will £270 amount to £826 at 15% compound interest?

30. In what time will £500 amount to £1238 at 12% compound interest?

31. A National Savings Certificate bought for £200 was worth £475 after $6\frac{1}{2}$ years. What rate per cent p.a. compound interest was given?

32. A National Savings Certificate bought for £1 was worth £3.11 after 10 years. What rate per cent p.a. compound interest was paid?

33. A man bought a house for £20 000. If it appreciated at the rate of 8% p.a., find its value after 10 years.

34. A newly married couple bought a house for £18 000. If it appreciated at the rate of 12% p.a., how much was it worth 20 years later?

35. Two women invested £50 000 in a business property as a hedge against inflation. If the inflation rate over the period of their investment was $9\frac{1}{2}$% p.a. and the value of the property kept pace with inflation, what was its value after 12 years?

36. A boy buys an old postage stamp for £3. If it increases in value by 15% p.a., how much can he expect it to be worth in 35 years' time?

37. It is estimated that a gold sovereign found in 1980 increases in value by 12% p.a. If it was valued at £120 in 1980, what should it be worth in the year 2000?

38. A gold sovereign cost £1 in 1900. If it appreciated to £108 in 1980, find the rate per cent of compound interest over the period.

39. Petrol which cost 25 p per gallon 24 years ago costs £2 per gallon today. Find the rate per cent p.a. increase in its price over this period.

40. The population of a town is expected to increase by 4% each year. If the population is 25 000 today, what can it be expected to be in (a) 10 years, (b) 25 years?

41. Over a 25 year period the population of China quadrupled. Find the rate of increase per annum.

42. The rates on a house increase by 8% each year. If £400 is the annual amount at the present time, what will they be in 15 years' time?

43. Between 1801 and 1850 the population of Great Britain increased from $10\frac{1}{2}$ million to 21 million. Find the rate of increase per annum giving your answer correct to two decimal places.

44. Assuming that only eight people lived on the Earth in the time of Noah (4000 BC) and that the population doubled every hundred years, estimate the world's population in the year AD 2000.

45. Over a 15 year period the population of a region of the Scottish Highlands decreased at the rate of 3% p.a. If there were 40 000 people in the area at the beginning of the period, how many were there at the end?

46. A motor car bought for £15 000 depreciates in any 1 year by 25% of its value at the beginning of that year. What will the car be worth when it is 5 years old?

47. A motorcycle bought for £2000 depreciates in any 1 year by 20% of its value at the beginning of that year. What will it be worth when it is 8 years old?

48. A company buys new machinery for £50 000 which depreciates by 18% of its value (at the beginning of the year) each year. What will be its loss of value after 7 years?

49. Expensive machinery depreciates by 16% of its value each year. A company intends selling a machine when it has fallen in value to less than half its purchase price. How many years' use (to the nearest whole number) can they expect from the machine?

50. A washing machine depreciates from £400 to a scrap value of £25 in 10 years. Find the annual rate of depreciation, assumed constant.

21

BORROWING MONEY

Almost everyone wants to borrow money at some time or another. It may be to buy a motorcycle or car, to buy your own home, or simply to enjoy the 'holiday of a lifetime'. Probably the biggest single item of expenditure most of us anticipate is buying our own home. Money for this may be borrowed from a bank, building society or local council, and it is well worth shopping around before finally committing yourself. If you want to buy a car, or some furniture, or an electrical appliance, and do not have sufficient ready cash, you are quite likely to buy it on 'terms' or 'hire-purchase'. Should you wish to take an expensive holiday or extend your home, a personal loan may well be available from the bank.

Various ways of borrowing will now be considered.

MORTGAGES

Very probably the time will come when you will want to own your own home. However, when the day arrives it will be most unlikely that you will have enough money to buy the house of your choice outright. You will need to borrow money, i.e. to take out a *mortgage*, but before you commit yourself, beware — it pays to shop around. It is possible to to borrow money from a bank or the local council, but most house buyers borrow from a building society. These range in size from a giant like the Halifax Building Society with assets of millions of pounds, to the small societies with only a single office.

The principle is a simple one. You may want to borrow £20 000, and are prepared to pay interest on the loan. At the same time perhaps twenty people are willing to lend £1000 each provided they feel that their cash is quite safe and that they receive a satisfactory return on their capital. The twenty lend their money to a building society at, say, $12\frac{1}{2}\%$ p.a. gross, and the building society in turn lends it to you at, say,

15% p.a. gross. The difference between the rate of interest received and the rate of interest paid enables the building society to operate — this money pays their staff and their accommodation costs and provides their profit. Many safeguards have been laid down by Acts of Parliament, and these make the building society a very safe place to invest your money or to borrow money from.

EXAMPLE 1

A married couple want to buy a house costing £40 000. They are able to sell their present home for £15 000 and need to take out a mortgage for the difference. If they take out a 20 year mortgage which costs £14.06 per £1000 per calendar month, calculate the total cost of the new house. Express this cost as a percentage of the cost price.

Advertised cost price of house $= $ £40 000

Value of present house (their deposit) $= $ £15 000

$\therefore$ Sum to be borrowed $= $ £25 000

A loan of £1000 costs £14.06 per calendar month for 20 years.

$\therefore$ A loan of £25 000 costs £14.06 $\times$ 25 $= $ £351.50 per calendar month for 20 years.

i.e. repayments in 1 year $= $ £351.50 $\times$ 12
$$= £4218$$

$\therefore$ Total repayments in 20 years $= $ £4218 $\times$ 20
$$= £84\,360$$

Total cost of house $= $ total repayments $+$ deposit
$$= £84\,360 + £15\,000$$
$$= £99\,360$$

$\therefore$ Required percentage $= \dfrac{\text{total cost}}{\text{advertised cost price}} \times 100$

$$= \dfrac{£99\,360}{£40\,000} \times 100$$

$$= 248.4\%$$

EXAMPLE 2

Mr Brown takes out a £12 000 mortgage over 25 years at $14\frac{1}{2}\%$. This means that his monthly repayments are £12.51 per calendar month per £1000 borrowed.

(a) Find (i) his gross annual repayments,
         (ii) his net annual repayments after a tax allowance of 30%.

(b) If the interest rate rises to 16% (i.e. £13.67 per calendar month per £1000 borrowed) while the tax allowance increases to 35%, calculate the annual amount by which Mr Brown is better or worse off.

(a) (i) Since gross monthly repayment on £1000 = £12.51

$$\text{Gross monthly repayment on £12 000} = £12.51 \times 12$$

$$= £150.12$$

$$\therefore \text{ Gross annual repayment} = £150.12 \times 12$$

$$= £1801.44$$

(ii) Tax allowance $= £1801.44 \times \dfrac{30}{100}$

$$= £540.43$$

$$\therefore \text{ Net annual repayments} = £1801.44 - £540.43$$

$$= £1261.01$$

(b) If the mortgage rate rises to 16%:

$$\text{New gross annual repayment} = £13.67 \times 12 \times 12$$

$$= £1968.48$$

If tax allowance rises to 35%:

$$\text{Tax allowance} = £1968.48 \times \dfrac{35}{100}$$

$$= £688.97$$

$$\text{i.e. Net annual repayment} = £1968.48 - £688.97$$

$$= £1279.51$$

Mr Brown's net annual repayments increase by:

$$£1279.51 - £1261.01 = £18.50$$

EXERCISE 99

1. A man borrows £14 000 from a building society in order to buy a house. The society charges £11.51 per calendar month per £1000 borrowed. What are the monthly repayments?

2. Mr and Mrs Green borrow £18 000 from a building society when they move to a larger house. The repayments are £11.37 per calendar month per £1000 borrowed. Calculate their monthly repayments.

3. The Goodbrick Building Society grants Mr John a mortgage for £21 000. Repayments amount to £13.91 per calendar month per £1000 borrowed. Calculate Mr John's annual repayments.

4. A woman borrows £9000 from a building society in order to buy a flat. The mortgage repayments over 25 years are £13.67 per calendar month per £1000 borrowed. Calculate (a) the annual repayments, (b) the total repayments.

5. Mr and Mrs Davis agree to buy a house costing £25 000. They agree to pay £10 000 down and to take a mortgage for the remainder at $14\frac{1}{2}\%$. Over a 20 year period this works out at £12.95 per calendar month per £1000 borrowed. Calculate (a) their yearly mortgage repayments, (b) the total amount they will have paid for the house. Express (b) as a percentage of the cost price.

6. John and Dorothy Wood sell their house for £27 000. After allowing £2000 for expenses they put the remainder as a down payment on a house costing £42 000. On the outstanding balance they take out a mortgage at $13\frac{1}{2}\%$ for 25 years, the monthly repayments for which are £11.75 per calendar month for each £1000 borrowed. Find (a) the monthly mortgage repayments, (b) the total cost of the house.

7. Mary Williams obtains a 95% mortgage on a house costing £19 000 and agrees to pay an interest rate of 15%. This means that her calendar monthly repayments per £1000 borrowed may be either £16.61 for 10 years or £13.32 for 20 years. How much more would she pay if she chose to take the 20 year mortgage as opposed to the 10 year mortgage?

8. A young couple obtain a 90% mortgage on a house costing £18 000. If the mortgage repayments over 20 years are £12.77 per month per £1000 borrowed, calculate (a) the amount borrowed, (b) the annual repayments, (c) the total cost of the house.

HIRE-PURCHASE

Hire-purchase (HP) is a popular and convenient way of buying things when you cannot afford the full price out of your income or your savings. A high percentage of sales of such things as washing machines, cameras, hi-fi equipment, motorcycles, cars and furniture are paid for in this way. You have the advantage of being able to use something before you have sufficient cash to pay for it, since someone else is lending you the money. As the term *hire-purchase* implies, you are really hiring the article until you have made the last payment. Only then is it legally yours. You must of course pay extra for the privilege of using the article before you can pay for it. An article bought on hire-purchase always costs more, sometimes significantly more, than if you pay cash. Following the lifting of government hire-purchase restrictions in July 1982, you may not be required to pay a cash deposit of part of the purchase price; traders now fix their own terms and conditions of hire-purchase.

A slight variation is a *credit sale*. In this type of sale the goods become yours as soon as you sign the agreement. If you fail to keep up the payments, the article cannot be taken away from you, but you could be taken to court in an attempt to recover the outstanding debt.

EXAMPLE 3

A motorcycle is priced at £1869. If bought on hire-purchase the terms are: $\frac{1}{3}$ deposit plus 36 monthly payments of £44.95. Find the HP price.

Deposit of $\frac{1}{3}$ of £1869 $= $ £623

Total of 36 monthly payments of £44.95 $= $ £44.95 $\times$ 36

$= $ £1618.20

$\therefore$ Total HP price $= $ £623 + £1618.20

$= $ £2241.20

EXAMPLE 4

The complete furnishings for a lounge display in a department store amount to £3560. If cash is paid a discount of 5% is given, but if sold on hire-purchase, the terms are calculated as follows:

A deposit of 25% is required.

The resulting balance is increased by 10% for each year of the hire-purchase agreement, and this total is divided by the number of calendar months over which the agreement runs, to give the monthly repayment.

If the whole display is purchased under such an HP agreement over 3 years, calculate:

(a) the cash price

(b) the deposit

(c) the total HP price

(d) the monthly repayment under the agreement

(e) the amount saved if the furnishings were bought for cash.

(a) Marked price of display $= £3560$

Discount for cash
is 5% of £3560 $= £3560 \times \dfrac{5}{100}$

$\qquad = £178$

$\therefore$ Cash price $= £3560 - £178$

$\qquad = £3382$

(b) Under the HP agreement:

Deposit $= 25\%$ of £3560

$\qquad = £3560 \times \dfrac{25}{100}$

$\qquad = £890$

(c) Balance due $= £3560 - £890 = £2670$

Since the agreement is for 3 years, and the balance is increased by 10% for each year, i.e. by 30%, the balance increases by $£2760 \times \dfrac{30}{100}$

$= £801$ to a total of $£2670 + £801 = £3471$

$\therefore$ Total HP price $= £890 + £3471$

$\qquad = £4361$

(d) Monthly repayment $= £\dfrac{3471}{36} = £96.42$

(correct to the nearest penny)

(e) Amount saved
by paying cash $=$ HP price $-$ cash price

$\qquad = £4361 - £3382$

$\qquad = £979$

EXERCISE 100

Find the total hire-purchase cost in each of the following cases:

1. Deposit £40 plus 12 monthly payments of £8

2. Deposit £36 plus 12 monthly payments of £6.75

3. Deposit £13.42 plus 12 monthly payments of £2.67

4. Deposit £2.37 plus 52 weekly payments of 39 p

5. Deposit £312 plus 24 monthly payments of £25.83

6. Deposit £17.37 plus 24 monthly payments of £6.27

7. Deposit £651 plus quarterly payments of £84.60 for 5 years

8. Deposit £86.70 plus weekly payments of £5.21 for 3 years

9. Deposit £2413 plus monthly payments of £212.33 for 2 years

10. Deposit £1937 plus monthly payments of £164.20 for three years.

11. The cash price of a dining suite is £784. Hire-purchase terms require 25% deposit together with 24 monthly repayments of £28.20. Calculate the amount saved by paying cash.

12. An electric lawn mower is offered for sale at £185.95. If bought on terms, a deposit of $\frac{1}{5}$ is required, followed by 24 equal monthly instalments of £7.19. Find the total HP price.

13. A cine-camera is advertised at £224. If bought on HP, the terms are: 25% deposit plus 12 monthly payments of £15.68. How much is saved by paying cash?

14. A grand piano is advertised at £2720. If bought on hire-purchase, the terms are: 20% deposit plus 18 monthly payments of £142. How much is saved by paying cash?

15. The cash price of a cut-glass water set is £85.50. The hire-purchase terms are $\frac{1}{5}$ deposit plus 52 weekly payments of 142 p. How much is saved by paying cash?

16. A man's suit can be bought for £126 cash or for a deposit of £42 plus 12 monthly instalments of £7.56.
    (a) How much more does the suit cost if bought on the instalment plan compared with the cash price?
    (b) Express the additional cost as a percentage of the cash price.

17. A motorcycle is offered for sale at £560. If bought on hire purchase, a deposit of $\frac{1}{4}$ is required together with 24 monthly payments of £21.49. Calculate the difference between the cash price and the hire-purchase price.

18. The marked price of a three-piece suite is £1290. A 5% discount is offered for a cash sale, but if bought on HP, the deposit is $\frac{1}{3}$, followed by 18 monthly payments of £57.33. Find the cash difference in the two ways of paying for the suite, and express this difference as a percentage of the *cash* price, giving your answer correct to three significant figures.

19. The marked price of an electric cooker is £330. If bought for cash, a discount of $2\frac{1}{2}$% is given, but if bought on hire-purchase, the terms are: $\frac{1}{3}$ deposit plus 24 monthly payments of £11.20. How much more does the cooker cost if bought on hire-purchase?

20. A freezer may be bought for £345 or for 24 monthly instalments of £13.76 following a deposit of £87. Find the total hire-purchase price. How much is saved by paying cash?

21. A bus company is offered a second hand coach for £6690. Since it cannot afford to pay cash it has two options:

Option 1: 6 half-yearly payments of £1286

Option 2: A deposit of $\frac{1}{3}$ plus 12 three-monthly payments of £486

Which option is the cheaper, and by how much?

22. Retiling a house will cost £2850. If paid for on hire-purchase, a deposit of $\frac{1}{5}$ is required together with 60 monthly payments of £53.20. Find the additional cost when bought on HP and express this as a percentage of the cash price.

23. A motorist decides to buy a new car, the list price of which is £7440. If he sells his old car privately for £2300 and then pays cash for the new car, he is given a discount of $12\frac{1}{2}\%$. However, if he offers his car in part-exchange, it is valued at £2500 and in addition he must make 36 monthly payments of £178. How much will he save if he sells his car privately and pays cash?

24. A carpet, which is suitable for use in a lounge measuring 5 m by 4 m, is offered for sale at £21.40 per square metre. Hire-purchase terms are as follows: $33\frac{1}{3}\%$ deposit, the balance to be increased by 12% and divided by 12 to give the monthly repayments for 1 year. Find:
(a) the monthly repayments
(b) the increased cost if bought on hire-purchase
(c) the increased cost expressed as a percentage of the cash price.

25. A food mixer may be bought by paying a deposit of £14.60 together with 26 equal payments of £2.17. If this is £8.54 more than the cash price, find the cash price.

26. A football may be bought by paying a deposit of £5.74 together with 52 equal instalments of 46 p. If this is £3.94 more than the cash price, find the cash price.

27. The cash price of an outfit is £176.40. Alternatively it may be paid for with a cash deposit of £44.10 followed by 23 monthly payments of £6.68. How much cheaper is it to pay cash?

28. The cash price of a colour television set is £385. On the instalment plan the deposit of 20% is followed by monthly payments of £27.97 for 1 year. For the second and subsequent years the set may be insured against failure for £32 p.a. If the same set had been rented, the rental fee would have been £9.47 per month for the first year and £8.96 for every additional month. Compare the hire-purchase costs with the rental costs over a 6 year period. Which is the cheaper and by how much?

345

29. A department store advertises a mink coat at £2100. Three different arrangements are offered if it is bought on credit:

    (i) a deposit of $\frac{1}{3}$ plus 12 monthly payments of £127.75

    (ii) a deposit of $\frac{1}{4}$ plus 12 monthly payments of £144.12

    (iii) a deposit of $\frac{1}{5}$ plus 12 monthly payments of £151.73

which is: (a) the cheapest, (b) the dearest, of these arrangements?

30. An electrical discount store calculates its HP prices as follows:

    (i) a deposit of 25% of the cash price

    (ii) the balance is charged interest at $12\frac{1}{2}\%$

    (iii) the balance plus interest is divided by the number of monthly instalments paid.

Using this information calculate:

    (a) the monthly repayments over one year on a video recorder marked £656

    (b) the total cost of a music centre, the list price of which is £372 if it is paid for over an 8 month period.

CREDIT CARDS

Everyone will have seen Access and Barclaycard notices at various shops, garages and other places of business. You will probably also be aware of television advertisements encouraging people to use American Express. These are only three examples of a comparatively new means of paying for goods and services — they are examples of *credit cards*. We are given plenty of information telling us of their advantages, but the fact that these advantages can be rather expensive is seldom pointed out with the same enthusiasm!

Credit cards operate as follows. Each card holder is given a credit limit, which depends on several factors, in particular on the individual's financial position and whether or not he or she is considered a good risk. Let us suppose that your credit limit is £500. This means that you can buy goods up to the value of £500, i.e. you may go on spending as long as your debt to the credit card company does not exceed £500. Before accepting your card the seller may check that you are still within your credit limit, and that everything relating to the account is in order.

If you are the holder of a credit card belonging to one of the major companies there are several advantages: (a) you need not carry very much cash about with you since the card takes its place, (b) you may use it abroad, (c) it doesn't cost you anything if you pay the credit card company promptly. Another advantage, that of buying without ready money, may turn out to be a snag, because some people are tempted into buying things they cannot really afford.

When you get your monthly statement from the credit card company, you will probably be asked to pay £5 or 5% of the debt, whichever is the greater. You have almost a month to decide how much to pay off the debt, because, provided you pay the minimum (£5 or 5%), you may pay as much or as little as you like. Any debt you have which is more than a month old is charged interest at $2\frac{1}{4}\%$ or $2\frac{1}{2}\%$ per month, a rate which may vary from time to time in accordance with the demand for and supply of money. It is worth noting that $2\frac{1}{2}\%$ per month, which does not sound very much, is equivalent to nearly 35% per annum, which is an extremely expensive way of borrowing money.

Cash may also be borrowed on a credit card, but whereas no interest is payable on borrowing to pay for goods or services until one month has elapsed, interest on borrowed cash is due immediately.

EXAMPLE 5 Anthony Williams decides to buy a camera costing £200 using Access. The terms are: a minimum payment of £5 or 5% of the balance, whichever is the greater, at the end of each month, with interest added each month at $2\frac{1}{4}\%$ per month. If he makes the minimum payment each month, how much does he pay at the end of the fifth month if he then clears the debt?

Original debt = £200

First payment at the end of the first month is 5% of £200 = £10, since this is greater than £5.

∴ Debt at end of first month after payment = £190

Interest for second month at $2\frac{1}{4}\%$ = £4.28

∴ Debt at end of second month before any repayment = £194.28

Second month repayment (5% of debt) = £9.71

∴ Debt at end of second month after payment = £184.57

Interest for third month at $2\frac{1}{4}\%$ = £4.15

∴ Debt at end of third month before any repayment = £188.72

Third month repayment (5% of debt) = £9.44

∴ Debt at end of third month after payment = £179.28

Interest for fourth month at $2\frac{1}{4}\%$	$= £4.03$
$\therefore$ Debt at end of fourth month before any repayment	$= £183.31$
Fourth month repayment (5% of debt)	$= £9.17$
$\therefore$ Debt at end of fourth month after payment	$= £174.14$
Interest for fifth month at $2\frac{1}{4}\%$	$= £3.92$
$\therefore$ Debt at end of fifth month before any repayment	$= £178.06$

$\therefore$ Amount due at the end of the fifth month is £178.06

EXAMPLE 6

Repeat Example 5 assuming that Anthony Williams decides to repay £30 at the end of each month.

Then compare the total paid to the credit card company in this example with the total payment in Example 5.

Original debt $= £200$

Payment at end of first month	$= £30$
Debt at end of first month after payment	$= £170$
Interest for second month at $2\frac{1}{4}\%$	$= £3.83$
$\therefore$ Debt at end of second month before repayment	$= £173.83$
Payment at end of second month	$= £30$
$\therefore$ Debt at end of second month after payment	$= £143.83$
Interest for third month at $2\frac{1}{4}\%$	$= £3.24$
$\therefore$ Debt at end of third month before repayment	$= £147.07$
Payment at end of third month	$= £30$
$\therefore$ Debt at end of third month after payment	$= £117.07$
Interest for fourth month at $2\frac{1}{4}\%$	$= £2.63$
$\therefore$ Debt at end of fourth month before repayment	$= £119.70$
Payment at end of fourth month	$= £30$
$\therefore$ Debt at end of fourth month after payment	$= £89.70$

Interest for fifth month at $2\frac{1}{4}\%$ =   £2.02

∴ Debt at end of fifth month
month before any repayment   =   £91.72

∴ Amount due at the end of the fifth month is
£91.72

Total paid
to credit   = £30 + £30 + £30 + £30 + £91.72
company

   = £211.72

Total paid to credit company in Example 5:
£10 + £9.71 + £9.44 + £9.17 + £178.06 =
   = £216.38

EXERCISE 101

1. Anne Phelps uses her credit card to buy an article costing £43.14. For her first payment at the end of the month she must pay at least £5 or 5% or her debt, whichever is the greater. Calculate her minimum repayment.

2. Alan Bates uses his credit card to buy a set of tyres costing £180 for his sports car. For the first repayment he must pay £5 or 5% of the debt, whichever is the greater. Calculate his initial minimum payment.

3. When the Viazzani family pay for their holiday, costing £1000, they use a credit card. They decide that the most they can afford to pay off the debt is £250 a month until the debt is cleared. If the interest rate is $2\frac{1}{4}\%$ per month, how long will the debt take to clear, and how much does the holiday really cost them?

4. Clive and Janet Peel pay for their new fitted kitchen costing £1500, using credit card facilities, the interest being $2\frac{1}{2}\%$ per month. If they pay £100 off their debt each month, how much will they owe before they make their payment at the end of the third month?

5. The Thompson family celebrate a birthday by going out to dinner. When the bill for £86 arrives Mr Thompson pays using his credit card, interest rates for which are $2\frac{1}{2}\%$ per month. If he pays £40 off the debt at the end of the first month, what must he pay at the end of the second month to clear the debt?

6. Spencer Rees' credit limit is £750. He buys articles to his credit limit and repays £100 per month, the interest rate being $2\frac{1}{2}\%$ per month after the first month. How much would he be able to spend to take him up to his credit limit, after he has made his payments up to and including the end of the third month?

7. The Aitken family buy a new dinner service, costing £150, from a large department store, paying for it with their credit card. If the interest rate is $2\frac{1}{2}\%$ per month and they decide to pay £40 each month off the debt, how much must they pay at the end of the fourth month in order to clear the debt?

8. John Roberts pays his garage bill of £180 using his credit card. If he pays £40 off the debt each month and the rate of interest is $2\frac{1}{2}\%$ per month, how much does he owe before he makes any payment at the end of the fifth month?

22
HOUSEHOLD AND MOTOR EXPENSES

RATES

The borough and county councils are responsible for providing very many things which make life easier and better for us — services which we would find it difficult to do without. Schools must be built and need maintaining and staffing; a police force is necessary to uphold the law; street lighting to make it safer and easier to move about at night; roads for our various vehicles; public libraries, sports centres, swimming pools, parks; cleansing departments to collect refuse and keep the streets clean; planning officers to control what is built and where it is built; a public health department; the county archives to preserve the past; cemeteries and crematoria; sewage disposal; homes for senior citizens, and so on.

All these services must be paid for, and it is the residents of an area, supplemented by a substantial grant from central government, who pay for them. This money is obtained from the local inhabitants in the form of *rates*. The system has been in use for a very long time. Even so, in some ways it is a very unfair system which may well be replaced in the not too distant future.

The rating system works as follows. Every property in the area is given what is called a *rateable value* (RV) which is related to the rent which the owner could expect to receive for the property in a year. All properties — houses, shops, garages, business premises and factories — are rated in this way. Assume that the total rateable value of the area is £10 000 000. With this in mind the council will consider very seriously their financial requirements for the year. Let us suppose that they estimate that they will require £5 000 000 more than all government grants they receive. They must raise £5 000 000 in cash and have a total rateable value of £10 000 000 to draw it from. They will therefore levy a rate of $£\dfrac{5\,000\,000}{10\,000\,000}$ i.e. $£\frac{1}{2}$ or 50 p in the £.

Every £1 rateable value will bring in an income of 50 p. Thus if your house has a rateable value of £200, you will have to pay 200×50 p or £100 to the council. If a local shopkeeper has a property with a rateable value of £750, he will have to pay 750×50 p = £375 in rates.

Perhaps the following year the required income rises to £8 000 000. The rate in the £ will be increased to $£\dfrac{8\,000\,000}{10\,000\,000} = £0.8 = 80$ p, i.e. the rateable value remains fixed, but the rate in the £ is increased thus increasing the amount each property owner has to pay. An attempt is made to keep the rate in the £ below 100 p by reviewing the rateable values at approximately 10 year intervals.

The relationship to remember is:

$$\text{Rate in the £} = \frac{\text{cash}}{\text{rateable value}}$$

from which it follows that

$$\text{Cash} = \text{RV} \times \text{rate in the £}$$

and

$$\text{RV} = \frac{\text{cash}}{\text{rate in the £}}$$

The chief advantage of this system is the ease with which the required money may be collected, combined with the relatively low cost of collection. Every property is owned by someone, and the owner is responsible for seeing that the rates are paid. Conversely, what seems grossly unfair about the system is that it bears no relationship to your ability to pay. Consider two identical houses. In one is a widow, left alone in the family home with a small pension. In the other is a family of six with four grown-up children; perhaps in this house there are six wage earners. Under the present system identical rates are due on the two properties. It goes without saying that the six get very much more for their money than does the widow!

EXAMPLE 1

Find the income from a penny rate in the Borough of Westford if the total rateable value of the borough is £4 340 000.

If each £1 rateable value gives an income of one penny then £4 340 000 rateable value will give an income of 4 340 000 pence i.e. £43 400.

Although rateable value is always preceded by the £ sign, for all calculations it should be considered as a number since it is impossible to multiply money by money.

EXAMPLE 2

The rateable value of my house is £274. How much will I pay in rates if the council levy a rate of 66 p in the £?

What is the rateable value of my neighbour's house if his rates bill amounts to £194.70?

Since:

Rates paid = RV × rate in the £

My rates bill for the year amounts to:

274×66 p = £180.84

And since:

$$RV \text{ in £s} = \frac{\text{rates paid}}{\text{rate in the £}}$$

$$RV \text{ of my neighbour's house in £s} = \frac{£194.70}{66 \text{ p}}$$

$$= 295$$

i.e. Rateable value = £295

EXERCISE 102

Calculate the income from a penny rate for each of the following areas:

	AREA	RATEABLE VALUE (RV)
1.	Coalwood	£1 437 000
2.	Downminster	£2 142 000
3.	Atherton	£37 090 000
4.	Blackleigh	£62 540 000
5.	Hanley Bliss	£52 870 000.

6. The rateable value of Tredegartown is £750 000. What sum will be produced by a rate of:
    (a) 1 p in the £
    (b) 50 p in the £
    (c) 75 p in the £
    (d) 86 p in the £
    (e) 120 p in the £?

Find the rateable value of each of the following areas if the income from a penny rate is as given:

7. Bexley: £52 645

8. Lochnagar: £23 659

9. Warkley: £93 640

10. Southfield: £61 537

11. Northhill: £137 200.

Find the rates payable on each of the following:

	RATEABLE VALUE	RATE IN THE £
12.	£100	75 p
13.	£150	60 p
14.	£125	85 p
15.	£90	67 p
16.	£300	92 p
17.	£225	110 p
18.	£450	58 p
19.	£136	73 p
20.	£159	82 p
21.	£850	93 p.

Calculate the rate in the £ for each of the following:

	RATEABLE VALUE	RATES DUE
22.	£200	£160
23.	£130	£80.60
24.	£176	£144.32
25.	£113	£85.88
26.	£182	£98.28
27.	£146	£135.78
28.	£164	£172.20
29.	£252	£304.92
30.	£317	£275.79
31.	£454	£549.34.

Find the rateable value of properties on which the following rates are due when the rate in the £ is as given:

	RATES DUE	RATE IN THE £
32.	£108	60 p
33.	£161.70	77 p
34.	£257.48	82 p
35.	£103.85	67 p
36.	£128.78	94 p
37.	£349.32	123 p
38.	£476.44	86 p
39.	£310.34	118 p
40.	£372.48	97 p
41.	£397.07	59 p.

42. Mr Bonner lives in a house with a rateable value of £246 while the rateable value of his neighbour's house is £204. How much more does Mr Bonner pay in rates than his neighbour if the rate in the £ is 94 p?

43. Jack Coots lives in a house in Eastley with a rateable value of £207 and pays rates at 87 p in the £, while his sister lives in a house in Southley with a rateable value of £255, but paying rates at 72 p in the £. Which one pays the greater rates and by how much?

44. Mr Downs pays £142.10 in rates on a property with a rateable value of £245. If Mrs Dash lives in the same area and has a property with a rateable value of £186, how much will she have to pay in rates?

45. Mr Snow and Mrs Black live in houses in the same borough with rateable values £193 and £216 respectively. If the difference in the amount they pay in rates is £24.61, calculate the rate in the £ and the amount paid by each in rates.

46. The total rateable value of Longtown Borough is £2 364 000. Find the income from a penny rate. If 46.4 p in the £ is required to pay for education, find the total cost of the educational services for the area, raised from the rates.

If the education costs are estimated to rise by £400 000 for the following year, by how much must the rate in the £ be increased, assuming that the rateable value of the area remains unaltered?

47. Mr Brown and Mr Green live in houses in the same borough with rateable values £236 and £283 respectively. If Mr Green pays £36.66 more in rates than Mr Brown, find the rate in the £, and the amount paid by each in rates.

48. The Taylor family pay rates of £156.96 when the rate in the £ is 72 p. They make improvements to the property which result in the rateable value being increased by £55. How much will they have to pay in rates the following year if the rate in the £ has increased to 87 p?

49. Mr and Mrs Wall pay rates of £181.50 when the rate in the £ is 75 p. They receive a council grant and make considerable improvements to their home whereby the rateable value is increased by £48. Find the new rateable value of their property and the amount they must pay in rates the following year if the rate in the £ rises by 18 p.

50. Out of a rate of 84 p in the £, 4.7 p is used towards providing the police force. How much is a shopkeeper, owning a property with rateable value £2650, paying towards the maintenance of the police?

51. I live in a house with a rateable value of £334 and pay rates at 77 p in the £. It is estimated that $1\frac{1}{2}\%$ of my payment will go towards providing the library service. What is my contribution towards this service?

52. My neighbour's house has a rateable value of £296 and the rate in the £ about to be levied is 84 p. If $5\frac{1}{2}\%$ of the council's budget goes towards refuse collection, how much does it cost him for his refuse to be collected?

53. Tintley Borough has a total rateable value of £1 890 000. It decides to levy a rate of 63 p in the £ and to spend $2\frac{1}{2}\%$ of the total sum collected on 'the arts'. How much will they spend on 'the arts'?

54. The general rate on Mr John's house amounts to £167.04 and his water rate £76.56. If the general rate is 96 p in the £, calculate the rateable value of his house and the rate in the £ levied by the water board.

Hence calculate the total rates (general + water) due on Miss England's house, in the same borough, which has a rateable value of £182.

55. Two householders live in houses in the same borough with rateable values £152 and £298. If the difference in the amount they pay in rates is £80.30, calculate the rate in the £ and the amount paid by each in rates.

GAS BILLS

Many homes in the United Kingdom depend on gas for heating and cooking. Much of this gas is 'natural gas' which is piped to us from under the North Sea. Natural gas gives nearly twice the amount of heat for a given volume compared with gas which is manufactured from coal.

The heat value, or calorific value, of gas is measured in British thermal units per cubic foot (Btu/ft^3), but it is more convenient to measure the amount of gas used by volume and convert this volume into units of heat. The size of your gas bill depends on the quantity of heat you use; the most usual unit when setting the price is the therm (1 therm = 100 000 Btu). The gas meter shows the number of 100s of cubic feet used, a figure which must be converted into therms before the cost of the gas used may be calculated.

On any gas bill you will find meter readings which show the number of 100s of cubic feet used, together with the calorific value of the gas supplied. These figures enable you to calculate the number of therms used as follows:

$$\text{Number of therms} = \frac{\substack{\text{number of} \\ \text{cubic feet}} \times \substack{\text{calorific value} \\ \text{in } Btu/ft^3}}{100\,000}$$

Thus if 180 units or 18 000 ft^3 were used, and the calorific value was 1035 Btu/ft^3, the number of therms used would be:

$$\frac{18\,000 \times 1035}{100\,000} = 186.3$$

Eventually the metric therm will be in common use, a metric therm being equal to 100 megajoules or 10^8 joules. The calorific or heat value is already given on bills sent out by British Gas, a typical value being 38.6 megajoules per cubic metre (MJ/m^3). A problem is that most gas meters give readings in cubic feet rather than in cubic metres.

EXAMPLE 3   A household uses 368 therms between 1 January and 31 March. If the standing charge, or fixed charge, is £10 and each therm costs 32 p, calculate the cost of gas for the quarter.

Standing charge = £10

Cost or commodity charge of 368 therms at 32 p per therm = 368 × 32 p

= £117.76

∴ Total cost for quarter = £127.76

EXAMPLE 4   The gas meter readings at the beginning and end of a quarter in the Perkins household are respectively 009364 and 009627. If 1 unit is equivalent to 1.035 therms, calculate the cost of gas for the quarter given that the standing charge is £9 and the cost per therm 33 p.

Standing quarterly charge $= £9$

Number of units used $= 009627 - 009364$
$$= 263$$

$\therefore$ Number of therms used $= 263 \times 1.035$
$$= 272.2$$

Cost or commodity charge of 272.2 therms at 33 p per therm $= 272.2 \times 33 \,p$
$$= £89.83$$

$\therefore$ Total cost of gas for the quarter $= £9 + £89.83$
$$= £98.83$$

EXAMPLE 5

The Green household pay for their gas on the Domestic Prepayment Tariff, the charges for which are: a standing charge of £3.75 per quarter + the first 45 therms per quarter at 50 p per therm + remaining therms at 35 p per therm.

Calculate their gas bill for a quarter when they use 240 therms.

If they changed to Credit Tariff, there would be a standing charge of £10 per quarter and each therm used would cost 33 p. Would they gain or lose by changing tariffs?

Domestic Prepayment Tariff:

Standing quarterly charge $= £3.75$

Commodity charge for 45 therms at 50 p per therm $= 45 \times 50 \,p$
$$= £22.50$$

Commodity charge for the remaining 195 therms at 35 p per therm $= 195 \times 35 \,p$
$$= £68.25$$

$\therefore$ Total quarterly charge $= £3.75 + £22.50 + £68.25$
$$= £94.50$$

Credit Tariff:

Standing charge $= £10$

Commodity charge for 240 therms at 33 p per therm $= 240 \times 33 \,p$
$$= £79.20$$

$$\therefore \text{ Total quarterly charge } = \text{£}89.20$$

$$\text{Amount saved by changing tariffs } = \text{£}94.50 - \text{£}89.20$$

$$= \text{£}5.30$$

EXERCISE 103

Calculate the quarterly bill for each of the following:

	NUMBER OF THERMS USED	STANDING CHARGE	COST OF GAS PER THERM
1.	200	£5	26 p
2.	300	£7	31 p
3.	350	£10	38 p
4.	420	£8.50	35 p
5.	222	£7.40	30 p
6.	182	£8.40	34 p
7.	453	£9.30	36 p
8.	198	£6.80	28 p
9.	422	£11	38 p
10.	634	£14	42 p

Calculate the quarterly bill for each of the following:

	NUMBER OF UNITS USED	EQUIVALENT VALUE OF ONE UNIT IN THERMS	STANDING CHARGE	COST OF GAS PER THERM
11.	200	1.040	£7	30 p
12.	400	1.035	£8	35 p
13.	500	1.037	£8.50	33 p
14.	750	1.038	£10	38 p
15.	352	1.039	£12.50	40 p
16.	187	1.035	£14	45 p
17.	272	1.036	£15.50	50 p
18.	840	0.52	£13.40	46 p
19.	1040	0.53	£15	52 p
20.	560	0.54	£20	55 p

Calculate the quarterly bill for each of the following:

| | METER READING | | UNITS | EQUIVALENT VALUE OF | STANDING | COST OF |
	PRESENT	PREVIOUS	USED	ONE UNIT IN THERMS	CHARGE	GAS PER THERM
21.	001447	001347		1.040	£8	30 p
22.	009093	008843		1.040	£10	35 p
23.	002468	002118		1.040	£12	40 p
24.	005871	005451		1.035	£14	45 p
25.	001293	001113		1.035	£13.50	42 p
26.	008769	008199		1.035	£12.60	38 p
27.	012654	012014		1.038	£10	40 p
28.	006574	006306		0.52	£14	40 p
29.	003764	003480		0.53	£16	45 p
30.	078582	077435		0.54	£17	50 p

In each of the following, calculate whether or not (and by how much) it is cheaper to use the Credit Tariff than the Domestic Prepayment Tariff:

| | NUMBER OF THERMS USED | CREDIT TARIFF | | DOMESTIC PREPAYMENT TARIFF | | |
		STANDING CHARGE	PRICE PER THERM	STANDING CHARGE	PRICE PER THERM OF INITIAL THERMS	PRICE PER THERM OF FURTHER THERMS
31.	400	£10	30 p	£4	50 p for first 40 therms	32 p
32.	550	£12	35 p	£5	50 p for first 50 therms	34 p
33.	180	£15	40 p	£8	45 p for first 50 therms	38 p
34.	362	£14	44 p	£10	54 p for first 60 therms	40 p
35.	247	£16	48 p	£6	58 p for first 45 therms	45 p

ELECTRICITY BILLS

Virtually every home in the United Kingdom is linked to an electricity supply. It provides our lighting, powers our washing machines, television sets and labour saving tools, and for many is the only source of heat. Electricity is sold in units called *kilowatt hours*. One kilowatt means 1000 watts, so that 1 kilowatt hour (kW h) is the electricity consumed in 1 hour by an appliance which has a rating of 1000 W. Each property has a meter which records the number of units used over a given period. A modern meter enables the user to read off a 5 figure number. The number of units used is then found by subtracting the previous reading from the present one.

Electrical equipment is therefore rated in watts — the *rating* telling us how much electricity a given appliance will use in a given time. This is illustrated with a few examples:

a 1 kW fire will use 1 unit of electricity in 1 hour

a 3 kW fire will use 3 units in 1 hour (or put another way, for 1 unit you may use the fire for $\frac{1}{3}$ hour or 20 minutes)

a 100 W bulb will use $\frac{1}{10}$ unit or $\frac{1}{10}$ kW in 1 hour (or it will burn for 10 hours on 1 unit)

The higher the wattage rating, the more expensive the appliance is to run. While a 25 W bulb will burn for 40 hours on 1 unit of electricity, a 5 kW cooker will only run for 12 minutes. Lighting from electricity is very cheap but heating can be expensive.

To calculate how expensive it is to operate a particular appliance:

$$\text{Number of units used} = \begin{array}{l}\text{appliance rating in kW} \\ \times \text{number of hours in use}\end{array}$$

Then

$$\text{Cost} = \text{number of units used} \times \text{price per unit}$$

EXAMPLE 6

Find the cost of using a 2.5 kW fire for 60 hours if electricity costs 6 p per unit.

$$\text{Number of units used} = \begin{array}{l}\text{rating in kW} \\ \times \text{number of hours}\end{array}$$

$$= 2.5 \times 60$$

$$= 150$$

$$\text{Cost} = \text{number of units used} \times \text{price per unit}$$

$$= 150 \times 6 \text{ p}$$

$$= 900 \text{ p}$$

$$= £9$$

EXAMPLE 7   Find the cost of using a 60 W light bulb for 80 hours if one unit of electricity costs 6 p.

$$\text{Number of units used} = \frac{\text{rating in kW}}{1000} \times \text{number of hours}$$

$$= \frac{60}{1000} \times 80$$

$$= 4.8$$

$$\therefore \text{ Cost } = 4.8 \times 6\,p$$

$$= 28.8\,p$$

$$= 29\,p \text{ correct to the nearest penny}$$

Two types of meter are available: a prepayment coin-in-the-slot arrangement, and a credit meter where the supply is unlimited. A prepayment meter will take 10 p or 50 p coins. The meter is set to give the correct number of units in relation to the value of the money put into it. When this prepaid number of units has been used the electricity is automatically cut off, and remains off until more money is put in the meter.

The credit meter is more convenient since you are rarely without heat or light, but it does tempt you to use more electricity than you need, or sometimes more than you can afford. Normally the meter is read by an Electricity Board official approximately every thirteen weeks, i.e. quarterly. The number of units consumed is recorded and a bill follows some days later.

Electricity is a difficult form of energy to store. Since it is convenient to be producing it 24 hours a day, the Boards have special Off Peak or White Meter rates under which electricity is sold to domestic users at cheap rates.

EXERCISE 104

1. Complete the given table below which shows the meter readings in a household for a year:

DATE	METER READING	NUMBER OF UNITS USED IN QUARTER
6 November	14563	First
10 February	15543	Second
4 May	16567	Third
12 August	16993	Fourth
8 November	17635	

2. If electricity is charged at 6 p per unit in addition to a quarterly standing charge of £7.50, calculate the quarterly electricity bills using the data given in Question 1.

3. Mr Chinn's electricity meter displays a reading of 23563 on 10 January and 24477 on 10 April. How many units has he used during the quarter? Calculate the cost of this electricity at each of the following tariffs:

	STANDING CHARGE	PRICE PER UNIT
(a)	£6.50	5 p
(b)	£8.00	8 p
(c)	£9.25	9 p
(d)	£10.50	10 p
(e)	£12.60	12 p
(f)	£15.15	18 p
(g)	£8.40	6.40 p
(h)	£9.20	7.37 p
(i)	£10.16	5.56 p
(j)	£7.34	8.72 p

4. How many hours will each of the following run on 1 unit of electricity?
   (a) a 100 W lamp
   (b) a 12 W lamp
   (c) a 2 kW fire
   (d) a 500 W iron
   (e) a 2.5 kW kettle.

5. How many units of electricity are used if:
   (a) a 150 W lamp burns for 10 hours
   (b) a 2 kW fire is used for 5 hours
   (c) a 3 kW kettle is boiling for 4 minutes
   (d) a 750 W iron is used for 4 hours?

6. The Smith household estimate that the numbers of units of electricity used for various appliances during a week are as follows:

Lighting	8 units
Cooker	32 units
Refrigerator and freezer	20 units
Television	5 units
Heating	48 units

   If the standing charge *per quarter* is £7.80 and a unit of electricity costs 6 p, calculate the cost of electricity for a week.

7. Mr Short's electricity bill for the quarter amounts to £108. The standing charge is £7.50 and the price of electricity is $7\frac{1}{2}$p per unit. How many units has he used?

8. Miss Deakin's electricity bill for a quarter amounts to £68.16. If she has used 946 units of electricity costing 6.45 p per unit, calculate the quarterly standing charge.

9. Calculate the total cost of using the following at 7.54 p per unit:

   a 3 kW fire for 26 hours
   eight 100 W lamps, each for 38 hours
   a 750 W iron for 4 hours
   a 350 W television set for 45 hours.

   Give your answer correct to the nearest penny.

10. Calculate the total cost of using the following if electricity costs 5.92 p per unit:

    two 150 W lamps, each for 15 hours
    eight 60 W lamps, each for 24 hours
    a 2.5 kW kettle for 2 hours
    a 4 kW cooker for 15 hours.

    Give your answer correct to the nearest penny.

11. Peter Glenn's electricity bills for a year amount to £273.32. The bills showed that he used 1284, 947, 513 and 828 units during the first, second, third and fourth quarters, respectively, of the year. If the standing quarterly charge was £7.24, calculate the cost of electricity per unit, giving your answer in pence correct to three significant figures.

12. Jane Lock uses White Meter electricity for her storage heaters and for heating domestic water. Her quarterly bill shows the following details:

METER READING		UNITS USED	UNIT CHARGES		£
PRESENT	PREVIOUS		5.75 p	3.22 p	
32617	33634	1017	1017		
Quarterly standing charge					7.55
38301	39543	1242		1242	
Time switch					1.95
			Amount due		

Complete the table and hence calculate the amount due.

13. During the winter quarter a family with storage heaters consumes 4325 units of Off Peak electricity at 3.64 p per unit, and 1820 units of electricity for other purposes at 5.84 p per unit. If the standing quarterly charge is £6.85, and £1.84 is charged for the hire of the time switch, calculate the bill for the quarter. What therefore is the average per week?

TELEPHONE BILLS

The telephone system in the United Kingdom is provided by British Telecom. Today it is possible to dial direct to almost anywhere in the country using Subscriber Trunk Dialling (STD), and to many places abroad using International Direct Dialling (IDD). From your own home you may dial a sequence of numbers and then speak to a relative or friend in Australia or America.

If you have a telephone at home you pay a quarterly rental. If this telephone line is shared with a neighbour, the rental cost is marginally lower, while the rental of business telephones is approximately 50% higher.

The cost of each telephone call you make depends on the following factors:

(a) The distance in kilometres between you and the person you want to call,

(b) The length of the time of the call,

(c) The time of day at which the call is made.

These three factors are combined in various ways for any one call and converted into metered charge units. The subscriber is then charged according to the number of units used during the quarter, the total due being calculated by adding VAT to the sum of the quarterly rental and total cost of the metered units.

In terms of distance, calls within the United Kingdom are divided into three categories: local calls, calls up to 56 km (35 miles), and calls over 56 km (35 miles). The time of day when the telephone is used is also charged at different rates: the peak rate, between 9.00 a.m. and 1.00 p.m. Monday to Friday; the cheap rate, between 6.00 p.m. and 8.00 a.m. each week day plus all day on Saturday and Sunday; and the standard rate at all other times.

The following gives some idea of the time allowed for 1 charge unit, which costs approximately 6 p.

(a) A local call at the cheap rate (i.e. evenings or weekend): 8 minutes

(b) A local call between 9.00 a.m. and 1.00 p.m. any weekday: $1\frac{1}{2}$ minutes

(c) A call over 56 km (35 miles) at the peak rate: 10 seconds

(d) A similar call at the cheap rate: 48 seconds

EXAMPLE 8

Between 5 April and 6 July Eli Dunn's telephone bill showed that he had used 846 charge units at 4.5 p per unit. If the quarterly standing charge was £15 and VAT was added to the total at 15%, calculate his telephone bill for the quarter. Calculate, correct to the nearest 10 p, the average weekly cost of the telephone.

	£
Telephone rental for the quarter	15
846 units at 4.5 p per unit	38.07
Total (exclusive of VAT)	53.07
VAT at 15%	7.96
Total payable	61.03

∴ His quarterly bill is £61.03 which averages per week to:

$$\frac{£61.03}{13} = £4.695 = £4.70$$

correct to the nearest 10 p

EXAMPLE 9

Billy Beck decides to telephone his girlfriend, who lives 150 miles away, at 11.00 a.m. on a Tuesday morning when 1 charge unit will buy 10 seconds. If the call lasted 10 minutes, how much would he have saved by waiting until 9.00 p.m. when 1 charge unit buys 48 seconds? Assume that the cost of 1 charge unit is 6 p.

(a) Tuesday morning:

If 10 seconds in the morning costs 1 charge unit

10 minutes will cost 60 charge units

Cost of 60 units at 6 p per unit $= £3.60$

(b) Tuesday evening:

If 48 seconds in the evening costs 1 charge unit

10 minutes will cost $\dfrac{10 \times 60}{48} = 12\frac{1}{2}$ units

Cost of 13 units (the meter records fractions of a unit as a whole unit) at 6 p per unit $= 78\,\text{p}$

$\therefore$ Amount saved by telephoning in the evening $= £3.60 - 78\,\text{p}$

$= £2.82$

So remember to telephone in the evenings or at weekends!

EXERCISE 105

Calculate the total telephone bill for each of the following:

	NAME	QUARTERLY RENTAL	UNITS USED	COST PER UNIT	VAT RATE
1.	Mr Grant	£13.50	734	5 p	15%
2.	Miss Freeman	£14.00	849	6 p	15%
3.	Mrs Workman	£15.00	483	6.5 p	20%
4.	Mr Price	£15.50	936	8 p	20%
5.	Miss Bloss	£16.00	1240	10 p	15%
6.	Mr Potter	£14.50	684	7.5 p	18%

The table given below shows the time allowed for 1 charge unit for calls over different distances at different times of the day:

TYPE OF CALL	CHARGE RATE	TIME ALLOWED FOR 1 CHARGE UNIT ON ANY ONE CALL
Local calls	Cheap	8 minutes
	Standard	2 minutes
	Peak	1 min 30 s
Calls up to 56 km (35 miles)	Cheap	144 s
	Standard	45 s
	Peak	30 s
Calls over 56 km (35 miles)	Cheap	48 s
	Standard	12.8 s
	Peak	10 s

Use this information to calculate the cost of each of the following calls:

	TYPE OR DISTANCE OF CALL	CHARGE RATE OR TIME OF CALL	LENGTH OF CALL	UNIT CHARGE
7.	Local	Peak	2 min	5 p
8.	Local	Cheap	8 min	5 p
9.	60 km	Standard	3 min	5 p
10.	80 miles	Cheap	4 min	5 p
11.	100 km	Peak	12 s	5 p
12.	200 km	Peak	20 s	8 p
13.	200 miles	Standard	$5\frac{1}{2}$ min	8 p
14.	75 km	Cheap	$9\frac{1}{2}$ min	8 p
15.	85 miles	Cheap	$8\frac{1}{2}$ min	10 p
16.	Local	10.00 a.m.	50 s	10 p
17.	50 miles	11.15 p.m.	8 min	10 p

18. Helen Miles rings her father, who lives 100 miles away, during her morning break when 1 unit will buy 10 seconds. The call lasts 5 minutes. If she had waited until the evening, 1 unit would have bought 48 seconds. If the cost of 1 unit is 5 p, how much would she have saved by waiting until the evening?

19. Peter rings his parents on Friday at 4.00 p.m. when 1 unit will buy 45 seconds. He speaks to them for 4 minutes. How many units must he pay for? If a unit will buy 144 seconds at the cheap rate, how long could his conversation have been for the same price had he waited until the evening?

20. An important business call at 9.30 a.m. takes 14 minutes when 1 unit buys 10 seconds. If a unit costs 8 p, how much would the same length of call cost if made at 4.00 p.m. in the afternoon of the same weekday when 1 unit buys 12.8 seconds?

COST OF RUNNING A MOTORCYCLE OR CAR

The chances are high that you will spend more on motorcycles and cars than on any other single item, except possibly a house. In this section we look into the costs of running them.

EXAMPLE 10   Jeff's motorcycle expenses for a year are given below:

> Road tax   £40
> Fully comprehensive insurance   £750
> Depreciation   £250
> Fuel   1200 litres at 50 p per litre
> Servicing and repairs   £35

If Jeff travels 24 600 km during the year, calculate:

(a) his total fuel costs,

(b) his total costs,

(c) how far he can travel on each litre of fuel,

(d) his overall cost per kilometre, giving your answer correct to the nearest tenth of a penny.

(a) Total fuel cost $= 1200 \times 50\,\text{p}$
$$= \text{£}600$$

(b) Total cost $= \text{£}40 + \text{£}750 + \text{£}250 + \text{£}600 + \text{£}35$
$$= \text{£}1675$$

(c) Number of kilometres per litre $= \dfrac{\text{distance travelled}}{\text{number of litres used}}$

$$= \frac{24\,600}{1200}$$

$$= 20.5$$

(d) Overall cost per kilometre $= \dfrac{\text{total cost}}{\text{number of kilometres travelled}}$

$$= \text{£}\frac{1675}{24\,600}$$

$$= \frac{1675}{246}\,\text{p}$$

$$= 6.809\,\text{p}$$

$$= 6.8\,\text{p}$$

correct to the nearest tenth of a penny

EXAMPLE 11   John's motoring expenses for a year were:

> Road tax   £85
> Insurance   £174
> Depreciation   30% of the purchase price of
> £11 000
> Fuel   2100 litres at 45 p per litre
> Servicing and repairs   £116

If John's car averages 11.5 km per litre, calculate:

(a) the distance he travelled in the year,

(b) the total cost of his petrol,

(c) his total motoring costs,

(d) his petrol costs as a percentage of his total costs, giving your answer correct to the nearest whole number,

(e) the average cost per kilometre, in pence, correct to the nearest whole number.

(a) Distance travelled in the year $= 2100 \times 11.5$ km

$$= 24\,150 \text{ km}$$

(b) Total cost of petrol $= 2100 \times 45$ p

$$= £21 \times 45$$

$$= £945$$

(c) Depreciation at 30% of £11 000 $= £11\,000 \times \dfrac{30}{100}$

$$= £3300$$

∴ Total cost of motoring $= £85 + £174 + £3300 + £945 + £116$

$$= £4620$$

(d) Petrol costs as a percentage of motoring costs

$$= \frac{\text{petrol costs}}{\text{total costs}} \times 100\%$$

$$= \frac{£945}{£4620} \times 100\%$$

$$= 20.45\%$$

$$= 20\% \text{ correct to the nearest whole number}$$

(e) Average cost per kilometre $= \dfrac{\text{total motoring costs}}{\text{total distance travelled}}$

$$= £\frac{4620}{24\,150}$$

$$= \frac{462}{2415} \times 100 \text{ p}$$

$$= 19.13 \text{ p}$$

$$= 19 \text{ p}$$

correct to the nearest whole number

EXERCISE 106

1. Tyres for a car cost £35 each and have a life of 35 000 km. Calculate the cost of tyres per kilometre.

2. Penny Coombes' car averages 35 miles per gallon on 4-star petrol. Calculate the cost of petrol per mile when it costs £2 per gallon. Give your answer in pence correct to two decimal places.

3. Joe travels 17 850 km in a year on his motorcycle. If it averages 21 km to the litre, calculate how much he spends on petrol when petrol costs 40 p per litre. If petrol amounts to 25% of his total costs, how much per kilometre does his motorcycle cost him over the year? Give your answer in pence correct to three significant figures.

4. Fred Street's motorcycle uses 11 litres of petrol each week and will travel on average 19.5 km on a litre. How many kilometres does he travel in a year?

   Assuming that expenses, other than for petrol, amount to £875, how much will he spend in the year if petrol costs 42 p per litre?

5. The cost of running a motorcycle for a year is made up of: road tax £38, insurance £520, depreciation £30 per month, tyres £48 and the cost of petrol. If petrol costs 50 p per litre and the bike averages 20 km a litre, calculate:
   (a) the cost of petrol if 24 000 km are travelled during the year
   (b) the total annual cost
   (c) the average cost per kilometre in pence, correct to three significant figures.

6. The cost of running Mandy's car for a year, excluding servicing and repairs is: road tax £95, insurance £182, depreciation £570, petrol 1650 litres at 53 p per litre.

   In a year when she travelled 30 000 kilometres, she estimates that motoring, including servicing and repairs, averaged out at 6.2 p per kilometre. How much did she spend on servicing and repairs?

7. David Burrows estimates that he drives his car on average 18 000 miles each year. He has to choose between a car which does 36 miles to the gallon and another which does 30 miles to the gallon. Calculate:
   (a) the difference in annual petrol consumption between the two cars
   (b) the cost of this difference if petrol is £2 per gallon.

8. Anthony Page drives on average 30 000 kilometres each year. His present car averages 50 km per gallon of petrol. He decides to buy a new car which only gives 40 km per gallon. How much more fuel will he use in a year? If petrol is priced at £1.95 per gallon, find the annual increase in his petrol bill.

9. Chris Jenkins is a salesman who averages 50 000 kilometres each year. His company car averages 12 km per litre of petrol, but the company decide to change his car to one which averages 15 km per litre. How many fewer litres should he use in a year. How much will be saved in petrol costs if the price of petrol is 42 p per litre?

10. Due to a change in job, my yearly mileage increases from 15 000 miles to 21 000 miles. How much more petrol will I use if my car averages 35 miles per gallon? Calculate also the increase in my petrol bill each year if petrol costs £1.86 per gallon.

11. As a result of spending £63 on improving the performance of my car, the number of kilometres it will travel on 1 litre of petrol increases from 12 to 13.5. Assuming that the annual distance I travel is 24 000 kilometres and that petrol costs 42 p per litre, will I be financially better off after 1 year, and if so by how much?

12. John Bull keeps detailed records of his motoring costs for a year. They were: road tax £80, insurance £156, depreciation £800, petrol 1500 litres at 45 p per litre, tyres £65, servicing and repairs £27 per month. Calculate:
    (a) the cost of petrol for the year
    (b) the number of kilometres travelled in the year if the car averages 14 km on each litre
    (c) the total costs for the year
    (d) the total cost per kilometre.

13. Sally Brown listed her motoring expenses for a year as follows: road tax £90, insurance £215, depreciation £750, petrol £2 per gallon (the car averaging 30 miles to the gallon), tyres £84, servicing and repairs averaging £26 per month.

    In a year when Sally travels 12 000 miles, calculate:
    (a) the total cost of petrol
    (b) the total annual cost
    (c) the total cost per mile, giving your answer correct to the nearest tenth of a penny.

14. The cost of running a particular car for a year is as follows: road tax £100, insurance £313, depreciation 25% of its purchase price of £12 000, petrol 1800 litres at 50 p per litre, two tyres at £33 each, servicing and repairs averaging £24 per month.

    Calculate the total average cost per kilometre if the car averages 12 km for each litre of fuel.

15. The cost of running my car for a year is as follows: road tax £90, insurance £215, depreciation £950, petrol 1950 litres at 48 p per litre, servicing and repairs £175. Calculate:
   (a) the total cost of the fixed charges, including servicing and repairs
   (b) the total petrol costs for the year
   (c) the total cost of motoring for the year
   (d) the distance I travel if the car averages 12.5 km per litre
   (e) the total average cost per kilometre, giving your answer in pence correct to three significant figures.

   Express the petrol costs as a percentage of the total costs, giving your answer correct to the nearest whole number.

HOUSEHOLD INSURANCE

Insurance is a method of spreading risks. As soon as you buy a property you must insure it against the risk of damage. When you furnish your home you need to insure the contents. You are insuring against events you hope will never happen, but are realistic enough to accept that it is possible that they might happen. Every year, in the United Kingdom, hundreds of properties are destroyed or badly damaged by fire, storms or floods.

Since every property is at risk, but comparatively few suffer damage, an insurance company will undertake to pay for the repair of your property. They collect a small sum of money, called a *premium*, from everyone who takes out a policy with them. In return they will pay out to people who make claims on their policies, but they always try to arrange the premiums so that, apart from paying out claims, they can cover their running costs and make a profit. The premiums are calculated by mathematicians called actuaries. It follows that insurance companies will have good years and bad years. Severe weather and/or major disasters will seriously affect the profitability of the company, and may cause premiums to increase.

A house cannot move around and cannot be carried away. It is therefore comparatively cheap to insure. A common premium is £1 per £1000 insured, but it should be understood that the full value of the property must be insured. Today this means increasing the value every year, or as the insurance companies like to say 'index linking' it. When you take out your first insurance policy it is important that you shop around. Do not forget to read the small print.

EXAMPLE 12   Calculate the annual insurance premium on a house
valued at £35 500 if the rate is £1 per £1000. What
would the premium be in 2 years' time if the policy
is index linked and the inflation rate is 10%?

For each £1000 insured the premium is £1 p.a.

∴ Premium for a house valued at £35 500 is:

$$£\frac{35\,500}{1000} \times 1 = £35.50$$

$$\text{Value of house 1 year later} = £35\,500 \times \frac{110}{100}$$

$$= £39\,050$$

$$\text{Value of house 2 years later} = £39\,050 \times \frac{110}{100}$$

$$= £42\,955$$

∴ $$\text{Premium 2 years later} = £42\,955 \times \frac{1}{1000}$$

$$= £42.955$$

$$= £42.96$$

correct to the nearest penny

The risk of the contents of a home being damaged or removed is much
greater than with the property itself. Accordingly the premium is more,
a typical rate being 30 p per £100 insured. Again it is important that
the full value of your possessions is covered.

EXAMPLE 13   Find the annual premium on the contents of a house,
valued at £12 500, if the rate is 30 p per annum per
£100 insured.

Annual premium on £100 is 30 p

∴ Annual premium on £12 500 is $$\frac{12\,500}{100} \times 30\,\text{p}$$

$$= £37.50$$

If you want to include articles such as cameras or other valuables, even
when they are taken outside the home, the premiums will be increased
since the risks become much higher. These articles are covered for 'all
risks', a typical rate being 90 p per £100.

EXAMPLE 14   Find the cost of insuring a camera valued at £350 under the 'all risks' section of a policy if the rate is 90 p per £100.

$$\text{Premium due per annum} = \frac{350}{100} \times 90 \, p = £3.15$$

We conclude with an example which includes all three rates.

EXAMPLE 15   Mr and Mrs Caton live in a house valued at £45 000. They value the contents of their home at £18 000, but wish to cover £3000 of this for 'all risks'. Using the rates given in Examples 12 to 14, calculate the total premium due (a) per annum, (b) per week. Supposing that the policy is index linked, what would be the annual premium in 2 years' time? Assume an inflation rate of 12%.

House insurance at £1 per £1000 = £45

Contents insurance at 30 p per £100 or £3 per £1000 on £18 000 − £3000 = £15 000 is:

£15 × 3 = £45

'All risks' insurance on £3000 at 90 p per £100 or £9 per £1000 is:

£9 × 3 = £27

∴ Total premium due = £45 + £45 + £27

= £117 p.a.

i.e. Weekly premium = $£\dfrac{117}{52}$ = £2.25

At 12% inflation the premium due 1 year later will be:

$$£117 \times \frac{112}{100} = £131.04 \text{ p.a.}$$

Assuming the same rate of inflation, the premium due 2 years later will be:

$$£131.04 \times \frac{112}{100} = £146.76$$

correct to the nearest penny

EXERCISE 107

Calculate the annual insurance premiums payable for properties which
have the given values, assuming a rate of £1 per £1000 insured:

1.	£5000	2.	£8000	3.	£10 000
4.	£12 000	5.	£13 500	6.	£14 750
7.	£18 000	8.	£22 000	9.	£35 000
10.	£45 000	11.	£56 000	12.	£76 000
13.	£88 500	14.	£100 000.		

15. A property valued at £40 000 is insured at a rate of £1 per £1000
by a policy which is index linked. If the inflation rate is 10%,
calculate the annual premium (a) now, (b) in 1 year's time,
(c) in 2 years' time.

16. Repeat Question 15 for a property valued at £22 000.

17. A property valued at £30 000 is insured at a rate of £1 per £1000
by a policy which is index linked. If the inflation rate is 12%,
calculate the annual premium (a) now, (b) in 1 year's time, (c) in
2 years' time.

18. A property valued at £50 000 is insured at a rate of £1 per £1000
by a policy which is index linked. If the inflation rate is 8%,
calculate the annual premium (a) now, (b) in 1 year's time, (c) in
2 years' time.

Calculate the annual premium payable for contents which are valued
as given below, assuming a rate of 30 p per £100:

19.	£6500	20.	£8000	21.	£12 000
22.	£13 500	23.	£21 250	24.	£33 400
25.	£67 800.				

Calculate the annual premium on articles covered for 'all risks' if they
are valued as given below. Assume that the rate is 90 p per £100:

26.	£3000	27.	£4500	28.	£6250
29.	£8500	30.	£10 200	31.	£25 300
32.	£55 500	33.	£120 000		

In each of the following calculate (a) the total premium, (b) the weekly premium, to insure for the values shown:

	PROPERTY VALUE	RATE	CONTENTS	RATE	'ALL RISKS'	RATE
34.	£15 000	£1 per £1000	£8000	30 p per £100	£4000	90 p per £100
35.	£25 000	£1 per £1000	£12 000	30 p per £100	£5000	90 p per £100
36.	£38 000	£1 per £1000	£22 000	30 p per £100	£8000	90 p per £100
37.	£56 000	£1 per £1000	£37 500	30 p per £100	£10 500	90 p per £100
38.	£88 000	£1 per £1000	£50 000	30 p per £100	£14 600	90 p per £100
39.	£120 000	£1 per £1000	£84 000	30 p per £100	£24 300	90 p per £100
40.	£150 000	£1 per £1000	£120 000	30 p per £100	£80 000	90 p per £100

MOTORCYCLE AND CAR INSURANCE

Before you can take your car or motorcycle on a public road you must have *third party liability* insurance. This enables you to meet any expenses if you are unfortunate enough to injure anyone or damage any property. If, however, you value your vehicle, you will require a *fully comprehensive* policy. This policy covers not only *third party*, *fire and theft*, but also damage to your own vehicle.

Calculating the actual cost of your policy can be quite an involved affair since there are several possible additions and subtractions to the basic premium. The most important of these will be your *no claim discount* (NCD). This is a discount given on renewal of the policy if you have not made a claim on that policy during the previous year. It is nothing to do with whether or not you were to blame in an accident.

The following are typical no claim discounts:

NCD at first renewal	30%
NCD at second consecutive renewal	40%
NCD at third consecutive renewal	50%
NCD at fourth or subsequent renewal	60%

(If only one claim is made at a time when you have 'earned' a discount of 50% or 60%, the discount at the next renewal will be 30% or 40% respectively and then as above.)

The basic premium depends on several factors including: the value, type and power of your car or motorcycle, the area in which you live, your age, and the type of cover you want, i.e. third party, or third party, fire and theft, or fully comprehensive.

EXAMPLE 16   Fred Knight is quoted an annual premium of £350 when he takes out a fully comprehensive insurance policy on his new car. Assuming the no claim discounts given in the text, calculate his annual premium:

(a) for the first six years, assuming that there have been no claims,

(b) for the sixth year, assuming that a claim was made during the fourth year.

How much did this claim cost Fred in lost discounts?

(a) Premium first year £350

Premium second year (i.e. first renewal) $= £350 -$ discount at 30%

Discount $= £350 \times \dfrac{30}{100} = £105$

$\therefore$ Premium $= £350 - £105 = £245$

Premium third year (i.e. second renewal) $= £350 -$ discount at 40%

Discount $= £350 \times \dfrac{40}{100} = £140$

$\therefore$ Premium $= £350 - £140 = £210$

Premium fourth year (i.e. third renewal) $= £350 -$ discount at 50%

Discount $= £350 \times \dfrac{50}{100} = £175$

$\therefore$ Premium $= £350 - £175 = £175$

Premium fifth year (i.e. fourth renewal) $= £350 -$ discount at 60%

Discount $= £350 \times \dfrac{60}{100} = £210$

$\therefore$ Premium $= £350 - £210 = £140$

Provided that there are no claims, the annual premium will remain at this figure for subsequent years.

i.e. Premium sixth year $= £140$

(b) During the fourth year the premium was £175. This included a 50% no claim discount.

For the fifth year the discount would revert to 30%, i.e. the premium would be the same as for the first renewal.

$\therefore$ Premium fifth year $= £245$

For the sixth year the discount progresses again up the scale, the next rate being 40%.

$\therefore$ Premium sixth year $= £350 -$ discount at 40%

$= £350 - £140$

$= £210$

Comparing (a) and (b)

Lost discount fifth year $= £245 - £140$

$= £105$

Lost discount sixth year $= £210 - £140$

$= £70$

$\therefore$ Total lost discounts $= £105 + £70$

$= £175$

EXERCISE 108

In the following questions, use the no claim discount percentages given in the text.

1. John is quoted an annual premium of £900 for fully comprehensive insurance on his motorcycle. What would the premium be for the third renewal, assuming no claim is made?

2. Sam's first premium for his motorcycle is £1200. What would this reduce to on the fourth renewal, assuming no claim is made?

3. Mr Morgan's first premium for insuring his new car is £560. How much would he expect to be paying for the sixth year, i.e. the fifth renewal, assuming no claim is made?

4. Jenny Davis buys a second hand car and is quoted a first annual premium of £320. Assuming that she makes no claims, how much can she expect to pay during the fourth year?

5. Robin Box is quoted an initial premium of £240 for third party cover for his motorcycle. After 2 years of accident-free motorcycling he makes an insurance claim during the third year. What will his renewal premium be for the fourth year?

6. A fully comprehensive insurance policy for Trevor Jones' car costs him £450 for the first year. Assuming that there are no claims, how much will the premium be for the sixth year?

   If he decides to pay the premium in four equal quarterly instalments, 10% is added to the premium. Calculate his quarterly premium.

7. The basic premium for comprehensive insurance cover for Alan's car is £750. A reduction of $7\frac{1}{2}\%$ is given because he agrees to pay the first £25 of each and every claim. His no claim discount is calculated on the balance. Calculate his premium (a) for the first year, (b) when full NCD is in operation.

8. My basic premium for fully comprehensive cover for my car is £400. A reduction of $12\frac{1}{2}\%$ of this premium is allowed because I agree to pay the first £50 costs for each and every claim. No claim discounts are allowed on the balance. How much will I be asked to pay if I am (a) on 40% NCD, (b) on full NCD?

9. The rates quoted by an insurance company for insuring my motorcycle are as follows:

Third party	£500
Third party, fire and theft	£690
Fully comprehensive	£1200

   At the third renewal (a) how much cheaper would third party cover be than fully comprehensive cover? (b) How much cheaper is third party cover than cover for third party, fire and theft?

10. The annual rates quoted by an insurance company for insuring Mr Thomas' car were as follows:

Third party, fire and theft	£300
Fully comprehensive	£450

    How much more would he be paying on the sixth renewal if he had chosen to take out a fully comprehensive policy? Assume that no claims were made during the period.

11. Peter Wells was not the luckiest of drivers. During his first 7 years' motoring he was forced to make claims during the third, fifth and sixth years. What was his renewal premium for the seventh year if the basic premium was £400?

12. James Lang was an exceptionally good driver and drove without any problems for 5 years. During his sixth year he was unfortunate enough to be involved in two 'skirmishes' which led to claims being made. If his basic premium was £500, how much would the premium be on his seventh renewal?

13. The insurance premium on my car this year amounts to £126.40 and includes a 60% no claim discount. Calculate the basic premium.

14. The insurance premium for Margaret's car amounts to £252 this year. If this amount includes a 40% no claim discount, how much can she expect to pay (a) next year, (b) the following year?

15. I receive a $12\frac{1}{2}$% discount on the basic premium for my car insurance because I agree to pay the first £50 of each and every claim. This year the amount I must pay, which includes the full no claim discount, is £155.40. Calculate the basic premium.

23

HOLIDAYS AND TRAVEL

DISTANCE TABLES

Most books of road maps give tables which enable us to find out quite quickly how far it is between any two major towns or cities in the country.

EXERCISE 109

Use the information given below to answer Questions 1 to 5:

	London	Birmingham	Bristol	Cambridge	Cardiff	Edinburgh	Leeds	Sheffield
Birmingham	111							
Bristol	114	82						
Cambridge	52	100	145					
Cardiff	155	101	44	180				
Edinburgh	378	286	367	338	365			
Leeds	190	111	206	148	212	199		
Sheffield	162	75	163	124	176	235	36	
York	196	134	215	157	242	186	24	56

Distances are in miles.

1. How far is it:
   (a) from Bristol to York
   (b) from Leeds to Edinburgh?

2. Which city is nearer to Bristol and by how much: Sheffield or Cambridge?

3. Which city is:
   (a) nearest to London
   (b) furthest from London?

4. Which city is:
   (a) furthest from Edinburgh
   (b) nearest to Leeds?

5. Which two cities are:
   (a) nearest together
   (b) furthest apart?

Use the information given below to answer Questions 6 to 10:

	London	Aberdeen	Brighton	Exeter	Liverpool	Manchester
London	—					
Aberdeen	806	—				
Brighton	89	895	—			
Exeter	275	911	275	—		
Liverpool	330	538	418	385	—	
Manchester	309	534	398	389	55	—
Worcester	183	689	270	217	169	164

Distances are in kilometres.

6. Which two places are nearest together?

7. Which two places are furthest apart?

8. What is the difference in the distances between Exeter and London, and Exeter and Manchester?

9. How far is Brighton from Manchester?

10. How far is it from Worcester to Manchester and then on to Liverpool?

THE 24 HOUR CLOCK

Frequently in rail, bus and airline timetables the 24 hour clock is used in preference to the more familiar 'a.m. and p.m.'.

In the 24 hour clock, four figures are always used. The first two figures show the number of hours past midnight, and the last two figures the number of minutes past the hour. A point is often used to separate the hours from the minutes, e.g. 09.20 on the 24 hour clock is the same as 9.20 a.m. or twenty minutes past nine in the morning, while 20.10 on the 24 hour clock is 8.10 p.m. or ten minutes past eight in the evening.

EXERCISE 110

1. Complete the following table:

24 HOUR CLOCK TIME	a.m./p.m. TIME	TIME IN WORDS
16.05	4.05 p.m.	Five minutes past four in the afternoon
17.35	5.35 p.m.	Twenty-five minutes to six in the afternoon
05.45	5.45 a.m.	A quarter to five in the morning
11.22	11.22 a.m.	Twenty-two minutes past eleven in the morning
21.15		
19.35		
04.10		
10.30		
18.40		
	3.15 p.m.	
	10.30 a.m.	
	9.45 p.m.	
	7.38 p.m.	
	2.15 a.m.	
		Five to eleven in the morning
		Half past ten in the evening
		Ten past four in the morning
		A quarter to twelve at night

2. How many hours and minutes are there between the following times?
   (a) 07.00 and 11.00   (b) 12.00 and 18.00

(c) 08.30 and 13.00
(d) 14.20 and 16.40
(e) 05.15 and 09.37
(f) 09.36 and 20.41
(g) 07.21 and 18.15
(h) 12.47 and 15.53
(i) 16.39 and 19.14
(j) 02.32 and 21.56.

You are now in a position to answer some questions on timetables which use the 24 hour clock.

Timetable A

BLACKTOWN-NEWVILLE

Blacktown	dep.	07.34	08.15	10.04	11.48
Crosskeys	dep.	07.46	08.27	10.16	12.00
Isca	dep.	08.02	08.43	10.32	12.16
Oxley	dep.	08.21	08.58	10.51	12.35
Parkley	dep.	08.34	09.08	11.04	12.48
Newville	arr.	08.46	09.20	11.16	13.04

3. Use timetable A, which gives details of buses travelling from Blacktown to Newville, to answer the following questions:
    (a) At what time should I leave Blacktown to make the fastest journey to Newville?
    (b) If I arrive 5 minutes too late to catch the 08.15 bus from Blacktown, how long must I wait for the next bus?
    (c) Which bus is the slowest?
    (d) How long does it take to travel from Crosskeys to Isca?
    (e) I live in Crosskeys and have an appointment in Parkley at 10.45. If it takes 10 minutes to walk to the bus stop, what is the latest time I must leave home to keep the appointment?

Timetable B

TRAIN TIMES TO LONDON

Button	dep.	—	09.24	10.42	11.42	—	12.56
Alford	dep.	—	09.35	10.52	11.52	—	13.06
Chipley	dep.	—	—	11.05	12.05	—	—
Mellow	dep.	—	—	—	12.30	—	—
Saxton	dep.	—	11.03	12.00	13.00	—	14.10
Sealey	dep.	—	11.08	12.05	13.06	—	14.16
Corby	dep.	11.25	11.30	12.38	13.30	14.42	14.38
Stamford	dep.	11.39	11.43	12.52	13.43	14.39	14.52
London	arr.	13.18	13.23	14.31	15.22	16.18	16.37

4. The following questions refer to timetable B:
   (a) How much longer does it take to travel to London from Button on the 10.42 train than on the 11.42?
   (b) How many trains stop at Mellow?
   (c) What time must I leave Chipley to reach London by 4 o'clock in the afternoon?
   (d) On which train must I leave Alford to get to Corby by 13.20?

5. Use timetable B to answer the following questions:
   (a) How many trains stop at all the stations?
   (b) Which train from Chipley makes the least number of stops?
   (c) If Alford is 525 km from London, find the average speed of the fastest train from Alford to London.

Timetable C

Distance in km from Glasgow

Glasgow Central	dep.	08.20	—
Carlisle	arr. dep.	09.04 09.06	165
Crewe	arr. dep.	10.11 10.14	390
Rugby	arr. dep.	10.54 10.56	510
Watford	arr. dep.	11.25 11.28	625
London (Euston)	arr.	11.35	650

6. Use timetable C to answer the following questions:
   (a) How long is the journey from Glasgow to London?
   (b) What is the average speed of the train for this journey?
   (c) Find the total time the train stops at stations.
   (d) How long does it take to travel from Crewe to Watford?

7. Use timetable C to answer the following questions:
   (a) Which two stations are nearest together?
   (b) How long does the train take to travel between these two stations?
   (c) What was the average speed of the train between these two stations? Give your answer correct to the nearest whole number.
   (d) What was the longest distance travelled by the train without a stop?

TIME ZONES

If you fly to Majorca for a holiday in the summer, and leave the United Kingdom at 5 o'clock in the morning, you will find that when you arrive in Majorca the time is 8 o'clock in the morning, even though the flight has taken only 2 hours. On the other hand, if you leave Majorca at 3 o'clock in the afternoon to return home, you will arrive home at 4 o'clock in the afternoon, but again you have had a 2 hour flight. The reason is that *local* or *clock time* in Majorca is 1 hour ahead of local time in the United Kingdom.

At any given hour it will be midnight somewhere on the Earth, but midday somewhere else. So that we all know where we are, we divide the Earth's surface area into *time zones*. Clock time in all these zones is related to Greenwich Mean Time (GMT). In countries to the east of Greenwich the sun rises earlier — their time is therefore ahead of GMT. In countries to the west of Greenwich the sun rises later and therefore their time is behind GMT.

EXAMPLE 1
Local time in Hong Kong is 8 hours ahead of GMT while local time in Washington is 5 hours behind GMT. What time is it (a) GMT when it is 4 p.m. in Hong Kong, (b) GMT when it is 5 p.m. in Washington, (c) in Washington when it is 3 a.m. in Hong Kong?

(a) Since Hong Kong is 8 hours ahead of GMT, GMT is 8 hours behind Hong Kong. Therefore if it is 4 p.m. in Hong Kong, it will be 4 p.m. − 8 hours i.e. 8 a.m. GMT.

(b) Since Washington is 5 hours behind GMT, GMT is 5 hours ahead of Washington. Therefore if it is 5 p.m. in Washington, it will be 5 p.m. + 5 hours i.e. 10 p.m. GMT.

(c) Washington is $8 + 5 = 13$ hours behind Hong Kong. Therefore if it is 3 a.m. in Hong Kong, it will be 3 a.m. − 13 hours = 2 p.m. the previous day in Washington.

EXERCISE 111

For Questions 1 to 10, assume that London time and GMT are the same.

1. Clock time in Calcutta is $5\frac{1}{2}$ hours ahead of GMT. What time is it:
   (a) in London when it is 1 p.m. in Calcutta
   (b) in Calcutta when it is 8 a.m. in London?

2. The time in New York is 5 hours 'slow' on GMT. What time is it:
   (a) in New York when it is 12 noon in London
   (b) in London when it is 6 p.m. in New York?

3. The time in Mexico City is 6 hours behind GMT. Find:
   (a) the time in London when it is 10 a.m. in Mexico City
   (b) the time in Mexico City when it is 2 p.m. in London.

4. San Francisco time is 8 hours behind GMT and Rome time is 1 hour ahead of GMT. Find:
   (a) the time in Rome when it is 11 a.m. in San Francisco
   (b) the time in San Francisco when it is midday in Rome.

5. Hong Kong time is 8 hours ahead of GMT and Rio de Janeiro time is 3 hours behind GMT. Find:
   (a) the time in Rio de Janeiro when it is 1 p.m. in Hong Kong
   (b) the time in Hong Kong when it is 10 a.m. in Rio de Janeiro.

6. Clock time in Lagos is 1 hour ahead of GMT and in Washington is 5 hours behind GMT. What is the time:
   (a) in Washington when it is 2 a.m. in Lagos
   (b) in Lagos when it is 2 p.m. in Washington?

7. The time in Moscow is 3 hours ahead of London time, while the time in Toronto is 5 hours behind London time. What time is it:
   (a) in Moscow when it is 10 a.m. in Toronto
   (b) in Toronto when it is midnight in Moscow?

8. Cairo is 2 hours ahead of GMT and Tokyo is 9 hours ahead. At 4 a.m. GMT in London, what time is it (a) in Cairo, (b) in Tokyo?
   When it is 4 a.m. in Tokyo what time is it (c) in Cairo, (d) in London?

9. The distance from Bombay to London is approximately 4500 miles. An aeroplane leaves Bombay at 5 a.m. local time and flies to London at an average speed of 500 mph. At what time (GMT) will it arrive in London if Bombay time is $5\frac{1}{2}$ hours ahead of GMT?

10. An aeroplane leaves Rome at 8 a.m. to fly to Sydney, which is approximately 10 500 miles away. If Rome time is 1 hour ahead of GMT and Sydney time is 10 hours ahead of GMT, find the local time of arrival at Sydney if the aeroplane travels at an average speed of 500 mph.

11. If the time in Washington is 5 hours behind GMT, and in Singapore is $7\frac{1}{2}$ hours ahead of GMT, find:
    (a) the time in Singapore when it is 4 a.m. in Washington
    (b) the time in Singapore and in Washington when it is 1 p.m. in London on 8th May.

During the summer months, i.e. from the end of March to the end of October, the United Kingdom uses British Summer Time (BST) which is 1 hour ahead of GMT.

12. When it is 6 a.m. BST in London what time is it:
    (a) in Tokyo, which is 9 hours ahead of GMT
    (b) in Buenos Aires, which is 4 hours behind GMT?

13. Karachi time is 5 hours ahead of GMT and Hong Kong time is 8 hours ahead of GMT. What time is it in Hong Kong at 5 a.m. in Karachi? What would be the BST time in London when it is 8 a.m. in Karachi?

14. The time in Johannesburg is 2 hours ahead of GMT while the time in Bombay is $5\frac{1}{2}$ hours ahead of GMT. When it is 12 noon BST in London what time is it (a) in Johannesburg, (b) in Bombay?

    When it is 2 p.m. in Johannesburg what time is it (c) in Bombay, (d) in BST in London?

15. An aeroplane leaves London at 12 noon BST and flies to Toronto which is 3500 miles away, at an average speed of 500 mph. Find the local time of arrival at Toronto which is 5 hours behind GMT.

FOREIGN EXCHANGE

If you have been abroad on holiday you will know that you cannot take UK money with you and expect to be able to spend it in the local shops at the holiday resort — you must have the currency of the country you are visiting, e.g. francs in France, pesetas in Spain, dollars in the United States. Similarly in the business world, if a company sells cars to a foreign country, the buyers will want to know how much they will cost in their own currency. If you buy Spanish oranges, you are not interested in what they cost in pesetas, but you do want to know what they cost in pence.

These questions can only be answered if the money of one country can be converted into the money of another, i.e. there must be a *rate of exchange* between the two currencies. Many factors determine the rate of exchange between two currencies and you may well have heard such phrases as 'The pound is weak against the West German mark' or 'The yen was strong against the US dollar'. In the early 1950s £1 could be exchanged for 12 Deutschmarks, whereas in the 1980s you would receive approximately 4 Deutschmarks for your £1. Over the 30 year period the Deutschmark has become much stronger, i.e. worth more, in relation to the pound.

The following table shows the monetary system for several countries together with typical rates of exchange.

COUNTRY	MONETARY UNIT	RATE OF EXCHANGE i.e. VALUE OF £1
Austria	schilling	30
Belgium	franc (f.)	80
Denmark	krone	14.30
France	franc (f.)	9
West Germany	Deutschmark (DM)	4.29
Greece	drachma (dr.)	112
Italy	lira (L.)	2300
Norway	krone	10.76
Portugal	escudo	125
Spain	peseta (pta.)	190
Sweden	krona	10.45
United States	dollar ($)	1.80

EXAMPLE 2

Convert £120 into French francs, given that £1 is equivalent to 9.80 f.

£1 is equivalent to 9.80 f.

∴ £120 is equivalent to 120×9.80 f.

i.e. £120 is equivalent to 1176 f.

EXAMPLE 3

Convert 1408 US dollars into pounds, given that $1 is equivalent to 55 p.

$1 is equivalent to 55 p

∴ $1408 is equivalent to 1408×55 p

i.e. $1408 is equivalent to $£\dfrac{1408 \times 55}{100} = £774.40$

EXAMPLE 4

The cost of a seat in the bullring in Malaga was 1400 pesetas. Calculate the equivalent cost in pounds if £1 ≡ 175 pta.

175 pta. is equivalent to £1

∴ 1 pta. is equivalent to $£\dfrac{1}{175}$

i.e. 1400 pta, is equivalent to $£\dfrac{1}{175} \times 1400 = £8$

EXAMPLE 5

A set of tools in West Germany costs 184 Deutschmarks. If £1 ≡ DM 3.88, calculate the equivalent cost in the United Kingdom, giving your answer correct to the nearest penny.

DM 3.88 is equivalent to £1

$\therefore$ DM 1 is equivalent to $£\dfrac{1}{3.88}$

i.e. DM 184 is equivalent to $£\dfrac{1}{3.88} \times 184 = £47.42$

correct to the nearest penny

EXAMPLE 6

A set of Sheffield cutlery is offered for sale at £172 in London, 1600 f. in Paris and 20 000 escudos in Lisbon. Given that £1 $\equiv$ 8.64 f. $\equiv$ 124 escudos, in which city is the set (a) cheapest, (b) dearest?

We must express each sale price in the same currency. The most convenient is pounds, but either of the other two would do.

Cost of cutlery set in London $= £172$

Cost of the cutlery set in Paris $= 1600$ f.

$$= £\dfrac{1600}{8.64}$$

$$= £185.19$$

Cost of cutlery set in Lisbon $= 20\,000$ escudos

$$= £\dfrac{20\,000}{124}$$

$$= £161.29$$

$\therefore$ The set is cheapest in Lisbon and dearest in Paris.

EXERCISE 112

1. If £1 $\equiv$ \$1.80, convert £216 into US dollars.
2. If £1 $\equiv$ 10.80 f., convert £84 into French francs.
3. If £1 $\equiv$ DM 3.94, convert £540 into Deutschmarks.
4. If £1 $\equiv$ 180 pta., convert £36.50 into pesetas.
5. If £1 $\equiv$ 108 dr., convert £82.25 into drachmas.
6. If £1 $\equiv$ 28 schillings, convert 350 Austrian schillings into pounds.
7. If £1 $\equiv$ 14 kroner, convert 1176 Danish kroner into pounds.
8. If £1 $\equiv$ 1.76 R, convert 303.16 South African rand into pounds.
9. If £1 $\equiv$ 430 Y, convert 23 220 Japanese yen into pounds.
10. If £1 $\equiv$ 2200 L., convert 34 056 lire into pounds.

11. If 1 f. ≡ 11 p, convert 76 f. into pounds.

12. If DM 1 ≡ 23 p, convert DM 104 into pounds.

13. If 5 escudos ≡ 4 p, convert 765 escudos into pounds.

14. If 50 dr ≡ 77 p, convert 475 drachma into pounds.

15. If 7 pta. ≡ 4 p, convert 1869 pesetas into pounds.

16. If 4 f. ≡ 5 p, convert £8.45 into Belgian francs.

17. If 5 dr. ≡ 7 p, convert £19.67 into drachmas.

18. If 3 schillings ≡ 10 p, convert £34.40 into Austrian schillings.

19. If 2 riyals ≡ 33 p, convert £50.16 into Saudi Arabian riyals.

20. If $HK 3 ≡ 76 p, convert £72.20 into Hong Kong dollars.

21. Calculate the rate of exchange if a tourist receives 903 US dollars
     for £525.

22. Calculate the rate of exchange if a holidaymaker receives 9520
     pesetas for £56.

23. Calculate the rate of exchange if a businessman receives 2688
     Austrian schillings for £84.

24. Calculate the rate of exchange if a bank exchanges 840 Deutsch-
     marks for £224.

25. Calculate the rate of exchange if a tourist receives 2288 Danish
     kroner for £160.

26. If a pair of shoes sells for 5940 pesetas in Barcelona, calculate
     the equivalent price in Liverpool if £1 ≡ 165 pta.

27. A bottle of whisky costs £8.40 in London. If £1 ≡ 10.20 f., what
     would it cost in Paris?

28. A book selling for 5000 lire in Rome is to be sold in the United
     Kingdom. If £1 ≡ 1500 L., find the equivalent UK price.

29. In Norway a man's haircut cost 28 kroner. If £1 ≡ 10.2 kroner,
     find the equivalent cost in Glasgow.

30. How much would a meal costing £15 in London cost in Lisbon if
     125 escudos are equivalent to £1?

31. The single fare from London to Johannesburg with a certain air-
     line is 394 South African rand. Find the equivalent price in pounds
     if £1 ≡ 1.84 R.

32. A pack of six cans of lager sells for 5.25 Deutschmarks in Bonn.
     What is the equivalent price in Manchester if £1 ≡ DM 4.20?

33. Spanish wine is sold in Madrid at 250 pesetas a bottle. Find the
     equivalent price in Belfast if 100 pesetas ≡ 54 p.

34. A suite of furniture selling in the United Kingdom for £1450 is to be marketed in the United States. If $1 is equivalent to 55 p, find the price in dollars giving your answer correct to the nearest $10.

Holidays and Travel

35. A tourist changed £90 on board ship into escudos at a rate of £1 ≡ 190 escudos. He did not spend anything ashore but when he returned to the ship he was only offered £1 for each 200 escudos. How much did he lose on the deal?

36. When an American tourist arrived at Gatwick Airport he changed 400 US dollars and 380 Canadian dollars into pounds. If £1 ≡ 2.18 US dollars ≡ 1.82 Canadian dollars, calculate, correct to the nearest pound, the value of his dollars in pounds.

37. If the first-class return train fare from Bonn to Stuttgart is 144.40 Deutschmarks, calculate the equivalent cost in pounds, given that £1 ≡ DM 3.80.

38. A tourist buys a bottle of wine in the duty-free shop at Malaga for 550 pesetas. How much did he save if the same wine was selling at £3.85 in the United Kingdom? (£1 ≡ 180 pta.)

39. Janet Burris buys a bottle of perfume in the duty-free shop at Rome airport for 27 600 lira. If £1 ≡ 2300 L., how much does she save if a similar bottle is selling for £14.80 in London?

40. Tom Jones buys a Japanese camera in Cannes for 2000 francs. When he arrives home he finds a similar camera on sale in a local shop for £180. If 10 f. ≡ 98 p, determine whether or not he made a good buy in Cannes.

41. A Limoges china vase is offered for sale in Paris at 1200 French francs, while in London the price of a similar vase is £125. If £1 ≡ 9.80 f., which is the better buy and by how much?

42. A British car sells in Belgium for 800 000 f. When the car is sold in the United Kingdom its price is increased by 15%. If £1 ≡ 80 f., find the UK price of the car.

43. Violins made by a particular craftsman in West Germany sell for 10 080 Deutschmarks. If 15% is added to their price when they are imported into the United Kingdom, find their selling price in this country. (£1 ≡ DM 4.20)

44. A car which sells for $18000 in the United States is imported into the United Kingdom. If this price is increased by 25% when sold to a customer in the United Kingdom, find its price, correct to the nearest £100, given that £1 ≡ $1.75.

45. A tourist changed £100 into French francs when he entered France and the exchange rate was £1 ≡ 9.80 f. He did not spend anything in France and when he crossed into Spain his francs were changed into pesetas at the rate of 1 f. ≡ 17 pta. Again it was unnecessary to spend any of this money so that when he returned to London he changed his money into pounds at the rate of 190 pta. ≡ £1. Compared with when he left the United Kingdom, how much had he gained or lost?

46. A radio in a French shop costs 418 f. What would it cost in West Germany if 11 f. ≡ DM 4?

47. Wooden chairs are sold in an Italian shop for 19 320 lire. What would be their price in Athens if 230 L. ≡ 11 dr.?

48. The price of a set of French saucepans in a Spanish store is 9880 pesetas. If 38 pta. ≡ 25 escudos, find their equivalent price in Lisbon.

49. Before Mr and Mrs Baxter went to France for a 14 day holiday they changed £500 into francs at a rate of 10.20 f. to the pound. While they were away they spent 70 f. a day each on accommodation, 85 f. each a day on meals, and 730 f. in total on other expenses. When they returned home the local bank exchanged their unspent francs into pounds at a rate of 10 f. to the pound. Find the amount they received in pounds.

50. A young couple changed £600 into Belgian francs, at a rate of £1 ≡ 80 f., before setting out on holiday. They spent five days in Belgium, spending 472 f. each per day on food and accommodation plus 1280 f. between them on other expenses. On the sixth day they travelled into West Germany, changing their remaining Belgian francs into Deutschmarks at the rate of 21 f. ≡ DM 1. In Germany, where they stayed for 8 days, they spend DM 84 each per day on food and accommodation, together with DM 516 between them on other expenses. The remaining Deutschmarks were exchanged into pounds when they returned to Britain. If the rate of exchange was DM 7 ≡ £2, how much did they receive for them?

PACKAGE HOLIDAYS

Most people who go on holiday buy what we call a *package holiday*, i.e. for a given sum of money the travel agent or tour company arranges virtually everything. The prices they quote include all transportation, hotel accommodation, and probably the services of a courier.

Given below is a typical price list for two imaginary hotels during the holiday season.

	HOTEL EXCELSIOR (HALF BOARD)				HOTEL ATHENA (FULL BOARD)			
NO. OF NIGHTS	7	14	7	14	7	14	7	14
DEP. DAY IN WEEK COMMENCING	SAT		WED		SAT		WED	
May 2	164	204	155	185	192	252	183	235
9	169	209	160	190	197	257	188	240
16	174	214	172	202	202	262	200	252
23	189	234	182	212	220	280	214	266
30	195	240	175	210	230	290	212	264
June 6	184	229	179	214	225	285	216	268
13	192	242	183	218	229	299	220	272
20	201	251	192	227	237	307	228	282
27	209	259	200	235	240	310	231	295
July 4	225	275	216	251	253	323	245	309
11	233	283	224	259	261	336	252	317
18	244	304	235	270	273	348	264	330
25	256	316	247	282	283	358	274	340
Aug 1	255	325	246	286	281	356	272	337
8	253	323	244	284	279	354	270	334
15	251	321	242	282	277	352	268	332
22	247	317	238	278	266	341	257	320
29	244	304	235	270	259	334	250	312
Sept 5	234	284	225	260	248	321	239	300
12	220	270	211	246	246	319	237	297
19	207	257	198	233	242	306	233	292
26	201	246	192	227	231	280	222	280
Oct 3	195	235	186	216	223	270	214	272

Child reductions (2-11 inclusive): 25%.

Deposit: £35 per person; £20 for children 2-11.

Cancellation charge: more than 56 days before departure 30%, 15-56 days 40%, 1-14 days 50%.

EXERCISE 113

Use the above information to answer the following questions:

1. When is the most expensive time to take a holiday at Hotel Excelsior?

2. Why are holidays which begin on a Saturday more expensive than those which begin on a Wednesday?

3. If I leave for my holiday on Wednesday 8 September, which hotel gives me the cheapest 14 day holiday?

4. How much would a 7 day holiday at the Hotel Athena, leaving on 31 July (a Saturday) cost Mr Wilcox for a family of five — Mr and Mrs Wilcox plus their children aged 7, 12 and 15 years? How much would they have to pay in deposits?

5. How much would two adults save by leaving on Wednesday 14 July instead of Wednesday 21 July, for a 14 day holiday at the Hotel Excelsior?

6. The Khan family, consisting of mother, father and four children aged 5, 8, 10 and 12 years, decided to take a 7 day holiday at the Hotel Athena leaving on Wednesday 15 September. Find:
   (a) the deposit
   (b) the total paid to the travel agent if there was a sum additional to the above of £10 per person for airport charges.

   When they had been at the resort for a few days they were sorry that they had not booked into the other hotel for 14 days. How much more would this have cost them?

7. Mr and Mrs Jacob and their daughter Ruth, aged 8, had booked and paid for a 7 day holiday at the Hotel Excelsior leaving on Saturday 8 May. Unfortunately 3 weeks before they were due to go they were forced to cancel the holiday. How much would the cancellation charge be?

8. What is the difference in cost between:
   (a) a 14 day holiday at the Hotel Athena for a family of four (mother, father and children aged 10 and 14), leaving on Wednesday 4 August; and
   (b) a 14 day holiday for two adults at the Hotel Excelsior leaving on Saturday 14 August?

TRAVEL INSURANCE

One thing which is frequently forgotten by holidaymakers is adequate *insurance cover*. This is particularly important for travellers going abroad, where, for example, medical expenses can be very high. Many companies offer comprehensive packages by the unit. A typical 'unit' covers the following:

Section A. Medical and additional expenses up to £1500.

Section B. Personal accident up to £1000 per limb or eye, and £10 per week for temporary disablement.

Section C. Baggage and personal effects up to £500.

Section D. Personal money up to £150.

Section E. Lost deposits up to £300.

Section F. Personal legal liability up to £350 000.

Section G. An optional addition (at an extra premium) to cover additional car expenses up to a maximum of £1000.

The table below gives some idea of the cost of one unit of the above cover. Two units would cost almost twice as much, with similar rates for further units.

PREMIUM SCALE PER PERSON FOR SECTIONS A TO F		
PERIOD	PREMIUM OVER 16 YEARS	PREMIUM UNDER 16 YEARS
Up to 10 days	£3.00	£2.00
Up to 17 days	£3.50	£2.50
Up to 31 days	£4.00	£3.25

These premiums are for European countries and countries bordering the Mediterranean. For other countries the above premiums should be doubled.

PREMIUM SCALE FOR SECTION G		
PERIOD	CAR UP TO 7 YEARS OLD	CAR UP TO 10 YEARS OLD
Up to 10 days	£6.50	£9.00
Up to 17 days	£9.00	£13.50
Up to 31 days	£13.00	£17.00

EXAMPLE 7

Calculate the premium due to cover a family of five (two adults plus their children aged 9, 11 and 13 years) taking their 8 year old car to France for a 3 week holiday if they choose one unit for the car and for each member of the family. Use the rates given in the text.

One unit for each of the two adults for 21 days costs:

$2 \times £4 = £8$

One unit for each of the three children for 21 days costs:

$3 \times £3.25 = £9.75$

One unit for the 8 year old car $= £17.00$

$\therefore$ Total premium due $= £34.75$

EXAMPLE 8

Calculate the premium due to cover a family of four (father, mother and two children aged 17 and 19 years) going on a 2 week holiday to Corfu. If they had gone to Canada instead, what difference would it have made to the premium?

Since both children are more than 16 years old both are counted as adults.

One unit for 4 adults for two weeks costs:

$4 \times £3.50 = £14$

∴ Total premium due is £14

If they had gone to Canada, the premium would have been doubled i.e. £28.

EXERCISE 114

In this Exercise use the premium rates given in the text.

1. Calculate the premium due to cover a family of three (father, mother and child aged 10 years) on a 12 day package holiday to France.

2. Calculate the premium due to cover a family of six, including four young children, on a 2 week European holiday in their 3 year old car.

3. Mr and Mrs White and their children Joanne (aged 8), Jonathan (aged 11) and Martin (aged 17) propose taking a 3 week touring holiday in their 5 year old car in Spain. What would the premium be if one unit is taken for each person and the car?

4. Peter and Betty Johnson are taking their 18 year old daughter to the United States for a 2 week holiday. If they decide to take out two units of travellers' insurance for each person, how much will the premium amount to?

5. Chris and Ray Williams propose taking their daughter Alison (aged 17) and their son Alan (aged 19) to Italy in their 6 year old car for a 28 day holiday. If they select two units of insurance for the car and one driver, but one unit for the other three travellers, what would be the total premium payable?

   If they were forced to change their plans and decided to leave the car at home but go to New Zealand instead, how much more (or less) would they pay for insurance? (Assume that all four travellers now take one unit.)

24

STOCKS AND SHARES; BANKRUPTCY

STOCKS

Governments, local authorities and other public bodies frequently need to borrow large sums of money either to repay old loans or to finance new schemes. They raise this money by issuing *stock* which is 'redeemable', meaning that it will be paid back at *par* (*face value*) within a fixed period, and on which they pay interest at a fixed rate. A person investing money in stock receives a certificate showing the *nominal value* of the stock (usually issued in multiples of £100) and the rate of interest expressed as a percentage of the nominal or face value. The price of stock varies according to the simple laws of supply and demand. If more people wish to buy than are prepared to sell, the price rises. Conversely if there are more sellers than buyers, the price will fall. The *market value* of stock is given as the price to be paid for £100 stock, even though it is possible to buy fractions of £100.

If you turn to the financial section of your newspaper you will find a list entitled *British Funds*. A typical entry in the list might read:

$$\text{Treasury} \quad 9\% \quad (1992\text{-}96) \quad 72 \quad +\tfrac{3}{4}$$

This means that £100 worth of Treasury stock may be purchased for £72, that it will be redeemed at £100 sometime between 1992 and 1996, and that the fixed rate of interest is 9% of the nominal value, interest being paid half-yearly. The last entry of $+\tfrac{3}{4}$ indicates that £100 stock rose in value by £$\tfrac{3}{4}$ as a result of the previous day's dealings.

Another entry might read:

$$\text{War Loan} \quad 3\tfrac{1}{2}\% \quad 27\tfrac{7}{8} \quad +\tfrac{1}{4}$$

War Loan, as the name implies, was stock issued to help finance a war. It was bought by large numbers of ordinary people and proved to be a very poor financial investment. It pays $3\frac{1}{2}$% interest on the nominal value and £100 stock may be purchased for £$27\frac{7}{8}$. As with the Treasury stock, the entry shows that, on the previous day, more investors were interested in buying than selling and therefore its price rose by £$\frac{1}{4}$ for £100 stock.

In questions on stocks great care should be taken to distinguish between the nominal or face value, on which the interest is calculated, and the market or cash value which enables an investor to calculate the *yield* or true rate of interest received.

EXAMPLE 1

A man buys £1200 Treasury $5\frac{1}{2}$% stock at 62. How much does it cost him?

What annual income can he expect to receive from it?

£100 nominal value will cost £62 cash

∴ £1200 nominal value will cost:

$$\frac{£62}{100} \times 1200 = £744 \text{ cash}$$

Yearly interest on £100 stock is £5.50

∴ Yearly interest on £1200 stock is:

$$\frac{£5.50 \times 1200}{100} = £66$$

EXAMPLE 2

A woman invests £1800 in Liverpool $9\frac{3}{4}$% stock at 90. Calculate how much stock she buys and the annual income from it.

£90 cash buys £100 stock

∴ £1800 cash buys $\dfrac{£100}{90} \times 1800 = £2000$ stock

£100 stock yields yearly interest of £9.75

∴ £2000 stock yields yearly interest of:

$$\frac{£9.75 \times 2000}{100} = £195$$

EXAMPLE 3   A small company buys £25 000 Consols $2\frac{1}{2}$% at 30.
Calculate (a) the cost of the stock, (b) the annual
income, (c) the yield.

(a) £100 stock costs £30 cash

$$\therefore \underset{\text{stock costs}}{\text{£25 000}} \quad \frac{£30}{100} \times 25\,000 = £7500 \text{ cash}$$

(b) £100 stock gives an income of £2.50

$$\therefore \underset{\text{an income of}}{\text{£25 000 stock gives}} \frac{£2.50 \times 25\,000}{100} = £625$$

(c) £7500 cash gives an income of £625

$$\therefore \underset{\text{an income of}}{\text{£100 cash gives}} = \frac{£625 \times 100}{7500} = £8\tfrac{1}{3}$$

i.e. Yield or true rate of interest is $8\frac{1}{3}$%

NOTE: $$\text{Yield \%} = \frac{\text{interest or dividend payable}}{\text{investment or cost of stock}} \times 100\%$$

BROKERAGE

Stocks are bought or sold for an investor by a stockbroker, who earns
his living by charging commission at a given percentage on the total sum
paid or received. This commission is called the *brokerage*. When buying,
the brokerage is added to the price paid, but when selling it is deducted.
The rates of commission vary according to the size of the deal, e.g. $1\frac{1}{4}$%
on the first £20 000, $\frac{3}{4}$% on the next £55 000 and $\frac{3}{5}$% on the excess.

EXAMPLE 4   A man sells £5400 Gas 3% stock at 40. How much
will he receive from the sale assuming brokerage at
$1\frac{1}{4}$%?

$$\underset{\text{selling £5400 stock at 40}}{\text{Amount received by}} = \frac{£5400}{100} \times 40$$

$$= £2160$$

$$\text{Brokerage at } 1\frac{1}{4}\% = £\frac{2160}{100} \times \frac{5}{4} = £27$$

$\therefore$ Net cash received after paying brokerage = £2133

EXAMPLE 5   An investor sells £6800 Electricity 9% stock at 75
and invests the proceeds in Consols 4% stock at 28.
How much new stock will he be able to buy if
brokerage is 2% for each transaction? Calculate his
change in income.

Income from £6800
stock at 9% $= £\dfrac{6800}{100} \times 9 = £612$

Cash from sale of £6800
Electricity stock at 75 $= £\dfrac{6800}{100} \times 75 = £5100$

Brokerage on £5100 cash at 2% $= £\dfrac{5100}{100} \times 2 = £102$

∴ Cash available for reinvestment $= £5100 - £102$
$$= £4998$$

Since brokerage is to be paid on the new investment,
the cash available to buy stock at the market price
is:

$$£4998 \times \dfrac{100}{102} = £4900$$

Amount of Consols 4% at 28 which may be purchased
for £4900 is:

$$£\dfrac{4900}{28} \times 100 = £17\,500$$

Income from £17 500
stock at 4% $= £\dfrac{17\,500}{100} \times 4 = £700$

∴ Increase in income $= £700 - £612$
$$= £88$$

EXERCISE 115

Find the cost of and income due from:

1. £500 War Loan $3\frac{1}{2}$% at 38

2. £1300 GLC $12\frac{1}{2}$% stock at 102

3. £4300 Funding 6% stock at 93

4. £3600 Exchange $11\frac{1}{4}$% stock at 95

5. £6200 Gas 3% stock at 42

6. £3100 Electricity 12% stock at 90.

Calculate the amount of stock which may be purchased, and the yearly income obtained by investing:

7. £420 in Electricity 10% stock at 70

8. £588 in Railway 12% stock at 84

9. £1 500 in Belgian 8% stock at 125

10. £1 275 in Cardiff 11% stock at 85

11. £4 275 in German $10\frac{1}{2}$% stock at 95

12. £2 460 in War Loan $3\frac{1}{2}$% stock at 30.

Find the amount of cash received by selling:

13. £1 200 Exchange $12\frac{1}{4}$% stock at 92

14. £800 Glasgow $9\frac{1}{4}$% stock at 101

15. £750 Conversion $3\frac{1}{2}$% stock at 34

16. £1 800 New Zealand 8% stock at 65

17. £950 Canadian 10% stock at 84

18. £3 400 Indian 6% stock at 53.

Find the yield per cent from each of the following stocks:

19. Manchester 6% stock at 50

20. Electricity 9% stock at 75

21. Consols 4% stock at 40

22. Australian 8% stock at 64

23. Treasury 15% stock at 90

24. Funding 14% stock at 98.

25. Fred Street sells £2800 Consols $2\frac{1}{2}$% stock at 36 and invests the proceeds in West German 8% stock at 84. How much West German stock does he buy and what is his change in income?

26. Lord Blackwood sells £8000 Canadian 12% stock at 90 and invests the proceeds in South African 10% stock at 80. Calculate how much South African stock he buys and the change in income.

27. Sally Martin sells £4800 Glasgow Corporation 7% stock at 50 and invests the proceeds in Treasury 12% stock at 80. Find the amount of Treasury stock bought and the change of income.

28. Lady Luck sells £14 000 War Loan $3\frac{1}{2}$% stock at 32 and invests the proceeds in Canadian Pacific 12% stock at 112. Calculate the change in income.

29. Mr Brown sells £11 700 Electricity 9% stock at 78 and invests the proceeds in Greater London 12% stock at 65. Find the change in income.

30. Mrs Davis sells £2450 $6\frac{1}{2}$% stock at 54 and invests the proceeds in $4\frac{1}{2}$% stock at 42. Find the change in her income.

31. Find the income after tax at 30% on £5868 which is invested in Gas $7\frac{1}{2}$% stock at 72.

32. Find the income after tax at 40% on £1806 which has been invested in Treasury 11% stock at 86.

33. Calculate the net income, after income tax at 35% has been deducted, if £8208 is invested in Government 14% stock at 108.

34. Calculate the net income, after income tax has been deducted at 30%, if £4324 is invested in American $12\frac{1}{2}$% stock at 94.

35. A man invests £10 950 in Government $8\frac{3}{4}$% stock at 73. Find his net interest, if tax is deducted at 33%.

36. What sum of money must be invested in 12% stock at 92 to give an income of £432?

37. What sum of money must be invested in $9\frac{1}{2}$% stock at 87 to give an income of £408.50?

38. What sum of money must be invested in $13\frac{1}{2}$% stock at 94 to give an income of £472.50?

39. What sum of money must be invested in $10\frac{3}{4}$% stock at 78 to give an income of £258?

40. By investing £2795 in an 8% stock an investor obtained an income of £344. Find the price of the stock.

41. By investing £8256 in a $12\frac{1}{2}$% stock an investor obtained an income of £1075. Find the price of the stock.

42. By investing £5508 in a 14% stock an investor obtained an income of £756. Find the price of the stock.

43. By investing £3572 in an $11\frac{3}{4}$% stock an investor obtained an income of £446.50. Find the price of the stock.

44. By investing £4056 in a 6% Government stock an investor obtained an income of £468. Find the price of the stock and yield per cent on the investment correct to one decimal place.

45. Mr George sells £4200 New Zealand 8% stock at 64. How much will he receive after paying brokerage at $1\frac{1}{2}$%?

46. Lord London sells £6000 Treasury 6% stock at 85. How much will he receive after paying brokerage at $1\frac{1}{4}$%?

47. Lady Dorking buys £9500 Australian 8% stock at 58. How much will this cost her after paying brokerage at $1\frac{1}{2}$%?

48. Fred Brown buys £2800 Glasgow $9\frac{1}{4}$% stock at 102. How much will it cost him after allowing for brokerage at $1\frac{1}{4}$%?

49. Mr White spends £2740.50, including brokerage at $1\frac{1}{2}$%, on Treasury 15% stock at 90. How much stock did he buy? How much did he pay in brokerage charges?

50. An investor spends £4872, including brokerage at $1\frac{1}{2}$%, in order to buy Exchange $12\frac{1}{4}$% stock at 80. How much stock did he buy? How much did he pay in brokerage?

Shares

If someone wants to start a business, he or she tends to use personal savings, or if friends, relatives, or the bank manager are sufficiently impressed, it may be possible to borrow the necessary money from them. If all goes well and the business is successful, a stage is reached when additional money or *capital* must be obtained if the venture is to prosper and expand. An important step in a rapidly expanding business is therefore to 'go public', i.e. to appeal to the general public for cash. In this way several million pounds may be made available to a business. The total amount required, say £2 000 000, is invested by people who feel that the business will be very successful, i.e. that they, the investors, will make a profit. They buy small units, or *shares*, each unit costing perhaps £1 or 25 p or even 5 p. Usually investors may buy as many or as few shares as they wish.

When the investor has paid for the shares, he or she will receive a *share certificate*. This details the number of shares bought, together with their *nominal* or *face value*. Immediately their *cash* or *market value* will be different from their face value. The law of supply and demand comes into operation. Quite simply, if more people wish to buy the shares than wish to sell, the price will rise. Conversely, if there are more sellers than buyers, the price will fall.

In most companies there are several different types of shares, the most common of which are outlined below. A *bond* or *debenture* is a security issued by the company acknowledging debt to the bondholder and giving details of the interest rate payable and the dates on which the interest is due. Debenture holders have the right to demand their interest or *dividend* even when the company is trading at a loss.

A *preference share*, as the name implies, is a preferred share, i.e. a share, at a fixed rate of interest, which ranks before ordinary or deferred shares for dividends.

Money invested in *ordinary shares* forms the real 'risk capital' of the business. The dividend due on these shares will vary considerably from year to year, and is due only after interest on debentures and preference shares has been made.

It is these ordinary shares which are listed in the daily newspapers. Typical entries would read:

Barclays Bank (£1)	480	−1
Boots (25 p)	207	+3
British Oxygen Co. (25 p)	162xd	+2
British Petroleum (25 p)	280xr	−2

These details refer to the dealings on the Stock Exchange the previous day and tell us that:

(a) Barclays Bank shares have a nominal value of £1; their market value was 480 p each, this being one penny lower than the price the previous day.

(b) Shares in Boots have a face value of 25 p. They cost 207 p each. This was 3 p more expensive than the previous day.

(c) Shares in British Oxygen Company have a nominal value of 25 p. Their price was 162 p, an increase of 2 p on the previous day. The letters xd after the share price indicate that they are sold 'ex-dividend', i.e. the seller retains the right to the next dividend.

(d) Shares in British Petroleum have a nominal value of 25 p and cost 280 p each, 2 p cheaper than the previous day. The letters xr after the price indicate that they are sold 'ex-rights', i.e. the seller retains the right to new shares which are about to be issued.

Suppose a public company is formed with a share capital of £1 000 000 consisting of 250 000 10% preference shares at £1 each, together with £750 000 ordinary shares at £1 each. Let us suppose that after 1 year the company has made a profit of £165 000. This profit may be distributed as follows:

$$\text{Dividend on preference shares} = 10\% \text{ of } £250\,000$$
$$= £25\,000$$

$$\begin{array}{l}\text{Profit retained by the company}\\ \text{for future expansion/emergencies}\end{array} = £50\,000$$

$$\begin{array}{l}\text{Profit remaining to be divided}\\ \text{among ordinary shareholders}\end{array} = £90\,000$$

Each share therefore qualifies for a dividend of $£\dfrac{90\,000}{750\,000} = £0.12$ or 12 p. Thus the ordinary shareholders will receive a dividend of 12 p for each £1 share, or a dividend of 12%.

Perhaps the cash value of each share would now have risen to £2. A seller after 1 year would thus have made a profit of £1 per share in addition to the dividend of 12 p.

Let us continue the story for a further year in the life of the company. A new investor buys ordinary shares at £2 each. At the end of the second year the recorded net profit for the company amounts to a disappointing £90 000. The profit is divided as follows:

$$\text{Dividend on preference shares} = \text{£25 000}$$

(exactly the same as the previous year)

$$\text{Profit retained by the company} = \text{£50 000}$$

(again unchanged)

$$\therefore \text{ Profit to be divided between ordinary shareholders} = \text{£15 000}$$

$$\text{i.e. Dividend per ordinary £1 share} = \text{£}\frac{15\,000}{750\,000}$$

$$= 2\,\text{p or 2\% of the nominal value}$$

The consequence of such poor results could be that the share price would fall. If it had fallen to 165 p, and the investor decided to sell, he or she would have lost 35 p on each share, but would have received a dividend of 2 p. The net loss would thus have been 33 p on each share.

The skill of the shrewd investor is therefore deciding when to buy and when to sell. It is easier to lose money than it is to make it!

The following may help the reader to understand some of the mysteries of the financial pages of a daily newspaper.

The *par value* of a share is the nominal or face value as indicated on the share certificate. It bears no relation to its cash value.

A share stands at a *premium* if its value is more than its par value or issue price. If it stands at a *discount*, its cash value is less than its nominal value. One of the most important words in share dealings is the dividend *yield*. The yield expresses the earnings on a share in terms of its market or cash value, as opposed to its nominal value. If we refer to the company discussed above, the dividend was 2 p on each £1 share, but since each share had cost the investor £2 the actual dividend or yield was 2 p on £2, i.e. 1%.

A *broker* is an agent who buys or sells for a client.

A *jobber* is a dealer in securities (stocks and shares) who is approached by brokers with clients wishing to buy or sell the particular securities in which the jobber deals.

EXAMPLE 6

Find the cost of buying 240 Sainsbury 25 p ordinary shares at 540 p. If the company pays a dividend of 40%, calculate the income.

Cost of 1 Sainsbury share is 540 p

∴ Cost of 240 Sainsbury shares is:

540×240 p $=$ £1296

Nominal value of 1 share $=$ 25 p

Nominal value of 240 shares $=$ 240×25 p

$=$ £60

A dividend of 40% means that the income will be 40% of the *nominal value* of the holding

i.e. Income $=$ £60 $\times \dfrac{40}{100} =$ £24

EXAMPLE 7

A woman sold 525 Marks & Spencer 25 p shares at 140 p and invested the proceeds in Powell Duffryn £1 shares at 250 p. How many Powell Duffryn shares was she able to buy?

The cash produced by selling 525 shares at 140 p each $=$ 525×140 p

250 p will buy 1 Powell Duffryn share

∴ 525×140 p will buy $\dfrac{525 \times 140}{250} =$ 294 such shares

i.e. 294 Powell Duffryn shares may be bought from the proceeds of selling the Marks & Spencer shares.

NOTE:

Frequently it is unnecessary to multiply large numbers together. They will often simplify later on in a question.

EXAMPLE 8

Find the income derived from investing £2700 in Beecham 25 p ordinary shares at 225 p if the declared dividend is 18%. Hence calculate the yield per cent on the investment.

225 p or £2.25 will buy 1 Beecham 25 p share

∴ £2700 will buy $\dfrac{2700}{2.25} =$ 1200 shares

Nominal value of 1200 25 p shares is:

£1200 $\times \dfrac{25}{100} =$ £300

Since the declared dividend is 18%, the income will be 18% of the nominal value of the shares held.

$$\therefore \text{ Income } = £300 \times \frac{18}{100}$$

$$= £54$$

$$\text{Yield per cent } = \frac{\text{income from investment}}{\text{amount of cash invested}} \times 100$$

$$= \frac{£54}{£2700} \times 100$$

$$\therefore \text{ Yield } = 2\%$$

BROKERAGE

Brokerage is calculated in exactly the same way as for stocks. Different rates of commission may operate at different times, and for dealings of different values.

EXAMPLE 9   Mr Smith buys 7450 Vickers £1 shares at 172 p. How much will this cost him if he pays brokerage at $1\frac{1}{2}\%$?

7450 Vickers £1 shares at 172 p each will cost

$£7450 \times 1.72 = £12\,814$

$$\text{Brokerage on this at } 1\tfrac{1}{2}\% = £12\,814 \times \frac{1.5}{100}$$

$$= £192.21$$

$$\text{Total cost of purchase } = £12\,814 + £192.21$$
$$= £13\,006.21$$

EXERCISE 116

Find the cost of buying the following shares:

1. 250 Glaxo 50 p shares at 478 p

2. 525 Tate & Lyle £1 shares at 204 p

3. 2400 Tesco 5 p shares at 56 p

4. 3500 Dunlop 50 p shares at 70 p

5. 724 Bowater £1 shares at 248 p

6. 543 Midland Bank £1 shares at 333 p

7.   973 Whitbread 25 p shares at 104 p

8.   457 Richard Costain 25 p shares at 268 p

9.   695 Chubb 20 p shares at 108 p

10. 3450 Campari 20 p shares at 59 p.

Find the amount received by selling the following shares:

11. 750 Rediffusion 25 p shares at 200 p

12. 435 Pearl Insurance 5 p shares at 380 p

13. 290 Dunhill 25 p shares at 250 p

14. 1250 Godfrey Davis 25 p shares at 89 p

15. 596 Comet 5 p shares at 104 p

16. 2400 Burton 50 p shares at 159 p

17. 3675 P & O £1 shares at 127 p

18. 982 Trafalgar House 20 p shares at 117 p

19. 739 Metal Box £1 shares at 174 p

20. 626 Unilever 25 p shares at 664 p.

21. How many £1 ordinary shares at 105 p may be bought for £441?

22. How many 50 p ordinary shares at 64 p may be bought for £112?

23. How many £1 ordinary shares at 478 p may be bought for £3011.40?

24. How many 25 p ordinary shares at 125 p may be bought for £992.50?

25. How many 50 p ordinary shares at 237 p may be bought for £760.77?

Find the purchase price of each of the following shares given that:

26. 420 £1 ordinary shares cost £504

27. 165 50 p ordinary shares cost £396

28. 275 £1 ordinary shares cost £440

29. 372 25 p ordinary shares cost £1607.04

30. 784 50 p ordinary shares cost £658.56.

Find the cost of, and income deriving from, the following preference shares:

31. 300 Guest Keen 5% (£1) shares at 150 p

32. 1240 ICI $7\frac{1}{2}$% (£1) shares at 300 p

33. 750 Lloyds Bank 8% (£1) shares at 460 p

34. 660 Tesco 9% (50 p) shares at 190 p

35. 25 000 Luxo 8% (50 p) shares at 550 p.

Find the income which will result from investing:

36. £330 in 8% £1 preference shares at 150 p

37. £1512 in 6% £1 preference shares at 360 p

38. £1215 in £1 ordinary shares at 225 p which pay a dividend of 12%

39. £2816 in 50 p ordinary shares at 320 p which pay a dividend of 8%

40. £1140.48 in 25 p ordinary shares at 88 p which pay a dividend of 15%.

Calculate the yield obtained by investing in:

41. 5% £1 preference shares at 250 p

42. 8% £1 preference shares at 160 p

43. 6% £1 preference shares at 240 p

44. $7\frac{1}{2}$% £1 preference shares at 90 p

45. 10% £1 preference shares at 250 p

46. £1 ordinary shares at 200 p paying 10%

47. £1 ordinary shares at 150 p paying 12%

48. £1 ordinary shares at 75 p paying 9%

49. 50 p ordinary shares at 200 p paying 16%

50. 50 p ordinary shares at 650 p paying 26%.

51. Mrs Jones invests £2511 in De La Rue shares at 465 p and sells when they have risen to 690 p. Calculate the profit.

52. A woman invests £3486 in Eagle Star 25 p ordinary shares at 415 p, and is forced to sell them when they have fallen to 378 p. How much does she lose?

53. John Strong bought 1665 Austin Reed 25 p shares at 82 p and sold them six months later when they had fallen to 67 p. How much did he lose?

54. An investor bought 354 Britannic Insurance shares at 214 p and sold when the price had risen to 288 p. Find the gain.

55. A father with £2000 to invest wants to buy Unilever ordinary shares at 674 p. Any unused cash he agrees to give to his son. How many shares is he able to buy? How much will his son receive?

56. Mr Davis invests £1069.50 in Glynwed 50 p shares at 138 p and is forced to sell when their price has fallen to 114 p. How much has he lost?

57. Mr Brown sells 1460 Boots $5\frac{1}{2}\%$ preference shares (£1) at 225 p and invests the proceeds in ICI 9% preference shares (£1) at 365 p. Calculate:
    (a) the number of ICI shares he is able to buy
    (b) his change in income.

58. Mr Garstang sells 936 Bryant's £1 ordinary shares, which pay a dividend of 6%, at 204 p. The resulting cash is invested in Callgood 50 p ordinary shares at 221 p which pay a dividend of 12%. Calculate:
    (a) How many Callgood shares he is able to buy
    (b) his annual change in income.

59. Mrs Thomas sells 792 Civic £1 ordinary shares, which pay a dividend of 7%, at 235 p. She invests the proceeds in Downtown 25 p ordinary shares at 94 p. If these shares pay a dividend of 12%, calculate:
    (a) the number of Downtown shares purchased
    (b) the annual change in income.

60. Lord Stock sells 600 Nogood 50 p ordinary shares which pay a dividend of $7\frac{1}{2}\%$, at 176 p. He invests the proceeds in Allard £1 ordinary shares at 275 p. If these shares pay a dividend of 7%, calculate:
    (a) the number of Allard shares purchased
    (b) the annual change in income.

61. Lady Singhe sells 1176 P & O 5% (£1) preference shares at 126 p, and with the proceeds is able to buy 336 Lloyds Bank (£1) ordinary shares which pay a dividend of 18%. Calculate:
    (a) the cost of a Lloyds Bank share
    (b) the annual change in income.

62. A woman invested £4500 in Austin Reed 25 p shares paying a dividend of 8%, and costing 75 p each. When they had risen to 95 p she sold them and invested the proceeds in British Leyland 50 p shares at 20 p which paid a dividend of $1\frac{1}{4}\%$. How many British Leyland shares did she buy and what was the change of income?

Calculate the cost, income and yield per cent from:

63. 800 Woolworth 25 p shares at 60 p when the dividend is 5%

64. 950 Vickers £1 shares at 165 p when the dividend is 8%

65. 432 British Home Stores 25 p shares at 145 p when the dividend is $12\frac{1}{2}\%$

66. 2340 Thorn EMI 25 p shares at 440 p paying a dividend of 20%

67. 764 Currys 25 p shares at 174 p paying a dividend of 16%.

68. Alcock & Brown have a capital value of £800 000 made up as follows:

    100 000 $7\frac{1}{2}$% £1 preference shares
    700 000 £1 ordinary shares

    If the total net profits in a particular year amount to £63 500, calculate the dividend on the ordinary shares.

69. Colman & Co. have issued capital made up as follows:

    50 000 $7\frac{1}{2}$% first preference shares at £1
    100 000 9% second preference shares at £1
    500 000 £1 ordinary shares

    Calculate the dividend on the ordinary shares in a year when the net profits amount to £72 750, and hence find the income received by an investor holding 950 ordinary shares.

70. Thomas & Evans have issued capital made up as follows:

    200 000 4% first preference shares at £1
    350 000 $5\frac{1}{2}$% second preference shares at £1
    800 000 25 p ordinary shares

    Calculate the dividend on the ordinary shares in a year when the net profits amount to £55 250. If the ordinary share is valued at 70 p, calculate the yield per cent.

71. Mr Millard sells 3000 £1 shares, paying a dividend of 16%, at 240 p each. He reinvests $\frac{2}{3}$ of the proceeds in some 50 p shares at 192 p which pay a dividend of 8%, and the remainder in a Government 7% stock at 32. Calculate:
    (a) the amount of new stock bought
    (b) the change in his annual income.

72. Two brothers John and Edgar each have £5000 to invest. John buys 'blue chip' industrial £1 shares costing 625 p each which pay a dividend of 12%, while his brother invests in a Government $3\frac{1}{2}$% stock at 40. After 1 year the blue chip has risen to 685 p and the Government stock to 42. If the brothers now sell, which one has made the better investment (including income) and by how much?

73. Jane and Allison are each given £1200 to invest. Jane buys 50 p shares in a grocery company at a cost of 160 p each, the company paying a dividend of 18%. Allison invests her money in War Loan $3\frac{1}{2}$% stock at 48. If the War Loan dividend is paid without deduction of income tax, but the company dividend is paid *after* deduction of tax at 30%, find the income payments made to each.

74. Dr Ali sells 2048 50 p shares at 252 p which pay a dividend of 18%. He invests $\frac{3}{4}$ of the proceeds in some £1 shares at 256 p which pay a dividend of 12%, and the remainder in 25 p shares at 63 p which pay a dividend of 6%. Calculate his change in income.

If, 1 year later, the 50 p shares stood at 294 p, the £1 shares at 265 p and the 25 p shares at 80 p, was it wise to sell or should Dr Ali have held his original shares?

75. The following table gives details of shares held by Mr McKay:

SHARE	NO. OF SHARES HELD	PRICE AT BEGINNING OF YEAR	PRICE AT END OF YEAR	DIVIDEND
Brown & Co. £1	524	467 p	502 p	16%
Readimade 50 p	156	79 p	52 p	$5\frac{1}{2}$%
Straightcut 25 p	760	213 p	296 p	20%
Cooksey & Son £1	446	374 p	342 p	14%

Use this information to calculate:
(a) his income from these shares during the year
(b) the amount by which the value of his *capital* increases during the year.

If he had sold all his shares at the beginning of the year and invested the proceeds in a building society paying 8%, would he have been better or worse off? (Include all income payments.)

76. Mr Garrett buys 573 £1 ordinary shares in Johnson & Co. at 392 p. How much will this cost him including brokerage at $1\frac{1}{2}$%?

77. Mrs Black buys 388 50 p ordinary shares in Dombey & Son at 176 p. How much will this cost her including brokerage at $1\frac{1}{4}$%?

78. Mr Green sells 1362 50 p shares in Newmonk & Co. at 74 p each. How much will he receive from the sale allowing for brokerage at $1\frac{1}{2}$%?

79. Miss Ratner sells 487 25 p Eagle Star ordinary shares at 375 p. How much will she receive allowing for brokerage at $1\frac{1}{4}$%?

80. David Thomas sells 510 £1 ordinary shares at 260 p each and invests the proceeds in 25 p ordinary shares at 196 p. If the brokerage is 2% whether buying or selling, calculate how many 25 p shares he is able to buy.

BANKRUPTCY

When someone's financial position becomes quite hopeless, i.e. when debts (*liabilities*) become much greater than income (*assets*), legal proceedings may be taken against the person resulting in his or her being declared a *bankrupt*. The object of the bankruptcy laws is to free the debtor whose financial position has become impossible. The bankrupt's assets are divided as fairly as possible between the people or companies to whom he or she is indebted, i.e. the *creditors*. A bankruptcy settlement releases the bankrupt from all further liability for those debts.

Creditors are called secured creditors, for example a banker who holds securities for an overdraft; preferential creditors, such as the Inland Revenue who will require the taxes for the previous year(s) to be paid; or the more common unsecured creditors, who are paid in proportion to the bankrupt's debt to them after the other creditors have been paid in full.

If a bankrupt has total assets of £50 000 but total debts or liabilities of £200 000 then the *dividend* or rate in the £ which it would be possible to pay would be:

$$£\frac{50\ 000}{200\ 000} = 25\,p$$

i.e. a creditor who was owed £1200 would receive 25 p for each £1 of the debt i.e. $25 \times 1200\,p = £300$.

EXAMPLE 10   A bankrupt has assets of £62 968 and a dividend of 34 p is declared. Calculate the liabilities.

Since the declared dividend is 34 p in the £, an asset of 34 p will cover a debt of £1

i.e. Assets of £62 968 will cover debts of:

$$£\frac{62\ 968}{0.34} = £185\ 200$$

∴ Total liabilities = £185 200

EXAMPLE 11   The assets of a bankrupt are £22 176. If £12 530 is due to the Inland Revenue in unpaid taxes and £34 450 is owed to unsecured creditors, what dividend can be paid? If an unsecured creditor receives £242.48, how much did the bankrupt owe the creditor?

Total assets of bankrupt $= £22\,176$

Debts which must be paid in full $= £12\,530$

$\therefore$ Cash remaining to pay
unsecured creditors $= £22\,176 - £12\,530$

$= £9646$

Dividend or rate in the £
available to unsecured creditors $= \dfrac{\text{available assets}}{\text{liabilities}}$

$= £\dfrac{9646}{34\,450}$

$= £0.28$

$\therefore$ Dividend payable is 28 p in the £

28 p or £0.28 is paid to a creditor on a debt of £1

$\therefore$ £242.48 is paid to a creditor on a debt of

$£\dfrac{242.48}{0.28} = £866$

Thus if the creditor receives £242.48 cash, the
bankrupt owed the creditor £866.

EXERCISE 117

What rate in the £ is a bankrupt with the given assets and liabilities able
to pay in each of the following cases?

1. Assets £1967, liabilities £5620

2. Assets £1719, liabilities £9550

3. Assets £2982, liabilities £42 600

4. Assets £6699, liabilities £23 100

5. Assets £11 343, liabilities £59 700

6. Assets £17 802, liabilities £77 400

7. Assets £26 176, liabilities £163 600

8. Assets £26 433, liabilities £293 700

9. Assets £81 136, liabilities £737 600

10. Assets £1 118 229, liabilities £5 324 900.

The following questions give a bankrupt's assets together with the rate
in the £ that can be paid to the creditors. In each case calculate the
bankrupt's liabilities.

11. Assets £8688, rate in the £   16 p

12. Assets £2889, rate in the £   9 p

13. Assets £7689, rate in the £   11 p

14. Assets £8325, rate in the £   15 p

15. Assets £34 270, rate in the £   23 p

16. Assets £50 337, rate in the £   17 p

17. Assets £11 194, rate in the £   29 p

18. Assets £54 444, rate in the £   13 p

19. Assets £180 704, rate in the £   32 p

20. Assets £294 462, rate in the £   14 p.

Find the total assets of a bankrupt who has the given liabilities and is able to pay the given rate in the £ in each of the following cases:

21. Liabilities £8260, rate in the £   15 p

22. Liabilities £15 340, rate in the £   15 p

23. Liabilities £42 400, rate in the £   23 p

24. Liabilities £36 920, rate in the £   25 p

25. Liabilities £66 450, rate in the £   16 p

26. Liabilities £53 350, rate in the £   24 p

27. Liabilities £17 200, rate in the £   8 p

28. Liabilities £95 250, rate in the £   12 p

29. Liabilities £1 372 000, rate in the £   19 p

30. Liabilities £5 240 000, rate in the £   27 p.

31. A bankrupt with assets of £2388 must pay £1328 to secured creditors. If liabilities to unsecured creditors amount to £4240, how much in the £ will they receive?

32. Mr White is declared a bankrupt with assets of £3751 and must pay the sum of £2456 in full to secured creditors. How much is he able to pay to a creditor who is owed £1720 if the total liabilities of unsecured creditors amount to £9250?

33. A small bankrupt grocery business with assets of £21 052 must pay £15 000 to secured creditors. If they are able to pay 17 p in the £ to unsecured creditors, calculate the total liabilities.

34. A leisure company is declared bankrupt with assets of £33 218. The company must pay £6596 to the Inland Revenue in outstanding taxes, after which it is able to pay unsecured creditors a rate of 27 p in the £. How much did the company owe to unsecured creditors?

35. A bankrupt with liabilities of £204 300 was able to pay unsecured creditors 9 p in the £. If a tax debt of £12 763 was also paid in full, calculate the bankrupt's total assets.

36. A bankrupt office machines company with assets of £52 356 must pay £24 500 to the bank as a secured creditor, plus £16 597 in taxes to the Inland Revenue as a preferential creditor, before a dividend can be calculated for the unsecured creditors. If the total liabilities for the unsecured creditors amount to £62 550, what rate in the £ can be declared? How much would a creditor who is owed £5794 receive?

37. A week before Mr Evans was declared a bankrupt, Mr Brown delivered goods to him valued at £4950. When the dividend payments were made Mr Brown received £1584. If Mr Evans' total assets were £17 622 including £5830 due to secured creditors, calculate the dividend in the £ paid, and his total liabilities.

38. The total assets of Poppy, Gunn & Co. Ltd when it was liquidated amounted to £15 404. If expenses of £1924 were paid, followed by £6767 to secured creditors, what dividend can be declared for the unsecured creditors to whom the company has debts of £47 950?

39. When Black, White & Co. were forced into liquidation their assets were sold for £46 481. After expenses of £2792 were paid, and £16 473 had been paid to secured creditors, a dividend of 28 p in the £ was paid to unsecured creditors. Find the total liabilities of the company when they were liquidated.

40. When Rekal Airways went bankrupt its liabilities were £65 028 181 while its assets only amounted to £20 710 000. £5 750 000 was owed to an aircraft manufacturing company who were secured creditors, and £2 460 000 was due in unpaid taxes. What rate in the £ was declared? How much could an oil company who were owed £595 400 for fuel expect to receive?

25

IMPERIAL UNITS

Imperial units have been in use in the United Kingdom for a very long time. While we are gradually changing to the SI system, some knowledge of the imperial system is still very useful. Some industries and many shops and markets still measure in imperial units.

No worked examples are given. All the necessary techniques have been considered earlier in the book.

Length:	12 inches (in.) = 1 foot
	3 feet (ft) = 1 yard
	1760 yards (yd) = 1 mile
Area:	144 square inches (in.^{2}) = 1 square foot
	9 square feet (ft^2) = 1 square yard
	4840 square yards (yd^2) = 1 acre
Volume:	1728 cubic inches (in.^{3}) = 1 cubic foot
	27 cubic feet (ft^3) = 1 cubic yard
Capacity:	8 pints = 1 gallon
Mass (Weight):	16 ounces (oz) = 1 pound
	14 pounds (lb) = 1 stone (st)
	112 lb = 1 hundredweight (cwt)
	20 cwt = 1 ton

LENGTH

EXERCISE 118

Express in inches:

1. 2 ft
2. 3 ft 4 in.
3. 5 ft 9 in.
4. 10 ft 5 in.
5. $3\frac{1}{2}$ ft
6. $4\frac{3}{4}$ ft

7. $7\frac{1}{3}$ ft **8.** 2 yd 2 ft **9.** 3 yd 1 ft 8 in.

10. 4 yd 9 in. **11.** 1 yd 2 ft 7 in. **12.** 16 yd 1 ft 5 in.

Express in feet and inches:

13. 156 in. **14.** 300 in. **15.** 648 in. **16.** 256 in.

17. 137 in. **18.** 724 in. **19.** 936 in. **20.** 1000 in.

How many yards are there in:

21. 2 miles **22.** half a mile

23. three-quarters of a mile **24.** $3\frac{1}{4}$ miles

25. 14 miles **26.** 26 miles 385 yd?

27. Find the perimeter of a square of side 7 in.

28. Find the perimeter of a square of side 1 ft 4 in.

29. Find the perimeter of a rectangle measuring (a) 6 in. by 4 in., (b) 1 ft 2 in. by 10 in.

30. The perimeter of a square is 3 ft 4 in. Find the length of one side.

31. The perimeter of a square is 1 yd 2 ft 8 in. Find the length of one side.

32. A circle has a radius of 35 in. Find its circumference. $(\pi = 3\frac{1}{7})$

33. A bicycle wheel has a 28 in. diameter. How far will the bicycle move forward for each revolution of the wheel? How many revolutions will the wheel make in travelling 1 mile? $(\pi = \frac{22}{7})$

34. A bicycle wheel has a diameter of 14 in. How far, in miles, will the bicycle travel if each wheel makes 5280 revolutions? $(\pi = \frac{22}{7})$

35. If 1 in. = 2.54 cm, express the following distances in centimetres (a) 1 foot, (b) 1 yard, (c) 1 ft 3 in., (d) 2 yd 1 ft 5 in.

36. The length of the Olympic marathon is 26 miles 385 yd. If 1 yard is approximately equal to 0.914 metres, find the length of the marathon in (a) metres, (b) kilometres. Give each answer correct to three significant figures.

37. On a map the scale is given as 2 inches to 1 mile. Express this in the form $1:n$. How far apart will two villages be which are 4.5 in. apart on the map?

38. On a map the scale is given as $\frac{1}{10}$ inch to the mile. Express this in the form $1:n$. What distance on this map will separate two towns 26 miles apart?

39. If 1 metre = 39.4 in., how many feet are there in a kilometre? Give your answer correct to three significant figures.

40. Find the difference in inches between 100 metres and 100 yards, if 1 metre = 39.4 inches.

Area

Exercise 119

Find the area of the rectangles with the following dimensions. Give your answer in the units given in brackets.

	LENGTH	BREADTH	
1.	5 in.	3 in.	(in.^{2})
2.	14 in.	9 in.	(in.^{2})
3.	7 in.	6 in.	(in.^{2})
4.	$6\frac{1}{2}$ in.	4 in.	(in.^{2})
5.	18 in.	12 in.	(ft^2)
6.	4.5 in.	2.5 in.	(in.^{2})
7.	3.4 in.	2.6 in.	(in.^{2})
8.	2 ft	8 in.	(in.^{2})
9.	3 ft 6 in.	2 ft 6 in.	(ft^2)
10.	5 ft 9 in.	3 ft 3 in.	(ft^2).

Find the area of the triangles with the following dimensions. Give your answer in the units given in brackets.

	LENGTH OF BASE	PERPENDICULAR HEIGHT	
11.	8 in.	6 in.	(in.^{2})
12.	14 in.	8 in.	(in.^{2})
13.	10 ft	6 ft	(ft^2)
14.	5 ft	3 ft	(ft^2)
15.	9 yd	5 yd	(yd^2)
16.	2 ft	18 in.	(ft^2)
17.	4 ft	27 in.	(ft^2)
18.	3 yd	2 ft	(ft^2)
19.	2 yd	2 ft 6 in.	(ft^2)
20.	1 yd 8 in.	2 ft 3 in.	(in.^{2}).

21. A path 12 yd long and 4 ft wide is to be laid using square paving slabs of side 2 ft. How many slabs are required?

22. A rectangular lawn measuring 44 ft by 27 ft is surrounded by a uniform path 1 yd wide. Find, in square yards, the area of (a) the lawn, (b) the path.

23. The floor of a room measuring 28 ft by 14 ft is to be covered with wooden blocks measuring 6 in. by 3 in. How many blocks are needed?

24. A rectangular pitch measuring 110 yd by 80 yd is used for rugby. Find its area in (a) square yards, (b) acres (correct to three significant figures).

25. A farm has an area of 34 acres. If each animal the farmer intends to keep requires on average a minimum of 5000 yd^2, what is the maximum number of animals the farmer should keep?

26. A circle has a diameter of 28 in. Find its area. $(\pi = \frac{22}{7})$

27. A circle has a radius of 63 in. Find its area in (a) in.^{2}, (b) ft^2. $(\pi = \frac{22}{7})$

28. Find the radius of a circle which has an area of 1386 in^2. $(\pi = \frac{22}{7})$

29. Find the radius of a circle which has an area of $38\frac{1}{2}$ ft^2.

30. On a map the scale is given as 1 inch to 1 mile. Express this ratio in the form $1:n$. What area on the map will represent an area of 10 square miles?

31. On a map the scale is given as 4 inches to 1 mile. Express this ratio in the form $1:n$. What area is represented by an area of 4 square inches on the map? Give your answer in acres.

32. If 1 in. = 2.54 cm, how many square centimetres are there in (a) a square inch, (b) a square foot, (c) a square yard? Give all answers correct to three significant figures.

33. If 1 yd = 0.914 metres, how many square metres are there in (a) a square yard, (b) a square foot? Give your answers correct to three significant figures.

34. How much larger, in square inches, is a circular flower bed 2 metres in diameter than one which is 2 yards in diameter? (Take 1 m = 39.4 in.)

35. The diagram shows the cross-section through a piece of wood which is 2 ft long. The cross-section is in the shape of a trapezium through which is bored a hole of diameter $3\frac{1}{2}$ in. If the dimensions of the trapezium are as given in the diagram, calculate:
    (a) the area of the circle which is removed (take $\pi = \frac{22}{7}$)
    (b) the area of cross-section of the timber
    (c) the volume of the wood in cubic feet, giving your answer correct to three significant figures.

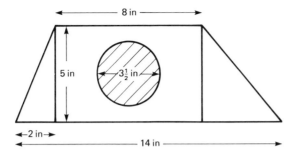

VOLUME AND CAPACITY

EXERCISE 120

1. Find the volume of a cube if the length of each edge is (a) 3 in., (b) 5 in., (c) 8 in.

2. How many 6 in. cubes can be made from a cubic foot of lead?

3. How many 12 in. cubes can be made from a cubic yard of timber?

4. What is the volume of a rectangular block measuring 8 in. by 7 in. by 3 in.?

5. Find the volume of a brick which measures 9 in. by $4\frac{1}{2}$ in. by 3 in. How many bricks would be required to build a pillar which has a volume of $1\,yd^3$?

6. Find the volume of a concrete block which measures 18 in. by 9 in. by 3 in. If 288 blocks are required to build a wall, find the volume of the wall in cubic yards.

7. A certain wood costs £27 per cubic foot. What would be the price of a 12 ft length of wood if its cross-section was a rectangle measuring 4 in. by 1 in.?

8. The carrying space of a lorry is in the shape of a cuboid measuring 5 yd by 3 yd by 2 yd. How many rectangular boxes measuring 1 yd by 1 yd by $\frac{1}{2}$ yd could be loaded on to this lorry?

9. How many cubes, each with a volume of 10 in.^{3} would fit into a hollow cube with an internal edge of 10 in.?

10. A room has sufficient space for 24 people on the assumption that each person needs $120\,ft^3$ of air space. If the room measures 18 ft by 16 ft, how high is the ceiling?

11. My cold water tank is 3 ft long with square ends of side 2 ft. How many gallons of water will it hold when full? ($1\,ft^3 = 6.24$ gallons)

12. 500 gallons of water are poured into an empty rectangular tank which is 8 ft long and 3 ft wide. Find the depth of water. (1 ft^3 = $6\frac{1}{4}$ gallons)

13. A milk lorry carries 960 milk crates, each crate containing 24 one pint bottles. How many gallons of milk have been loaded?

14. If a gallon of oil has a mass of $8\frac{1}{2}$ lb, find the mass in hundredweights of 500 gallons of oil. Give your answer correct to the nearest whole number.

15. A water tank holds 800 gallons. If a gallon of water has a mass of 10 lb, how many gallons remain after 12 cwt of water has been drawn off?

MASS (WEIGHT)

In accordance with common practice, no distinction is made between mass and weight in this exercise.

EXERCISE 121

Express in ounces:

1. 3 lb	2. 7 lb	3. $5\frac{1}{2}$ lb
4. $3\frac{3}{4}$ lb	5. 8 lb 2 oz	6. 12 lb 14 oz
7. 21 lb 3 oz	8. 6 lb 7 oz	9. 9 lb 10 oz.

Express in pounds:

10. 4 st	11. 11 st	12. 9 st
13. 8 st 7 lb	14. 6 st 3 lb	15. 18 st 10 lb
16. 5 st 3 lb	17. 15 st 8 lb	18. 25 st 6 lb
19. 5 cwt	20. 12 cwt	21. $3\frac{1}{2}$ cwt
22. 2 cwt 4 st	23. 3 cwt 5 st	24. 8 cwt 7 st
25. 8 tons	26. 5 tons 12 cwt	27. 3 tons 4 cwt
28. 15 tons 11 cwt	29. 8 tons 2 cwt	30. 10 tons 16 cwt.

If 1 lb is approximately equal to 0.454 kilograms, express the following in kilograms correct to three significant figures:

31. 2 lb	32. 5 lb	33. 14 lb
34. $8\frac{1}{2}$ lb	35. $12\frac{1}{4}$ lb	36. $24\frac{3}{4}$ lb.

If 1 ton is approximately equal to 1.016 tonnes, express the following in tonnes correct to three significant figures:

37. 5 tons

38. 12 tons

39. 53 tons

40. $8\frac{1}{2}$ tons

41. $4\frac{1}{3}$ tons

42. $16\frac{3}{4}$ tons.

43. The combined weight of a father and his son is 19 st 6 lb. If the father has a weight of 11 st 13 lb, what is the weight of the son?

44. The total weight of a lorry and its load is 14 tons 1 cwt 60 lb. When one-third of its load has been delivered, the total weight is reduced to 11 tons 60 lb. Find the weight of the lorry.

45. A lorry leaves the depot carrying a 10 ton load of coal. It makes deliveries of 2 tons 8 cwt, 1 ton 12 cwt, 3 tons 17 cwt and 11 cwt. What weight remains on the lorry?

46. What is the cost of a 6 lb chicken at 56 p per pound?

47. What is the cost of a 15 lb turkey at 85 p per pound?

48. What is the cost of a 12 lb 4 oz turkey at 96 p per pound?

49. Find the price of a joint of beef weighing 5 lb 8 oz at 188 p per lb.

50. Find the cost of $4\frac{1}{2}$ oz of cooked ham at 146 p per pound.

51. The suggested cooking time for roasting pork is 30 minutes to the pound. How long should be allowed to cook a joint weighing $3\frac{1}{2}$ lb?

52. The suggested cooking time for roasting beef is 40 minutes to the pound. How long should be allowed to cook a joint weighing 4 lb 4 oz?

53. A recipe book recommends a cooking time of 30 minutes per pound plus 30 minutes over, for a particular type of joint. How long would this mean for a joint weighing (a) $2\frac{1}{2}$ lb, (b) $5\frac{1}{2}$ lb?

54. A van capable of carrying 6 cwt is loaded with boxes each of weight 32 lb. What is the maximum number of boxes which should be loaded?

55. Which is the heavier, and by how much, a girl weighing 9 st 5 lb or a boy weighing 62.5 kg? (1 lb = 0.454 kg)

26
CHANGE OF UNITS

Frequently it is necessary to change from one set of units to another. For instance, we are used to seeing distance in miles on signposts in the United Kingdom whereas in Europe they are given in kilometres. Since most of us 'think' in miles it is useful to be able to convert from one unit to another.

A kilometre is approximately $\frac{5}{8}$ mile

$$\therefore \qquad 240 \, \text{km} = 240 \times \frac{5}{8} \, \text{miles} = 150 \, \text{miles}$$

Conversely: $\qquad 220 \, \text{miles} = 220 \times \frac{8}{5} \, \text{km} = 352 \, \text{km}$

A fairly easy way of converting kilometres into miles is as follows: find half the number of kilometres, then add one-quarter of this value. Work only in whole numbers.

e.g. $\qquad 40 \, \text{km} \approx 20 + 5 = 25 \, \text{miles}$

$$168 \, \text{km} \approx 84 + 21 = 105 \, \text{miles}$$

$$250 \, \text{km} \approx 125 + 31 = 156 \, \text{miles}$$

A slightly more difficult problem is to convert the cost of petrol in francs per litre into the more familiar pence per gallon.

EXAMPLE 1　　Petrol in France costs 2.85 francs per litre. If £1 ≡ 7.50 f., 1 litre = $1\frac{3}{4}$ pints and 8 pints = 1 gallon, calculate the equivalent price in pence per gallon.

Since we want our last line to read: 1 gallon costs ? pence, we write our initial line with volume first, followed by cost:

1 litre costs 2.85 f.

$1\frac{3}{4}$ pints cost 2.85 f.

1 pint costs $2.85 \times \dfrac{4}{7}$ f.

8 pints cost $2.85 \times \dfrac{4}{7} \times 8$ f.

1 gallon costs $2.85 \times \dfrac{4}{7} \times 8$ f.

1 gallon costs $£2.85 \times \dfrac{4}{7} \times \dfrac{8}{7.50}$

i.e. 1 gallon costs $2.85 \times \dfrac{4}{7} \times \dfrac{8}{7.50} \times 100\,$p $= 173.7\,$p

∴ Equivalent price of petrol is $173.7\,$p per gallon or $174\,$p correct to the nearest whole number

EXAMPLE 2

In Spain milk costs 48 pesetas per half litre. Find the equivalent cost in the United Kingdom in pence per pint, given that $£1 \equiv 180\,$pta. and 1 litre $= 1\frac{3}{4}$ pints.

We wish to end our solution with the line: 1 pint of milk costs ? pence. We therefore begin the first line with a volume, followed by the price:

0.5 litres of milk costs 48 pta.

1 litre of milk costs 96 pta.

$1\frac{3}{4}$ pints of milk costs 96 pta.

1 pint of milk costs $96 \times \dfrac{4}{7}$ pta.

1 pint of milk costs $£96 \times \dfrac{4}{7} \times \dfrac{1}{180}$

1 pint of milk costs $96 \times \dfrac{4}{7} \times \dfrac{100}{180}$p $= 30.48\,$p

∴ Equivalent price of milk is $30.48\,$p per pint i.e. $30\,$p correct to the nearest penny

EXERCISE 122

Use the following equivalents: 1 km $= \frac{5}{8}$ mile, 1 kg $= 2.2$ lb, 1 litre $= 1\frac{3}{4}$ pints, 1 gallon $= 8$ pints, 1 inch $= 2.54$ cm.

1. Express 60 mph in (a) kilometres per hour, (b) metres per second.

2. Express 70 km/h in metres per second.

3. Express 70 mph in (a) kilometres per hour, (b) metres per second.

4. Express 1500 km/h in miles per minute.

5. If a loaf of bread with mass 1.8 lb is sold in the United Kingdom for 60 p, find the equivalent cost in francs for a loaf of mass 1 kg if £1 ≡ 8 f.

6. Petrol in France costs 3.2 francs per litre. Find the equivalent UK price per gallon if £1 ≡ 9 f.

7. A length of cloth costs 900 lire per metre in Rome. What would be its price per yard in London if 1 metre = 1.094 yards and £1 ≡ 2200 L.

8. Beer costing 12.50 francs per litre in Paris is sold by the pint in London. Find its price correct to the nearest penny. (£ ≡ 8 f.)

9. Potatoes are sold in Italy at 580 lire per kilogram. Find the cost in pence per pound if £1 ≡ 2300 L.

10. A basket of canned foods averages 60 p per pound in a UK supermarket. What would be the equivalent price in West Germany in Deutschmarks per kilogram? (£1 ≡ DM 3.50)

11. In the United Kingdom milk costs 24 p per pint and in France it costs 1.70 f. per half litre. In which country is its cheaper? (1 f. ≡ 13 p)

12. The pressure in the tyre of a car is to be 32 lb per square inch. Find the equivalent pressure in kilograms per square centimetre. (1 lb = 0.454 kg)

13. The oil pressure in an engine should be 70 lb per square inch. Find the equivalent pressure in kilograms per square centimetre.

14. Petrol in West Germany costs 125 pfennigs a litre. If £1 ≡ DM 3.50, 1 Deutschmark = 100 pfennigs and 1 litre = 1.75 pints, find the equivalent cost of petrol in pence per gallon.

15. Petrol in the United States costs $3.20 per US gallon. If 1 US gallon = 0.83 UK gallons and $1 ≡ 55 p, find the equivalent cost in pence per gallon.

16. The cost of petrol in Brittany is 3 francs per litre. If $1 ≡ 4.58 f. and 1 US gallon = 3.79 litres, find the equivalent cost in dollars per US gallon.

17. An imperial gallon of petrol in the United Kingdom costs £2. Find the equivalent cost in the United States in dollars per US gallon. (£1 ≡ $1.79, 1 imperial gallon = 1.20 US gallons)

18. Farmland costs £2000 per acre. If 1 acre = 0.001 563 square miles, and 1 mile = 1.61 km, find the cost of farmland per square kilometre.

19. Wine bought for 12 francs a litre is sold at 75 p per 30 centilitre glass. Find the profit (or loss) per cent. (£1 ≡ 8 f.)

20. Wine bought at 1500 f. per hectolitre is sold at £1.80 per pint. Find the gain (or loss) per cent. (£1 ≡ 10 f.)

21. In New York petrol is sold at $1.20 per US gallon. What would be the equivalent price in London? (£1 ≡ $1.90, 1 imperial gallon = 1.20 US gallons)

22. A 2 lb jar of jam costs 96 p. If 1 lb = 454 g and £1 ≡ 150 pta., find the cost per kilogram in pesetas.

23. A 500 g tin of tomatoes costs 650 lire in Italy. Find the equivalent cost per lb in the United Kingdom if £1 ≡ 900 L. and 1 lb = 454 g.

24. Gold bought at £100 per troy ounce is sold in francs per gram. Find its selling price if it is sold at a 50% profit. (12 troy ounces = 1 troy pound = 0.8229 lb, £1 ≡ 8.50 f., 1 lb = 454 g)

25. A plot of building land has an area of 60 acres and costs £5000 per acre. It is sold off in plots, each with an area of 0.04 hectares. Find the price of a plot if it is (a) sold at cost, (b) sold at a profit of 80%. (1 acre = 0.001 563 square miles, 1 mile = 1.6 km and 1 km^2 = 100 hectares)

REVISION PAPERS
76-100

PAPER 76

1. Find (a) the simple interest, (b) the compound interest, on £580 invested for 2 years at 14%.

2. The marked price of a washing machine is £320. If bought for cash, a discount of $2\frac{1}{2}\%$ is allowed. If bought under a hire-purchase agreement, the terms are: deposit of $\frac{1}{4}$ the marked price, plus 24 monthly repayments of £11.20. Calculate: (a) the cash price, (b) the hire-purchase price.

   How much is saved by paying cash?

3. The pie chart below shows how a family spend their weekly income of £176. How much does each slice stand for? How much is spent on (a) food, (b) the car, (c) entertainment?

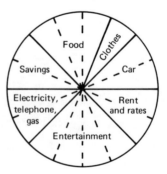

4. A thread of mercury, 13.5 cm long, is run out of a straight tube of uniform bore and found to have a mass of 0.1 g. Find the radius of the tube in millimetres, correct to three significant figures, given that 1 cm³ of mercury has a mass of 13.6 g. (Take $\pi = 3.142$)

5. A glass test tube may be considered as an open cylinder, internal diameter 1 cm, which is closed at one end by a hemispherical glass shell. If 6 cm^3 of liquid is poured into the upright test tube, calculate:

(a) the depth of the liquid
(b) the area of glass in contact with the liquid.

PAPER 77

1. A shopkeeper pays £65 for a bicycle and marks it up so that he makes a profit of 30%. Find the selling price. If he reduces all goods in his shop by 10% in a sale, how much profit will he then make on the bicycle?

2. Simplify $\left(\dfrac{5}{7} + \dfrac{3}{4}\right) \div \left(\dfrac{3}{4} - \dfrac{1}{3}\right)$.

3. How long is it necessary to invest £730 at 12% simple interest to give £481.80 in interest?

4. On a day when £1 was worth 1.695 US dollars and 9.64 French francs find the value of 1200 f. in dollars. Give your answer correct to three significant figures.

5. A cylindrical cooking pot has a diameter of 44 cm and is 30 cm deep. It contains soup to one-third of its depth which is served to campers in a hemispherical ladle of diameter 9 cm. How many campers may be served if each receives one full ladle?

PAPER 78

1. Simplify (a) 0.05×0.2, (b) $0.05 \div 0.2$, (c) $0.2 - 0.05$.

2. A salesman receives a basic wage of £40 per week, plus commission at $1\frac{1}{2}\%$ on the value of goods sold in excess of £5000. How much will he earn in a week when he sells goods to the value of £23 000?

3. On a working day a factory worker estimates that he spends 8 hours working, 7 hours sleeping, 2 hours eating, 2 hours watching TV, 3 hours gardening and the remainder in other ways. Draw a pie chart to illustrate this information.

4. Find the cost of 750 General Electric Company 25 p shares at 915 p each. If a dividend of $10\frac{1}{2}\%$ is declared, what income will these shares give?

5. A woman's take-home pay is £615 per month after deductions. These deductions, which are all based on gross salary, are: company pension scheme at 6%, national insurance contributions at 8% and income tax at 30% after the first £2200 each year. Calculate her gross annual salary.

PAPER 79

1. (a) What is the rate of simple interest if £1050 amounts to £1407 in 4 years?
   (b) In a local election Brown receives $\frac{1}{4}$ of the votes, Smith $\frac{1}{5}$, Thomas $\frac{2}{5}$ and White $\frac{1}{20}$. The remaining votes cast, which amounted to 86, were spoilt. Who won the election? What was the winner's majority?

2. A school Outdoor Pursuits group left school at 8.45 a.m. on a Saturday morning for a walk. The graph representing their journey is shown below. Use this graph to determine:
   (a) the time they returned to school
   (b) the total time spent resting
   (c) the fastest speed at which they walked
   (d) their speed on the last section of the journey
   (e) the total length of the walk.

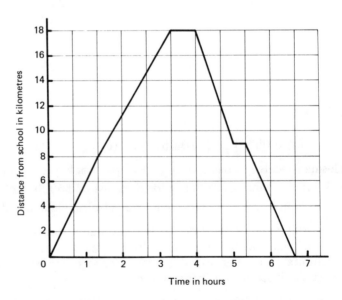

3. The cash price of a lawnmower is £128. The hire-purchase price is £32 deposit, together with 12 monthly instalments of £8.64. Calculate the amount saved by paying cash.

4. In a factory producing pumps it takes a workforce of 250 working a 38 hour week to produce 6650 pumps. How large a workforce would be required to produce 7056 pumps if they worked a 36 hour week?

5. A shopkeeper sold switches at a profit of 40% but when he reduced his selling price by 10% he found that his sales increased by 60%. Find the percentage increase in (a) his takings, (b) his profit.

PAPER 80

1. (a) Express (i) $\frac{9}{16}$ as a decimal, (ii) 0.225 as a fraction in its lowest terms.
    (b) Express 40.0986 correct to (i) the nearest whole number, (ii) three significant figures, (iii) two decimal places.

2. Find the compound interest on £1020 invested for 3 years at $12\frac{1}{2}\%$.

3. Use a calculator to evaluate as a decimal correct to four decimal places, the sum of the first six terms of each of the following series:
    (a) $\dfrac{1}{1\times2}+\dfrac{1}{2\times3}+\dfrac{1}{3\times4}+\dfrac{1}{4\times5}+\ldots$
    (b) $\dfrac{1}{1\times2\times3}+\dfrac{1}{2\times3\times4}+\dfrac{1}{3\times4\times5}+\ldots$

4. Cylindrical tubing is made from copper which has a mass of 8.9 g per cubic centimetre. A particular central heating system uses 50 m of 25 mm diameter tube, the wall of which is 2 mm thick, together with 150 m of 5 mm diameter tube, the wall of which is 1.2 mm thick. Calculate the total mass of copper used in kilograms correct to three significant figures.

5. The liner *Canberra* sets sail from Southampton at 19.00 hours on a Saturday for New York which is 3100 nautical miles away. If she sails at a steady 25 knots, how long will the journey take? If New York time is 5 hours behind GMT, at what time (local time) will she arrive?

PAPER 81

1. A car travels 350 m on 15 cm³ of petrol. Express this rate of petrol consumption in kilometres per litre.

2. The ratio of the ages of two brothers is 5:6. If the older boy is 18 years old, how old is the younger one? What will be the ratio of their ages in 6 years' time?

3. The income from a penny rate in the borough of Newlands is £25 120. Find the rateable value of Newlands. If the council decide to levy a rate of 75.5 p in the £ for the year and my rates bill amounts to £196.30, find the rateable value of my house.

   The rateable value of my neighbour's house is £244. How much will he be expected to pay in rates?

   If the sum spent by the council on leisure amenities represents a rate of 15.4 p in the £, calculate the total sum spent on leisure in the year.

4. If a sum of money is invested at $11\frac{1}{2}\%$ simple interest, how many complete years must elapse before the total interest is larger than the sum invested?

5. A lorry driver is paid at a basic rate of £3.50 per hour for a $37\frac{1}{2}$ hour working week. Calculate his basic wage.

   Overtime is paid at the rate of time-and-a-quarter Monday to Friday, and time-and-a-half on a Saturday. Find his total wage for a week when he works an extra 2 hours on each of Thursday, Friday and Saturday.

PAPER 82

1. Find the sum of money which amounts to £4287.50 if invested for 6 years at $12\frac{1}{2}\%$ simple interest.

2. Evaluate $\left(5\dfrac{5}{8} \times \dfrac{3}{14}\right) \div \left(\dfrac{3}{4} + \dfrac{3}{14}\right)$.

3. Taking 1 litre = 1.76 pints and £1 ≡ 8.24 f. find, in pence per pint, the equivalent cost of wine which sells at 12.50 f. per 75 centilitre bottle in France.

4. An ink bottle 6.5 cm high contains $50\,\text{cm}^3$ of ink. How much would a similar bottle 7.8 cm high contain?

5. The value of a machine depreciates each year by 15% of its value at the beginning of the year. If its purchase price is £4500, what will it be worth after 3 years? Give your answer correct to the nearest pound.

PAPER 83

1. (a) Multiply 0.045 21 by 0.12.
   (b) Divide 0.003 312 by 460.

   Give each answer in standard form.

2. Divide 7.05 into two parts, one of which is 1.105 larger than the other.

3. The rateable value of my house is £260 and that of my neighbour is £285. If my neighbour's rates for the year amount to £210.90, calculate (a) the rate in the £, (b) the amount I must pay in rates.

4. A solid sphere of radius 3 cm fits into a hollow cube so that it touches all six sides. Calculate the volume of unfilled space inside the cube.

5. The bar chart below shows the average number of hours of sunshine per day at a Mediterranean resort during the holiday period.
   (a) Which is probably the best month to go on holiday there?
   (b) What is the average number of hours of sunshine (i) per day, (ii) per week, during the month of August?
   (c) What is the average number of hours of sunshine per day over the whole period?

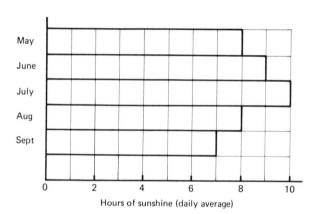

Hours of sunshine (daily average)

PAPER 84

1. (a) What is the least number which must be added to $5\frac{4}{7}$ to make it an integer?

   (b) What is the least number which must be subtracted from $8\frac{2}{7}$ to make it an integer which is a multiple of 3?

2. (a) Find the number of Unit Trust units which can be bought for £1147 if each unit costs 155 p.
   (b) Find the amount received by selling 860 units in a Unit Trust if the selling price is 86 p per unit.

3. Tyres for a small car cost £35.20 each plus VAT at 15%. If the life of a tyre is 42 000 km, calculate the cost per kilometre for tyres for the car, giving your answer in pence correct to three significant figures.

4. Local time in Bombay is $5\frac{1}{2}$ hours ahead of GMT and in New York is 5 hours behind GMT. Find:
   (a) the time in Bombay when it is 5 a.m. in New York
   (b) the time in New York when it is 5 a.m. in Bombay.

5. If 5 men *or* 7 women can make a certain machine in 37 hours, in what time will 5 men *and* 7 women make five such machines?

PAPER 85

1. Simplify $\left(\dfrac{3}{4}+\dfrac{5}{8}\right) \div \left(\dfrac{3}{4}-\dfrac{2}{3}\right)$.

2. Find:
   (a) the cost of buying 623 Pharmer 50 p shares at 126 p each,
   (b) the amount received by selling 416 Liqui 25 p shares at 87 p each.

3. In a certain year the first £2450 of Peter Walker's income was exempt from income tax, while the remainder was taxed at 30%. If he paid £2634 in tax, calculate his gross income.

4. A car takes $2\frac{3}{4}$ hours for a journey of 209 km. Calculate its average speed in (a) kilometres per hour, (b) miles per hour (8 km = 5 miles).

5. A hollow metal sphere has internal and external radii of 4.52 cm and 4.66 cm respectively. Calculate the volume of metal used. If 1 cm^3 of the metal has a mass of 8.6 g, calculate the mass of the sphere. Give each answer correct to three significant figures. ($\pi = 3.142$)

PAPER 86

1. If £1 ≡ $1.72, convert:
   (a) £185 into dollars
   (b) $838.50 into pounds.

2. If a manufacturer makes a profit of 25%, the wholesaler a profit of 40% and the shopkeeper a profit of 60%, what is the cost of making an article which is sold to the consumer for £14.56?

3. Calculate the volume of a sphere which has a surface area of 100 cm², giving your answer correct to three significant figures. ($\pi = 3.142$)

4. The basic premium for fully comprehensive cover for my car is £512. A reduction of $12\frac{1}{2}\%$ is allowed because I agree to pay the first £50 of each and every claim, and a no claim discount is allowed on the balance. How much will my premium be if:
   (a) I am on 20% no claim discount
   (b) I am on the full 60% no claim discount?

5. (a) Calculate the price of a 12% Government stock if it gives the same return on money invested as a 9% Government stock at 87.
   (b) Mr Hart invests £4140 in TP 25 p shares at 345 p and receives an annual income of £78. Calculate (i) the number of shares bought, (ii) the declared dividend.

PAPER 87

1. On a day when £1 was worth 430 yen and 188 pesetas, find the value of 1950 pesetas in yen, giving your answer correct to three significant figures.

2. Find the compound interest on £780 invested for 2 years at $14\frac{1}{2}\%$.

3. A motorcycle uses 25 cm³ of petrol to travel 550 m. Express this rate of consumption in kilometres per litre.

4. Wendy Lewis estimates that she watches television on average for $2\frac{1}{2}$ hours each evening Monday to Friday, and for 5 hours on each of Saturday and Sunday. If the annual licence fee is £80, calculate, correct to three significant figures, the cost of her viewing in pence per hour.

   What percentage of each week does she spend viewing?

5. A cylindrical jug, whose height is twice its diameter, will hold a volume of liquid equal to the sum of the volumes contained by two hemispherical glasses, one of radius 3 cm, the other of radius 3.5 cm. Find the height of the jug, giving your answer correct to three significant figures.

PAPER 88

1. John walks from home to school at 3 km/h and returns home at 4 km/h. Find his average speed for the whole journey.

2. A Unit Trust Company buys 2500 of its units from Mr Brown at 176.5 p each and sells them to Mr White for 182.4 p each. Calculate the gross profit made by the company.

3. The Smith household used 474 units of gas between 1 December and 1 March, each unit being equivalent to 1.038 therms. Gas is charged at 37 p per therm and there is a standing charge of £12.50 per quarter. How much does it cost them for gas during the quarter?

4. At what time between 5 and 6 o'clock are the hands of a grandfather clock together?

5. Mr and Mrs Parfit obtain a mortgage for £18 000 over 25 years. The monthly repayments are £11.82 per £1000 borrowed. Calculate (a) their total annual repayments, (b) their total repayments.

PAPER 89

1. What sum of money would amount to £846.75 if invested for $3\frac{1}{2}$ years at $11\frac{3}{4}\%$ simple interest?

2. A gold coin is bought for £150 and rises in value at 8% each year. How much will it be worth in 5 years' time?

3. (a) Calculate the exchange rate for pesetas if 26 505 pta. is equivalent to £142.50.
   (b) If £25 is equivalent to 91 Swiss francs, find (i) the value of 743 Swiss francs in pounds, (ii) the value of £270 in Swiss francs.

4. A house valued today at £42 000 is insured at a rate of £1 per £1000 by a policy which is index linked. If the inflation rate is 8%, calculate the annual premium (a) now, (b) last year, (c) next year, (d) the year after.

5. Peter Lee invested £4410 in 6% Government stocks at 90. When the stock had risen to $93\frac{1}{2}$ he sold and invested the proceeds in 9% Government stock at 98. Find his change in income.

PAPER 90

1. Evaluate $\dfrac{(0.2)^3}{0.48} \times \dfrac{2.43}{(0.3)^3}$.

2. (a) A 'printer's ream' of paper (516 sheets) is 12 cm thick. Calculate the thickness of a single sheet in millimetres, correct to three significant figures.

   (b) The speed limits on certain roads on the Continent are (i) 60 km/h, (ii) 70 km/h, and (iii) 90 km/h. What is the maximum integer (whole number) speed in mph within each of these limits?

3. Miss Roderick invested £2738 in Triley 25 p shares at 148 p which paid a dividend of 22%. How many shares did she buy and what was her annual income?

   At the same time Mr Witchel invested a sum of money in a Government 9% stock at 74 which gave him an annual income of £162. Calculate the amount of stock bought and the amount of cash invested.

   Calculate, correct to the nearest penny, the income which Miss Roderick and Mr Witchel received from each £100 invested.

4. A rectangular pane of glass measures 1.5 m by 95 cm and is 4 mm thick. If 1 cm^3 of glass has a mass of 2.6 g, calculate the mass of the pane in kilograms correct to three significant figures.

5. Two express trains, one in the United Kingdom and the other on the Continent, run at speeds of 125 mph and 195 km/h respectively. If 1 mile = 1.609 km, find the ratio of the speed of the UK train to that of the Continental train in the form $1:n$.

   What would be the difference in the time taken by the two trains to complete a journey of 300 miles?

PAPER 91

1. Simplify $\dfrac{2}{5} + \dfrac{1}{11}\left(\dfrac{2}{3} + \dfrac{4}{5}\right)$.

2. The population of a town increases by 12% each year. If the present population is 6272, what was the population (a) last year, (b) 2 years ago?

3. A Government 3% stock at 80 has 3 years to run before it will be redeemed at par. Including the six half-yearly dividends, calculate the profit on each £100 invested over the 3 year period.

4. In a factory a workforce of 200 produce 5016 articles when they work a 38 hour week. What workforce is required to produce 7236 articles if the working week is reduced to 36 hours?

5. In 1975 it cost £10.92 to produce an electric mixer. The cost was made up of labour, materials and administrative costs in the ratio 7:5:2. By 1985 the labour costs had trebled, the cost of materials had increased fourfold and the administrative costs had doubled. Calculate:
   (a) the 1975 cost of materials
   (b) the 1985 cost of materials
   (c) the 1985 cost of the mixer.

PAPER 92

1. (a) If 434 is a number in base 8, express it as a base 10 number.
   (b) Express the denary number 434 as a number in base 5.
   (c) Find the smallest whole number which is exactly divisible by 936 and 294.

2. Robert Parker wants to buy a new car, priced at £13 000, on hire-purchase. The terms at Northcar Motors are: deposit $\frac{1}{5}$, plus 36 monthly payments of £363; while the terms at Southcar Motors are: deposit $\frac{1}{6}$, plus 24 monthly payments of £536. Calculate the total cash difference in the terms offered by the two garages.

3. Mrs Comerford's motoring expenses for a year were: road tax £100, insurance £216, depreciation £650, fuel costs 3200 litres at 43 p per litre, servicing and repairs £174.
   If Mrs Comerford's car averages 12 km per litre, calculate:
   (a) the distance travelled during the year
   (b) the fuel costs for the year
   (c) the total motoring expenses for the year
   (d) the average cost per kilometre, giving your answer in pence correct to three significant figures.

4. George Chappel invests £30 000 in a country cottage. He spends a further £5000 on furniture and repairs and estimates that rates will amount to £175 per annum. He proposes to let the cottage and charge a rent which gives him a 10% return on his original outlay. What weekly rent should be charged if it is his intention to let the cottage for 25 weeks during the year?

5. £186 is to be divided between six boys and nine girls so that the ratio of a boy's share to a girl's share is 5:7. How much will each receive?
   What is the ratio of the total amount given to boys to the total amount given to girls?

PAPER 93

1. (a) Express 24.9375 m correct to (i) the nearest metre, (ii) the nearest centimetre, (iii) the nearest millimetre.

    (b) Divide 56 p in the ratio $\frac{1}{3} : \frac{1}{5}$.

2. Evaluate $\dfrac{\sqrt[3]{2.642} \times 0.94}{0.734^2 \times \sqrt{16.4}}$

    giving your answer correct to three significant figures.

3. When a shopkeeper sells an electric lamp for £53.10 he makes a profit of 18%. What must he sell it for in order to make a profit of 25%?

4. My last telephone bill showed that I had used 445 units of time at 5.6 p per unit. If the telephone rental was £16 for the quarter and VAT at 15% was added to the whole, calculate my telephone bill for the quarter.

5. Jim, Scott and Terry go for a day out together and agree to divide the expenses in the ratio $1 : 2 : 2$. If Scott paid £7.50 for petrol and Terry £10.35 for a meal, how much should Jim give to each of the other two?

PAPER 94

1. Find the smallest whole number which is exactly divisible by all the whole numbers up to and including 10.

2. A music centre is offered for sale at £425.50. If bought on hire-purchase the terms are: deposit $\frac{1}{4}$ plus £3.72 per week for 2 years. How much is saved by paying cash?

3. Peter John invests £3240 in British Transport 3% stock at 72. How much stock does he buy? How much will his annual income be from this stock?

4. A spherical soap bubble has a radius of 1.25 cm. If this radius increases by 25%, find:
    (a) the new external surface area
    (b) the percentage increase in surface area.

5. An insurance company offers a householder insurance cover at the following terms:

    House: £1 per £1000
    Contents: 30 p per £100
    'all risks': 90 p per £100

    If the householder estimates the value of his house to be £35 000 and the contents to be £12 000, £2500 of which is to be 'all risks', calculate the annual premium.

PAPER 95

1. Convert 28.5 knots into kilometres per hour, given that 1 knot = 1 nautical mile per hour, 1 nautical mile = 1.152 statute miles (i.e. miles measured overland) and 1 statute mile = 1.610 kilometres.

2. Find the income derived from investing £2420 in Cuboid 25 p ordinary shares at 275 p if the declared dividend is $22\frac{1}{2}\%$. Hence calculate the yield per cent, giving your answer correct to three significant figures.

3. Cliff Hall drives on average 65 000 km each year and his present car averages 55 km per gallon. If he changes his car to one which gives 46 km per gallon, calculate the increase in his petrol bill, if petrol costs £1.86 per gallon.

4. The electricity meter in the Sansom household reads 53643 on 1 January and 54315 on 1 April. How many units have been consumed during the quarter?

   If electricity is charged at 7.4 p per unit and there is a standing charge of £9.40 per quarter, calculate the cost of electricity for (a) the quarter, (b) an average week.

5. Local time in Moscow is 3 hours ahead of GMT while local time in Hong Kong is 8 hours ahead of GMT. Find:
   (a) the time in Hong Kong when it is 10 a.m. in Moscow
   (b) the time in Moscow when it is 4 p.m. in Hong Kong.

PAPER 96

1. Simplify (a) $\dfrac{5\frac{1}{5} \times 4\frac{1}{4}}{5\frac{1}{5} - 4\frac{1}{4}}$ (b) $\dfrac{\frac{5}{7} - \frac{2}{3}}{\frac{1}{6} \div \frac{3}{11}}$.

2. By selling potatoes at £5.72 a bag a wholesaler made a loss of 12%. What would he have gained or lost per cent if he had raised the price of a bag to £7.28?

3. The Grant household use 724 units of gas in a quarter, each unit being equivalent to 1.039 therms. If there is a standing charge of £11.75 and each therm costs 42 p, calculate the average weekly cost of gas for the Grant household, giving your answer correct to the nearest penny.

4. Joan runs from her home at 8 mph to post a letter and walks back at 3 mph. Calculate her average speed for the whole journey.

5. A hemispherical cut-glass salad bowl has an internal diameter of 22 cm and is everywhere 7.5 mm thick. If 5% of the original glass has been removed by the cutting of the design, calculate the volume of glass in the resulting bowl, giving your answer in cubic centimetres correct to three significant figures.

PAPER 97

1. One jug will hold $\frac{7}{11}$ of a litre and a second jug will hold $\frac{5}{9}$ of a litre. If the larger jug is filled and then used to fill the smaller jug, how much remains in the larger jug?

2. Mr Lubbock sells £4200 War Loan $3\frac{1}{2}\%$ stock at 30, and invests the proceeds in Gas $7\frac{1}{2}\%$ stock at 70. Find his change in income.

3. Kevin's motorcycle expenses last year were: road tax £40, comprehensive insurance £675, depreciation £300, fuel 1400 litres at 45 p per litre, servicing and repairs £42. If he had travelled 30 800 km, calculate:
   (a) his average distance travelled on 1 litre of fuel
   (b) his total fuel costs
   (c) his total costs
   (d) the overall cost per kilometre, giving your answer correct to the nearest penny.

4. A Swiss watch sells for 182.52 Swiss francs in Zurich. What would be its equivalent price in London if £1 $\equiv$ 3.12 Swiss francs?

5. A cylindrical hole of diameter 2.5 cm is bored centrally through a solid wooden cube of side 3 cm, the axis of the hole being perpendicular to the base of the cube. If each cubic centimetre of the wood has a mass of 0.85 g, find the mass of the resulting block, giving your answer in grams correct to three significant figures. ($\pi = 3.142$)

PAPER 98

1. Two similar solids have volumes of 1715 cm^3 and 320 cm^3 respectively. Find the ratio of (a) their linear dimensions, (b) their surface areas.

2. In a 100 m race Peter and Paul were timed at 11 s and 11.3 s respectively. How far ahead, in centimetres, was Peter when he passed the finishing tape?

3. In the Football League at the end of each season three clubs are promoted and three relegated, between the first and second divisions and between the second and third divisions, while four clubs are promoted and four relegated between the third and fourth divisions. How many clubs change divisions each season?

4. The distance around a rectangular field is 1.2 km and it is surrounded by a five-strand wire fence, each strand being 3 mm in diameter. If each cubic centimetre of the wire has a mass of 8.2 g, find the total mass of wire used in kilograms correct to three significant figures. ($\pi = 3.142$)

5. The diagram below shows an open metal mould which is used for casting concrete blocks measuring $30 \text{ cm} \times 20 \text{ cm} \times 10 \text{ cm}$. If the walls and base of the mould are 0.5 cm thick, calculate:
   (a) the volume of metal in the mould
   (b) the side of the resulting solid cube if the mould is melted down and recast without any change in volume.

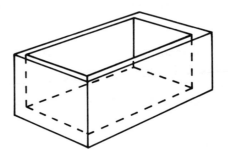

PAPER 99

1. Divide £2.52 between four girls in the ratio $5:6:8:9$. If the girl with the largest amount gives 18 p to the girl with the smallest amount, find the new ratio of the amounts the four girls now have.

2. Local time in Tokyo is 9 hours ahead of GMT whereas local time in Toronto is 5 hours behind. Find:
   (a) the time in Toronto when it is 12 noon in Tokyo
   (b) the time in Tokyo when it is 16.30 in Toronto.

3. Evaluate (a) $\dfrac{2.074 \times 199.2}{(13.64)^2}$, (b) $\sqrt[3]{\dfrac{826}{59.26 \times 39.61}}$.

4. A coach joined the motorway at 10 a.m. and travelled north at a steady speed of 100 km/h until 11.30 a.m. when it stopped at a service area. It remained there for 18 minutes and then continued its journey north at a steady speed of 90 km/h until it left the motorway at 1.08 p.m.

At 11.30 a.m. a car joined the motorway 90 km north of the service area and travelled south at a steady speed of 110 km/h.

Using suitable scales draw the two graphs and from them find:
(a) the time at which the car passed the service area
(b) when and where the coach and car passed
(c) the distance between the vehicles at 12.45 p.m.

5. A solid glass sphere has twice the mass of a solid metal sphere. If 1 cm^3 of the metal has a mass of 7.5 g and 1 cm^3 of the glass has a mass of 2.5 g, find the ratio of the radius of the glass sphere to the radius of the metal sphere in the ratio $x : 1$. Give x correct to three significant figures.

PAPER 100

1. (a) Convert 543_8 into a denary number.
   (b) Convert 368_{10} into an octal number.
   (c) Find the following, working only in octal numbers: (i) $4 + 6$, (ii) $24_8 + 12_8$, (iii) $24_8 - 12_8$, (iv) $24_8 \times 16_8$, (v) $124_8 \div 14_8$.

2. When the price of a set of china is increased by 12% its new price is £47.60. Find the cash increase.

   In a sale all marked prices are reduced by 10%. How much more (or less) is the sale price than the *original* price of the set?

3. Calculate the net income, after tax at 45% has been deducted, if £7820 is invested in Government $11\frac{3}{4}\%$ stock at 92. What yield (before tax) does this investment give? Give each answer correct to three significant figures.

4. How long does it take Judy to walk 4.5 km if she takes 100 steps of length 90 cm each minute?

5. A car loses 20 per cent of its value each year. It is now 2 years old and is valued at £9600. How much did it cost when new? What will be its value in 3 years' time?

EXAMINATION QUESTIONS PAPERS 1-15

PAPER 1

1. (a) A rectangular block of stone is 1.2 m long, 0.3 m wide and 0.2 m high. Calculate its volume in cubic metres.
    (b) A sum of £156 is to be divided between two people in the ratio 5 : 7. Calculate the amount received by each.
    (c) Taking 1.90 dollars as the equivalent of £1, find the equivalent in pounds of 760 dollars. (O & C)

2. (i) Calculate $1 \div 0.4$.
    (ii) Write 6×10^{-2} as a decimal, not in standard form.
    (iii) Express 0.0024 in the standard form $A \times 10^n$, where n is an integer and A is a number between 1 and 10.
    (iv) Given that $\dfrac{561 \times 27}{99} = 153$, find the exact value of $\dfrac{0.561 \times 2.7}{990}$.
    (AEB 1979)

3. Five hundred and twelve metal ball bearings of diameter 3 cm are melted down to form one sphere. Calculate the radius of this sphere.
    If 1 cm^3 of the metal weighs 9.21 g, calculate the weight of the sphere in kilograms.
    (Volume of a sphere of radius r is $\frac{4}{3}\pi r^3$ and take $\pi = 3.142$)
    (WJEC)

4. A cookery book gives the instructions for cooking a leg of lamb as 'Allow 20 minutes, together with 40 minutes per kilogram'

Find:
 (i) the time, in minutes, required to cook a joint of mass $2\frac{1}{2}$ kg
 (ii) the mass of a leg of lamb which can be cooked in 1 hour 50
      minutes
 (iii) the latest time a leg of lamb, which has a mass of 1.75 kg,
       should be placed in the oven to be cooked by 1300 hours
 (iv) the formula for the total cooking time, T minutes, for a leg of
      lamb of mass M kilograms. (AEB 1980)

5. A ship is 120 m long and a model of it is made on the scale of 1 to
   12. If the mast of the model is 1.5 m high, how high is the mast of
   the actual ship?

   If it costs £648 to paint part of the ship, how much will it cost to
   paint the corresponding part of the model?

   If the tank of the model holds 2 gallons of fuel oil, how much will
   the tank on the ship hold? (SU)

PAPER 2

1. (a) Without using tables, find the value of $9.388 \div 46$.
   (b) Subtract the binary number 1 1 0 1 from the binary number
       1 1 0 1 0, giving the answer in binary form.
   (c) 53 is a number to base 8. Express it as a number to base 2.
       (O & C)

2. (a) Find the weight of a cylindrical telegraph pole of length 10 m
       and radius 7 cm if 1 cm^3 of the wood from which it is made
       weighs 3 g. (Take $\pi = 3\frac{1}{7}$)
   (b) Find the rateable value of a town where a rate of 94 p in the £
       produces an income of £496 320.
   (c) Divide 85 in the ratio $2:3$ and also in the ratio $a:b$.
   (d) Two similar figures have volumes of 250 cm^3 and 54 cm^3.
       What are the ratios of (i) their linear dimensions, (ii) their
       surface areas? (SU)

3. A retailer selling machinery to his customers charges a basic retail
   price plus value added tax (VAT) which is a percentage of the
   basic retail price. In 1974, when the VAT rate was 8%, the basic
   retail price of machine A was £543 and the VAT on machine B
   was £94. Calculate:
   (i) the actual VAT paid by a customer buying machine A
   (ii) the basic retail price of machine B.

   In 1975 the VAT rate was increased to $12\frac{1}{2}\%$ and the retailer
   increased the price to the customer of machine B to £1377. Calculate:

447

(iii) the basic retail price of machine *B* in 1975

(iv) the increase in the basic retail price of machine *B* in 1975 and express this increase as a percentage of the basic retail price in 1974, giving the answer to the nearest tenth of one per cent.

Calculate also the actual increase in VAT on machine *B* from 1974 to 1975. (AEB 1979)

4. *ABCD* is the cross-section of a bar of metal with $AB = 6$ cm, $BC = 13$ cm, $AD = 12$ cm, and $D\widehat{A}B = A\widehat{D}E = D\widehat{E}B = 90°$.

If the bar is 1 m long calculate:
 (i) the length of *EC* and hence *DC*
 (ii) the area of the cross-section
 (iii) the volume of the bar of metal
 (iv) the weight of the bar of metal, in kilograms, given that 1 cm³ of metal weighs 2.3 grams. (WJEC)

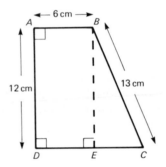

5. The figure below represents a lead 'sinker' consisting of a solid cone of height 2.8 cm, base radius 2.1 cm, attached to a solid hemisphere of the same radius. Calculate the weight of the sinker given that 1 cm³ of lead weighs 11.34 grams.

Assuming there is no wastage, how many such sinkers could be made from a cylindrical block of lead of height 112 cm and radius 31.5 cm? (The volume of a cone of height *h*, base radius *r* is $\frac{1}{3}\pi r^2 h$, and of a sphere of radius *r* is $\frac{4}{3}\pi r^3$; take $\pi = \frac{22}{7}$) (WJEC)

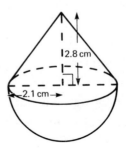

PAPER 3

1. Of the 28 pupils in a class, in an examination the top 10 have an average mark of 75.4. The average mark of the bottom 8 pupils is 18.25. Calculate the average mark of the remaining 10 pupils, if the average mark for the whole class is 49.　　　　(WJEC)

2. (a) Express as a fraction in its lowest terms $(\frac{3}{4} - \frac{2}{5}) \div 3\frac{1}{2}$.
   (b) Add the binary number $1\,0\,0\,1$ to the binary number $1\,0\,1\,1$, giving the answer as a number (i) to base 2, (ii) to base 10.
   (c) 52 is a number to base 8. Find the result of multiplying this number by 2, giving the answer as a number to base 8. (O & C)

3. A married couple wish to buy a three-piece suite for which the cash price is £230. It can be bought by means of a 10% deposit with simple interest charged on the balance. The interest and balance is paid by means of 52 weekly payments of £4.90. Calculate the total cost of the suite, and the rate of interest that is being charged, giving your answer to the nearest whole number.

   Alternatively, the cash price could be borrowed from the bank and repaid in twelve equal monthly payments, the rate of interest being 15% per annum charged on the initial loan. What would be each monthly repayment to the nearest penny?　　　　(SU)

4. A small open trough is made of thin plastic material. The trough has a horizontal rectangular base of length 50 cm and width 10 cm. Its ends are vertical and each is a trapezium with base 10 cm, sloping edges 13 cm and top edge 20 cm. Calculate:
   (i) the depth of the trough
   (ii) the maximum capacity of the trough in litres
   (iii) the area of the plastic material required to make the trough
   (iv) the volume of liquid in the trough when it is filled to one-third of the maximum depth.　　　　(JMB)

5. (a) A headmaster of a school with 450 pupils drew a graph to help him to change his daily attendances into percentages. Using 2 cm to represent 10% on one axis and 2 cm to 50 pupils on the other axis, draw this graph. Use your graph to find: (i) the percentage attendance, when the total attendance was 387, (ii) the number of pupils which would give a 94% attendance.
   (b) A solid sphere weighs 30 g. Calculate the weight, in kilograms, of a solid sphere of the same material whose radius is 5 times the radius of the given sphere.　　　　(WJEC)

PAPER 4

1. (a) Evaluate $13.4 \times 26.6 + 13.4^2$.
   (b) If 8.64 French francs = £1, express 3 francs in pence to the nearest penny.
   (c) 80 cm³ of liquid weighing 1.3 g per cm³ are mixed with 160 cm³ of liquid weighing 1.9 g per cm³. Find the weight of 1 cm³ of the mixture. (SU)

2. (a) For the first 15 miles of a 30 mile journey, the average speed of a car was 30 mph. If the journey was completed in 50 minutes, calculate the average speed of the car over the second 15 miles.
   (b) Calculate the compound interest on £20 000 invested for 2 years at $8\frac{1}{2}$% per annum.
   (c) One pipe delivers water at the rate of 2 gallons every 7 seconds, and a second pipe at 1000 gallons per hour. Calculate which pipe delivers water at the faster rate. (WJEC)

3. The figure below represents a rubber stopper of vertical height 4 cm which has been formed from a cone of solid rubber by removing the lower (i.e. dotted) part. The diameter at the top is 4 cm and at the bottom 2.2 cm. Calculate (a) the slant height of the stopper, (b) (using similar triangles) the vertical height of the cone of which the stopper was a part, (c) the volume of the stopper. (The volume of a cone, base-radius r, vertical height h is $\frac{1}{3}\pi r^2 h$; take $\pi = 3.142$) (WJEC)

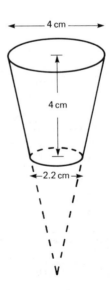

4. (a) A man went to France on holiday when the rate of exchange was 8.52 francs to the £. How many francs did he get for £75.50?

Whilst in France he bought a necklace for 80 francs which he could have obtained for £10 in England. Find the difference between the French and English prices of this necklace giving the answer in pence to the nearest penny.

He made a trip to Spain from France and changed 100 francs into 1720 Spanish pesetas. Calculate the equivalent rate of pesetas to the £ this change of cash represents.

(b) Given that $x^3 = \dfrac{2}{0.045\,71}$, use logarithms to calculate x.

(AEB 1979)

5. A motorist travelling at a steady speed along a motorway passed a point A at 12.00 noon. At 2.00 p.m. he left the motorway at a junction B which is 160 km from A. At 3.00 p.m. he rejoined the motorway further on at a junction C, a distance of 30 km from B measured along the motorway. He then continued along the motorway at a steady speed of 100 km/h in the same direction as before.

Taking 2 cm to 1 hour on one axis and 2 cm to 50 km on the other, draw the graphs representing the two stages of the motorist's journey on the motorway.

Hence, or otherwise, find the time at which the motorist arrived at a point D, a distance of 350 km from A measured along the motorway.

A second motorist passed D at 12.00 noon and travelled along the motorway towards A. He did not meet the first motorist on the motorway. Find, by drawing straight line travel-graphs or otherwise, the greatest and the least steady speeds at which this second motorist could have travelled. (O & C)

PAPER 5

1. (a) (i) An article which cost £25 is sold for £29. Express the profit as a percentage of the cost price.
    (ii) An article is sold for £30, thereby making a profit of 20% on the cost price. Calculate the cost price.
  (b) Two whole numbers are in the ratio 3:5. If the smaller number is 18, calculate the larger number.
  (c) Two whole numbers are in the ratio of 1:3. If the sum of the two numbers is 24, calculate the smaller number. (WJEC)

2. The following details are taken from a rate demand note for this year.

Estimated product of a penny rate   £79 500
Total amount to be raised   £5 326 500

Calculate for this year:
   (i) the rate, expressed as pence in the £, which must be levied
   (ii) the amount paid in rates by a householder whose house has a rateable value of £155.

The demand note also stated that, of the rate levied, 28.5 p in the £ was to be used for education. Calculate for this year:
   (iii) the total amount to be spent on education
   (iv) the annual contribution of the above householder towards education, giving the answer to the nearest ten pence.

Another householder estimated that, of the amount he paid in rates, his contribution towards education was £68.40. Calculate the rateable value of his house.   (AEB 1979)

3. (a) A journey of 23 km was completed in two stages by a train which took 30 minutes altogether. For the first stage the distance travelled was 8 km and the average speed was 40 km/h. Find the times taken for the two stages of the journey. Calculate, in kilometres per hour, the average speed for the second stage of the journey.
   (b) An alloy contains 54% by weight of copper and 46% by weight of zinc. Find the number of grams of copper which must be combined with 138 g of zinc to give an alloy with this composition.   (O & C)

4. A cone-shaped vessel is held with the vertex downwards and the axis vertical. The height is 12 cm and the radius at the open end is 9 cm. It contains a liquid whose surface is 8 cm below the level of the open end of the cone. Taking $\pi = 3.142$, calculate the volume of the liquid. (The volume of a cone of height h and radius r is $\frac{1}{3}\pi r^2 h$)   (WJEC)

5. A rate of 1p in the £ produces £64 000 from a certain borough. Calculate:
   (i) the total rateable value of the borough
   (ii) the rate needed to finance a project costing £200 000. (WJEC)

PAPER 6

1. (a) (i) Express $\frac{5}{16}$ in decimal form.
      (ii) Express 0.825 as a fraction in its lowest terms.
   (b) A motorist drives for 2 hours at a speed of 60 km/h, and then for 45 minutes at a speed of 16 km/h. Find his average speed for the whole journey.   (O & C)

2. (a) Find the highest common factor of the following numbers: 150, 480 and 720.
   (b) (i) Calculate in base 5, $13_5 \times 2$, $13_5 \times 3$, $13_5 \times 4$.
       (ii) Calculate in base 5, without changing to base ten, 1214 divided by 13. (WJEC)

3. A car accelerates from rest and readings are taken of the speed, in metres per second, and the time, in seconds.

Speed	0	5.2	10.1	14.2	17.1	18.9	20.2	21.1	21.7	22.0	22.2
Time	0	1	2	3	4	5	6	7	8	9	10

Choose suitable scales to plot the readings on a graph, taking speed as the y axis.

Use your graph to estimate:
(a) the speed after 3.5 seconds
(b) the time when the speed is 8.0 m s^{-1}
(c) the rate at which the speed was changing (i.e. acceleration) at 6 seconds;
(d) the distance travelled in the first ten seconds, to the nearest 5 m. (SU)

4. (a) During a certain period of time, the ratio of men candidates to women candidates who took a driving test was $11:9$. Of all the candidates who took the test, 72% were successful, and among these successful candidates the ratio of men to women was $5:3$. Calculate the fraction of the women candidates who were successful.
   (b) In a certain election there were two candidates only. Out of 32 000 voters in the electorate only 71.8% voted, and the successful candidate had a majority of 1714. Calculate the number of votes cast for the successful candidate. (WJEC)

5. A solid right circular cone has height 24 cm and base-radius 10 cm. Given that the volume of a right circular cone of height h and base-radius r is $\frac{1}{3}\pi r^2 h$ and that its curved surface area is $\pi r \sqrt{(r^2 + h^2)}$, calculate the volume of the cone and also its *total* surface area.

A right circular cone of height 6 cm is removed from the original cone by cutting it parallel to its base. Find the base-radius of the cone which is removed and also the volume of the solid which remains. (Take π as 3.142) (O & C)

PAPER 7

1. (a) Evaluate 13×5 using binary numbers, giving your answer in binary.
   (b) Calculate, without using tables the value of $(27)^{\frac{2}{3}} \times (\frac{3}{2})^{-2}$. (WJEC)

2. (a) Calculate the compound interest on £350 invested for 2 years
   at 12% per annum.
   (b) In a small firm employing 10 men, 6 men had a weekly wage
   of £46 each. The average weekly wage in the factory was £44.
   Calculate the average weekly wage of the other 4 men.
                                                                (WJEC)

3. Use mathematical tables to evaluate:
   (a) $\sqrt{(16.81)^2 + (7.48)^2}$
   (b) $(0.7)^6$
   (c) $\sqrt[3]{0.027\,41}$
   (d) $\dfrac{18.51 - 7.42}{18.51 + 7.42}$

4. A shopkeeper buys certain articles at 25 p each and during one
   week he sells 80 of these articles at a profit of 40% of his cost
   price. The following week he sells a further 120 of them at a
   discount of 20% of the previous selling price. Find the profit that
   he makes in each of these two weeks.

   In the third week he is able to raise the selling price of the same
   articles to 40 p each (the cost price remaining as before). What is
   the smallest number of articles he must sell in this third week in
   order that his average profit per article over the three week period
   is at least 8 p?   (SU)

5. The figure below represents the section of a tunnel of height 4.2 m.
   The section is part of a circle, centre O, of radius 2.8 m. Calculate
   (a) the width of the floor AB, (b) the angle AOB, (c) the area of
   the triangle AOB, (d) the area of the section of the tunnel. (Take
   π to be 3.142)   (WJEC)

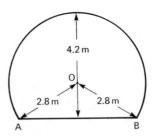

PAPER 8

1. (a) A man weighs 79 kg. If 1 kg = 2.205 lb, calculate, correct to 3
   significant figures, his weight in lb.
   (b) Evaluate $4\dfrac{3}{5} - \left(1\dfrac{7}{10} \times 2\dfrac{1}{2}\right)$.

(c) Find the price of a roll of wallpaper, before VAT has been added, if the total cost of 4 rolls is £15.64 after 15% VAT has been added.

(d) A plastic bottle, 12 cm high, contains 200 cm³ of hair shampoo. How much does a (mathematically) similar bottle, 18 cm high, hold? (SU)

2. (a) Express as a single fraction in its lowest terms $\dfrac{1}{5} + \dfrac{1}{2}\left(\dfrac{3}{4} + \dfrac{4}{5}\right)$.

(b) A sum of £1300 is divided between A and B in the ratio 3 : 2. Then A divides his share into three parts in the ratio 7 : 4 : 2. Find the value of the smallest of these parts. (O & C)

3. (a) The cash price of a vacuum cleaner is £40. The price by hire purchase is £14 deposit, together with 12 instalments of £2.64. Calculate the extra amount paid in buying by hire purchase as a percentage of the cash price.

(b) *Without using tables*, divide 15.7 by 0.32, giving the answer to four significant figures.

(c) In a given time a car travels 800 metres and uses 62.5 cubic centimetres of petrol. Calculate its rate of consumption in kilometres per litre. (WJEC)

4. The diagram below shows a large greenhouse which has the following dimensions: length 12 m, width 7.2 m, height of sides 4.5 m and height to roof-ridge (which is parallel to, and half-way between, the long sides) 6 m. Calculate:
   (i) the area of the end *ABFLE*
   (ii) the volume of air contained in the greenhouse
   (iii) the length of the slanting edge *EL*
   (iv) the total area of glass, consisting of the four walls and the roof. (O & C)

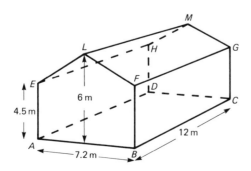

5. The figure below represents a vertical section through the axis of symmetry AB of a solid which consists of three parts, a cone, a cylinder, and a hemisphere, each having a radius of 4 cm.

Given that the height of the cone is 12 cm and that the area of the cylindrical curved surface is 110 cm^2, calculate:
 (i) the slant height of the cone,
 (ii) the total surface area of the solid,
(iii) the height AB of the solid.

(The surface area of a cone is πrl. The surface area of a sphere is $4\pi r^2$. Take π to be 3.142) (AEB 1980)

PAPER 9

1. (a) Find the number of units of a Unit Trust which can be bought for £600 if each unit costs 75 p.
   (b) Find each share if £244.80 is divided in the ratios $2:3:7$.
   (c) Add together 7.52×10^{-2} and 8.45×10^{-1}, expressing the answer in the form $a \times 10^{-n}$, where n is a whole number and a is a number between 1 and 10. (O & C)

2. (a) Evaluate $\dfrac{0.75^2 - 0.05^2}{12}$, without the use of tables, and give your answer (i) correct to 2 decimal places, (ii) correct to 2 significant figures.
   (b) Calculate, using logarithms (i) 8.26^3, (ii) $\sqrt[3]{0.0826}$.
   (c) The scale of an Ordnance Survey map is $1:25\,000$. A lake which is nearly rectangular in shape, measures 3 cm by 16 cm on the map. Calculate its approximate true area in km^2. (SU)

3. (a) A man invests £3000 for one year at a rate of interest of 15% per annum. He also invests £2000 for the same year at a rate of interest of 16% per annum. Find his total interest for the year and express this interest as a percentage of the total sum invested.

(b) Multiply 0.013 251 by 0.15, giving the exact answer in the form $a \times 10^b$, where a is a number lying between 1 and 10 and b is a positive or negative whole number. (O & C)

4. Mr White invested £1785 in £1 shares at 85 p which paid a dividend of $3\frac{3}{4}$ per cent. Calculate the number of shares that he bought and his annual income from those shares.

Mr Jones invested a sum of money in a 5 per cent stock at 108 and his annual income from this stock was £165. Calculate the amount of stock that he held and the sum of money that he invested in the stock.

Calculate, to the nearest penny, the income that Mr White received from each one hundred pounds invested, and calculate, to the nearest penny, the income that Mr Jones received for each one hundred pounds invested. State which of the two men received more per one hundred pounds invested. (AEB 1980)

5. A hollow tin cylinder is closed at both ends. Its length is 13 cm and its radius 7 cm.
   (i) Taking $\pi = 3\frac{1}{7}$, calculate the total surface area of the tin cylinder.
   (ii) Inside the cylinder is a ball-bearing of radius 2 cm. The axis of the cylinder is vertical and the ball-bearing rolls around so that it is always touching the curved surface of the cylinder and the flat base. Describe completely the locus of the centre of the ball-bearing. (WJEC)

PAPER 10

1. (a) Evaluate $[(6 \times 10^4) \times (9 \times 10^{-6})] \div (4 \times 10^{-3})$.
   (b) Use logarithms to calculate the cube root of 0.059.
   (c) The annual expenditure on education in a certain borough is £3 354 000. This is obtained by a rate of 43 p in the £. (i) Calculate the total rateable value of the borough. (ii) If a special project costs £273 000, calculate the additional rate in the £ needed to finance this project. (WJEC)

2. (a) When a dealer sells a car for £3534, he makes a profit of 24% on his cost price. Calculate his cost price.

(b) A shopkeeper sells two brands of carpet. The luxury brand he buys for £8 per square metre and sells at a profit of 20 per cent. The standard brand he buys for £6 per square metre and sells at a profit of 15 per cent. If he sells 1000 square metres of the luxury carpet and 2000 square metres of the standard carpet, calculate his profit as a percentage of his cost price.

(c) A cycle wheel is 2 m in circumference.
  (i) Calculate the number of revolutions of the wheel when the cycle travels 60 km.
  (ii) If the wheel makes 250 revolutions in one minute, calculate the average speed of the cycle in $km\,h^{-1}$.   (SU)

3. *In this question all speeds are constant.* A, B and C are three towns on the same road. From A to B is 25 miles and from A to C is 79 miles.

(a) A motorist sets out from A at 12 noon and travels to C, arriving there at 3.30 p.m.
  (i) Draw a graph of this journey, using 2 cm to represent 10 miles, and 6 cm to represent 1 hour. *Draw the time axis along the longer side of the graph paper.*
  (ii) *Use your graph* to find the speed of the motorist as accurately as you are able.

(b) A second motorist starts from A at 12.30 p.m., gets to B at 1.30 p.m., and having stopped there for half-an-hour, travels on to C at 36 mph.
  (i) On the same graph paper, draw the graph of this motorist's journey.
  (ii) At what time does this motorist arrive at C?

(c) A third motorist travels non-stop from C to A, starting from C at 1.14 p.m. and arriving at A at 3.18 p.m.
  (i) On the same graph paper, draw the graph of this motorist's journey.
  (ii) When and where will the third motorist pass the second motorist?   (WJEC)

4. During a certain year the quarterly rental charge for a private telephone was £8.25 and the time units used were charged at 3.0 p each. In addition a Value Added Tax (VAT) of 15% of the total of these two charges was added to the bill.
  (i) In the first quarter of the year, 345 time units were used. Calculate the total cost for this quarter.
  (ii) The total cost for the second quarter was £20.70. Calculate the cost before the addition of VAT and the number of time units used in this quarter.   (O & C)

5. Income tax is calculated on the taxable income; i.e. after a tax-free allowance has been deducted from the actual income. In 1976 on the first £4500 of taxable income a basic rate of 32 per cent was charged, and on the next £2000 of taxable income a higher rate of 40 per cent was charged. Calculate the tax paid by:

(i) Mr Smith whose actual income was £5800 with a tax-free allowance of £2400

(ii) Mr Robinson whose actual income was £8000 with a tax-free allowance of £2400.

Express Mr Robinson's tax as a percentage of his actual income.

In 1977 Mr Robinson's tax-free allowance and the 40 per cent rate were unaltered but the basic rate of tax was reduced. Mr Robinson had an increase in actual income of £500, and paid £1967.50 in tax. Calculate the new basic rate of tax. (AEB 1980)

PAPER 11

1. (a) In a 1000 m race Davies beats Jones by 40 m. In a similar race Jones beat Williams by 125 m. Assuming that they run at these speeds how far will Williams run in the time it takes Davies to run 1000 m?

(b) Calculate the sum of money which will amount to £290 when invested for 2 years at $12\frac{1}{2}$% per annum simple interest.

(c) An aeroplane flies 400 miles due North, and 90 miles due east. Calculate the distance from the starting point. (WJEC)

2. (a) A man calculated that in a particular year the family holiday had cost him $7\frac{1}{2}$ per cent of his income. The holiday cost £900. Calculate the man's income for that year.

(b) An accurate measuring device indicates that a particular length is 3.6282 m. State this measurement correct to (i) the nearest metre, (ii) the nearest centimetre, (iii) the nearest millimetre. (JMB)

3. (Throughout this question take π to be 3.142)

In the figure below, ABC is a semicircle centre O and radius 10 cm, PQRS is a rectangle with PQ = 8 cm and QR = 7 cm and CON is the line of symmetry of the figure.

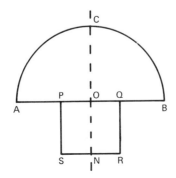

Calculate the area of the figure, giving the answer in cm^2.

  (i) If the above figure represents the uniform cross-section of a solid of length 200 cm, calculate the volume of the solid, giving the answer in m^3 correct to two significant figures.

 (ii) If the above figure is rotated through 180° about the line CON, calculate the total surface area in cm^2 of the solid generated, giving the answer correct to the nearest cm^2.

(The surface area of a sphere of radius r is $4\pi r^2$)   (AEB 1979)

4. (a) A car travelled for 12 minutes at an average speed of 45 miles per hour. During the next 9 minutes, the average speed was 50 miles per hour and for the next 6 minutes of the journey the average speed was 60 miles per hour. Calculate the average speed over this 27-minute period of the journey.

   (b) A man loaned £275 to a friend at 4% per annum, and another £120 to another friend at 5% per annum. After each had paid one year's interest, the first friend paid back the £275 in full, but the second friend went bankrupt and could only pay 20 p in the £1. Calculate the percentage of the £395 which he loaned that the man received back, including interest payments.   (WJEC)

5. A family man wishes to hire a car for a day. Three car-hire firms quoted their prices as follows:

   Alpha Agency charged £20 per day irrespective of the distance travelled

   Betta Travel charged £10 for any distance up to, and including 200 km, and then 6 p for every kilometre over the initial 200 km

   Cruiser Cars charged a basic £5 plus 4 p for every kilometre travelled.

  (i) Draw up a table that shows the cost of hiring a car for one day from each firm and using it to travel 0, 200 and 400 km in that day.

 (ii) Use your table to draw graphs on the same axes showing the cost of hiring a car from each firm for all distances up to 400 km in one day.

(Scales: take 2 cm to represent 50 km on the distance axis and 2 cm to represent £2 on the cost axis)

Use your graphs to estimate:

(iii) the range of distances for which Betta Travel is cheaper than Cruiser Cars,

(iv) the range of distances for which Alpha Agency is cheaper than either of the other two firms,

 (v) the maximum cost per kilometre that Cruiser Cars could have charged if the firm kept its basic £5 charge and was cheaper than both the other two firms up to distances of 400 km.

(AEB 1979)

PAPER 12

1. (a) Evaluate $10110 - 1011$, where the numbers are in the binary scale, giving your answer in the binary scale.
   (b) £270 is divided among three prize winners in the ratio $2:3:4$. Calculate the largest share.
   (c) The price of a book is increased by 10% to £4.95. Calculate the price before the increase.
   (d) A cylindrical container of radius 15 cm has a capacity of 27 litres. Calculate the radius of a similar container with a capacity of 8 litres. (JMB)

2. (a) Calculate $\dfrac{2\frac{1}{2} + 3\frac{3}{4}}{1\frac{1}{3} - \frac{7}{8}}$.
   (b) Express in standard form $35.8, 35\,800, 0.003\,58$.
   (c) Find the total cost of 6 metres of timber at 90 p a metre when an additional 15% VAT is charged.
   (d) A cylindrical tin, 7 cm high, holds 250 millilitres of paint. How much will a (mathematically) similar tin 14 cm high hold? (SU)

3. (a) When a cold rod is heated, its length increases by 4%. If the length of the rod after heating becomes 65 cm, calculate the length when cold.
   (b) The scale of a map is $1:50\,000$. Find the actual area in square kilometres, of a wood represented by an area of 7.6 square centimetres on the map.
   (c) Mercury weighs 13.6 grams per cubic centimetre. Calculate, *without using logarithms*, the volume in litres of the quantity of mercury which weighs 34 kilograms. (1 litre $= 1000$ cubic centimetres) (WJEC)

4. A barn, used for storing hay, is 30 m long and a sketch of its uniform cross-section is shown in the figure below. The vertical heights AE and CD are each 15 m and the curve of the roof is an arc ABC of a circle, centre F and radius 12 m, with the angle AFC $= 90°$.

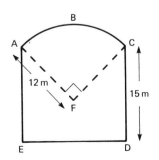

Calculate:

(i) the cost of weatherproofing the barn roof, correct to the nearest £10, at £2.50 per square metre.

(ii) the volume of hay that the barn contains when it is 80 per cent full, giving your answer correct to 2 significant figures. (Take π to be 3.142) (AEB 1980)

5. A block of copper is in the form of a cube of edge 20 cm. The density of copper is 8.9 g/cm^3. Calculate the mass of the block in kilograms.

The block is drawn out to form a cylindrical rod of diameter 8 cm. Find the length of the rod.

A portion of length 10 cm is cut from this rod, and melted down to form a sphere. Calculate the radius of the sphere. (The volume of a sphere of radius $r = \frac{4}{3}\pi r^3$. Take π as 3.142) (O & C)

PAPER 13

1. (a) (i) 235 is a number to base 8. Express it as a number to base 10.

(ii) Add together the binary numbers 1 1 0 1 1 and 1 1 0 1 0, giving the answer as a binary number.

(b) Express as a single fraction in its lowest terms

$$\left(\frac{2}{3} + \frac{1}{6}\right) \times \left(\frac{3}{2} - \frac{2}{5}\right).$$

(O & C)

2. A sweet manufacturer makes aniseed balls having a *diameter* of 1 cm. If 1 cubic centimetre of aniseed ball weighs 8.5 g, find (a) the volume of one ball, (b) the number of balls, to the nearest whole number, needed to weigh 250 g.

The manufacturer now decides to make Super Balls by changing the size to a *diameter* of 2 cm. How many balls, to the nearest whole number, will now be needed to weigh 250 g? (SU)

3. As an investment a man buys a holiday flat for £15 000 and spends a further £1500 on repairs. He expects to have to pay £150 a year for maintenance and the rates will be 84 p in the pound on a rateable value of £250. He intends to let the flat at such a rent that it will pay for the annual charges and, in addition, provide a return of 12% on his original cost of purchase and repairs.

(a) What will be his annual expenditure?

(b) What should he charge for a weekly rent if he lets the flat for just 30 weeks in the year?

(c) If instead he charges £75 a week for 25 weeks during the summer and £30 a week for 21 weeks during the rest of the year, what percentage return on his original cost does this provide? (SU)

4. At a steady speed of 48 km h^{-1} a car travels 17 kilometres on a litre of petrol. At 96 km h^{-1} the distance is reduced to 11 kilometres per litre. The relationship between the distance travelled by the car per litre of petrol consumed and the speed is linear. Sketch the graph showing the relationship and determine the distance travelled per litre at 112 km h^{-1}. (SU)

5. In a certain income tax year, the first £985 of income was exempt from tax. The next £750 of the income was taxed at the rate of 25%, and the remainder of the income was taxed at the rate of 30%.
   (i) Calculate the total tax paid on an income of £4690 for the year, and express this tax as a percentage of the income.
   (ii) Calculate the income on which a total tax of £963 was paid during the year. (O & C)

PAPER 14

1. (a) During a journey a motorist cruises for 3 hours on a motor-way at 112 km h^{-1} and drives along country roads for 2 hours at an average speed of 64 km h^{-1}. How long was the journey and what was the average speed?
   (b) A circular cylinder is made of thin paper and has both ends closed. Its height is 6 cm and the circumference of each end is 11 cm. Calculate the radius of the ends and its volume. (Take $\pi = \frac{22}{7}$) (SU)

2. A factory worker is paid at the basic rate of £2.80 per hour for a 35-hour working week. Calculate the basic weekly wage for 35 hours work.

Overtime work is paid at the rate of time and a quarter (that is, the basic rate is increased by one quarter) Monday to Friday, time and a half on Saturday and double time on Sunday. Find the weekly wage for a week that consists of the basic 35 hours plus 2 hours overtime on Tuesday, 2 hours overtime on Thursday, 3 hours overtime on Saturday and 3 hours overtime on Sunday.

The wage for a working week made up of the basic 35 hours plus overtime of 2 hours on each of the days Monday, Wednesday and Thursday with x hours overtime on Saturday is the same as the wage for a working week made up of the basic 35 hours plus 3 hours 40 minutes overtime on Saturday and x hours overtime on Sunday. Calculate the value of x. (JMB)

3. Metal drums in the form of circular cylinders with internal diameters 48 cm and internal lengths 85 cm are completely filled with
oil of density 850 kg/m^3.
   (i) Calculate the total volume of oil contained in 5 of these drums,
   giving the answer in cubic centimetres, correct to three significant figures. (Take π as 3.142)
   (ii) Express this volume in cubic metres.
   (iii) Calculate to the nearest kilogram the total mass of the oil.
   (iv) All the oil from the 5 drums is poured into a rectangular
   tank having a horizontal base of internal dimensions 1.80 m
   by 1.20 m. Calculate the depth of the oil, to the nearest centimetre.
   (v) Find the number of cans, each holding 5 litres, which can be
   filled from the oil in the tank. (O & C)

4. Over any period of ten years, the population of a certain city
increases by 6% of its size at the beginning of the period. If the
population was 53 000 in 1905, find the population, to the nearest
50, in (i) 1925, (ii) 1895. (WJEC)

5. A boy plans to cycle to a nearby town to visit a friend. He calculates for various average speeds (V kilometres per hour) the total
time (T hours) that he will take to travel to the town, visit his
friend and then return home. He bases his calculations on a
formula of the form $T = \dfrac{a}{V} + b$ where a and b are constants, and
the following table shows the results of some of his calculations.

V	6	8	10	12	15	20	25
T	7.9	6.3	5.3	4.7	4.1	3.5	3.1
$1/V$	.167		.1		.067		.04

Complete the table by finding the values of $\dfrac{1}{V}$ when $V = 8, 12$ and
20 and by plotting a graph of T against $\dfrac{1}{V}$ show that the values of
T and V agree with the formula. (Scales: take 2 cm to represent
0.02 units on the $\dfrac{1}{V}$-axis and 2 cm to represent 1 unit on the
T-axis)

Use your graph to estimate:
   (i) the probable value of a and, using this value, calculate b
   (ii) the value of T when $V = 18$
   (iii) the value of V when $T = 4.5$. (AEB 1979)

1. (a) Express a speed of 32.5 metres per second in kilometres per hour.

   (b) Find the value of $\dfrac{2.8 \times 10^{-2} \times 3.6 \times 10^{3}}{5.6 \times 10^{2}}$.

   (b) Find the pre-tax price of an article which is sold for £552 after a Value Added Tax of 15% has been added to the pre-tax price. (O & C)

2. (a) Write down the next term in each of the following sequences:

   (i) 1, 1, 2, 3, 5, 8, ... , (ii) $\dfrac{3}{4}, \dfrac{1}{2}, \dfrac{1}{3}, \dfrac{2}{9}, \dfrac{4}{27}, \ldots$.

   (b) A boy spent one-third of his pocket money on sweets, and a half of the money remaining he spent on a magazine. Given that he had 20 p left, find how much money he had originally.

   (c) Find the length of an edge of the cube whose total surface area is $13.5 \, \text{cm}^2$. (JMB)

3. The plan view of a horizontal observation platform at a seaside holiday resort is shown in the figure below. The platform consists of a rectangle ABCE, with AE = BC = 1.5 m, and a segment of a circle CDE with centre O and radius 2.5 m. The angle COE is $90°$.

   Calculate:
   (i) the length of EC and hence the perimeter of the platform,
   (ii) the total area of the platform. (Take π to be 3.142)

   (AEB 1979)

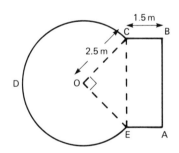

4. (a) A hollow sphere is made of metal 3 cm thick. Given that the external radius is 9 cm, calculate the volume of metal used, giving your answer as a multiple of π.

   (b) (i) Re-arrange the formula $\frac{4}{3}\pi r^3 = V$ so as to express r as a function of V.

      (ii) A solid metal rectangular block whose dimensions are 9 cm by 11 cm by 49 cm is melted down and recast as a solid sphere. Calculate the radius of this sphere, taking the value of π as $\frac{22}{7}$.

   (The volume of a sphere of radius r cm is $\frac{4}{3}\pi r^3 \, \text{cm}^3$) (JMB)

5. The following table gives the number of miles a car will travel on one gallon of petrol under various conditions.

| TYPE OF DRIVING | ENGINE SIZE | | |
| | 1100 cc | 1300 cc | 1600 cc |
	MILES PER GALLON		
Car driven at constant 56 m.p.h.	50	48	45
Car driven at constant 75 m.p.h.	36	40	30
Normal town driving	32	30	25

All petrol costs £1.20 per gallon.

(i) Calculate the cost of driving a 1300 cc model 120 miles at a constant 75 m.p.h.

(ii) Find the estimated annual petrol bill of a motorist with a 1600 cc model who drives 150 miles per week, all of it in towns.

(iii) Calculate the distance an 1100 cc model would travel at a constant 56 m.p.h. on £100 worth of petrol. Give your answer in miles to two significant figures.

(iv) Calculate, to the nearest quarter of an hour, the length of time a 1600 cc model could travel on 8 gallons of petrol at a constant 56 m.p.h.

(v) A motorist with a 1600 cc model fits a device costing £60 to his engine. This device improves his petrol consumption from 25 m.p.g. to 30 m.p.g. Show that if he drives 600 miles, he saves £4.80 worth of petrol, and calculate how far he must drive before the device has paid for itself. (m.p.g. = miles per gallon) (SU)

USEFUL FACTS AND FORMULAE

MEASURES

Length:
$$10\,\text{mm} = 1\,\text{cm}$$
$$100\,\text{cm} = 1\,\text{m}$$
$$1000\,\text{mm} = 1\,\text{m}$$
$$1000\,\text{m} = 1\,\text{km}$$

Area:
$$10^2\,\text{mm}^2 = 1\,\text{cm}^2$$
$$100^2\,\text{cm}^2 = 1\,\text{m}^2$$
$$10\,000\,\text{m}^2 = 1\,\text{hectare}$$
$$100\,\text{hectares} = 1\,\text{km}^2$$

Volume:
$$10^3\,\text{mm}^3 = 1\,\text{cm}^3$$
$$100^3\,\text{cm}^3 = 1\,\text{m}^3$$
$$1000\,\text{cm}^3 = 1\,\text{litre}$$

Mass:
$$1000\,\text{g} = 1\,\text{kg}$$
$$1000\,\text{kg} = 1\,\text{tonne}$$

PERCENTAGE PROFIT AND LOSS

$$\% \text{ Profit} = \frac{\text{SP} - \text{CP}}{\text{CP}} \times 100 \quad \text{or} \quad \frac{\text{Profit}}{\text{CP}} \times 100$$

$$\% \text{ Loss} = \frac{\text{CP} - \text{SP}}{\text{CP}} \times 100 \quad \text{or} \quad \frac{\text{Loss}}{\text{CP}} \times 100$$

MENSURATION

Circumference of circle, $C = \pi D = 2\pi r$

Arc length of circle $= 2\pi r \times \dfrac{\theta}{360}$

(if θ is the angle subtended by the arc at the centre)

Area of circle, $A = \pi r^2$

Area of annulus, $A = \pi(R^2 - r^2)$

Area of sector of circle $= \pi r^2 \times \dfrac{\theta}{360}$

Area of triangle $= \frac{1}{2}$ base $\times$ perpendicular height

Area of trapezium $= \frac{1}{2}$ sum of parallel sides $\times$ distance between them

Volume of pyramid $= \frac{1}{3}$ base area $\times$ perpendicular height

Volume of solid with uniform cross-section $=$ area of cross-section $\times$ length (or height)

Cylinder:

Curved surface area $= 2\pi rh$

Total surface area $= 2\pi r(r + h)$

Volume $= \pi r^2 h$

Cone:

Curved surface area $= \pi rl$
(where l is the slant height)

Total surface area $= \pi r(r + l)$

Volume $= \frac{1}{3}\pi r^2 h$

Sphere:

Total surface area $= 4\pi r^2$

Volume $= \frac{4}{3}\pi r^3$

Similar solids:

Ratio of their areas is the same as the ratio of the squares of corresponding linear dimensions.

Ratio of their volumes is the same as the ratio of the cubes of corresponding linear dimensions.

FLOW OF LIQUID

Quantity flowing $=$ area of cross-section of pipe $\times$ speed of flow

AVERAGE

$$\text{Average value} \ = \ \frac{\text{total of all values}}{\text{number of values}}$$

$$\text{Average speed} \ = \ \frac{\text{total distance}}{\text{total time}}$$

PYTHAGORAS' THEOREM

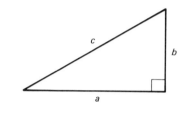

$$c^2 \ = \ a^2 + b^2$$

RATES AND RATEABLE VALUE

$$\text{Rates paid} \ = \ \text{RV} \times \text{rate in the £}$$

INTEREST

$$\text{Simple interest, } I \ = \ \frac{PRT}{100}$$

$$\text{Compound interest, } A \ = \ P\left(1 + \frac{R}{100}\right)^n$$

ANSWERS

EXERCISE 1

1. 3027
2. 5176
3. 9500
4. 4842
5. 16 050
6. 12 872
7. 1783
8. 22 900
9. 400 000
10. 110 000
11. 18 040
12. 4003
13. 1 300 000
14. 8630
15. 100 072
16. 7087
17. 47 865
18. 550 700
19. 2 500 000
20. 13 000 572
21. Four hundred and twenty-six
22. Nine hundred and twenty-seven
23. One hundred and twenty-six
24. Four hundred and thirty
25. Six hundred and fifty-five
26. Nine hundred and twenty-six
27. One thousand five hundred
28. Three thousand seven hundred and fifty
29. Eighty-two thousand
30. Sixty-seven thousand five hundred
31. Three hundred and forty-seven thousand and five
32. Five hundred and ninety-two thousand and seventy
33. One hundred and forty-two thousand five hundred and sixty
34. Eight hundred and seventy-two thousand six hundred and sixty
35. Three hundred and ninety-four thousand
36. Four hundred and sixty-two thousand five hundred
37. Five hundred thousand eight hundred and seventy-three
38. Eight hundred and ninety-two thousand six hundred and sixty
39. One million two hundred and seventy thousand
40. Three million fifty thousand and forty-seven

EXERCISE 2

1. 77
2. 77
3. 98
4. 89
5. 98
6. 70
7. 90
8. 90
9. 80
10. 70
11. 41
12. 71
13. 94
14. 91
15. 86
16. 110
17. 106
18. 142
19. 104
20. 121
21. 757
22. 879
23. 777
24. 688
25. 998
26. 777
27. 879
28. 987
29. 699
30. 899
31. 565
32. 852
33. 963
34. 1002
35. 980
36. 1049
37. 988
38. 999
39. 781
40. 907
41. 1888
42. 1886
43. 1598
44. 2479
45. 1959
46. 794
47. 1865
48. 686
49. 1819
50. 1699
51. 1835
52. 1345
53. 1612
54. 1619
55. 1853
56. 1192
57. 1990
58. 1640
59. 2250
60. 1379
61. 9621
62. 8213
63. 6311
64. 7418
65. 8884
66. 4274
67. 6977
68. 7066
69. 3811
70. 5023
71. 10 261
72. 6702
73. 7368
74. 9079
75. 9854
76. 9106
77. 8729
78. 10 413
79. 7947
80. 9891
81. 17 482
82. 15 760
83. 18 252
84. 10 905
85. 15 268
86. 8444
87. 13 997
88. 14 806
89. 10 651
90. 13 368
91. 17 025
92. 11 163
93. 10 975
94. 19 033
95. 19 401
96. 15 425
97. 18 857
98. 18 211
99. 22 074
100. 23 611
101. 154 059
102. 165 633
103. 240 948
104. 193 176
105. 225 612
106. 259 957
107. 271 409
108. 223 429
109. 243 353
110. 339 269
111. 1433
112. 1156
113. 2155
114. 1913
115. 1772
116. 1502
117. 10 113
118. 16 886
119. 14 834
120. 15 520
121. 51 899
122. 21 236
123. 15 133
124. 41 380
125. 96 954
126. 54 075
127. 162 931
128. 154 249
129. 114 602
130. 154 922
131. 210
132. 1554
133. 483
134. 150
135. 2763
136. 61 571
137. 83 955
138. 23
139. 225
140. 5318

EXERCISE 3

1. 15
2. 31
3. 11
4. 22
5. 43
6. 212
7. 231
8. 110
9. 114
10. 171
11. 18
12. 17
13. 5
14. 16
15. 46

16. 115	17. 329	18. 217	19. 428	20. 207
21. 288	22. 228	23. 365	24. 136	25. 538
26. 1041	27. 2311	28. 1120	29. 3311	30. 5333
31. 3779	32. 5072	33. 8038	34. 2643	35. 3046
36. 1489	37. 1896	38. 3609	39. 4888	40. 3834
41. 49 013	42. 17 145	43. 2740	44. 16 865	45. 67 818
46. 2971	47. 6554	48. 3603	49. 7687	50. 7369
51. 4821	52. 112	53. 16 628	54. 9106	55. 6985
56. 200	57. 367	58. 104	59. 85	60. 136
61. 91	62. 851	63. 1354	64. 710	65. 627
66. 4192	67. 289	68. 18 734	69. 6125	70. 463
71. 307	72. 616	73. 11 629	74. 4453	75. 20 512
76. 40 490	77. 2683	78. (a) 1474, (b) 1259		79. 674
80. 148				

Exercise 4

1. 170	2. 252	3. 203	4. 416	5. 288
6. 470	7. 234	8. 423	9. 1210	10. 1141
11. 2084	12. 1526	13. 2604	14. 2826	15. 4944
16. 3664	17. 1845	18. 2736	19. 1687	20. 2640
21. 3080	22. 6390	23. 24 840	24. 22 550	25. 45 540
26. 31 360	27. 11 120	28. 26 190	29. 2597	30. 1554
31. 742	32. 1512	33. 2144	34. 3525	35. 848
36. 3212	37. 5488	38. 3362	39. 1368	40. 1458
41. 1827	42. 1218	43. 3213	44. 3096	45. 6370
46. 2365	47. 2336	48. 2542	49. 247	50. 1458
51. 2205	52. 2948	53. 6059	54. 7728	55. 9312
56. 3230	57. 4620	58. 3888	59. 10 016	60. 13 695
61. 13 520	62. 30 408	63. 13 872	64. 18 998	65. 22 692
66. 37 296	67. 38 232	68. 63 336	69. 23 800	70. 29 524
71. 29 664	72. 9153	73. 60 088	74. 35 896	75. 40 256
76. 33 320	77. 50 778	78. 59 878	79. 72 556	80. 79 584
81. 27 280	82. 159 840	83. 203 835	84. 460 152	85. 131 352
86. 112 251	87. 269 861	88. 324 216	89. 397 188	90. 198 654
91. 495 759	92. 308 448	93. 378 721	94. 159 333	95. 155 964
96. 530 366	97. 206 700	98. 394 723	99. 425 078	100. 696 352
101. 6885	102. 7335	103. 50 985	104. 28 635	105. 572 265
106. 5340	107. 2070	108. £5638	109. 648 miles	

110. (a) 1568 miles,   (b) 81 536 miles

Exercise 5

1. 153	2. 307	3. 241	4. 763
5. 42	6. 175	7. 595	8. 98
9. 624	10. 424	11. 127	12. 516
13. 298	14. 254	15. 74	16. 314
17. 172	18. 69	19. 422	20. 232
21. 82	22. 621	23. 424	24. 245
25. 793	26. 537	27. 317	28. 826
29. 169	30. 98	31. 48 R 4	32. 75 R 4
33. 76 R 5	34. 145 R 3	35. 55 R 7	36. 77 R 0
37. 40 R 3	38. 77 R 2	39. 52 R 6	40. 89 R 5
41. 172 R 12	42. 342 R 7	43. 434 R 18	44. 309 R 20
45. 328 R 12	46. 44 R 50	47. 147 R 3	48. 80 R 13
49. 114 R 28	50. 150 R 19	51. 30 R 77	52. 737 R 122
53. 198 R 86	54. 81 R 148	55. 36 R 120	56. 126 R 191
57. 78 R 329	58. 411 R 311	59. 104 R 737	60. 753 R 550

61. 247	**62.** 80 R 186	**63.** 335	**64.** 124
65. 57	**66.** 6	**67.** 4	**68.** 2856
69. 22 R 62	**70.** 50 R 84	**71.** 93	**72.** 26, 19
73. 16	**74.** 17	**75.** 65	**76.** 285
77. 709	**78.** 526	**79.** 2500	**80.** 167, 4
81. 6 seconds	**82.** 44	**83.** 40 000	**84.** 45
85. 117			

EXERCISE 6

1. 830	**2.** 6988	**3.** 2289	**4.** 97, 1 m	**5.** 2083
6. 10	**7.** 18	**8.** (a) £5072, (b) £1287		**9.** £1983
10. 42				

EXERCISE 7

1. 5, 6	**2.** $-12, -16$	**3.** 12, 14	**4.** 16, 32
5. 19, 22	**6.** $1\frac{1}{2}, \frac{3}{4}$	**7.** 125, 216	**8.** $-18, -25$
9. $125, -216$	**10.** 48, 55	**11.** $-11, -14$	**12.** $-2, -2$
13. 25, 33	**14.** 20, 30	**15.** $+9, +11$	**16.** $+25, +36$
17. $+30, +35$	**18.** $+25, -36$	**19.** $0, -10$	**20.** $+6, +5$
21. $4, -2$	**22.** $-10, +25$	**23.** $+\frac{1}{10}, +\frac{1}{100}$	**24.** $+0.8, +0.16$
25. $+3, -1$	**26.** $+33, +65$	**27.** $+9, +4$	**28.** $+8, +2$
29. $-1, +5$	**30.** $+100, +180$		

EXERCISE 8

1. $3^4 \times 5^2 \times 7^2$	**2.** $2^2 \times 11^3$	**3.** $2^5 \times 3 \times 5^2$
4. $3^3 \times 5^3 \times 7^2$	**5.** 3^7	**6.** 2^7
7. 5^4	**8.** 3^3	**9.** $2^2 \times 3^2$
10. 2^9	**11.** 10^5	**12.** 10^5
13. 2^4	**14.** 1	**15.** $2^2 \times 3^4$
16. 36	**17.** 180	**18.** 1800
19. 432	**20.** 2700	**21.** $2^2 \times 3^2$
22. $2^4 \times 3$	**23.** $2^2 \times 3^3$	**24.** $2^2 \times 3^2 \times 7$
25. $2^4 \times 3^2$	**26.** $3^3 \times 5^2$	**27.** 5×7^3
28. $2^3 \times 3^3$	**29.** $2^5 \times 7^2$	**30.** $2 \times 3 \times 5 \times 7$
31. $2^5 \times 3^3$	**32.** $5^3 \times 7$	**33.** $3^2 \times 5^3$
34. $3^4 \times 5 \times 7$	**35.** $3^5 \times 5^2$	**36.** $2^8 \times 5$
37. $2^4 \times 11^2$	**38.** $2^3 \times 11 \times 13$	**39.** $7^3 \times 11^2$
40. $2 \times 3 \times 5 \times 7 \times 11 \times 13$	**41.** No	**42.** Yes
43. Yes	**44.** No	**45.** Yes
46. No	**47.** Yes	**48.** No
49. No	**50.** Yes	**51.** No
52. Yes	**53.** 2	**54.** 6
55. 15	**56.** 3	**57.** 3
58. 9	**59.** 4	**60.** 7
61. 2	**62.** 7	**63.** 21
64. $2^6 \times 3^2$, 24	**65.** $3^4 \times 5^2$, 45	**66.** $5^2 \times 7^2$, 35
67. $2^8 \times 3^2$, 48	**68.** $2^2 \times 3^6$, 54	**69.** $2^6 \times 3^4$, 72
70. $3^2 \times 5^4$, 75	**71.** $2^6 \times 5^2 \times 11^2$, 440	**72.** $2^3 \times 3^3$, 6
73. 3^6, 9	**74.** $2^6 \times 3^3$, 12	**75.** $3^3 \times 5^3$, 15
76. $2^3 \times 3^6$, 18	**77.** $2^9 \times 3^3$, 24	**78.** 13, 260
79. 33, 198	**80.** 5, 275	**81.** 15, 525
82. 3, 6	**83.** 2, 12	**84.** 9, 63
85. 5, 35		

EXERCISE 9

1. 4	2. 10	3. 5	4. 6	5. 6
6. 17	7. 2	8. 15	9. 9	10. 7
11. 6	12. 7	13. 2	14. 3	15. 8
16. 1	17. 18	18. 17	19. 3	20. 14
21. 3×5	22. 5×7	23. 3^2	24. 7	25. $2^4 \times 3$
26. $2^2 \times 3^2$	27. $2^3 \times 3$	28. 3^3	29. 2×3	30. $2^4 \times 3$
31. 2×3^3	32. $2^3 \times 7$	33. $2^3 \times 3$	34. 7	35. $2 \times 3 \times 7$
36. 2^4	37. 5^2	38. $3^3 \times 5$	39. $2^3 \times 7$	40. 19
41. 2^5	42. 2×3^2	43. 3×13	44. $2^2 \times 7$	45. 5^2
46. 3×7^2	47. $2 \times 3^2 \times 7$	48. $2^3 \times 3^2$	49. $2^3 \times 7$	50. $3 \times 5 \times 7$

EXERCISE 10

1. 10	2. 50	3. 36	4. 60
5. 36	6. 60	7. 54	8. 84
9. 60	10. 105	11. $2^2 \times 3^2$	12. $2^3 \times 5^2$
13. $2^2 \times 3^4$	14. $2^2 \times 5^3$	15. $2^2 \times 3^4$	16. $3^3 \times 5^2$
17. $3^3 \times 5^3$	18. $2^2 \times 3^2 \times 5^3$	19. $2^2 \times 3^2 \times 5$	20. $2^4 \times 3^3 \times 5^2$
21. $2 \times 3 \times 5$	22. $2^4 \times 3^2$	23. $2^4 \times 3 \times 7$	24. $3^4 \times 7^2$
25. $2^2 \times 3 \times 5^3$	26. $2^2 \times 3^3 \times 7$	27. $2^6 \times 3 \times 5 \times 7$	28. $2^3 \times 3 \times 13^2$
29. $2^2 \times 3 \times 11^2$	30. $2^4 \times 3^3$	31. $2^3 \times 3^2 \times 7$	32. $2^2 \times 3 \times 7$
33. $3^2 \times 5^2 \times 7 \times 13$	34. $2 \times 3 \times 11^2 \times 13$	35. $2^2 \times 3^3 \times 7$	

EXERCISE 11

1. $\frac{1}{2}, \frac{5}{8}, \frac{7}{20}, \frac{13}{64}, \frac{9}{32}$
2. Nine-twentieths, three-eighths, twenty-one twenty-ninths, thirty-one hundredths, one hundred and thirty-seven two hundredths
3. 5 p, 75 p, £1.75, 20 cm, 6 minutes, 16 hours

EXERCISE 12

1. (a) $\frac{3}{5}$ (b) $\frac{3}{4}$ (c) $\frac{4}{9}$ (d) $\frac{3}{25}$ (e) $\frac{9}{16}$ (f) $\frac{5}{12}$ (g) $\frac{181}{338}$ (h) $\frac{7}{15}$ (i) $\frac{23}{29}$ (j) $\frac{23}{39}$
   (k) $\frac{7}{19}$ (l) $\frac{2}{7}$ (m) $\frac{17}{21}$ (n) $\frac{31}{36}$ (o) $\frac{19}{24}$

2. (a) 12 (b) 20 (c) 8 (d) 63 (e) 64 (f) 14 (g) 8 (h) 8 (i) 9 (j) 432

3. (a) $\frac{1}{4}, \frac{1}{3}, \frac{3}{8}$ (b) $\frac{5}{9}, \frac{4}{7}, \frac{2}{3}$ (c) $\frac{1}{3}, \frac{7}{20}, \frac{7}{16}$ (d) $\frac{3}{8}, \frac{5}{12}, \frac{7}{16}, \frac{23}{48}$
   (e) $\frac{31}{36}, \frac{41}{45}, \frac{15}{16}, \frac{77}{81}$ (f) $\frac{23}{60}, \frac{49}{120}, \frac{37}{90}, \frac{13}{30}$ (g) $\frac{12}{25}, \frac{29}{60}, \frac{39}{80}, \frac{22}{45}$ (h) $\frac{13}{60}, \frac{2}{9}, \frac{7}{30}, \frac{4}{15}$

4. (a) $\frac{3}{4}, \frac{11}{16}, \frac{5}{8}$ (b) $\frac{8}{25}, \frac{36}{125}, \frac{1}{5}$ (c) $\frac{11}{14}, \frac{5}{7}, \frac{13}{20}$ (d) $\frac{4}{9}, \frac{1}{3}, \frac{2}{7}, \frac{1}{5}$
   (e) $\frac{2}{3}, \frac{9}{14}, \frac{11}{18}, \frac{10}{21}$ (f) $\frac{2}{7}, \frac{5}{21}, \frac{2}{9}, \frac{5}{28}$ (g) $\frac{11}{12}, \frac{13}{15}, \frac{19}{24}, \frac{23}{32}$ (h) $\frac{11}{42}, \frac{7}{30}, \frac{8}{35}, \frac{13}{60}$

5. (a) $3\frac{1}{3}$ (b) $1\frac{1}{2}$ (c) $14\frac{2}{3}$ (d) 5 (e) 4 (f) $5\frac{5}{13}$ (g) 40 (h) $7\frac{1}{4}$ (i) $4\frac{5}{8}$
   (j) 30 (k) $5\frac{5}{8}$ (l) $7\frac{3}{13}$ (m) $3\frac{10}{21}$ (n) 14 (o) $3\frac{12}{13}$ (p) $4\frac{1}{2}$ (q) $27\frac{3}{4}$ (r) $12\frac{13}{19}$
   (s) $2\frac{6}{31}$ (t) $21\frac{17}{73}$

6. (a) $\frac{16}{3}$ (b) $\frac{31}{7}$ (c) $\frac{91}{9}$ (d) $\frac{41}{3}$ (e) $\frac{57}{4}$ (f) $\frac{31}{4}$ (g) $\frac{42}{5}$ (h) $\frac{77}{8}$ (i) $\frac{127}{6}$ (j) $\frac{162}{11}$
   (k) $\frac{81}{5}$ (l) $\frac{382}{9}$ (m) $\frac{130}{19}$ (n) $\frac{157}{32}$ (o) $\frac{228}{31}$ (p) $\frac{324}{23}$ (q) $\frac{508}{7}$ (r) $\frac{301}{8}$ (s) $\frac{717}{7}$ (t) $\frac{4085}{17}$

EXERCISE 13

1. 1	2. $\frac{2}{3}$	3. $\frac{9}{17}$	4. $\frac{1}{2}$	5. $\frac{3}{5}$
6. 1	7. 1	8. $\frac{5}{8}$	9. $1\frac{11}{24}$	10. $1\frac{1}{10}$

11. $1\frac{17}{40}$ 12. $\frac{82}{99}$ 13. $\frac{13}{16}$ 14. $\frac{15}{16}$ 15. $\frac{31}{32}$

16. $\frac{11}{24}$ 17. $1\frac{1}{12}$ 18. $1\frac{29}{60}$ 19. $1\frac{5}{12}$ 20. $1\frac{11}{12}$

21. $1\frac{17}{30}$ 22. $\frac{11}{24}$ 23. $1\frac{13}{18}$ 24. $1\frac{8}{9}$ 25. $2\frac{1}{4}$

26. $3\frac{3}{4}$ 27. $7\frac{1}{2}$ 28. $6\frac{5}{8}$ 29. $10\frac{1}{8}$ 30. $14\frac{1}{6}$

31. $17\frac{13}{14}$ 32. $4\frac{1}{26}$ 33. $5\frac{1}{6}$ 34. $3\frac{19}{28}$ 35. $7\frac{5}{24}$

36. $14\frac{13}{16}$ 37. $4\frac{1}{4}$ 38. $6\frac{7}{8}$ 39. $13\frac{17}{40}$ 40. $17\frac{3}{5}$

41. $18\frac{1}{8}$ 42. $5\frac{2}{3}$ 43. $7\frac{2}{7}$ 44. $14\frac{3}{10}$ 45. $2\frac{71}{72}$

46. $7\frac{5}{8}$ 47. $5\frac{17}{36}$ 48. $6\frac{4}{7}$ 49. $14\frac{11}{36}$ 50. $12\frac{2}{5}$

EXERCISE 14

1. $\frac{2}{5}$ 2. $\frac{4}{15}$ 3. $\frac{1}{2}$ 4. $\frac{3}{17}$ 5. $\frac{7}{24}$

6. $\frac{5}{12}$ 7. $\frac{1}{8}$ 8. $\frac{1}{9}$ 9. $\frac{7}{32}$ 10. $\frac{19}{100}$

11. $\frac{23}{42}$ 12. $\frac{13}{48}$ 13. $\frac{9}{35}$ 14. $\frac{3}{35}$ 15. $\frac{1}{16}$

16. $\frac{2}{9}$ 17. $\frac{1}{4}$ 18. 0 19. $\frac{21}{50}$ 20. $\frac{5}{48}$

21. $\frac{11}{12}$ 22. $\frac{7}{36}$ 23. $\frac{5}{6}$ 24. $1\frac{1}{10}$ 25. $1\frac{1}{6}$

26. $3\frac{3}{8}$ 27. $7\frac{1}{6}$ 28. $6\frac{1}{4}$ 29. $2\frac{5}{12}$ 30. $3\frac{1}{8}$

31. $\frac{3}{4}$ 32. $4\frac{5}{8}$ 33. $2\frac{11}{24}$ 34. $\frac{37}{60}$ 35. $7\frac{5}{21}$

36. $1\frac{7}{10}$ 37. $2\frac{1}{8}$ 38. $4\frac{1}{12}$ 39. $1\frac{1}{35}$ 40. $2\frac{29}{48}$

41. $1\frac{5}{7}$ 42. $2\frac{5}{12}$ 43. $2\frac{5}{8}$ 44. $9\frac{1}{3}$ 45. $\frac{1}{18}$

46. $\frac{1}{12}$ 47. $3\frac{33}{100}$ 48. $1\frac{47}{72}$ 49. $3\frac{1}{4}$ 50. $3\frac{17}{40}$

EXERCISE 15

1. $3\frac{1}{2}$ cm 2. $2\frac{1}{4}$ m 3. £$4\frac{2}{3}$ 4. $1\frac{12}{13}$

5. $9\frac{3}{5}$ p 6. $10\frac{1}{2}$ litres 7. $3\frac{1}{3}$ pints 8. 3 gallons

9. $7\frac{1}{5}$ g 10. $2\frac{2}{3}$ seconds 11. 6 p 12. $3\frac{3}{4}$ kg

13. $9\frac{3}{5}$ 14. $1\frac{1}{5}$ 15. $1\frac{11}{13}$ 16. $13\frac{1}{3}$

17. 6 18. 35 19. 16 20. 36

21. 18 22. 44 23. 72 24. $29\frac{1}{4}$

25. $24\frac{1}{2}$ 26. $16\frac{1}{4}$ 27. 14 28. $4\frac{3}{8}$

29. $\frac{10}{27}$ 30. $\frac{7}{20}$ 31. $\frac{10}{39}$ 32. $1\frac{2}{3}$

33. $\frac{9}{98}$ 34. $\frac{1}{12}$ 35. $2\frac{1}{2}$ 36. $\frac{6}{19}$

37. 2 38. $1\frac{5}{8}$ 39. 2 40. $4\frac{29}{40}$

41. $1\frac{17}{30}$ 42. $2\frac{1}{2}$ 43. $2\frac{7}{10}$ 44. $\frac{5}{8}$

45. $28\frac{1}{2}$ 46. $11\frac{1}{3}$ 47. 18 48. $13\frac{13}{20}$

49. $13\frac{1}{2}$ 50. 3

EXERCISE 16

1. $\frac{1}{8}$ 2. $\frac{1}{9}$ 3. $\frac{1}{8}$ 4. $\frac{2}{21}$ 5. $\frac{1}{26}$ 6. $\frac{2}{7}$

7. $\frac{1}{2}$ 8. $\frac{2}{3}$ 9. 8 10. 18 11. 10 12. 96

13. $\frac{1}{2}$ 14. $1\frac{1}{2}$ 15. $\frac{1}{4}$ 16. 5 17. $\frac{9}{16}$ 18. $1\frac{11}{24}$

19. $3\frac{1}{9}$ 20. $\frac{3}{4}$ 21. 3 22. $\frac{3}{4}$ 23. $1\frac{1}{9}$ 24. $1\frac{1}{20}$

25. $1\frac{1}{2}$ 26. 8   27. $1\frac{1}{3}$ 28. $\frac{19}{26}$ 29. $2\frac{1}{4}$ 30. $1\frac{1}{2}$

31. $1\frac{5}{7}$ 32. $1\frac{1}{3}$ 33. $1\frac{2}{3}$ 34. $\frac{4}{9}$ 35. $\frac{3}{7}$ 36. $\frac{7}{32}$

37. $1\frac{1}{4}$ 38. $4\frac{2}{3}$ 39. $\frac{4}{5}$ 40. $\frac{4}{9}$ 41. $1\frac{7}{13}$ 42. $\frac{2}{3}$

43. $2\frac{1}{2}$ 44. $1\frac{1}{6}$ 45. $\frac{3}{14}$ 46. $5\frac{1}{3}$ 47. $\frac{3}{10}$ 48. $1\frac{3}{32}$

49. $6\frac{3}{7}$ 50. $\frac{27}{98}$

EXERCISE 17

1. 75   2. £72   3. 147   4. 36

5. 240 miles   6. 500 gallons   7. £857 500   8. £4.80

9. 5 litres   10. 414   11. £14 560

12. A, £938, B £804, C £938   13. 336   14. $2\frac{2}{5}$

15. $8\frac{1}{6}$ 16. 56   17. $5\frac{1}{4}$ m   18. $8\frac{8}{9}$ minutes

19. $3\frac{1}{3}$ 20. $3\frac{3}{7}$

EXERCISE 18

1. 12.3   2. 4.56   3. 83.73   4. 7.346   5. 24.05

6. 105.604   7. 726.08   8. 10.536   9. 400.23   10. 6104.508

	THOUSANDS	HUNDREDS	TENS	UNITS	TENTHS	HUNDREDTHS	THOUSANDTHS
11.				8	6		
12.				4	2	7	
13.			2	6	8	3	
14.				4	9	2	6
15.			2	7	9	4	2
16.		6	3	6	4	2	1
17.			1	6		4	
18.			3	3			5
19.			3		9	2	
20.		4		6	5		7
21.		1	2	6	5	4	3
22.		5				6	3
23.		7	3	5	7		7
24.	3			7	6		7
25.	7	3		5		4	2
26.					6	4	
27.					2	4	7
28.						9	3
29.					1	1	4
30.							8

31. 0.3   32. 0.7   33. 0.37   34. 0.54   35. 0.357

36. 0.174   37. 0.352   38. 0.497   39. 0.913   40. 0.705

41. 0.037   42. 0.052   43. 0.234   44. 5.3   45. 4.72

46. 1.23   47. $\frac{4}{10}$ 48. $\frac{2}{10}+\frac{7}{100}$ 49. $\frac{8}{10}+\frac{3}{100}$ 50. $\frac{2}{10}+\frac{4}{100}+\frac{6}{1000}$

51. $\frac{7}{10}+\frac{3}{100}+\frac{7}{1000}$ 52. $\frac{8}{10}+\frac{2}{100}+\frac{9}{1000}$ 53. $\frac{6}{100}+\frac{2}{1000}$ 54. $\frac{3}{100}+\frac{5}{1000}+\frac{9}{10\,000}$

55. $\frac{53}{10}+\frac{7}{100}$ 56. $\frac{42}{10}+\frac{9}{100}$ 57. $\frac{100}{10}+\frac{7}{100}$ 58. $\frac{359}{10}+\frac{3}{1000}$ 59. $\frac{3}{10}$

60. $\frac{38}{100}$ 61. $\frac{94}{100}$ 62. $\frac{357}{1000}$ 63. $\frac{848}{1000}$ 64. $\frac{718}{1000}$

65. $\frac{51}{1000}$ 66. $\frac{248}{10\,000}$ 67. $\frac{473}{100}$ 68. $\frac{824}{10}$ 69. $\frac{6945}{1000}$

70. $\frac{23\,052}{1000}$ 71. $\frac{4}{5}$ 72. $\frac{3}{4}$ 73. $\frac{9}{20}$ 74. $\frac{13}{20}$

75. $\frac{3}{8}$ 76. $\frac{5}{8}$ 77. $\frac{16}{25}$ 78. $\frac{7}{25}$ 79. $\frac{9}{25}$

80. $\frac{157}{250}$ 81. $\frac{111}{250}$ 82. $\frac{7}{8}$ 83. $\frac{11}{20}$ 84. $\frac{39}{50}$

85. $\frac{1}{8}$

EXERCISE 19

1. 67.3	2. 142.1	3. 8.92	4. 3614
5. 4.29	6. 164.2	7. 4960	8. 235
9. 96.4	10. 4280	11. 39.43	12. 1692
13. 2392	14. 4368	15. 912	16. 7
17. 122.9	18. 264	19. 7340	20. 82 000
21 7.02	22. 0.842	23. 24.64	24. 0.0526
25. 4.315	26. 0.623	27. 0.051 76	28. 0.009 16
29. 0.734	30. 1.92	31. 0.082 64	32. 4.34
33. 0.0009	34. 0.9	35. 0.742	36. 6.06
37. 0.006 34	38. 0.000 74	39. 0.0436	40. 0.9096

EXERCISE 20

1. 6.8	2. 9.8	3. 7.9	4. 8.8
5. 9.9	6. 9.2	7. 9.5	8. 8.2
9. 13.3	10. 12.5	11. 8.86	12. 7.74
13. 7.98	14. 14.40	15. 13.01	16. 56.38
17. 84.86	18. 44.24	19. 104.8	20. 71.25
21. 142.28	22. 325.62	23. 233.13	24. 580.37
25. 422.52	26. 23.514	27. 23.037	28. 78.195
29. 5.412	30. 40.923	31. 79.639	32. 115.837
33. 112.53	34. 172.567	35. 370.176	36. 28.32
37. 209.725	38. 504.157	39. 169.895	40. 779.857
41. 260.42	42. 599.049	43. 88.562	44. 135.476
45. 466.487	46. 977.814	47. 71.81	48. 164.76
49. 888.212	50. 934.347	51. 29.3	52. 107.86
53. 88.13	54. 95.107	55. 313.013	56. 382.4
57. 5.123	58. 19.936	59. 375.186	60. 125.824
61. 2.2	62. 3.2	63. 11.3	64. 11.2
65. 24.3	66. 2.52	67. 13.11	68. 11.42
69. 8.221	70. 11.24	71. 13.1	72. 2.96
73. 54.39	74. 4.55	75. 3.97	76. 24.593
77. 16.316	78. 313.49	79. 276.49	80. 50.439
81. 32.46	82. 469.54	83. 7.933	84. 74.785
85. 3.839	86. 4.153	87. 11.054	88. 41.855
89. 10.469	90. 25.114	91. 6.48	92. 22.86
93. 1.065	94. 2.457	95. 250.34	96. 19.81
97. 27.55	98. 50.65	99. 52.076	100. 79.263

EXERCISE 21

1. 1	2. 1.2	3. 5.6	4. 2.4
5. 0.21	6. 0.4	7. 0.48	8. 0.18
9. 0.48	10. 2.1	11. 1.82	12. 2.34
13. 8.65	14. 11.36	15. 47.44	16. 43.44
17. 19.11	18. 61.46	19. 15.64	20. 46.75
21. 10.4	22. 35.5	23. 28.8	24. 21.9
25. 1.26	26. 35	27. 1.98	28. 174
29. 802.8	30. 2555	31. 367	32. 5.46
33. 24.25	34. 57.96	35. 21.42	36. 0.18

37. 0.35	38. 0.72	39. 0.08	40. 0.1458
41. 72	42. 0.2448	43. 0.4488	44. 0.1608
45. 1.9602	46. 0.2232	47. 3.5834	48. 3,4808
49. 50.68	50. 247.59	51. 231.08	52. 609.74
53. 115.456	54. 417.444	55. 659.022	56. 2298.75
57. 22.169 43	58. 5.677 83	59. 366.1424	60. 25.0177
61. 3	62. 2	63. 5	64. 9.870
65. 3.145	66. 4.190	67. 35.68	68. 2.047
69. 0.024	70. 0.24	71. 1.632	72. 0.84
73. 1.092	74. 1.24	75. 2.952	76. 3.066
77. 0.785	78. 0.5481	79. 17.064	80. 5.8752

EXERCISE 22

1. 1.32	2. 1.47	3. 1.78	4. 35.6
5. 5.14	6. 27.34	7. 7.93	8. 4.27
9. 1.25	10. 0.8	11. 0.6	12. 1.6667
13. 0.482	14. 0.212	15. 0.153	16. 0.118
17. 0.031	18. 0.042	19. 0.0155	20. 0.0098
21. 2.2	22. 3.75	23. 2.25	24. 1.375
25. 0.375	26. 6.2	27. 0.875	28. 2.5
29. 6.75	30. 3.5	31. 8.6	32. 2.125
33. 4.72	34. 3.95	35. 8.471	36. 6.304
37. 0.0093	38. 0.0216	39. 0.000 734	40. 0.0295

EXERCISE 23

1. 2.73	2. 1.84	3. 5.63	4. 8.4	5 3.22
6. 5.42	7. 6.3	8. 4.5	9. 7.4	10. 8.6
11. 8.2	12. 8.8	13. 7.2	14. 1.3	15. 6.7
16. 21.4	17. 54.2	18. 257	19. 0.44	20. 0.65
21. 0.94	22. 65	23. 65.4	24. 172	25. 7.55
26. 3.14	27. 4.08	28. 5.6	29. 2.95	30. 60.5
31. 3.6975	32. 35	33. 53	34. 42	35. 68.5

EXERCISE 24

1. 14.4	2. 39.5	3. 8.9	4. 12.9	5. 3.4
6. 295.0	7. 1027.6	8. 55.0	9. 7.6	10. 73.9
11. 0.9	12. 0.3	13. 0.4	14. 0.6	15. 0.9
16. 0.1	17. 0.1	18. 92.6	19. 61.1	20. 40.1
21. 14.27	22. 50.10	23. 37.35	24. 9.29	25. 7.67
26. 70.25	27. 63.60	28. 42.56	29. 8.26	30. 3.50
31. 0.93	32. 1.00	33. 0.68	34. 0.35	35. 0.14
36. 0.62	37. 0.42	38. 0.74	39. 0.83	40. 0.19
41. 4	42. 4	43. 16	44. 28	45. 36
46. 19	47. 53	48. 42	49. 73	50. 128
51. 232	52. 528	53. 414	54. 300	55. 405
56. 1	57. 1	58. 9	59. 7	60. 714
61. 70	62. 40	63. 220	64. 590	65. 170
66. 820	67. 940	68. 220	69. 520	70. 6840
71. 60	72. 10	73. 10	74. 20	75. 70
76. 5640	77. 4980	78. 8000	79. 60	80. 50
81. 7400	82. 6200	83. 200	84. 600	85. 400
86. 100	87. 3400	88. 1800	89. 100	90. 700
91. 5400	92. 1300	93. 34 000	94. 56 400	95. 673 500
96. 400	97. 800	98. 31 500	99. 83 800	100. 10 000

1. 328
2. 413
3. 763
4. 843
5. 193
6. 61.3
7. 80.9
8. 36.7
9. 40.3
10. 59.3
11. 2.34
12. 3.93
13. 5.66
14. 9.89
15. 7.34
16. 0.556
17. 0.621
18. 0.738
19. 0.812
20. 0.544
21. 1240
22. 6930
23. 8280
24. 4340
25. 3930
26. 0.0647
27. 0.0295
28. 0.0857
29. 0.0592
30. 0.0225
31. 36 500
32. 27 600
33. 814 000
34. 54 700
35. 50 100
36. 5.93
37. 16.9
38. 207
39. 62 600
40. 0.554
41. 73.6
42. 193 000
43. 0.009 27
44. 5.45
45. 920 000
46. 0.002 94
47. 0.0457
48. 604 000
49. 82.9
50. 327
51. 540
52. 730
53. 54
54. 17
55. 35
56. 27 000
57. 9.5
58. 18
59. 390
60. 4.3
61. 0.93
62. 0.39
63. 0.73
64. 0.0095
65. 0.037
66. 200
67. 16
68. 9.0
69. 8.2
70. 55 000
71. 52 730
72. 17 420
73. 39 250
74. 725.0
75. 363.0
76. 44.25
77. 32.94
78. 3.142
79. 2.988
80. 0.6432
81. 0.5679
82. 0.028 67
83. 8.625
84. 37.14
85. 98.95
86. 23.56
87. 0.045 94
88. 473 800
89. 83.46
90. 0.3543
91. 75, 74.6, 74.62
92. 19, 18.5, 18.54
93. 25, 24.9, 24.93
94. 524, 524, 524.15
95. 618, 618, 618.33
96. 828, 828, 828.19
97. 8, 7.92, 7.92
98. 42, 42.4, 42.43
99. 9, 8.55, 8.55
100. 365, 365, 364.62

1. 2.46
2. 6.53
3. 8.20
4. 9.84
5. 5.27
6. 8.53
7. 9.45
8. 0.65
9. 0.24
10. 0.52
11. 0.16
12. 5.47
13. 7.73
14. 3.75
15. 1.70
16. 0.04
17. 18.57
18. 3.96
19. 0.71
20. 0.02
21. 1.065
22. 0.781
23. 1.998
24. 0.674
25. 0.709
26. 0.492
27. 2.352
28. 1.169
29. 1.624
30. 0.397
31. 0.092
32. 0.018
33. 1.703
34. 0.873
35. 7.321
36. 3.89
37. 4.22
38. 1.59
39. 1.29
40. 0.397
41. 0.369
42. 0.0197
43. 0.0167
44. 0.0148
45. 528
46. 658
47. 9510
48. 740
49. 186
50. 5800

1. 7.26×10^1
2. 1.834×10^2
3. 5×10^3
4. 4.242×10^2
5. 8.24×10^4
6. 1.23×10^6
7. 5×10^{-1}
8. 4.3×10^{-1}
9. 8.42×10^{-1}
10. 7×10^{-2}
11. 9×10^{-3}
12. 4.12×10^{-2}
13. 9.3×10^{-3}
14. 2×10^{-5}
15. 5.43×10^{-5}
16. (i) 1.23×10^4, (ii) 3.6×10^6, (iii) 4×10^1
17. (i) 7.5×10^4, (ii) 1.25×10^9, (iii) 2×10^0, (iv) 5×10^{-1}
18. (i) 1.44×10^2, (ii) 9×10^6
19. (i) 4.26×10^{-3}, (ii) 4.14×10^{-3}, (iii) 2.52×10^{-7}, (iv) 7×10^1
20. (i) 1.764×10^2, (ii) 4×10^{-11}

1. 3 min slow
2. -5 min fast
3. Take £20 out
4. Put in £50
5. 100 m down
6. Up -6 stairs
7. 50 litres flows out
8. 3 km due N
9. Decrease 6%
10. Increases -20%
11. Decreases 2000
12. Lost by 2 goals

EXERCISE 29

1. 5	2. 4	3. 3	4. 3	5. −2	6. −8
7. −10	8. −6	9. −7	10. −12	11. −13	12. −30
13. 17	14. 24	15. −11	16. 4	17. 15	18. −12
19. −2	20. −25	21. 0	22. 2	23. 0	24. −2
25. 8	26. 11	27. 3	28. 10	29. −14	30. −15
31. −18	32. 5	33. −3	34. −15	35. −3	36. −1
37. 10	38. 11	39. 11	40. 7		

EXERCISE 30

1. −12	2. −8	3. 20	4. −42	5. −42	6. −70
7. 39	8. −15	9. −1	10. −4	11. −8	12. 3
13. −2	14. −4	15. 3	16. 3	17. −9	18. −8
19. 11	20. −4	21. −4	22. 2	23. −8	24. 2
25. −2	26. −3	27. 9	28. $\frac{1}{3}$	29. 6	30. −35
31. 12	32. 5	33. −15	34. 8	35. 48	36. 54
37. 2	38. −5	39. −3	40. −3	41. −3	42. 2
43. 6	44. 5	45. 8	46. 2	47. 4	48. −4
49. 0	50. 64	51. −64	52. −64	53. 64	54. 4
55. −4	56. 8	57. −4	58. −4	59. 0	60. 4
61. 6	62. 4	63. 1	64. −1	65. 6	66. −6
67. $\frac{1}{4}$	68. −1	69. 1	70. $-\frac{2}{3}$	71. −3	72. −72
73. 3	74. $-5\frac{1}{3}$	75. −16			

EXERCISE 31

1. (a) 4 cm   (b) 5 cm   (c) 3 cm   (d) 5 cm
2. (a) 24 mm   (b) 42 mm   (c) 28 mm   (d) 55 mm
3. (a) 3.3 cm, 33 mm   (b) 3 cm, 30 mm   (c) 2.4 cm, 24 mm
   (d) 6.95 cm, 69.5 mm
6. (a) metre   (b) centimetre   (c) metre   (d) kilometre   (e) millimetre
7. (a) 12 000   (b) 4320   (c) 680   (d) 5.29   (e) 43.6   (f) 0.26
   (g) 0.734   (h) 0.038   (i) 60 240   (j) 0.497
8. (a) 2400   (b) 360   (c) 49   (d) 2.6   (e) 4.4   (f) 63.4
   (g) 0.731   (h) 0.004   (i) 173 200   (j) 2640
9. (a) 370   (b) 135   (c) 91.2   (d) 4.6   (e) 8400   (f) 27 000
   (g) 730   (h) 24   (i) 1 243 000   (j) 92 000
10. (a) 5   (b) 10   (c) 0.75   (d) 4.36   (e) 0.83   (f) 0.1763
   (g) 0.4936   (h) 0.007 63   (i) 0.1434   (j) 7.23
11. (a) 13.66   (b) 3.86   (c) 11.186   (d) 3090.4   (e) 985
12. (a) 10   (b) 19.7   (c) 10.7 m   (d) 0.288 m   (e) 1.574 m
13. (a) 30 m 24 cm   (b) 24 m 36 cm   (c) 7 m 49 cm   (d) 24 m 16 cm   (e) 92 m 60 cm
   (f) 67 m 24 cm   (g) 103 m 4 cm
14. (a) 2.29 m   (b) 5.43 m   (c) 6.01 m   (d) 1.7 m   (e) 0
15. 250   16. 4000   17. 556   18. 8   19. 56   20. 250

EXERCISE 32

1. (a) kilogram   (b) tonne   (c) milligram   (d) milligram   (e) kilogram
2. (a) 0.25 g   (b) 5.7 g   (c) 73.4 g   (d) 4.73 g   (e) 5420 g   (f) 20 400 g
   (g) 730 g   (h) 49.3 g
3. (a) 7.6 kg   (b) 0.491 kg   (c) 0.0972 kg   (d) 6.04 kg
   (e) 0.9264 kg   (f) 0.055 45 kg   (g) 0.000 374 kg   (h) 0.008 497 kg
4. (a) 54 000 mg   (b) 429 000 mg   (c) 1240 mg   (d) 460 mg
   (e) 1 200 000 mg   (f) 44 000 mg   (g) 217 000 mg   (h) 840 mg

5. (a) 3.42 t   (b) 1740 kg   (c) 47 kg   (d) 83.44 t   (e) 504.6 t
6. (a) 694 kg   (b) 4.6 kg   (c) 1.848 kg   (d) 0.743 kg   (e) 716 kg
7. (a) 34.09 g   (b) 62.2 g   (c) 17.22 g   (d) 148.1 g
8. (a) 700 g   (b) 3910 g   (c) 0.62 g   (d) 3.01 g   (e) 0.5959 g
9. (a) 9 kg 43 g   (b) 1 kg 691 g   (c) 3 kg 450 g   (d) 13 kg 740 g   (e) 28 kg 400 g
10. 16.56 kg   11. 21.792 kg   12. 7.12 kg   13. £15   14. 9.54 t
15. 1.25 kg   16. 12.74 kg   17. 6.318 t   18. 14.81 kg   19. 846 kg
20. 436 g   21. 2195 g   22. 23.69 kg   23. 8.188 t   24. 42
25. 31.36 t

REVISION PAPER 1

1. 8235   2. 24 035   3. $2^6 \times 3^4$, 72   4. $\frac{3}{7}$ 5. 30, 2.5 m

REVISION PAPER 2

1. 1341   2. 134   3. $3^2 \times 7^2 \times 13$, 13   4. 39.984 kg
5. 4, −1

REVISION PAPER 3

1. 15 530   2. 5.33 p.m.   3. 67   4. $3^3 \times 7^3$, 21   5. (a) $\frac{5}{6}$ (b) $\frac{7}{6}$

REVISION PAPER 4

1. 120   2. 18, 23   3. HCF 18, LCM 60 480
4. (a) $1\frac{1}{14}$ (b) $\frac{5}{14}$ 5. $38\frac{3}{4}$ hours

REVISION PAPER 5

1. 2173   2. 4.318 kg, 146 g less   3. $9\frac{1}{3}$
4. (a) 109.9 (b) 138.8   5. 3 km

REVISION PAPER 6

1. $\frac{3}{16}$ 2. $3\frac{1}{2}$ 3. (a) 0.76   (b) 0.32
4. (a) 5 h 20 min   (b) 26 h 40 min   (c) 1040 h   5. 4380, 1752

REVISION PAPER 7

1. 81   2. 714   3. 792
4. (a) 0.084   (b) 0.002   5. 24, 25

REVISION PAPER 8

1. 19   2. 2667   3. (a) 6.72   (b) 530
4. 63.79 m   5. (a) 16   (b) 6

REVISION PAPER 9

1. 82.555   2. 2409   3. 3.47   4. 1.2 kg   5. 450

REVISION PAPER 10

1. 2
2. 58 R 37
3. 2205 kg, 735 kg
4. (a) 300   (b) 294   (c) 293.75
5. 777

REVISION PAPER 11

1. $2^4 \times 7^2 \times 19$, 19
2. (a) 2.028   (b) $5\frac{2}{125}$
3. 77.2472
4. (a) $-1\frac{3}{4}$ (b) 1
5. $2\frac{2}{3}$ m

REVISION PAPER 12

1. 240
2. 24.6
3. 6.39
4. $2^2 \times 3 \times 5^2$
5. $\frac{2}{3}$

REVISION PAPER 13

1. 168.6
2. $+133 + 197$
3. (a) $\frac{31}{40}$ (b) $\frac{67}{250}$
4. 6.01
5. 28 gallons

REVISION PAPER 14

1. (a) 71   (b) 70.75   (c) 70.7
2. (a) 0.08   (b) 0.027
3. $1\frac{1}{6}$
4. $4\frac{1}{2}$ t
5. 56

REVISION PAPER 15

1. $2^3 \times 3 \times 5 \times 7^2$, Yes
2. 4 h 46 min
3. $\frac{5}{13}, \frac{7}{15}, \frac{4}{7}$
4. (a) 0.346 58   (b) 33.4
5. 184

REVISION PAPER 16

1. (a) 490, 493   (b) 493.1
2. $\frac{10}{11}, \frac{11}{12}$
3. $\frac{9}{16}, \frac{11}{24}, \frac{9}{20}$
4. 328.08
5. 2.4 h

REVISION PAPER 17

1. (a) 1.30   (b) 1.299
2. $\frac{14}{125}$
3. $2\frac{23}{24}$
4. $\frac{29}{32}$
5. 8 days

REVISION PAPER 18

1. $25\frac{1}{5}$
2. -3
3. 2.095
4. 14 h 27 min
5. 420

REVISION PAPER 19

1. (a) 4.32   (b) 5.333   (c) 3.9
2. $2^4 \times 3^2 \times 5^2$, 60
3. (a) 67   (b) 67.5   (c) 67.46
4. $\frac{11}{25}$
5. 5, 29 cm

REVISION PAPER 20

1. $1\frac{3}{8}$
2. (a) -1.5 (b) 33
3. 15, 20
4. 144
5. 12 m

REVISION PAPER 21

1. (a) 3   (b) 12
3. Christine 1635 g, Susan 1565 g

2. (a) 0.3125   (b) 0.032
4. 124

5. 14 min

REVISION PAPER 22

1. 2
4. 1666, 300 g

2. (a) $\frac{7}{8}$ (b) $\frac{7}{32}$
5. 120

3. (a) 24.576   (b) 5.3

REVISION PAPER 23

1. $1\frac{2}{5}$
4. $\frac{117}{250}$

2. $2\frac{2}{5}$
5. 6.23 a.m.

3. (a) 216.783   (b) 0.276

REVISION PAPER 24

1. (a) 1000   (b) 961   (c) 960.7
3. $\frac{3}{20}$

2. $2\frac{1}{2} \div \frac{2}{3}$ by $2\frac{1}{12}$
4. 2

5. 13.76 m

REVISION PAPER 25

1. $1\frac{1}{20}$
3. (a) 1   (b) 0.93   (c) 0.926
5. 80 litres

2. (a) 1.92   (b) 120   (c) 0.012
4. (a) $\frac{17}{80}$ (b) 0.2125

EXERCISE 33

1. 243_8 2. 547_8 3. 433_5 4. 142_5 5. 221_3
6. 540_7 7. 333_8 8. 565_8 9. 412_5 10. 333_5
11. 343_6 12. 19, 354, 183, 348
13. 8, 23, 50, 67   14. 14, 27, 58, 110
15. (a) 114, 2032, 4114   (b) 46, 531, 1362   16. (a) 1112_5 (b) 124_5
17. (a) 562_8 (b) 237_8 18. (a) 42007_8 (b) 131_8
19. (a) 143143_5 (b) 1012_3 20. (a) 1416_7 (b) 223_4
21. (a) 1101_3 (b) 5410_6 (c) 20_6 22. (a) 1071_9 (b) 14412_7 (c) 343_5
23. (a) 13013_5 (b) 4061_8 (c) 110001_3 24. (a) 5465_7 (b) 211302_4 (c) 25_8
25. (a) $2\,R\,165_8$ (b) $2\,R\,101_5$

EXERCISE 34

1. 1001   2. 1011   3. 10001   4. 10011
5. 11000   6. 11011   7. 100100   8. 101101
9. 111001   10. 1000101   11. 1100000   12. 1101001
13. 1111110   14. 10001001   15. 10011001   16. 10101100
17. 11000001   18. 11011010   19. 11111101   20. 101010110
21. 6   22. 7   23. 9   24. 12   25. 11
26. 13   27. 22   28. 25   29. 23   30. 19
31. 31   32. 42   33. 51   34. 46   35. 39
36. 57   37. 31   38. 127   39. 110   40. 1100
41. 10101   42. 111000   43. 1011   44. 10101
45. 11000   46. 101011   47. (a), (b), (e)   48. (a), (c), (d)
49. (b), (c)   50. (c)
51. (a) 1101111, 1110000, 1110001   (b) 1101101, 1101111, 1110001
    (c) 101110, 110000
52. 110011   53. 11101   54. 110100   55. 101110

EXERCISE 35

1. 1101	**2.** 10010	**3.** 10001	**4.** 1110
5. 10111	**6.** 101000	**7.** 100110	**8.** 1001011
9. 10101	**10.** 10110	**11.** 11110	**12.** 101100
13. 1011100	**14.** 1010110	**15.** 11	**16.** 10
17. 101	**18.** 1010	**19.** 10111	**20.** 1110
21. 100101	**22.** 10111	**23.** 10010	**24.** 100001
25. 100100	**26.** 111100	**27.** 111100	**28.** 1000110
29. 1111000	**30.** 1111001	**31.** 11111100	**32.** 101
33. 1001	**34.** 100	**35.** 1110	**36.** 1110
37. 10 R 1	**38.** 110 R 100	**39.** 1010 R 100	**40.** 100 R 101

EXERCISE 36

1. £0.79	**2.** £0.99	**3.** £0.88	**4.** £0.88
5. £0.95	**6.** £0.78	**7.** £0.98	**8.** £0.95
9. £1.73	**10.** £1.93	**11.** £2.03	**12.** £2.21
13. £14.40	**14.** £16.76	**15.** £23.19	**16.** £39.42
17. £18.57	**18.** £50.25	**19.** £16.04	**20.** £15.45
21. £1.63$\frac{1}{2}$	**22.** £1.20$\frac{1}{2}$	**23.** £0.91$\frac{1}{2}$	**24.** £1.37$\frac{1}{2}$
25. £15.01$\frac{1}{2}$	**26.** £10.06	**27.** £13.69	**28.** £22.29
29. £104.28$\frac{1}{2}$	**30.** £118.24$\frac{1}{2}$	**31.** £377.58	**32.** £178.87
33. £555.33	**34.** £796.52	**35.** £482.32	**36.** £173.91
37. £741.32	**38.** £2035.22	**39.** £2120.78	**40.** £2330.89$\frac{1}{2}$
41. £59.67$\frac{1}{2}$	**42.** £195.86$\frac{1}{2}$	**43.** £147.92$\frac{1}{2}$	**44.** £165.40
45. £365.58	**46.** £279.77	**47.** £447.52$\frac{1}{2}$	**48.** £1166.31$\frac{1}{2}$
49. £32.17			

50. a = £167.96, b = £199.74, c = £234.60, d = £2887.22, e = £3984.12, f = £3051.56
g = £2861.38, h = £2455.56, i = £2715.28, j = £2492.98, k = £10 525.20

EXERCISE 37

1. £3.22	**2.** £3.04	**3.** £2.12	**4.** £2.31
5. £4.64	**6.** £4.32	**7.** £1.49	**8.** £2.18
9. £2.45$\frac{1}{2}$	**10.** £3.84$\frac{1}{2}$	**11.** £2.97$\frac{1}{2}$	**12.** £5.93$\frac{1}{2}$
13. £6.06$\frac{1}{2}$	**14.** £43.15$\frac{1}{2}$	**15.** £28.82$\frac{1}{2}$	**16.** £47.92$\frac{1}{2}$
17. £40.62	**18.** £115.84	**19.** £142.06	**20.** £15.86
21. £392.12$\frac{1}{2}$	**22.** £187.16$\frac{1}{2}$	**23.** £273.64$\frac{1}{2}$	**24.** £165.14$\frac{1}{2}$
25. £1183.06	**26.** £62.39	**27.** £1548.75$\frac{1}{2}$	**28.** £3615.79$\frac{1}{2}$
29. £21.66	**30.** £12.13	**31.** £86.49	**32.** £132.56
33. £95.24	**34.** £157.13	**35.** £134.75	**36.** £8.45$\frac{1}{2}$
37. £52.15$\frac{1}{2}$	**38.** £6.06	**39.** £88.12	**40.** £765.75
41. £3.35	**42.** £7.84$\frac{1}{2}$	**43.** £9.72	**44.** £23.15$\frac{1}{2}$
45. £196.26$\frac{1}{2}$	**46.** £1.84	**47.** £13.50$\frac{1}{2}$	**48.** £14.60$\frac{1}{2}$
49. £290.65	**50.** £640.62$\frac{1}{2}$		

EXERCISE 38

1. £7.32	**2.** £24.52	**3.** £23.65	**4.** £9.78
5. £36.33	**6.** £68.72	**7.** £37.40	**8.** £87.57
9. £47.52	**10.** £46.48	**11.** £70.72	**12.** £18.40

13. £19.48   14. £55.56   15. £10.96   16. £34.95
17. £60.12   18. £31.85   19. £20.23$\frac{1}{2}$ 20. £22.12$\frac{1}{2}$
21. £74.47$\frac{1}{2}$ 22. £82.88   23. £105.44   24. £167.76
25. £22.05   26. £66.64   27. £163.78   28. £80.82
29. £107.47$\frac{1}{2}$ 30. £77.31   31. £628.16   32. £2420.22
33. £2665.98   34. £610.13   35. £5245.71   36. £5863.12
37. £1667.27   38. £1073.25   39. £1938.89   40. £4490.95$\frac{1}{2}$
41. £3024.17$\frac{1}{2}$ 42. £2362.81$\frac{1}{2}$ 43. £6274.40   44. £8444.16
45. £29 568.52   46. £30 214.70   47. £27 692.50   48. £8762.21
49. £6208.91   50. £35 903.30

EXERCISE 39

1. £1.63   2. £2.27   3. £1.14   4. £2.08   5. £1.35
6. £2.16   7. £5.42   8. £4.36   9. £2.73   10. £7.16
11. £4.13   12. £1.89   13. £5.54   14. £7.92   15. £6.58
16. £4.13   17. £9.26   18. £3.78   19. £1.62   20. £2.44
21. £5.18   22. £4.76   23. £12.91   24. £18.34   25. £6.24
26. £8.93   27. £7.64   28. £10.24   29. £1.64   30. £18.27
31. £9.66   32. £8.38   33. £24.11   34. 44   35. 38
36. 92   37. 64   38. 78   39. 58   40. 36
41. 53   42. 48   43. 102   44. 204   45. 94
46. £1.52$\frac{1}{2}$ 47. £3.78$\frac{1}{2}$ 48. £6.80$\frac{1}{2}$ 49. £16.31$\frac{1}{2}$ 50. £4.62$\frac{1}{2}$
51. £8.16$\frac{1}{2}$ 52. £1.93$\frac{1}{2}$ 53. £2.41$\frac{1}{2}$ 54. £7.42$\frac{1}{2}$ 55. 38
56. 57   57. 73   58. 116   59. 304   60. 193

EXERCISE 40

1. £1.19   2. 5, £1   3. £34.58
4. £122.20   5. £226.82   6. £2475
7. £769.23   8. £65.14   9. £4.77
10. 147, £20.12, £26.46   11. £152.69   12. 71
13. 26, 24 p   14. 80   15. £6.50
16. £718.08   17. £19.48   18. £20.47$\frac{1}{2}$
19. £299.03   20. £1.09   21. 14
22. 53   23. £7.78   24. £42.48
25. £601.20   26. £63.12   27. £3482
28. £2048.70   29. £1668.96   30. £139.12
31. £7854   32. £4914   33 £16.94
34. £7276   35. £1082.64   36. £668.80
37. 15 p   38. 6$\frac{1}{2}$ p   39. £14 852
40. Increase £944.50   41. Profit £32   42. £2544.64
43. £24.40   44. 53 p   45. 1404
46. £532.40   47. £2340   48. £573.50
49. £47 000   50. £4.05

EXERCISE 41

1. 14   2. 54   3. 40
4. 12.6   5. 40.2   6. 11 h
7. 57 mph   8. 90 km/h   9. 3$\frac{3}{4}$ mph
10. 18 mph   11. 5 km/h   12. 5.5
13. 11.52 runs per wicket   14. 42.96   15. 27.4
16. 3.8   17. 681   18. 147 cm

485

19. 24 mpg
20. 24.6 mph
21. 16.36 mph
22. 50 mph
23. 272 cm
24. 55.7 kg
25. 157.4 cm
26. 940 mm
27. 70.9 kg
28. 22 400
29. 75.5 mph
30. 60 mph

EXERCISE 42

1. $\frac{2}{3}$ **2.** $\frac{5}{9}$ **3.** $\frac{2}{3}$ **4.** $\frac{7}{9}$ **5.** $\frac{3}{7}$ **6.** $\frac{9}{11}$

7. $\frac{5}{3}$ **8.** $\frac{8}{7}$ **9.** $\frac{1}{3}$ **10.** $\frac{3}{4}$ **11.** $\frac{9}{7}$ **12.** $\frac{45}{14}$

13. $\frac{7}{10}$ **14.** $\frac{2}{3}$ **15.** $\frac{8}{1}$ **16.** $\frac{3}{7}$ **17.** $\frac{4}{13}$ **18.** $\frac{2}{3}$

19. $\frac{4}{11}$ **20.** $\frac{2}{3}$ **21.** $\frac{1}{4}$ **22.** $\frac{40}{11}$ **23.** $\frac{1}{2}$ **24.** $\frac{7}{100}$

25. $\frac{13}{30}$ **26.** $\frac{1}{3}$ **27.** $\frac{20}{1}$ **28.** $\frac{3}{4}$ **29.** $\frac{1}{4}$ **30.** $\frac{9}{20}$

31. $\frac{15}{4}$ **32.** $\frac{7}{2}$ **33.** $\frac{3}{1}$ **34.** $\frac{7}{12}$ **35.** $\frac{49}{108}$ **36.** $\frac{3}{4}$

37. $4:5$ **38.** $9:2$ **39.** $10:7$ **40.** $14:9$ **41.** $5:7$ **42.** $7:8$

43. $26:7$ **44.** $20:9$ **45.** $\frac{2}{5} = \frac{8}{20} = \frac{14}{35}$ **46.** $\frac{3}{7} = \frac{12}{28} = \frac{24}{56}$

47. $\frac{14}{13} = \frac{42}{39} = \frac{70}{65}$ **48.** $\frac{7}{11} = \frac{56}{88} = \frac{77}{121}$ **49.** $\frac{4}{9} = \frac{12}{27} = \frac{60}{135}$ **50.** $\frac{7}{8} = \frac{49}{56} = \frac{147}{168}$

51. £25   **52.** £9.10   **53.** 1008 cm   **54.** 20.4 m   **55.** 297 g

56. £12.27   **57.** 49 p   **58.** 102 mm   **59.** 17.5 km   **60.** 27.6 kg

61. $7:9$ **62.** $4:3$ **63** (a) $9:11$ (b) $11:20$

64. $13:15$ **65.** (a) $1:2$ (b) $2:3$ **66.** $8:7$

67. $14:9$ **68.** $5:4$ **69.** $25:102$

70. $1:5$ **71.** $64:81$ **72.** $4:9$

73. $24:25$ **74.** $9:7$ **75.** (a) $2:7$ (b) $1:3$

76. (a) $7:3$ (b) $11:3$ **77.** $5:6$ **78.** $3:7$

79. (a) 2527   (b) 361   **80.** $15:17$ **81.** $54:55$

82. $6:7$ **83.** $4:5$ **84.** (a) $13:11$ (b) $2:13$

85. 18 kg oranges, 36 kg sugar, 9 lemons, 9 litres water

86. 1.26 kg flour, 1.3125 kg sugar, 21 eggs, 21 tablespoons jam

87. $21:16$ **88.** Better, in ratio $52:45$ **89.** £4.47

90. £15.35

EXERCISE 43

1. $\frac{1}{100\,000}$ **2.** $\frac{1}{40\,000}$ **3.** $\frac{1}{5000}$

4. $\frac{1}{200}$, 3 cm by 2 cm   **5.** $\frac{1}{250}$, 4 m by 6 m   **6.** 11 cm by 8 cm

7. $\frac{1}{100}$ km^2 **8.** 32 cm^2 **9.** 846 km^2

10. 3.96 km   **11.** $\frac{1}{1000}$ **12.** 213 000 hectares

13. 83.72 cm   **14.** (a) 2.8 km   (b) 1.74 miles

15. 4.856 cm^2

EXERCISE 44

1. £24, £18   **2.** 22 p, 33 p   **3.** 21 cm, 33 cm

4. 1.6 m, 2 m   **5.** 6 km, 14 km   **6.** £12, £24, £30

7. 14 p, 21 p, 35 p   **8.** 65 mm, 52 mm, 39 mm   **9.** 46 cm, 115 cm, 161 cm

10. 90 g, 126 g, 234 g   **11.** £18, £12, £9   **12.** 48 p, 24 p, 16 p

13. 240 g, 320 g, 400 g   **14.** 35 cm, 56 cm, 63 cm   **15.** 70 cm, 56 cm, 28 cm

16. 81, 63   **17.** 32, 72   **18.** 60, 45

19. 77, 121   **20.** 5 m, 3.75 m × 2.5 m   **21.** A 14 p, B 35 p, C 49 p

22. 16 cm, 28 cm, 36 cm   **23.** 17.5 cm, 21 cm, 24.5 cm   **24.** £36 000, £12 000

25. $12\frac{1}{4}$ t, $8\frac{3}{4}$ t, $15\frac{3}{4}$ t   **26.** £1040, £1520   **27.** $3:4:10$

28. $12:15:16$ **29.** $9:15:25$ **30.** $9:6:2$

31. £30, £15, £10   **32.** £150, £75, £25   **33.** £348
34. 665 kg, 1596 kg   **35.** 10 g, 35 g, 20 g

EXERCISE 45

1. £14.20	**2.** £8.04	**3.** £7.48	**4.** £19.08
5. £5.76	**6.** £3.50	**7.** £352	**8.** 308 miles
9. 13 gallons	**10.** 448 km	**11.** $15\frac{1}{2}$ litres	**12.** £592
13. £516	**14.** 235	**15.** £224.64	**16.** $7\frac{1}{3}$ cm
17. 397	**18.** £485.04	**19.** 342 kg, 608 kg	**20.** £24.32
21. $17\frac{1}{2}$ p	**22.** 1792 kg	**23.** £33.60	**24.** £11 358
25. £108.75			

EXERCISE 46

1. 3 hours	**2.** 84 mph	**3.** 7	**4.** 6 days	**5.** 10 days
6. 160	**7.** 3.5 cm^3	**8.** 10	**9.** 51	**10.** 55
11. 1200	**12.** 32	**13.** 77	**14.** 30 cm	**15.** 15
16. 144	**17.** 40	**18.** 12 days	**19.** 20	**20.** 11

EXERCISE 47

1. £308	**2.** £96	**3.** £480	**4.** £7.56	**5.** £480
6. 1764	**7.** 12	**8.** 12 t	**9.** 85	**10.** 343
11. $£816\frac{2}{3}$	**12.** 12	**13.** £8	**14.** £57.60	**15.** Fall by £60

EXERCISE 48

1. 50%, 25%, $12\frac{1}{2}$%, $37\frac{1}{2}$%, $62\frac{1}{2}$%
2. $87\frac{1}{2}$%, $33\frac{1}{3}$%, $66\frac{2}{3}$%, $112\frac{1}{2}$%, $212\frac{1}{2}$%
3. 20%, 40%, 80%, 120%, 160%
4. 55%, 12%, $83\frac{1}{3}$%, 45%, 34%
5. 116%, $133\frac{1}{3}$%, 290%, 110%, $187\frac{1}{2}$%
6. 25%, 35%, 47%, 6%, 72%
7. 123%, 200%, 304%, $65\frac{1}{2}$%, 1224%
8. $\frac{1}{4}, \frac{1}{2}, \frac{3}{4}, \frac{2}{5}, \frac{3}{5}$; 0.25, 0.5, 0.75, 0.4, 0.6
9. $\frac{11}{20}, \frac{12}{25}, \frac{16}{25}, \frac{19}{25}, \frac{7}{20}$; 0.55, 0.48, 0.64, 0.76, 0.35
10. $\frac{1}{8}, \frac{3}{8}, \frac{5}{8}, \frac{7}{8}, \frac{1}{6}$; 0.125, 0.375, 0.625, 0.875, 0.166 66

11. 68%	**12.** 21%	**13.** 28%	**14.** 28%	**15.** 37%	**16.** 14%

17. 38%
18. (a) 25%   (b) 10%   (c) 25%   (d) 200%   (e) 25%
19. (a) 20%   (b) 33%   (c) $133\frac{1}{3}$% (d) 40%   (e) 81%
20. (a) 25%   (b) 5%   (c) 10%   (d) 55%   (e) 42.2%
21. (a) 80%   (b) 30%   (c) 85%   (d) 35%   (e) 72%
22. (a) 2.4 m   (b) 3.25 cm   (c) 2.125 km   **23.** (a) 90 g   (b) 246 kg   (c) 45 g
24. (a) 31.08   (b) 26.5 cm   (c) 25.74 m   **25.** 120

26. £192	**27.** 65%	**28.** 80 kg	**29.** 24 510	**30.** 21 756
31. 36	**32.** 156	**33.** 70%	**34.** 40	**35.** 125
36. £6	**37.** £9.60	**38.** £124	**39.** 3	**40.** £62 500
41. 30%	**42.** 15%	**43.** 35%	**44.** 1.5 kg	**45.** 2760 cm^3
46. 71.5%	**47.** 65%	**48.** 391	**49.** 73	**50.** £357.72

EXERCISE 49

1. (a) $\frac{120}{100}$ (b) $\frac{150}{100}$ (c) $\frac{135}{100}$ (d) $\frac{220}{100}$ (e) $\frac{300}{100}$
2. (a) $\frac{80}{100}$ (b) $\frac{40}{100}$ (c) $\frac{88}{100}$ (d) $\frac{65}{100}$ (e) $\frac{25}{100}$
3. (a) 130   (b) 384   (c) 54   (d) 88   (e) 72

4. (a) 120 (b) $122\frac{1}{2}$ (c) 7 (d) 56
5. £67.20   6. £632.50   7. 70.2 kg   8. 174 cm   9. 546 cm^3
10. £188.80   11. 128 cm   12. 59 408   13. £62.90   14. £4480
15. 1.729 m   16. 78.24 kg   17. 3.5 kg   18. £48   19. 120
20. 840 m^2

EXERCISE 50

1. $\frac{6}{5}$ 2. $\frac{3}{2}$ 3. $\frac{29}{20}$ 4. $\frac{4}{3}$ 5. $\frac{4}{5}$
6. $\frac{2}{5}$ 7. $\frac{1}{4}$ 8. $\frac{1}{3}$ 9. $\frac{21}{20}$ 10. $\frac{28}{25}$
11. £2.40   12. £9   13. £7.50   14. £24   15. £19.50
16. £324   17. £48   18. £1.50   19. £5.58   20. £426
21. $\frac{5}{6}$ 22. $\frac{2}{3}$ 23. $\frac{4}{7}$ 24. $\frac{3}{5}$ 25. $\frac{5}{2}$
26. $\frac{10}{9}$ 27. $\frac{2}{1}$ 28. $\frac{8}{9}$ 29. $\frac{8}{5}$ 30. $\frac{20}{17}$
31. £120   32. £40   33. £3.40   34. 27 p   35. £2
36. 90 p   37. £10.80   38. £19.22$\frac{1}{2}$ 39. £20   40. £120
41. 15%   42. 20%   43. 12%   44. 25%   45. 60%
46. 25%   47. 30%   48. 70%   49. 80%   50. $12\frac{1}{2}$%

EXERCISE 51

1. £3   2. 80%   3. £53 760   4. £148.50   5. 18%
6. £14   7. £14.70   8. £7.20   9. £120   10. £6300
11. £2100   12. £45   13. $55\frac{5}{9}$%   14. $83\frac{1}{3}$%   15. £1200
16. £5400   17. £2.70   18. £3910   19. $37\frac{1}{2}$%   20. 80%
21. $33\frac{1}{3}$%   22. $12\frac{1}{2}$%   23. £5   24. £4896   25. 20%
26. £19.20   27. £7550   28. (a) 11 760   (b) 12 000
29. (a) 63   (b) 243   30. (a) £186   (b) £47.40

EXERCISE 52

1. A 21, B 17, C 29
2. D 25, E 16, F 22
3. (a) 26 cm   (b) 25 cm^2
4. (a) 32 cm   (b) 40 cm^2
5. (a) 32 cm   (b) 53 cm^2
6. (a) 44 cm   (b) 35 cm^2
7. (a) 34 cm   (b) 30 cm^2
8. (a) 46 cm   (b) 43 cm^2
9. (a) 30 cm   (b) 35 cm^2
10. (a) 28 cm   (b) 29 cm^2
11. (a) 34 cm   (b) 29 cm^2
12. (a) 46 cm   (b) 38 cm^2
13. (a) 34 cm   (b) 46 cm^2
14. (a) 36 cm   (b) 32 cm^2
15. (a) 8 cm   (b) 4 cm^2
16. (a) 12 km   (b) 9 km^2
17. (a) 20 m   (b) 25 m^2
18. (a) 28 mm   (b) 49 mm^2
19. (a) 2 cm   (b) 0.25 cm^2
20. (a) 3 km   (b) 0.5625 km^2
21. (a) 4.8 cm   (b) 1.44 cm^2
22. (a) 1.6 km   (b) 0.16 km^2
23. (a) 14 cm   (b) 12 cm^2
24. (a) 40 mm   (b) 96 mm^2
25. (a) 24 m   (b) 35 m^2
26. (a) 180 m   (b) 800 m^2
27. 250 mm^2 28. 4000 cm^2 29. 130 m^2 30. 1.125 km^2
31. 16.2 hectares
32. (a) 4 cm, 18 cm   (b) 15 cm, 150 cm^2 (c) 2.6 cm, 12 cm   (d) 12 mm, 216 mm^2
     (e) 0.75 m, 4.5 m
33. 42   34. 450, £171
35. (a) 77 m   (b) 255 m^2 36. 133
37. (a) 6 m   (b) 12 cm   (c) 30 cm   38. 1.25 m^2, 5

39. $814 \, \text{cm}^2$, $536 \, \text{cm}^2$ **40.** (a) £7.92   (b) $4.42 \, \text{kg}$
41. $17.44 \, \text{m}^2$ **42.** 296
43. (a) $1.7 \, \text{m}^2$ (b) $0.5 \, \text{m}^2$ **44.** (a) $10.8 \, \text{m}$ (b) $7.92 \, \text{m}^2$
45. $47.60 \, \text{m}^2$

EXERCISE 53

1. (a) $78 \, \text{cm}^2$ (b) $9.75 \, \text{cm}$ **2.** (a) $56 \, \text{cm}^2$ (b) $11.2 \, \text{cm}$
3. (a) $105 \, \text{cm}^2$ (b) $7.5 \, \text{cm}$ **4.** $AB = 12 \, \text{cm}$, $BC = 6 \, \text{cm}$
5. (a) $h = 4 \, \text{cm}$ (b) $H = 6 \, \text{cm}$
6. (a) $AB = 12 \, \text{cm}$ (b) $AD = 9 \, \text{cm}$ (c) $H = 12 \, \text{cm}$
7. $48 \, \text{cm}^2$ **8.** $130 \, \text{cm}^2$ **9.** $21.84 \, \text{cm}^2$ **10.** $6 \, \text{cm}^2$
11. $8 \, \text{cm}$ **12.** $6.5 \, \text{cm}$ **13.** $5.4 \, \text{cm}$ **14.** $80 \, \text{cm}^2$
15. $82.5 \, \text{cm}^2$ **16.** $22.2 \, \text{cm}^2$ **17.** $7 \, \text{cm}$ **18.** $16 \, \text{cm}$
19. $12 \, \text{cm}$, $8 \, \text{cm}$ **20.** $8.5 \, \text{cm}$

EXERCISE 54

1. (a) $512 \, \text{cm}^3$ (b) $64 \, \text{mm}^3$ (c) $125 \, \text{m}^3$ (d) $12.17 \, \text{cm}^3$ (e) $0.216 \, \text{km}^3$ (f) $0.216 \, \text{m}^3$
2. $60 \, \text{cm}^3$ **3.** $672 \, \text{m}^3$
4. $150.5 \, \text{cm}^3$ **5.** $18 \, \text{km}^3$
6. $0.5625 \, \text{m}^3$ **7.** (a) $6 \, \text{mm}$ (b) $0.5 \, \text{m}$ (c) $\frac{2}{3} \, \text{cm}$
8. $6 \, \text{cm}$ **9.** $11 \, \text{mm}$
10. $8 \, \text{cm}$ **11.** $5 \, \text{mm}$
12. $0.8 \, \text{cm}$ **13.** $\frac{3}{4} \, \text{m}$
14. $180 \, \text{m}^3$, 40   **15.** $3\frac{1}{3} \, \text{m}$
16. 480   **17.** £3.52
18. (a) $90 \, 240 \, \text{g}$ (b) $90.24 \, \text{kg}$ **19.** 96
20. $125 \, \text{cm}^3$ **21.** $41.54 \, \text{cm}$, $50 \, \text{cm}$
22. $1.2 \, \text{cm}^3$, $264 \, \text{cm}^3$ **23.** 30
24. (a) $792 \, \text{cm}^3$ (b) $288 \, \text{cm}^3$ **25.** (a) 540   (b) $8061 \, \text{cm}^3$
26. (a) $30 \, 400 \, \text{cm}^3$ (b) $0.0304 \, \text{m}^3$ **27.** (a) $43 \, 650 \, \text{cm}^3$ (b) $0.043 \, 65 \, \text{m}^3$
28. (a) $42 \, 900 \, \text{cm}^3$ (b) $343.2 \, \text{kg}$ **29.** $40 \, \text{cm}$
30. 64   **31.** $1350 \, \text{cm}^3$
32. $72 \, \text{cm}^3$ **33.** $0.203 \, \text{m}^3$
34. 6   **35.** (a) $90 \, \text{cm}^2$ (b) $31 \, 500 \, \text{cm}^3$ (c) $258 \, \text{kg}$

REVISION PAPER 26

1. 22, 10 p   **2.** 13 litres   **3.** £3.15, £5.40
4. (a) £1.98   (b) £1.62   **5.** £609.28

REVISION PAPER 27

1. (a) 65%, 175%   (b) $\frac{9}{20}$, $\frac{16}{5}$ **2.** £84.94
3. $\frac{100}{413}$ **4.** 7.21 rolls, i.e. 8 rolls
5. 4032, 162

REVISION PAPER 28

1. £11.20, £8.96, £15.68   **2.** (a) 4.519   (b) 0.004   **3.** 180
4. £637.90   **5.** 74

REVISION PAPER 29

1. $2\frac{49}{62}$ 2. 2.7 km 3. (a) -4.5 (b) -8
4. (a) £18.60 (b) £6.20 5. £82.50

REVISION PAPER 30

1. £93.88 2. 33 litres
3. (a) 21 (b) 21.1 (c) 20.06 4. £237.90 5. £396

REVISION PAPER 31

1. (a) 35% (b) $7\frac{1}{2}\%$ (c) $32\frac{3}{4}\%$ 2. $\frac{77}{156}$
3. £21.25 4. $17\frac{1}{2}$ days 5. $343\,\text{cm}^2$

REVISION PAPER 32

1. (a) £94.23 (b) £2.65 2. £7350, £8050, £6300 3. $£9.37\frac{1}{2}$, $66\frac{2}{3}$ miles
4. (a) $56\frac{1}{4}\%$ (b) $43\frac{3}{4}\%$ 5. 66

REVISION PAPER 33

1. $\frac{67}{80}$ 2. 20% 3. £2441.25 4. 134 5. 224, 19, 4

REVISION PAPER 34

1. 1071, 119 2. 211, 338
3. (a) 1 0 0 0 1 0 1 1 (b) 1 1 0 (c) 1 0 0 1 1 0 1 (d) 1 1 0
4. 17 5. 6

REVISION PAPER 35

1. (i) 288 (ii) 25 2. $5\frac{17}{84}$ 3. 423.5
4. 48 days 5. £151.74

REVISION PAPER 36

1. $1\frac{17}{24}$ 2. 20% 3. 30
4. £18.80, 200 km 5. £161.81

REVISION PAPER 37

1. (a) 0.16 (b) 0.16 2. £2.97 3. 1.5 kg
4. 144 kg 5. 792, 330

REVISION PAPER 38

1. (a) $-4\frac{1}{2}$ (b) 2
2. (a) (i) 1 0 1 1 1 0 0 1 1 1 (ii) 103 (b) (i) 102 (ii) 143_5
3. £337.50 4. 847 5. 35 p, Cheaper

Revision Paper 39

1. $\frac{1}{4}$ 2. £140.16   3. £34
4. 683, 48.79%   5. (a) 346.5 cm^3 (b) 133.5 cm^3

Revision Paper 40

1. (a) 0.159 96   (b) 5.25
2. (a) 14, 26, 14   (b) (i) 1 0 0 0 1 0 0 0 1   (ii) 1 1 1
3. 180 litres   4. £30 768   5. £9862.50, £2137.50

Revision Paper 41

1. $\frac{512}{665}$ 2. 42 min   3. 1200   4. £272.78   5. 108

Revision Paper 42

1. $3\frac{14}{15}$ 2. 100 m   3. (a) 18%   (b) $\frac{5}{8}$
4. 20 p, 24 p, 30 p, 36 p   5. $2\frac{1}{2}$ litres

Revision Paper 43

1. $3\frac{20}{63}$ 2. 2.4 kg   3. £1.45   4. 6.33 m^2, 1.485 m^3, 1485 kg
5. 90 p, 16

Revision Paper 44

1. 30 years   2. $3\frac{4}{57}$ 3. 6 knots   4. £646   5. $33\frac{1}{3}$ m^2

Revision Paper 45

1. $\frac{5}{8}, \frac{9}{16}, \frac{11}{20}, \frac{16}{30}$ 2. £5.32   3. $30\frac{1}{2}$%, £110   4. £97.79
5. (a) 1387 cm^3 (b) 341 cm^3

Revision Paper 46

1. 1   2. 347.48   3. 25 days   4. 9 gallons, £19.26   5. 28%

Revision Paper 47

1. £17.30   2. £112, £168, £224, £280   3. £62.40
4. £108   5. 2.3 kg, 2.3 kg, 3.5 kg

Revision Paper 48

1. $2\frac{4}{7}$ 2. (a) 48   (b) 109   (c) 1068
3. 2500   4. (a) 4 : 11   (b) 3 : 10   (c) 1 : 2
5. 22%

Revision Paper 49

1. £13.76   2. 78.4 m, 8, £36.48   3. 2250
4. £14 100   5. 813 cm^3

1. $\frac{55}{192}$

2. 144 kg

3. 0.0184 m^3

4. 18 cm, 234 cm^2

5. 1704 cm^3, 569.8 cm^3

EXERCISE 55

1.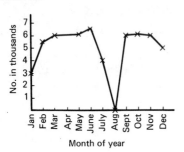

2.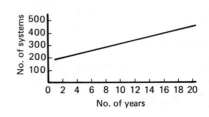

3.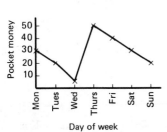

4.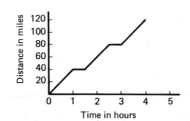

5.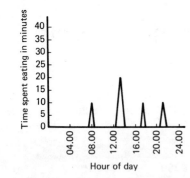

6.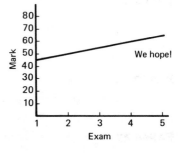

7.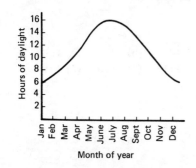

8. (a) 102 km　(b) 84 miles　(c) 29 mph　(d) 99 km/h
9. (a) 45.5 kg　(b) $70\frac{1}{2}$ lb　　　　　10. (a) 15°C, 71°C　(b) 122°F, 176°F
11. (a) 133°F　(b) 21°R　　　　　　12. (a) $240　(b) £124
13. (a) $9\frac{3}{5}$ gallons (64 litres = 14 gallons)　(b) 25 litres
14. (a) (i) increase　(ii) increase　(iii) constant
　　(b) (i) 1982　(ii) 1979　(c) (i) 23　(ii) 50
15. (a) (i) 64 cm^2　(ii) 168 cm^2　(b) (i) 5.6 cm　(ii) 7.6 cm

EXERCISE 56

1. (a) 84 km　(b) 161 km from Paddington at 05.04　(c) 25 km
2. (a) 1256　(b) 137 km/h　(c) 100 km from Caxton at 11.56　(d) 100 km/h
3. (a) 8.45 a.m.　(b) 50 mph　(c) 25 miles north of B at 9.30 a.m.
4. (a) 11.46 a.m.　(b) $16\frac{1}{2}$ km/h　(c) 7.3 km from Elmwood at 10.14 a.m.　(d) $2\frac{2}{5}$ km
5. (a) 40 km/h　(b) 12.09 p.m.　(c) 2 h 39 min　(d) 30 km/h
6. (a) 1.09 p.m.　(b) 64 miles from A at 1.40 p.m.　(c) 38 mph
7. (a) Dick, 21 minutes　(b) 2 miles from Axeter at 12.36 p.m. and 6.85 miles at 1.25 p.m.
　　(c) 49 minutes
8. (a) 50 miles from A at 1.54 p.m.　(b) They arrive at the same time　(c) 20 miles
9. (a) 11 km from Atley at 1.50 p.m.　(b) 2.45 p.m.　(c) 5.75 km
10. (a) $37\frac{1}{2}$ mph　(b) 1.14 p.m., 63 mph
　　(c) (i) 44 mph　(ii) 53 miles from A at 1.25 p.m. and $17\frac{1}{2}$ miles from A at 2.15 p.m.

EXERCISE 57

1. (a) 7, 11, 12, 10, 8　(b) Morocco　(c) London
2. (a) 50 cm, 17 cm, 35 cm　(b) Bangkok
3. (a) 12 500, 15 000, 1650　(b) 44 000

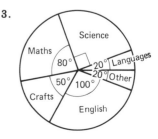

4. London
　 Costa Brava
　 Algarve
　 Dalmatian Coast

5. Housing
　 Refuse collection & disposal
　 Environmental health
　 Recreation & amenities
　 Industrial & commer‐ cial development
　 Planning & development
　 Interest payments

EXERCISE 58

1. Shoe size
   6　5　4　9　8　7　72°　45°　36°　108°　9°

2. Food 216°　Clothes 36°　54°　36°　18°　Heat　Light　Pleasure　Other

3. Science　Maths 80°　20° Languages　50°　20° Other　100°　Crafts　English

4.

5.

6.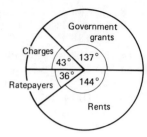

7.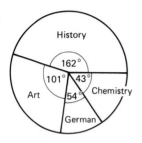

8. Individuals 43%, Insurance Co. 17%, Pension funds 10%, Banks 8%, Investment trust 10%, Overseas holders 5%, Other 7%

EXERCISE 59

1. (a) Pacific   (b) Arctic   (c) 120 million square miles
2. (a) A dog   (b) 6   (c) 58   (d) Dogs, cats, birds, rabbits, fish, gerbils
3. (a) Tuesday   (b) 830   (c) a holiday   (d) 80
4. (a) (i) July   (ii) February   (b) July and August   (c) 3000 km
   (d) 14 940 km   (e) April and June, March and September
5. (a) 32   (b) 22   (c) 11   (d) cycling

EXERCISE 60

1. (a) 28   (b) Size 5   (c) 14   2. (a) 73   (b) 57   (c) 100

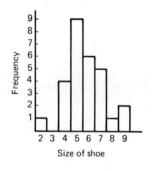

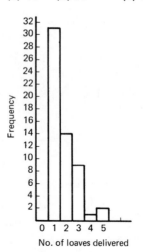

3. (a) 21   (b) 39   (c) 11   **4.** (a) 4   (b) 16   (c) 148

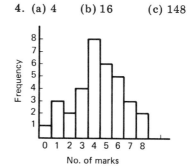

5. (a) 42   (b) 11   (c) 397   (d) 9

EXERCISE 61

	MEAN	MEDIAN	MODE
1.	18	16	16
2.	30	29	29
3.	75	73	70, 71
4.	10	9	8
5.	33	33	31
6.	42	31	12
7.	169 cm	169 cm	169 cm
8.	75	71	70
9.	1.5	1	0
10.	160 cm	160 cm	160 cm

11. Median £1.76, mean £1.80
12. Mean £2.17, median £2.10, mode £2.10
13. Mean 17 mm, median 21 mm
14. (a) 6   (b) 6   (c) 5, 6

15.	MEAN	MEDIAN	MODE
Boys	6.2	7	7
Girls	5.92	7	7
All	6.0	7	7

EXERCISE 62

1. 84   **2.** 118   **3.** 496   **4.** 230   **5.** 110

EXERCISE 63

1. (a) $\frac{1}{13}$ (b) $\frac{1}{52}$ (c) $\frac{1}{4}$ (d) $\frac{1}{2}$ (e) $\frac{4}{13}$ 2. (a) $\frac{1}{10}$ (b) $\frac{1}{2}$ (c) $\frac{1}{2}$

3. $\frac{1}{4}$ 4. (a) $\frac{1}{3}$ (b) $\frac{2}{3}$ (c) $\frac{2}{9}$

5. (a) $\frac{1}{2}$ (b) $\frac{33}{100}$ (c) $\frac{7}{50}$ 6. (a) $\frac{1}{8}$ (b) $\frac{3}{8}$ (c) $\frac{7}{8}$

7. (a) $\frac{7}{20}$ (b) $\frac{3}{10}$ (c) $\frac{17}{20}$ 8. (a) 0 (b) $\frac{1}{36}$ (c) $\frac{1}{36}$ (d) $\frac{5}{6}$

9. (a) $\frac{3}{10}$ (b) $\frac{2}{5}$ 10. (a) $\frac{3}{7}$ (b) $\frac{5}{7}$ (c) $\frac{4}{7}$

11. (a) $\frac{3}{7}$ (b) $\frac{4}{7}$ 12. $\frac{2}{5}$

13. (a) $\frac{3}{4}$ (b) $\frac{1}{4}$ 14. (a) $\frac{1}{8}$ (b) $\frac{1}{2}$

15. (a) $\frac{4}{11}$ (b) $\frac{7}{11}$ (c) $\frac{2}{11}$ 16. (a) $\frac{1}{5}$ (b) $\frac{1}{2}$ (c) $\frac{2}{3}$

17. (a) $\frac{1}{18}$ (b) $\frac{5}{36}$ 18. (a) $\frac{1}{6}$ (b) $\frac{1}{2}$ (c) $\frac{1}{2}$

19. (a) $\frac{1}{7}$ (b) $\frac{1}{12}$ (c) $\frac{1}{30}$ 20. (a) Don   (b) $\frac{1}{96}$ (c) $\frac{5}{8}$

EXERCISE 64

1. 1.96	2. 53.29	3. 84.64	4. 13.69
5. 27.04	6. 47.61	7. 72.25	8. 18.49
9. 0.6084	10. 0.5329	11. 0.8464	12. 0.1024
13. 0.4356	14. 0.2916	15. 0.4761	16. 1849
17. 1024	18. 3136	19. 5329	20. 6724
21. 841	22. 0.003 025	23. 0.001 156	24. 0.005 776
25. 5.9536	26. 35.05	27. 76.39	28. 0.5242
29. 0.8612	30. 0.2981	31. 1384	32. 3516
33. 7868	34. 0.007 674	35. 0.002 852	36. 0.000 466 6
37. 328 329	38. 712 336	39. 92 416	40. 35.12
41. 9.872	42. 58.42	43. 79.64	44. 2.362
45. 18.14	46. 0.3098	47. 0.062 15	48. 0.5846
49. 0.000 191 1	50. 0.000 159 8	51. 0.008 787	52. 206.5
53. 707.0	54. 3924	55. 2913	56. 5246
57. 1541	58. 247 200	59. 30 210	60. 65 740
61. 27.74	62. 0.0081	63. 0.1112	64. 1438
65. 205 600	66. 35 120 000	67. 0.2886	68. 0.000 019 01
69. 0.015 98	70. 2 068 000	71. 2857	72. 1874
73. 0.006 172	74. 0.000 006 215	75. 1.219×10^9	

EXERCISE 65

1. 2.627	2. 1.924	3. 2.145	4. 3.082
5. 2.881	6. 1.549	7. 9.695	8. 8.185
9. 7.348	10. 5.568	11. 4.359	12. 8.602
13. 0.9592	14. 0.7280	15. 0.5568	16. 0.9055
17. 0.6633	18. 0.8718	19. 2.435	20. 1.572
21. 2.482	22. 2.871	23. 3.028	24. 2.689
25. 3.899	26. 5.413	27. 7.707	28. 5.992
29. 7.987	30. 9.497	31. 0.7443	32. 0.6269
33. 0.8526	34. 0.9214	35. 0.7842	36. 0.9423
37. 20.66	38. 19.80	39. 23.15	40. 28.18
41. 28.76	42. 26.34	43. 2.888	44. 2.489
45. 1.773	46. 3.145	47. 2.765	48. 2.059
49. 8.285	50. 8.598	51. 5.243	52. 7.633
53. 6.328	54. 3.643	55. 21.99	56. 24.29
57. 15.61	58. 29.88	59. 18.53	60. 26.97
61. 0.7713	62. 0.8523	63. 0.9943	64. 0.5233
65. 0.6264	66. 0.9132	67. 0.046 26	68. 0.2315

69. 0.025 08	**70.** 0.1463	**71.** 0.089 05	**72.** 0.007 211
73. 0.2695	**74.** 0.057 84	**75.** 0.025 44	**76.** 65.30
77. 91.03	**78.** 96.75	**79.** 77.05	**80.** 59.09
81. 66.61	**82.** 0.9020	**83.** 0.049 97	**84.** 0.002 898
85. 2695	**86.** 288.6	**87.** 3513	**88.** 127.3
89. 2130	**90.** 787.4	**91.** 7.367	**92.** 0.5633
93. 6.261	**94.** 0.037 82	**95.** 0.009 487	**96.** 0.023 18
97. 2.219	**98.** 238.2	**99.** 0.3526	**100.** 9.968
101. 6.748	**102.** 17.87	**103.** 37.93	**104.** 101.1
105. 11.54	**106.** 3.962	**107.** 0.7000	**108.** 0.7414
109. 0.8295	**110.** 0.4707	**111.** 171.2	**112.** 106.5
113. 235.3	**114.** 14.05	**115.** 43.68	**116.** 1821
117. 2861	**118.** 26.21	**119.** 2.632	**120.** 0.2261

EXERCISE 66

1. 9.079 cm	**2.** 28.99 cm	**3.** 50.92 cm	**4.** 3.209 m
5. 1.069 m	**6.** 583.3 mm	**7.** 21.35 cm	**8.** 8.325 m
9. 76.70 cm	**10.** 7.211 m	**11.** 3.867 m	**12.** 6.395 m
13. 91.74 cm	**14.** 12.64 cm	**15.** 1.816 m	**16.** 0.9682 m
17. 15.95 m	**18.** 0.2 cm	**19.** 42.45 m	
20. 22.4 cm by 11.2 cm			

EXERCISE 67

1. 0.0014	**2.** 0.013 51	**3.** 1.351	**4.** 0.001 351
5. 0.079 37	**6.** 0.000 793 7	**7.** 7.937	**8.** 793.7
9. 0.015 56	**10.** 15.56	**11.** 0.000 154 9	**12.** 0.000 168 8
13. 2.756	**14.** 51.71	**15.** 184.7	**16.** 10.91
17. 0.000 228 8	**18.** 0.001 564	**19.** 0.011 86	**20.** 0.000 810 4
21. 0.010 85	**22.** 0.001 356	**23.** 0.000 194 1	**24.** 4.077
25. 1.744	**26.** 0.061 69	**27.** 0.016 85	**28.** 237.1
29. 0.000 127 3	**30.** 0.9960	**31.** 0.149	**32.** 0.007 92
33. 12.3	**34.** 0.000 363	**35.** 0.127	**36.** 0.0101
37. 12.2	**38.** 91.7	**39.** 540	**40.** 0.508
41. 0.247	**42.** 2.04	**43.** 3.64	**44.** 0.543
45. 0.0841	**46.** 1.88	**47.** 2.30	**48.** 0.470
49. 0.0529	**50.** 0.298		

EXERCISE 68

1. 4	**2.** 27	**3.** 25	**4.** $\frac{1}{4}$	**5.** $\frac{1}{27}$	**6.** 3
7. 4	**8.** 2	**9.** 4	**10.** 9	**11.** 1	**12.** 1
13. 1	**14.** $\frac{1}{4}$	**15.** $\frac{1}{81}$	**16.** $\frac{1}{125}$	**17.** 216	**18.** 1
19. 8	**20.** $\frac{9}{16}$				

EXERCISE 69

1. 0.7782	**2.** 0.9031	**3.** 0.6232	**4.** 0.7559	**5.** 0.9159
6. 0.6395	**7.** 0.1106	**8.** 0.8287	**9.** 0.7172	**10.** 0.8690
11. 0.3904	**12.** 0.5091	**13.** 0.8658	**14.** 0.8101	**15.** 0.9668
16. 0.1113	**17.** 0.6746	**18.** 0.9262	**19.** 0.8058	**20.** 0.5458
21. 4.400	**22.** 6.500	**23.** 7.540	**24.** 2.790	**25.** 8.910
26. 1.716	**27.** 5.541	**28.** 3.291	**29.** 1.962	**30.** 6.736
31. 7.000	**32.** 3.700	**33.** 5.649	**34.** 1.960	**35.** 2.674
36. 5.545	**37.** 7.473	**38.** 8.344	**39.** 5.855	**40.** 2.045
41. 8.232	**42.** 7.378	**43.** 5.729	**44.** 3.098	**45.** 8.609
46. 1.587	**47.** 1.526	**48.** 2.948	**49.** 2.551	**50.** 3.628

EXERCISE 70

1. 43.85	2. 31.04	3. 309.3	4. 81.53	5. 883.5
6. 931.7	7. 26.06	8. 266.0	9. 897.2	10. 2242
11. 441.2	12. 2117	13. 27 770	14. 9813	15. 31 670
16. 9391	17. 317.4	18. 4123	19. 1835	20. 9394
21. 2.245	22. 1.387	23. 2.103	24. 1.704	25. 2.513
26. 1.301	27. 1.706	28. 8.772	29. 2.541	30. 6.375
31. 1.586	32. 1.181	33. 2.288	34. 5.141	35. 19.97
36. 2.024	37. 4.997	38. 1.945	39. 16.54	40. 44.71
41. 18.65	42. 6.946	43. 26.33	44. 24.51	45. 16.81
46. 35.99	47. 166.9	48. 39.60	49. 4.101	50. 1.349
51. 1.261	52. 3.621	53. 15.67	54. 8.229	55. 8.921
56. 174.1	57. 29.17	58. 3.876	59. 1.538	60. 1.988

EXERCISE 71

1. $\bar{1}$.9243	2. $\bar{2}$.4150	3. $\bar{3}$.7559	4. $\bar{4}$.8451
5. $\bar{3}$.9657	6. $\bar{5}$.9345	7. $\bar{1}$.6470	8. $\bar{4}$.9739
9. $\bar{2}$.3508	10. $\bar{1}$.8124	11. $\bar{2}$.7127	12. $\bar{6}$.9123
13. 0.5370	14. 0.028 38	15. 0.000 532 1	16. 0.035 26
17. 0.000 084 55	18. 0.000 273 7	19. 0.000 000 794 3	20. 0.3480
21. 0.001 760	22. 0.036 45	23. 0.000 029 76	24. 0.0610
25. $\bar{3}$.0	26. $\bar{5}$.8	27. $\bar{3}$.0	28. $\bar{7}$.6
29. $\bar{1}$.3	30. $\bar{4}$.8	31. $\bar{6}$.3	32. $\bar{5}$.5
33. $\bar{8}$.5	34. $\bar{2}$.4	35. $\bar{7}$.1	36. $\bar{1}$.70
37. $\bar{1}$.6	38. $\bar{2}$.5	39. $\bar{1}$.8	40. $\bar{2}$.7
41. $\bar{2}$.6667	42. $\bar{3}$.4	43. $\bar{1}$.6	44. $\bar{7}$.6
45. 9.12	46. 2.72	47. 26.14	48. 0.1372
49. 0.3857	50. 0.061 37	51. 0.1584	52. 0.2868
53. 0.7968	54. 50.76	55. 1731	56. 317.6
57. 0.020 52	58. 0.001 125	59. 0.000 015 37	60. 21.28
61. 295	62. 11.25	63. 0.3777	64. 0.007 616
65. 0.1734	66. 0.5476	67. 0.3163	68. 0.000 077 44
69. 0.1374	70. 0.009 746	71. 0.000 007 108	72. 0.2064
73. 0.9562	74. 0.5218	75. 0.2437	76. 0.075 68
77. 0.2773	78. 0.9476	79. 0.1359	80. 0.2103
81. 0.043 54	82. 0.2359	83. 7.675	84. 0.9480
85. 699.9	86. 86.40	87. 1535	88. 51.22
89. 0.006 836	90. 4.225	91. 24.32	92. 7.497
93. 3.499	94. 3.085	95. 4.764	96. 0.4444
97. 5.400	98. -0.3969	99. 6.677	100. 7.027

EXERCISE 72

1. 21 600 cm^3 2. 8.768 cm^3 3. 231.28 cm^3 4. 5000 cm^3
5. 420 cm^3 6. 0.325 m^3 7. 108 litres   8. 73 500 litres
9. 1.62 m^3 10. 12 m^3 11. $\sqrt{3}$, 225$\sqrt{3}$ or 390 cm^3, 2.73 kg
12. 106 cm^3 13. 35 000 cm^3 14. 165 cm^3 15. 176 cm^3
16. 30 672 cm^3 17. 18 816 cm^3 18. 450 m^3, 7 h   19. 408 cm^2, 816 cm^3
20. 50 cm^2, 10 litres

EXERCISE 73

1. 100 cm^3 2. 270 cm^3 3. $66\frac{2}{3}$ cm^3
4. 81 cm^3 5. 72 cm   6. 8 cm

7. 225.8 cm^3 8. 512 cm^3 9. 5$\sqrt{5}$ cm or 11.18 cm
10. (a) 12 cm   (b) 12.51 cm   11. 7 cm
12. 8 cm × 16 cm   13. 210.6 cm^2 14. (a) 1000 cm^3 (b) 523 cm^3
15. 138.6 cm^3, $\sqrt{109}$ or 21.17 cm^2

EXERCISE 74

1. 44 cm	2. 132 cm	3. 30.8 m	4. 132 cm
5. 35.2 cm	6. 211.2 cm	7. 528 m	8. 23.76 m
9. 3.96 km	10. 31.42 cm	11. 5.027 m	12. 15.71 cm
13. 11 m	14. 942.5 cm	15. 18.85 km	16. 49 cm
17. 0.84 m	18. 91 cm	19. 182 m	20. 11.2 cm
21. 6.44 m	22. 36 cm	23. 150 mm	24. 158 cm
25. 308 mm	26. 532 mm	27. 354 cm	28. 114 m
29. 28.8 cm	30. 65 cm	31. 17.5 cm	32. 67.2 cm
33. 63.6 cm	34. 104.4 m	35. 150.4 cm	36. 490 mm
37. 396 m	38. 482	39. 52.5 m	40. 44 m
41. 88 mm	42. 63 mm	43. 34 cm	44. 66 m
45. 440 cm	46. 8800 m	47. 8.8 m, 0.477 m	48. 20 m
49. 452 cm	50. 0, 52.37 cm/s, 26.18 cm/s		51. 1.26 m
52. 14 cm, 7 cm	53. 35 m	54. 66 cm, 150	55. 603 cm

EXERCISE 75

1. (a) 616 mm^2 (b) 55.44 cm^2 (c) 0.1386 cm^2 (d) 50$\frac{2}{7}$ m^2 (e) 78$\frac{4}{7}$ m^2 (f) 491$\frac{1}{14}$ cm^2

2. (a) 7 cm (b) 1.4 m (c) 6.3 m		3. 77 cm^2	4. 1386 mm^2
5. 364 cm^2	6. 6174 mm^2	7. 5763 mm^2	8. 8771 cm^2
9. 894 m^2	10. 49.28 cm^2	11. 254.6 cm^2	12. 14.385 cm^2
13. 86.24 cm^2	14. 196.6 cm^2	15. 680.1 m^2	16. 1228 cm^2
17. 78.88 cm^2	18. 4:9	19. (a) 4:5 (b) 4:5 (c) 16:25	
20. 2:3	21. 6:7	22. 61$\frac{1}{2}$ cm^2	23. 132 m
24. (a) 154 cm^2 (b) 246 cm^2		25. 3850 m^2, 3696 m^2	26. 2238$\frac{1}{2}$ m^2
27. 5 cm	28. 5 cm	29. 2618 cm^2	30. 144$\frac{4}{7}$ mm^2

EXERCISE 76

1. 52.8 cm^2, 80.52 cm^2 2. 2640 cm^2, 32 057 cm^2 3. 12.1 m^2, 15.83 m^2
4. 211 cm^2, 140.25 cm^2 5. 99.79 cm^2, 265.3 cm^2

6.

7 cm	20 cm	1034 cm^2
10 cm	12.50 cm	1100 cm^2
5 m	8 m	594 m^2
12 mm	9 mm	1584 mm^2
8 cm	6 cm	704 cm^2
11 mm	31 mm	2904 m^2

7. 132 m^2, 606   8. 297 cm^2 9. 330 cm^2
10. 238.9 cm^2 11. 73.4 cm^2 12. 3.282 m^2
13. 22 m^2 14. 39.28 cm^3 15. 11.0 cm^2

EXERCISE 77

1. 6790 cm^3 2. 2010 cm^3 3. 1140 cm^3
4. 4580 cm^3, 1250 cm^3 5. 8.14 cm   6. 12.6 cm
7. 14.9 cm   8. 26.5 cm   9. 11.3 cm
10. 423 cm^3 11. 8   12. 73.7 cm^3
13. 19 mm   14. 3.08 cm^3, 6   15. 2.37 cm^3

16. 4.55 cm
17. Dia. = height = 5.55 cm, Dia. = height = 6.99 cm
18. 377 cm^3 (a) 36.3 cm^3 (b) 36.3 cm^3
19. 55 000 m^3
20. 6 min 38 s
21. Base radius 4.30 cm, height 17.2 cm
22. Base radius 9.27 cm, height 18.5 cm
23. Base radius 3.63 cm, height 14.5 cm
24. 251 mm^3
25. 45.5%
26. 349 cm^3
27. 50.3 cm^3, 0.448 kg
28. 1290 mm^3
29. 0.0130 m^3
30. 117 litres

EXERCISE 78

1. 100 cm^3
2. 168 cm^3
3. 79.3 cm^3
4. 769 cm^3
5. 314 cm^3
6. 469 cm^3
7. 837 cm^3
8. 163 cm^3
9. 37.7 cm^3
10. 2.41 cm^3
11. 176 cm^3
12. 1.36 cm^3
13. 754 cm^3
14. 500 cm^3
15. 10.6 cm^3
16. 22.9 cm^3
17. 226 cm^2
18. 401 cm^2
19. 424 cm^2
20. 38.2 cm^2
21. 6.79 cm
22. 8.57 cm
23. 20.1 m^2
24. 6.25 cm
25. 1 : 1.44
26. (a) 19.6 m^2 (b) 19.6 m^3
27. (a) 45.8 cm^3 (b) 5.73 cm^3
28. Salt 31.2 cm^3, pepper 34.4 cm^3
29. 8 : 19
30. 8.19 cm

EXERCISE 79

1. 314 cm^2, 524 cm^3
2. 228 cm^2, 324 cm^3
3. 1190 cm^2, 3860 cm^3
4. 672 cm^2, 1640 cm^3
5. 27.0 cm^2, 13.2 cm^3
6. 3350 cm^2, 18 200 cm^3
7. 6.20 cm, 483 cm^2
8. 4.99 cm, 313 cm^2
9. 3.98 cm, 199 cm^2
10. 0.463 cm, 2.70 cm^2
11. 489 cm^3
12. 1830 cm^3
13. 6860 cm^3
14. 217 m^3
15. 30.9 cm^3
16. 64 000
17. 1010 g
18. 0.201 cm
19. 2.01×10^{10} km^2, 2.68×10^{14} km^3
20. (a) 38.2 cm^3 (b) 340 g

EXERCISE 80

1. 92.4
2. 29 106 litres/min
3. 29 409 litres, 122 s
4. 152 000 litres/h
5. 829 gallons/min
6. 1 108 800 litres/h
7. 25 min
8. 11 900 gallons
9. (a) 78.6 cm^2 (b) 2590 litres/min   (c) 55.6 min
10. 9 hr 11 min

EXERCISE 81

1.
1 : 2	1 : 4	1 : 8
3 : 4	9 : 16	27 : 64
5 : 2	25 : 4	125 : 8
2 : 7	4 : 49	8 : 243
7 : 9	49 : 81	343 : 729
10 : 1	100 : 1	1000 : 1
3 : 2	9 : 4	27 : 8
5 : 2	25 : 4	125 : 8
5 : 3	25 : 9	125 : 27
10 : 3	100 : 9	1000 : 27
2 : 3	4 : 9	32 : 108

2. Middle 864 cm^3, smallest 500 cm^3
3. 10 cm, 12 cm
4. 512 cm^3, 216 cm^3
5. 422 g, 125 g
6. 64 : 61
7. 3.85 m, 4.2 m; 10.7 gallons, 13.8 gallons
8. (a) 400 cm^3 (b) $37\frac{1}{2}$ m^3
9. (a) 45 cm   (b) 9 : 4   (c) 135 g
10. 1080, 135

EXERCISE 82

1. 6.20 cm
2. 8.06 cm
3. Radius 4.40 cm, height 4.40 cm
4. $3\frac{3}{4}$
5. 125 000
6. 1.75 cm
7. 32
8. 3 : 1 : 2
9. 11
10. 5.64
11. 2.56 cm
12. (a) 113 cm^2 (b) 21.2 cm^3
13. 4.97 cm
14. 6.11 cm
15. 6.69 cm
16. 2160 cm^3, 50%
17. $16\frac{1}{3}$
18. 1250 kg   (a) 151 000 cm^2 (b) 151 m^2
19. 8.79 cm
20. 372 cm^3
21. $1\frac{1}{2}$ cm
22. (a) 8 cm   (b) 389 cm^2 (c) 913 cm^3 (d) 532 cm^3
23. (a) 13.9 cm^3 (b) 23.8 cm^3
24. $2\frac{1}{2}$ cm
25. (a) 356 cm^2 (b) 403 cm^3 (c) 3.64 cm

EXERCISE 83

1. £3000
2. £2400
3. £1500
4. £1350
5. £1110
6. £3600
7. £6000
8. £15 000
9. £18 000
10. £22 650
11. £2625
12. £2576
13. £1122
14. £6055
15. £3942
16. £1800
17. £1050
18. £1350
19. £2280
20. £1597.50
21. £2289
22. £2071.80
23. £2976
24. £979.50
25. £1758
26. £2211
27. £2464
28. £1293.60
29. £2847.25
30. £3017.84
31. £165.25
32. £138.25
33. £82.75
34. £201.85
35. £108.12
36. £33.81
37. £34.90
38. £59.27
39. £35.64
40. £66.57
41. £5675
42. £7900
43. £10 325
44. £20 650
45. £37 450
46. £48 250
47. £132 250
48. £270 250
49. (a) £5744   (b) £11 656   (c) £3496.80
50. (a) £5465.20   (b) £18 974.80   (c) £6261.68

EXERCISE 84

1. £97.75
2. £5.75
3. £690
4. £2.59
5. £31.05
6. £36.80
7. £14.37$\frac{1}{2}$
8. £40.82$\frac{1}{2}$
9. £2.07
10. £63.25
11. £97.75
12. £18.28$\frac{1}{2}$
13. £8.62$\frac{1}{2}$
14. £30.36
15. £73.94$\frac{1}{2}$
16. £17.48
17. £13.80
18. £48.30
19. £5.06
20. £29.32$\frac{1}{2}$
21. £19.09
22. £10.98
23. £43.70
24. £202.97$\frac{1}{2}$
25. £261.62$\frac{1}{2}$
26. £35
27. £420
28. £314.60
29. £33.60
30. £8.62$\frac{1}{2}$
31. £16.10
32. £120
33. £208.80
34. £517.50
35. £724.50

EXERCISE 85

1. £2100
2. £6300
3. £2880
4. £5280
5. £9150
6. £3480
7. £13 440
8. £5750
9. £55 825
10. £1 287 600
11. £32 000
12. £21 000
13. £10 600
14. £27 000
15. £570 000

EXERCISE 86

1. 0	2. £750	3. £2250	4. £6500
5. £25 450	6. £14 725	7. £600	8. £957 750
9. £168 850	10. £4500	11. 0	12. £12 300
13. £6350	14. 0	15. £26 750	16. £8625
17. £197 800	18. £381 350	19. £33 320	20. £30 325

EXERCISE 87

1. £70	2. £78.75	3. £93.75	4. £75.25
5. £78	6. £93.50	7. £98.58	8. £138
9. £104.72	10. £118.25	11. £80.87$\frac{1}{2}$, £4.62$\frac{1}{2}$	12. £146.30
13. £151.12$\frac{1}{2}$	14. (a) 8 h (b) 2$\frac{1}{2}$ h (c) £141.90		15. £125.40

EXERCISE 88

1. Dilys £48.86, Enid £48.30   2. £99   3. 72   4. £1.68
5. £3.04   6. Holland £113.72, Bennett £100.84, Hogan £100.08, Hyde £106.60
7. £97.45   8. £51.97   9. £116.68   10. £134.30

EXERCISE 89

1. £87.50	2. £600	3. £12 290
4. £8200	5. £542	6. (a) £330 (b) £780
7. £97	8. £102.60	9. £176.72$\frac{1}{2}$
10. George by £175.25		

EXERCISE 90

1. £1000	2. £672	3. £3050
4. £756	5. £1264	6. £1536
7. £2140	8. £3820	9. £666.67
10. £833.33	11. £9600	12. £14 400
13. £11 556	14. £10 488	15. £12 480
16. £7728	17. £6432	18. £44 640
19. £29 820	20. £64 200	21. Mr Manners by £918
22. Mr Deakin by £2688	23. £11 520	24. £9372.58
25. David by £97.93 per month or £1175.20 p.a.		

EXERCISE 91

1. £6.75	2. £8.82	3. £14.40	4. £20.70	5. £21.15
6. £8.37	7. £11.16	8. £14.85	9. £18.90	10. £21.15
11. £6.52	12. £9.19	13. £10.97	14. £14.06	15. £15.77
16. £5.90	17. £11.25	18. £13.44	19. £14.40	20. £16.80

EXERCISE 92

1. £31.20	2. £28.80	3. £61.60	4. £104	5. £65.25
6. £5.16	7. £6.07	8. £12.41	9. £12.60	10. £9

11. Lump sum £14 208, annual pension £4736 p.a.   12. Smaller by £281
13. £25 620, £8540   14. £26 880, £8960
15. Lump sum Peter £9640, Eric £10 725; Annual pension Peter 0, Eric £5005

EXERCISE 93

1. (a) £1300   (b) £1482   (c) £1703   (d) £1944.80   (e) £2740.40
2. (a) £29.20   (b) £34.70   3. (a) £29.25   (b) £1521   4. £1279.20, £72.80
5. 5, £3.73   6. (a) £6.37   (b) £44.59   7. (a) £9.45   (b) £47.25
8. £17 160   9. £21 736   10. £2732.60, £3416.40
11. (a) £42.46   (b) £45.86   12. £31.35   13. £32.35
14. £32.85   15. £32.85   16. £21.85
17. £26.85   18. £32.85   19. £32.85
20. £32.85

REVISION PAPER 51

1. (a) 250   (b) 247   (c) 246.7, 2.5×10^2
2. (a) 23.95   (b) 0.2395   (c) 0.001 744   3. £18.05$\frac{1}{2}$ 4. £51.60
5. (a) 392 cm^2 (b) 480 cm^3 (c) 7.83 cm   (d) 13 cm   (e) 15.3 cm

REVISION PAPER 52

1. (a) 6.092   (b) 0.42   (c) 14   2. 0.3864, 987.2, 2.175
3. 9.9 s   4. £7.40   5. £809.25

REVISION PAPER 53

1. 5$\frac{1}{4}$ 2. (a) 14.21   (b) 6.647   3. £7.80, 13%
4. (a) 28 700   (b) 3280   5. 106, 33 p

REVISION PAPER 54

1. $2^3 \times 3^2 \times 7^3$,   (a) 14   (b) 3   2. 1.643, 0.3617   3. £184
4. £4540, 25%   5. 4.96 cm

REVISION PAPER 55

1. (a) 18   (b) −4   2. Pearl £1785, Mary £2499, Nance £3213; £1428
3. £162   4. (a) 225 km   (b) 400 km/h^2 (c) 462.5 km
5. 4.08 mm

REVISION PAPER 56

1. £37.50   2. £7.40   3. £9.90   4. $\bar{1}$.7222, $\bar{1}$.9306
5. (a) 3.23 p.m.   (b) 29 mph   (c) 104 miles from A at 2.44 p.m.   (d) 72 miles

REVISION PAPER 57

1. (a) (i) 40% (ii) $\frac{13}{20}$ (b) 23   2. 90 p
3. 103 km/h   4. (a) $\frac{2}{3}$ (b) $\frac{1}{3}$ (c) 0
5. (a) 370.6 cm^3 (b) 269.5 g   (c) 59%

REVISION PAPER 58

1. (a) 103   (b) 142   2. (a) 0.5   (b) 40   (c) 0.125
3. (a) 4$\frac{1}{3}$ (b) 5   (c) 4   4. £14.20
5. Less by £186.20

REVISION PAPER 59

1. (a) 35%   (b) 48%   (c) $\frac{11}{20}$
2. (a) 25.58   (b) 0.001 529   (c) 0.4280
3. (a) 5.436×10^2 (b) 0.007 64   (c) 600
4. (a) £104   (b) £120
5. (a) £24   (b) £45   (c) £177

REVISION PAPER 60

1. $4\frac{15}{32}$
2. 12 km/h
3. (a) (i) 42 (ii) 1 0 1 0 1 0   (b) (i) 37 (ii) 45
4. (a) £175   (b) £50
5. $5\frac{1}{6}$ cm

REVISION PAPER 61

1. 2.68 km
2. 108 km/h
3. (a) (i) 0.001 82 (ii) 4.84   (b) 1.82×10^{-3}
4. (a) £50.05   (b) £19.25
5. (a) (i) 3 p.m. (ii) 4.42 p.m.   (b) 4.2 mph   (c) $1\frac{1}{4}$ miles from summit at 2.40 p.m.

REVISION PAPER 62

1. 5.307
2. 16 000 000 litres
3. 141 m
4. £645.16
5. $16\frac{2}{3}\%$

REVISION PAPER 63

1. (a) $4\frac{5}{6}$ (b) $1\frac{5}{6}$ (c) 5   (d) $2\frac{2}{9}$
2. £491.05, £39.28
3. (a) 564 cm   (b) 72.6 m^2 (c) 24.3 litres
4. (a) (i) 1 0 0 0 1 1 1 0 0 (ii) 124   (b) (i) 1000 (ii) 10050
5. 107 km

REVISION PAPER 64

1. (a) (i) 0.24 (ii) 0.681   (b) £46
2. (a) 243, 729   (b) $15\frac{1}{2}$, 20
3. (a) 360 m^2 (b) 2160 m^3 (c) 448 m^2 (d) 112 litres
4. 1.49 m, 1.75 m
5. 6.92 cm^2

REVISION PAPER 65

1. (a) 369.9   (b) 13.73
2. 16.13%
3. 125
4. £1500
5. (a) 53 m^2 (b) 954 000 litres   (c) 94 500 litres

REVISION PAPER 66

1. (a) 0.64   (b) 0.0144   (c) 0.4   (d) 0.6
2. (a) 3   (b) 2   (c) 4
3. 0.042
4. 3000
5. 86.6 cm

REVISION PAPER 67

1. (a) £4.35   (b) 1.08 kg
2. (a) (i) 0.216 (ii) 8   (b) (i) 0.49 (ii) 0 (iii) 30
3. 110 000 correct to two significant figures
4. $96.25\frac{1}{2}$
5. (a) $37\frac{1}{2}$ h   (b) £206.25   (c) $14\frac{1}{2}$ (d) $£336.87\frac{1}{2}$

REVISION PAPER 68

1. (a) $\frac{1}{40}$ (b) $\frac{6}{7}$ (c) 86.5 (d) 0.084 2. 70, £9100
3. 57, 68
5. £74, £82.88 4. (a) £2.67, £3.54 (b) £2.70, £3.51

REVISION PAPER 69

1. 13 weeks, £2.32 2. £1003 3. £42
4. £10 584 5. (a) 3040 m^2 (b) 18.2 m^3

REVISION PAPER 70

1. (i) 2.46×10^5 (ii) 2.34×10^5 2. (a) 100 (b) 59.82 (c) 59.82
3. (a) 145.9 (b) 0.7627 4. £7.50
5. (a) 60 mph, 12.50 p.m. (b) 18 miles (c) 40 min (d) 51 mph

REVISION PAPER 71

1. (a) 16 (b) 12 (c) -2 2. 90 km/h
3. (a) 188 (c) 13+ (d) 14+ (e) $\frac{3}{10}$ 4. $\frac{1}{8}$ (b) $\frac{3}{8}$ (c) $\frac{1}{2}$ 5. £30

REVISION PAPER 72

1. £73.29 2. (a) $<$ (b) $=$ (c) $=$ (d) $>$ 3. 270 cm^2
4. (a) 5 (b) 6 (c) 4.8 5. 1.2 m^3, 239 cm

REVISION PAPER 73

1. (a) 20 (b) 0.4 (c) 0.09 (d) 0.0121 (e) 0.000 027
2. (a) 74.36 m (b) 450 m (c) 3.174 m^2 (d) 2.624 kg
3. 5400 m 4. £600, 50%, 30% 5. 129 cm^2

REVISION PAPER 74

1. (a) 1.244 (b) 2594 2. 19 litres 3. (a) 47 h, £241.87$\frac{1}{2}$
4. 18.2% 5. £175

REVISION PAPER 75

1. (a) 499.5 (b) (i) 416 km (ii) 350 miles (iii) 12.8 km^2 2. 4.56
3.

CP	P	SP
£50	£20	£70
£60	£24	£84
£75	£30	£105

4. £115.10 5. (a) 4 m^3 (b) 100 kg

EXERCISE 94

1. £18 2. £24 3. £16.50 4. £60 5. £36
6. £40 7. £10 8. £9.50 9. £12 10. £7
11. £48 12. £210 13. £160 14. £54 15. £480
16. £252 17. £44 18. £112.50 19. £67.50 20. £297

	21. £114	22. £130	23. £125	24. £111	25. £105.50

21. £114   22. £130   23. £125   24. £111   25. £105.50
26. £248   27. £770   28. £412.50   29. £1428   30. £906.67
31. £60, £310   32. £133.20, £503.20   33. £43, £473
34. £287, £1107   35. £968, £1518   36. £324.80, £964.80
37. £72.20, £167.20   38. £167.40, £539.40   39. £79.69, £504.69
40. £64.48, £188.48   41. £93.50   42. £46
43. £85.58   44. £143.64   45. £799.68   46. £1009.80   47. £114.78
48. £9.31   49. £248.35   50. £40.17

EXERCISE 95

1.

P	R	T	SI	A
150	12	2	36	186
240	15	5	180	420
320	18	3	172.80	492.80
720	24	4	691.20	1411.20
405	8	$2\frac{1}{2}$	81	486
356	11	$3\frac{3}{4}$	146.85	502.85
534	13	7 months	$40.49\frac{1}{2}$	$574.49\frac{1}{2}$
890	17	9 months	$113.47\frac{1}{2}$	$1003.47\frac{1}{2}$

(All values in £)

2. £231 interest, total repayment £2431
3. £57.60   4. £18 810   5. £520   6. £12 000
7. 9 months   8. 73 days   9. 160 days   10. £15 000

EXERCISE 96

1. £50.40   2. £83.20   3. £178.08   4. £111.24
5. £88.41   6. £75.35   7. £155.51   8. £110.85
9. £35.82   10. £85.13   11. £109.59   12. £244.13
13. £135.25   14. £108.32   15. £293.09   16. £70.92
17. £156.65   18. £103.88   19. £323.94   20. £166.53
21. £271.43   22. £323.49   23. £127.15   24. £142.84
25. £63.09   26. £111.49   27. £328.05   28. £40.80
29. £129.30   30. £104.99   31. £168.78   32. £98.78
33. £4490.62   34. £11 278.40   35. £1873.84
36. Bank £1160, finance company £1268.24   37. £798   38. £1998.21
39. £2659.38
40. If he keeps the car its value is £409.60 + building society cash of £10 883.91.
    If he sells, his new £9000 car is worth £3686.40 after 4 years.

EXERCISE 97

1. £1.25   2. £114.84   3. £1852.60   4. £5518.20
5. £683.80   6. £5705.20   7. £1456.32   8. £48 315
9. £2000   10. £5000   11. £8000   12. £500
13. £6000   14. £1500   15. 14%   16. 13%
17. 8 years   18. 2 years   19. £2020   20. £3536

EXERCISE 98

1. 6.192   2. 190.0   3. 5.960   4. 1.714
5. 1.539   6. 8.198   7. 13.21   8. 1.216
9. 0.5987   10. 0.0617   11. 0.3939   12. 0.1001
13. 809.11   14. £14 856   15. £11 991   16. £716 853

17. £120 000
18. £25 124
19. £34 419
20. £7737
21. 14.9%
22. 11.8%
23. 14.7%
24. 5.88 years
25. 8.38 years
26. 2.81 years
27. £100
28. £10
29. 8 years
30. 8 years
31. 14.2%
32. 12%
33. £43 200
34. £174 000
35. £149 600
36. £400
37. £1160
38. 6.03%
39. 9.05%
40. 37 000, 66 600
41. 5.70%
42. £1270
43. 1.42%
44. 9.22×10^{18}
45. 25 300
46. £3560
47. £336
48. £12 500
49. 4 years
50. 24.2%

EXERCISE 99

1. £161.14
2. £204.66
3. £3505
4. (a) £1476   (b) £36 909
5. £2331, £56 620, 226.5%
6. (a) £199.75   (b) £84 925
7. £21 725
8. (a) £16 200   (b) £2482   (c) £51 450

EXERCISE 100

1. £136
2. £117
3. £45.46
4. £22.65
5. £931.92
6. £167.85
7. £2343
8. £899.46
9. £7508.92
10. £7848.20
11. £88.80
12. £209.75
13. £20.16
14. £380
15. £5.44
16. (a) £6.72   (b) $5\frac{1}{3}\%$
17. £95.76
18. £236.44, 19.3%
19. £57.05
20. £417.24, £72.24
21. Option 1 by £346
22. £912, 32%
23. £2198
24. (a) £26.63   (b) £34.24   (c) 8%
25. £62.48
26. £25.72
27. £21.34
28. To buy by £110.60
29. (a) (i)   (b) (ii)
30. (a) £46.12$\frac{1}{2}$ (b) £406.87$\frac{1}{2}$

EXERCISE 101

1. £5
2. £9
3. £1035.55
4. £1368.37
5. £47.15
6. £269.59
7. £35.43
8. £28.34

EXERCISE 102

1. £14 370
2. £21 420
3. £370 900
4. £625 400
5. £528 700
6. (a) £7500   (b) £375 000   (c) £562 500   (d) £645 000   (e) £900 000
7. £5 264 500
8. £2 365 900
9. £9 364 000
10. £6 153 700
11. £13 720 000
12. £75
13. £90
14. £106.25
15. £60.30
16. £276
17. £247.50
18. £261
19. £99.28
20. £130 38
21. £790.50
22. 80 p
23. 62 p
24. 82 p
25. 76 p
26. 54 p
27. 93 p
28. 105 p
29. 121 p
30. 87 p
31. 121 p
32. £180
33. £210
34. £314
35. £155
36. £137
37. £284
38. £554
39. £263
40. £384
41. £673
42. £39.48
43. His sister by £3.51
44. £107.88
45. £206.51, £231.12
46. £23 640, £1 096 896, 16.92 p
47. 78 p, £184.08, £220.74
48. £237.51
49. £290, £269.70
50. £124.55
51. £3.86
52. £13.67$\frac{1}{2}$
53. £29 767.50
54. £174, 44 p, £254.80
55. 55 p, £83.60, £163.90

EXERCISE 103

1. £57   2. £100   3. £143   4. £155.50   5. £74
6. £70.28   7. £172.38   8. £62.24   9. £171.36   10. £280.28
11. £69.40   12. £152.90   13. £179.61   14. £305.83   15. £158.79
16. £101.10   17. £156.40   18. £214.33   19. £301.62   20. £186.32
21. £39.20   22. £101   23. £157.60   24. £209.62   25. £91.75
26. £236.78   27. £275.73   28. £69.74   29. £83.73   30. £326.69
31. Credit by £9.20   32. Prepayment by £4.50   33. Credit by £7.10
34. Prepayment by £10.08   35. Credit by £11.56

EXERCISE 104

1. 980, 1024, 426, 642   2. £66.30, £68.94, £33.06, £46.02
3. 914,   (a) £52.20   (b) £81.12   (c) £91.51   (d) £101.90   (e) £122.28   (f) £179.67
(g) £66.90   (h) £76.56   (i) £60.98   (j) £87.04
4. (a) 10   (b) $83\frac{1}{3}$ (c) $\frac{1}{2}$ (d) 2   (e) 0.4   5. (a) $1\frac{1}{2}$ (b) 10   (c) 0.2   (d) 3
6. £7.38   7. 1340   8. £7.14   9. £9.59   10. £4.80
11. 6.84 p per cent
12.   58.48
        7.55
        39.99
        1.95
    —————
    £107.97

13. £272.41, £20.95

EXERCISE 105

1. £57.73   2. £74.68   3. £55.67   4. £108.46   5. £161
6. £77.64   7. 10 p   8. 5 p   9. 20 p   10. 25 p
11. 10 p   12. 16 p   13. £2.08   14. 96 p   15. £1.10
16. 10 p   17. £1   18. £1.15   19. 6, 14 min 24 s
20. £5.28

EXERCISE 106

1. 0.4 p   2. 5.71 p
3. £340, 7.62 p per km   4. 11 154 km, £1115.24
5. (a) £600   (b) £1566   (c) 6.53 p per km   6. £138.50
7. (a) 100 gallons   (b) £200   8. 150 gallons, £292.50
9. $833\frac{1}{3}$ gallons, £350   10. 171.4 gallons, £318.80
11. Yes by £30.33
12. (a) £675   (b) 21 000 km   (c) £2100   (d) 10 p
13. (a) £800   (b) £2251   (c) 18.8 p   14. 21.6 p
15. (a) £1430   (b) £936   (c) £2366   (d) 24 375 km   (e) 9.71 p; 40%

EXERCISE 107

1. £5   2. £8   3. £10   4. £12   5. £13.50
6. £14.75   7. £18   8. £22   9. £35   10. £45
11. £56   12. £76   13. £88.50   14. £100
15. (a) £40   (b) £44   (c) £48.40   16. (a) £22   (b) £24.20   (c) £26.62
17. (a) £30   (b) £33.60   (c) £37.63   18. (a) £50   (b) £54   (c) £58.32
19. £19.50   20. £24   21. £36   22. £40.50   23. £63.75
24. £100.20   25. £203.40   26. £27   27. £40.50   28. £56.25

29. £76.50   **30.** £91.80   **31.** £227.70   **32.** £499.50   **33.** £1080

34. (a) £75   (b) £1.44   **35.** (a) £107   (b) £2.04

36. (a) £176   (b) £3.38   **37.** (a) £263   (b) £50.60

38. (a) £369.40   (b) £7.10   **39.** (a) £590.70   (b) £11.36

40. (a) £1230   (b) £23.65

EXERCISE 108

1. £450
2. £480
3. £224
4. £160
5. £240
6. £180, £49.50
7. (a) £693.75   (b) £277.50
8. (a) £210   (b) £140
9. (a) £350   (b) £95
10. £60
11. £400
12. £500
13. £316
14. (a) £210   (b) £168
15. £444

EXERCISE 109

1. (a) 215 miles   (b) 199 miles
2. Cambridge by 18 miles
3. (a) Cambridge   (b) Edinburgh
4. (a) London   (b) York
5. (a) York and Leeds   (b) London and Edinburgh
6. Liverpool, Manchester
7. London and Aberdeen
8. 114 miles
9. 398 miles
10. 219 miles

EXERCISE 110

1.

9.15 p.m.	quarter past nine in the morning
7.35 p.m.	twenty-five to eight in the evening
4.10 a.m.	ten past four in the morning
10.30 a.m.	half past ten in the morning
6.40 p.m.	twenty to seven in the evening
15.15	quarter past three in the afternoon
10.30	half past ten in the morning
21.45	quarter to ten in the evening
19.38	twenty-two minutes to eight in the evening
02.15	quarter past two in the morning
10.55	10.55 a.m.
22.30	10.30 p.m.
04.10	4.10 a.m.
23.45	11.45 p.m.

2. (a) 4 h   (b) 6 h   (c) 4 h 30 min   (d) 2 h 20 min   (e) 4 h 22 min   (f) 11 h 5 min
     (g) 10 h 54 min   (h) 3 h 6 min   (i) 2 h 35 min   (j) 19 h 24 min
3. (a) 08.15   (b) 1 h 44 min   (c) 11.48   (d) 16 min   (e) 08.17
4. (a) 9 min   (b) 1   (c) 12.05   (d) 10.52
5. (a) 1   (b) 11.05   (c) 11.52, average speed 150 km/h
6. (a) 650 km   (b) 200 km/h   (c) 10 min   (d) 1 h 11 min
7. (a) Watford and London   (b) 7 min   (c) 214 km/h   (d) 225 km (Carlisle–Crewe)

EXERCISE 111

1. (a) 7.30 a.m.   (b) 1.30 p.m.
2. (a) 7 a.m.   (b) 11 p.m.
3. (a) 4 p.m.   (b) 8 a.m.
4. (a) 8 p.m.   (b) 3 a.m.
5. (a) 2 a.m.   (b) 9 p.m.
6. (a) 8 p.m. previous day   (b) 8 p.m.
7. (a) 6 p.m.   (b) 4 p.m.

8. (a) 6 a.m.　　(b) 1 p.m.　　(c) 9 p.m. previous day　　(d) 7 p.m. previous day
9. 8.30 a.m.　　　　　　　　　　　　　10. 2 p.m. next day
11. (a) 4.30 p.m.　(b) 7.30 p.m., 7 a.m.　　12. (a) 2 p.m.　　(b) 1 a.m.
13. 8 a.m., 4 a.m.
14. (a) 1 p.m.　　(b) 4.30 p.m.　　(c) 5.30 p.m.　　(d) 1 p.m.
15. 1 p.m.

EXERCISE 112

1. $388.80
2. 907.20 f.
3. DM 2127.60
4. 6570 pta.
5. 8883 dr.
6. £12.50
7. £84
8. £172.25
9. £54
10. £15.48
11. £8.36
12. £23.92
13. £6.12
14. £7.31$\frac{1}{2}$
15. £10.68
16. 676 f.
17. 1405 dr.
18. 1032 schillings
19. 304 riyals
20. $HK 285
21. $1.72 ≡ £1
22. 170 pta. ≡ £1
23. 32 schillings ≡ £1
24. DM 3.75 ≡ £1
25. 14.3 kroner ≡ £1
26. £36
27. 85.68 f.
28. £3.33
29. £2.74$\frac{1}{2}$
30. 1875 escudos
31. £214
32. £1.25
33. £1.35
34. $2640
35. £4.50
36. £392
37. £38
38. 79 p
39. £2.80
40. No, £16 cheaper at home
41. In Paris by £2.55
42. £11 500
43. £2760
44. £12 900
45. Lost £12.32
46. DM 152
47. 924 dr.
48. 6500 escudos
49. £3
50. £40

EXERCISE 113

1. 7 days leaving on Sat. of week commencing 25 July
   14 days leaving on Sat. of week commencing 1 August
2. Demand is higher on a Saturday than a Wednesday
3. Excelsior
4. £1344.25, £160
5. £22
6. (a) £165　　(b) £1304.25, £47.25
7. £180.40
8. £617.75

EXERCISE 114

1. £9.50　　　2. £26　　　3. £31.50　　　4. £42　　　5. £46, £14 less

EXERCISE 115

1. £190, £17.50
2. £1326, £162.50
3. £3999, £258
4. £3420, £405
5. £2604, £186
6. £2790, £372
7. £600, £60
8. £700, £84
9. £1200, £96
10. £1500, £165
11. £4500, £472.50
12. £8200, £287
13. £1104
14. £808
15. £255
16. £1170
17. £798
18. £1802
19. 12%
20. 12%
21. 10%
22. 12$\frac{1}{2}$%
23. 16$\frac{2}{3}$%
24. 14.29% or 14$\frac{2}{7}$%
25. £1200, £26 more
26. £9000, £60 less
27. £3000, up £24
28. £10 down
29. £631.80 up
30. £17.50 down
31. £427.87$\frac{1}{2}$
32. £138.60
33. £691.60
34. £402.50
35. £879.37$\frac{1}{2}$
36. £3312

37. £3741
40. 65
43. 94
46. £5036.25
49. £3000, £40.50

38. £3290
41. 96
44. 52, 11.5%
47. £5592.65
50. £6000, £72

39. £1872
42. 102
45. £2647.68
48. £2891.70

EXERCISE 116

1. £1195
4. £2450
7. £1011.92
10. £2035.50
13. £725
16. £3816
19. £1285.85
22. 175
25. 321
28. 160 p
31. £450, £15
34. £1254, £29.70
37. £25.20
40. £48.60
43. 2.5%
46. 5%
49. 4%
52. £310.80
55. 296, £4.96
58. (a) 864   (b) £4.32 less
61. (a) 441 p   (b) £1.68 more
64. £1567.50, £76, 4.85%
67. £1329.36, £30.56, 2.30%
70. 14%, 5%
73. Jane £47.25, Allison £87.50
75. (a) £188.57   (b) £629.36, worse by £349.68
76. £2279.85
79. £1803.42

2. £1071
5. £1795.52
8. £1224.76
11. £1500
14. £1112.50
17. £4667.25
20. £4156.64
23. 630
26. 120 p
29. 432 p
32. £3720, £93
35. £137 500, £1000
38. £64.80
41. 2%
44. $8\frac{1}{3}$%
47. 8%
50. 2%
53. £249.75
56. £186
59. £1980, £3.96 more
62. 28 500, £58.12$\frac{1}{2}$ more
65. £626.40, £13.50, 2.16%
68. 8%
71. £7500, 145 more
74. Rise of £27.84; worse by £349.37 for one year
77. £691.42
80. 650

3. £1344
6. £1808.19
9. £750.60
12. £1653
15. £619.84
18. £1148.94
21. 420
24. 794
27. 240 p
30. 84 p
33. £3450, £60
36. £17.60
39. £35.20
42. 5%
45. 4%
48. 12%
51. £1215
54. £261.96
57. (a) 900   (b) 70 p more
60. (a) 384   (b) £4.38 more
63. £480, £10, 2.08%
66. £10 296, £117, 1.14%
69. 12%
72. Edgar by £111.50

78. £992.76

EXERCISE 117

1. 35 p
5. 19 p
9. 11 p
13. £69 900
17. £38 600
21. £1239
25. £10 632
29. £260 680
33. £50 600
37. 32 p, £42 680
39. £97 200 to unsecured creditors and £16 473 to secured creditors
40. 22 p, £130 988

2. 18 p
6. 23 p
10. 21 p
14. £55 500
18. £418 800
22. £2301
26. £12 804
30. £1 414 800
34. £98 600
38. 14 p

3. 7 p
7. 16 p
11. £54 300
15. £149 000
19. £564 700
23. £9752
27. £1376
31. 25 p
35. £31 150

4. 29 p
8. 9 p
12. £32 100
16. £296 100
20. £2 103 300
24. £9230
28. £11 430
32. £240.80
36. 18 p, £1042.92

EXERCISE 118

1. 24 in.
5. 42 in.
9. 128 in.

2. 40 in.
6. 57 in.
10. 153 in.

3. 69 in.
7. 88 in.
11. 67 in.

4. 125 in.
8. 96 in.
12. 593 in.

13. 13 ft   14. 25 ft   15. 54 ft   16. 21 ft 4 in.
17. 11 ft 5 in.   18. 60 ft 4 in.   19. 78 ft   20. 83 ft 4 in.
21. 3520 yd   22. 880 yd   23. 1320 yd   24. 5720 yd
25. 24 640 yd   26. 46 145 yd   27. 28 in.   28. 64 in.
29. (a) 20 in.   (b) 4 ft   30. 10 in.   31. 17 in.   32. 220
33. 88 in., 720   34. $3\frac{2}{3}$ miles
35. (a) 30.48 cm   (b) 91.44 cm   (c) 38.1 cm   (d) 226.06 cm
36. (a) 42 200 m, 42.2 km   37. 1 : 31 680, $2\frac{1}{4}$ miles
38. 1 : 633 600, 2.6 in.   39. 3280 ft   40. 340 in.

EXERCISE 119

1. 15 in.^{2} 2. 126 in.^{2} 3. 42 in.^{2} 4. 26 in.^{2}
5. $1\frac{1}{2}$ ft^2 6. 11.25 in.^{2} 7. 8.84 in.^{2} 8. 192 in.^{2}
9. $8\frac{3}{4}$ ft^2 10. 18.6875 in.^{2} or $18\frac{11}{16}$ in.^{2} 11. 24 in.^{2}
12. 56 in.^{2} 13. 30 ft^2 14. $7\frac{1}{2}$ ft^2 15. $22\frac{1}{2}$ yd^2
16. $1\frac{1}{2}$ ft^2 17. $4\frac{1}{2}$ ft^2 18. 9 ft^2 19. $7\frac{1}{2}$ ft
20. 594 in.^{2} 21. 36   22. 132 yd^2, $51\frac{1}{3}$ yd^2 23. 3136
24. (a) 8800   (b) 1.82 acres   25 32   26. 616 in.^{2}
27. (a) 12 474 in.^{2} (b) $86\frac{5}{8}$ ft^2 28. 21 in.   29. $3\frac{1}{2}$ ft
30. 1 : 63 360, 10 in.^{2} 31. 1 : 15 840, $\frac{1}{4}$ sq mile
32. (a) 6.45 cm^2 (b) 929 cm^2 (c) 8360 cm^2
33. (a) 0.835 m^2 (b) 0.0928 m^2 34. 805 in.^{2}
35. (a) $9\frac{5}{8}$ in.^{2} (b) $45\frac{3}{8}$ in.^{2} (c) 0.630 ft^3

EXERCISE 120

1. (a) 27 in.^{3} (b) 125 in.^{3} (c) 512 in.^{3} 2. 8   3. 27
4. 168 in.^{3} 5. $121\frac{1}{2}$ in.^{3}, 384   6. 486 in.^{3}, 3 yd^3 7. £9
8. 60   9. 100   10. 10 ft   11. 74.88 gallons
12. $3\frac{1}{3}$ ft   13. 2880   14. 38 cwt   15. $665\frac{3}{5}$ gallons

EXERCISE 121

1. 48 oz   2. 112 oz   3. 88 oz   4. 60.08 oz
5. 130 oz   6. 206 oz   7. 339 oz   8. 103 oz
9. 154 oz   10. 56 lb   11. 154 lb   12. 126 lb
13. 119 lb   14. 87 lb   15. 262 lb   16. 73 lb
17. 218 lb   18. 356 lb   19. 560 lb   20. 1344 lb
21. 392 lb   22. 280 lb   23. 406 lb   24. 994 lb
25. 17 920 lb   26. 12 544 lb   27. 7168 lb   28. 34 832 lb
29. 18 144 lb   30. 24 192 lb   31. 0.908 kg   32. 2.27 kg
33. 6.36 kg   34. 3.86 kg   35. 5.56 kg   36. 11.2 kg
37. 5.08 tonnes   38. 12.2 tonnes   39. 508 tonnes   40. 8.64 tonnes
41. 4.40 tonnes   42. 17.0 tonnes   43. 7 st 7 lb   44. 4 tons 18 cwt 60 lb
45. 1 ton 12 cwt   46. £3.36   47. £12.75   48. £11.76
49. £10.34   50. 41 p   51. 105 min   52. 170 min
53. (a) 105 min   (b) 195 min   54. 21
55. The boy by 6.67 lb or 3.026 kg

Exercise 122

1. (a) 96 km/h (b) $26\frac{2}{3}$ m/s
2. 19.44 m/s
3. (a) 112 km/h (b) 31.11 m/s
4. 15.63 miles/min
5. 5.87 f.
6. $162\frac{1}{2}$ p
7. $37\frac{1}{2}$ p (37.39)
8. 89 p
9. $11\frac{1}{2}$ p
10. DM 4.62
11. UK by 1.26 p per pint
12. 2.252 kg/cm^2
13. 4.926 kg/cm^2
14. 163 p
15. 212 p/gallon
16. \$2.48
17. \$2.98
18. £493 700 per km^2
19. Gain $66\frac{2}{3}$%
20. 110%
21. 76 p
22. 159 pta.
23. 66 p
24. 40.95 f.
25. (a) £500 (b) £900

Revision Paper 76

1. (a) £162.40 (b) £173.77
2. (a) £312 (b) £348.80, £36.80
3. £11, (a) £33 (b) £22 (c) £44
4. 0.132 mm
5. (a) 7.805 cm (b) 24.52 cm^2

Revision Paper 77

1. £84.50, £11.05
2. $3\frac{18}{35}$
3. $5\frac{1}{2}$ years
4. \$211
5. 79

Revision Paper 78

1. (a) 0.01 (b) 0.25 (c) 0.15
2. £310
3.
4. £6862.50, £19.69

5. £12 000

Revision Paper 79

1. (a) $8\frac{1}{2}$% (b) Thomas by 129 votes
2. (a) 15.25 (b) 1 h (c) 9 km/h (d) $6\frac{3}{4}$ km/h (e) 36 km
3. £7.68
4. 280
5. (a) 44% (b) 4%

Revision Paper 80

1. (a) (i) 0.5625 (ii) $\frac{9}{40}$ (b) (i) 40 (ii) 40.1 (iii) 40.10
2. £432.30
3. (a) 1.6071 (b) 0.2411
4. 107 kg
5. 124 h, 18.00 the following Thursday

Revision Paper 81

1. $23\frac{1}{3}$ km/litre
2. 15 years, 7 : 8
3. £2 512 000, £260, £184.22, £386 848
4. 9 years
5. £131.25, £159.25

REVISION PAPER 82

1. £2450
2. $1\frac{1}{4}$
3. £1.15
4. $86.4\,\text{cm}^3$
5. £2764

REVISION PAPER 83

1. (a) 5.4252×10^{-3}　(b) 7.2×10^{-6}
2. 2.9725, 4.0775
3. 74 p, £192.40
4. $102.9\,\text{cm}^3$
5. (a) July　(b) (i) 8 h　(ii) 56 h　(c) 8.405

REVISION PAPER 84

1. (a) $\frac{3}{7}$　(b) $2\frac{2}{7}$
2. (a) 740, £739.60
3. 0.386 p
4. (a) 3.30 p.m.　(b) 6.30 p.m. the previous day
5. $92\frac{1}{2}$ h

REVISION PAPER 85

1. $16\frac{1}{2}$
2. (a) £784.98　(b) £361.92
3. £11 230
4. (a) 76 km/h　(b) $47\frac{1}{2}$ mph
5. $37.1\,\text{cm}^3$, 319 g

REVISION PAPER 86

1. (a) $318.20　(b) £487.50
2. £5.20
3. $94.0\,\text{cm}^3$
4. (a) £358.40　(b) £179.20
5. (a) 116　(b) (i) 1200　(ii) 26%

REVISION PAPER 87

1. 4460 yen
2. £242.60
3. 22 km/litre
4. 6.84 p, 13.4%
5. 9.07 cm

REVISION PAPER 88

1. $3\frac{3}{7}$ km/h
2. £147.50
3. £194.54
4. 27.27 min or $27\frac{3}{11}$ min past 5
5. (a) £2553.12　(b) £63 828

REVISION PAPER 89

1. £600
2. £220.40
3. (a) £1 ≡ 186 pta.　(b) (i) £204.12　(ii) 982.80 f.
4. (a) £42　(b) £38.89　(c) £45.36　(d) £48.99
5. Increase of £126.75

REVISION PAPER 90

1. 1.5
2. (a) 0.233 mm　(b) (i) 37 mph　(ii) 43 mph　(iii) 56 mph
3. 1850, £101.75, £1800, £1332, £3.72, £12.20
4. 14.8 kg
5. 1 : 0.970, 4.5 min

REVISION PAPER 91

1. $\frac{8}{15}$
2. (a) 5600　(b) 5000
3. £36.25
4. 335
5. (a) £3.90　(b) £15.60　(c) £35.10

REVISION PAPER 92

1. (a) 284   (b) 3214   (c) $2^3 \times 3^2 \times 7^2 \times 13 = 45\,864$ 2. £637.33
3. (a) 38 400 km   (b) £1376   (c) £2516   (d) 6.55 p per km
4. £147   5. £10, £14, 10 : 21

REVISION PAPER 93

1. (a) (i) 25 m   (ii) 2494 cm   (ii) 24 938 mm   (b) 35 p : 21 p   2. 0.596
3. £56.25   4. £47.06   5. 36 p to Scott and £3.21 to Terry

REVISION PAPER 94

1. 2520   2. £67.75$\frac{1}{2}$ 3. £4500, £135
4. (a) 30.68 cm^2 (b) 56.25%   5. £86

REVISION PAPER 95

1. 52.86 km/h   2. £49.50, 2.05%   3. £430
4. 672   (a) £59.13   (b) £4.55   5. (a) 3 p.m.   (b) 11 a.m.

REVISION PAPER 96

1. (a) $23\frac{5}{19}$ (b) $\frac{6}{77}$ 2. 12% gain   3. £25.21
4. $4\frac{4}{11}$ mph   5. 579 cm^3

REVISION PAPER 97

1. $\frac{8}{99}$ litres   2. £12 less   3. (a) 22 km   (b) £630   (c) £1687   (d) 5 p
4. £58.50   5. 10.4 kg

REVISION PAPER 98

1. (a) 7 : 4   (b) 49 : 16   2. 265 cm   3. 20
4. 348 kg   5. (a) 835.5 cm^3 (b) 9.419 cm

REVISION PAPER 99

1. 7 : 6 : 8 : 7
2. (a) 10 p.m. the previous night   (b) 6.30 a.m. the following day
3. (a) 2.221   (b) 0.706
4. (a) 12.19 p.m.   (b) At 12.05 p.m. 25 km north of the service area   (c) 133 km
5. 1.82 : 1

REVISION PAPER 100

1. (a) 355   (b) 560$_8$ (c) (i) 12   (ii) 36   (iii) 12   (iv) 430   (v) 7   2. £5.10, 34 p more
3. £549, 12.8%   4. 50 min   5. £15 000, £495.20

515

EXAMINATION QUESTIONS

PAPER 1

1. (a) $0.072\,\text{m}^3$ (b) £65, £91 (c) £400
2. (i) 2.5 (ii) 0.06 (iii) 2.4×10^{-3} (iv) 0.001 53
3. 12 cm, 66.67 kg
4. (i) 120 min (ii) $2\frac{1}{4}$ kg (iii) 1130 hours (iv) $T = (20 + 40M)\,\text{min}$
5. 18 m, £4.50, 3456 gallons

PAPER 2

1. (a) 0.203 (b) 1 1 0 1 (c) 1 0 1 0 1 1
2. (a) 4620 (b) £528 000 (c) $34:51, \frac{85a}{a+b}, \frac{85b}{a+b}$ (d) (i) $5:3$ (ii) $25:9$
3. (i) £43.44 (ii) £1175 (iii) £1224 (iv) £49, 4.2%, £59
4. (i) 5 cm, 11 cm (ii) $102\,\text{cm}^2$ (iii) $10\,200\,\text{cm}^3$ (iv) 23.46 kg
5. 366.7 g, 10 800

PAPER 3

1. 47.2
2. (a) $\frac{1}{10}$ (b) (i) 1 0 1 0 0 (ii) 20 (c) 124
3. £277.80, 23%, £22.04 per month
4. (i) 12 cm (ii) 9 litres (iii) $2160\,\text{cm}^2$ (iv) $2\frac{1}{3}$ litres
5. (a) (i) 86% (ii) 423 (b) $3\frac{3}{4}$ kg

PAPER 4

1. (a) 536 (b) 35 p (c) 1.7 g
2. (a) 45 mph (b) £3544.50 (c) the first
3. (a) 4.1 cm (b) $8\frac{8}{9}$ cm (c) $31.04\,\text{cm}^3$
4. (a) 643.26 francs, 61 p, 146.54 (b) 3.524
5. 4.36 p.m., least $53\frac{1}{3}$ km/h, greatest 95 km/h

PAPER 5

1. (i) 16% (ii) £25 (b) 30 (c) 6
2. (i) 67 p (ii) £103.85 (iii) £2 265 750 (iv) £44.20, £240
3. (a) 12 min, 18 min, 50 km/h (b) 162 g
4. $37.70\,\text{cm}^3$
5. (i) £6 400 000, 3.125 p

PAPER 6

1. (a) (i) 0.3125 (ii) $\frac{33}{40}$ (b) 48 km/h
2. (a) 30 (b) (i) 31, 44, 112 (ii) 43
3. (a) 15.8 m/s (b) 1.55 s (c) $1\,\text{m/s}^2$ (d) 160 m
4. (a) $\frac{3}{5}$ (b) 12 345
5. $2514\,\text{cm}^3$, $260\pi\,\text{cm}^2$ or $816.9\,\text{cm}^2$, $2\frac{1}{2}$ cm, $2474\,\text{cm}^3$

PAPER 7

1. (a) 1 0 0 0 0 0 1 (b) 4
2. (a) £89.04 (b) £41
3. (a) 18.40 (b) 0.1176 (c) 0.3015 (d) 0.4277
4. £8, £3.60, 63
5. (a) 4.850 m (b) 120° (c) $3.395\,\text{m}^2$ (d) $19.82\,\text{m}^2$

PAPER 8

1. (a) 174 lb   (b) $\frac{7}{20}$ (c) £3.40   (d) 675 cm^3
2. (a) $\frac{39}{40}$ (b) £120
3. (a) £5.68, 14.2%   (b) 49.06   (c) 12.8 km/litre
4. (i) 37.8 m^2 (ii) 453.6 m^3 (iii) 3.9 m (iv) 277.2 m^2
5. (i) 12.65 cm (ii) 369.5 cm^2 (iii) 20.38 cm

PAPER 9

1. (a) 800   (b) £40.80, £61.20, £142.80   (c) 9.202×10^{-1}
2. (a) 0.05, 0.047   (b) (i) 563.6 (ii) 0.4355 (iii) 3 km^2
3. (a) £770, 15.4%   (b) $1.987\,65 \times 10^{-3}$ 4. 2100, £78.75, £3300, £3564, Mr Jones
5. (i) 880 cm^2 (ii) A circle, radius 5 cm, situated 2 cm above the base

PAPER 10

1. (a) 135   (b) 0.3893   (c) £7 800 000, $3\frac{1}{2}$ p
2. (a) £2850   (b) 17%   (c) (i) 30 000 (ii) 30 km/h
3. (a) (ii) $22\frac{1}{2}$ mph   (b) (ii) 3.30 p.m.   (c) (ii) 37 miles from A at 2.20 p.m.
4. (i) £21.39 (ii) £18, 325   5. (i) £1088 (ii) £1880, 23.5%, $29\frac{1}{2}$%

PAPER 11

1. (a) 840 m   (b) £232   (c) 410 miles
2. (a) £12 000   (b) (i) 4 m (ii) 363 cm (iii) 3628 mm
3. 213.1 cm^2 (i) 0.043 m^3 (ii) 356π cm^2 or 1119 cm^2 4. (a) 50 mph   (b) 80%
5. (iii) 125 km to 350 km (iv) distances over 365 km better than B, over 375 km better than C
   (v) 2.5 p per km

PAPER 12

1. (a) 1 0 1 1   (b) £120   (c) £4.50   (d) 10 cm
2. (a) $13\frac{7}{11}$ (b) 3.58×10^1, 3.58×10^4, 3.58×10^{-3} (c) £6.21   (d) 2 litres
3. (a) 62.5 cm   (b) 1.9 km^2 (c) 2.5 litres   4. (i) £1410 (ii) 7100 m^3
5. 71.2 kg, 159.1 cm, 4.932 cm

PAPER 13

1. (a) (i) 157 (ii) 1 1 0 1 0 1   (b) $\frac{11}{12}$ 2. (a) $\frac{\pi}{6}$ or 0.5237 cm^3 (b) 56, 7
3. (a) £360   (b) £78   (c) 13%   4. 9 km
5. (i) £1074, 22.90%, £4320

PAPER 14

1. (a) 464 km, 92.8 km/h   (b) $1\frac{3}{4}$ cm, 57.75 cm^3 2. £98, £141.40, 4
3. (i) 769 000 cm^3 (ii) 0.769 m^3 (iii) 654 kg (iv) 36 cm (v) 153.8
4. (i) 170 000 (ii) 29 600   5. (i) a = 38, b = 1.554 (ii) 3.7 (iii) 12.9

PAPER 15

1. (a) 117 km/h   (b) 0.18   (c) £480
2. (a) (i) 13, 21 (ii) $\frac{8}{81}$, $\frac{16}{243}$ (b) 60 p   (c) 1.5 cm
3. (i) 3.536 m (ii) 23.16 m^2 4. (a) 684π cm^3 (b) (i) $\sqrt[3]{\frac{3V}{4\pi}}$ (ii) $10\frac{1}{2}$ cm
5. (i) £3.60 (ii) £374.40 (iii) 4200 miles (iv) $6\frac{1}{2}$ h (v) 7500 miles

INDEX

Addition
 of binary number 86
 of decimals 44
 of directed numbers 58
 of fractions 27
 of money 90
 of whole numbers 2
Annulus 240
Antilogarithms 215
Appreciation 334
Area
 general 135
 imperial units 421
 metric units 135
 of annulus 240
 of circle 240
 of cone 250
 of cylinder 244
 of parallelogram 144
 of rectangle 136
 of sector of a circle 242
 of similar shapes 258
 of sphere 254
 of square 136
 of trapezium 145
 of triangle 144
Averages and average speed 100

Bankruptcy 415
Bar charts 184
Bills
 electricity 361
 gas 356
 telephone 365
Binary arithmetic 84
Borrowing money 338
 credit cards 346
 hire-purchase 341
 mortgages 338
Building societies 338

Calculators and tables 200

Capacity
 imperial 423
 metric 147
Capital gains tax (CGT) 275
Capital transfer tax (CTT) 277
Car
 insurance 377
 running costs 368
Change of units 426
Circle
 arc length 241
 area 240
 circumference 234
 sector area 242
Cone
 surface area 250
 volume 251
Commission 287
Common fractions 22
Compound interest 324
 formula 331
 table 328
Compound proportion 118
Conversion of units 426
Cost of running a motorcycle/car 368
Credit cards 346
Cylinder
 surface area 244
 volume 246

Decimal places 51
Decimals 39
 addition of 44
 long division of 50
 multiplication of 47
 short division of 49
 subtraction of 46
Depreciation 334
Direct proportion 113
Directed numbers
 addition and subtraction 58
 multiplication and division 61

Distance tables 382
Division
 by a power of 10 42
 by whole numbers 10
 of binary numbers 87
 of decimals 49
 of directed numbers 61
 of fractions 35
 of money 95

Earning money 280
Electricity bills 361

Figures into words 2
Flow of liquid 255
Foreign exchange 389
Fractions
 addition of 27
 common 22
 decimal 39
 division of 35
 improper 24
 multiplication of 32
 proper 24
 subtraction of 30

Gas bills 356
Graphs
 conversion 169
 simple 167
 travel 172
 $y = 10^x$ 212
Greenwich mean time (GMT) 387
Gross wages/salaries 290

Highest common factor (HCF) 19
Hire-purchase 341
Histograms 188
Holidays and travel 382
 package holidays 394
Hourly pay 280
House insurance 373
House purchase 338
Houshold expenses 351

Imperial units 419
Income 280
Income tax 268
Indices 15
 fractional, negative, zero 210
Insurance
 car 377
 holiday 396
 household 373
 motorcycle 377
Interest 315
 compound 324
 simple 315
Inverse proportion 116

Least common multiple (LCM) 19
Length
 imperial 419
 metric 64
Logarithms 210
 of numbers less than 1 219

Mass
 imperial 424
 metric 68
Mean 190
Median 191
Metric system
 length 64
 mass 68
Mixed numbers 24
Mode 192
Money
 borrowing 338
 earning 280
 foreign 389
 UK, addition 90
  division 95
  multiplication 94
  subtraction 93
Mortgages 338
Motorcycle
 insurance 377
 running costs 368
Multiplication
 binary 87
 by a power of 10 42
 of decimals 47
 of directed numbers 61
 of fractions 32
 of money 94
 of whole numbers 8

National Insurance 290
Nearest whole number 51
Negative characteristics 219
Net wages/salaries 290
Number systems 81
 the binary system 84

Octal numbers 81

Package holidays 394
Parallelogram 144
Pay
 commission 287
 gross and net 290
 hourly 280
 piecework 285
 salaries 288
Pay As You Earn (PAYE) 268
Pensions 293

Percentages 121
    change 125
    profit and loss 127
Perimeter
    of a circle 234
    of a rectangle 136
Pictographs 178
Pie charts 180
Piecework 285
Prime factors 16
Prime numbers 15
Prism 226
Probability 195
Profit and loss 127
Proper fractions 24
Proportion 111
    compound 118
    direct 113
    inverse 116
Pyramid 231
Pythagoras' theorem 204

Rates and rateable value 351
Ratio 104
Reciprocals 207
Rectangle 136
Representative fraction 109
Retirement pensions 297

Salaries 288
Sector of a circle 242
Sequences 13
Series 13
Shares 405
Significant figures 53
Similar areas and shapes 258
Simple interest 315
    inverse problems 321
Social benefits 295
Sphere
    surface area 254
    volume 254
Square roots 202
Squares 200
Standard form 57
Statistics 178
Stocks 399

Subtraction
    binary 87
    directed numbers 58
    fractions 30
    money 93
    whole numbers 6
Superannuation (pensions) 293

Taxes
    capital gains tax 275
    capital transfer tax 277
    income tax 268
    value added tax 273
Telephone bills 365
Time
    24 hour clock 383
Time zones 387
Timetables
    bus and train 385
Trapezium 145
Travel insurance 396
Triangle
    area 144

Value added tax (VAT) 273
Volume
    cuboid 147
    cylinder 246
    imperial 423
    prism 226
    pyramid 231
    right circular cone 251
    similar 259
    sphere 254

Wages 290
Weight
    imperial 424
Whole numbers
    addition 2
    division 10
    multiplication 8
    nearest whole number 51
    subtraction 6
Words into figures 1
Working origin 194